Middle School 3-2

학교시험 완벽대비

2학기 전과정

적중100 plus

영어 기출문제집

중3

지학 | 민찬규

Best Collection

구성과 특징

교과서의 주요 학습 내용을 중심으로 학습 영역별 특성에 맞춰 단계별로 다양한 학습 기회를 제공하여
단원별 학습능력 평가는 물론 중간 및 기말고사 시험 등에 완벽하게 대비할 수 있도록 내용을 구성

Words & Expressions

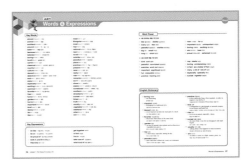

Step1 Key Words 단원별 핵심 단어 설명 및 풀이
Key Expression 단원별 핵심 숙어 및 관용어 설명
Word Power 반대 또는 비슷한 뜻 단어 배우기
English Dictionary 영어로 배우는 영어 단어

Step2 실력평가 단원별 수시평가 대비 주관식, 객관식 문제풀이

Step3 서술형 대비 학업성취도 및 수행능력평가 대비 서술형 문제풀이

Conversation

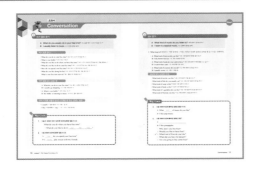

Step1 핵심 의사소통 소통에 필요한 주요 표현 방법 요약
핵심 Check 기본적인 표현 방법 및 활용능력 확인

Step2 대화문 익히기 교과서 대화문 심층 분석 및 확인

Step3 교과서 확인학습 빈칸 채우기를 통한 문장 완성 능력 확인

Step4 기본평가 시험대비 기초 학습 능력 평가

Step5 실력평가 단원별 수시평가 대비 주관식, 객관식 문제풀이

Step6 서술형 대비 학업성취도 및 수행능력평가 대비 서술형 문제풀이

Grammar

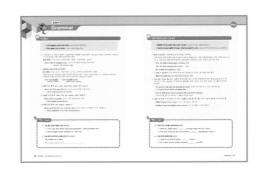

Step1 주요 문법 단원별 주요 문법 사항과 예문을 알기 쉽게 설명
핵심 Check 기본 문법사항에 대한 이해 여부 확인

Step2 기본평가 시험대비 기초 학습 능력 평가

Step3 실력평가 단원별 수시평가 대비 주관식, 객관식 문제풀이

Step4 서술형 대비 학업성취도 및 수행능력평가 대비 서술형 문제풀이

Reading

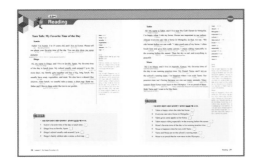

Step1 구문 분석 단원별로 제시된 문장에 대한 구문별 분석과 내용 설명
확인문제 문장에 대한 기본적인 이해와 인지능력 확인

Step2 확인학습A 빈칸 채우기를 통한 문장 완성 능력 확인

Step3 확인학습B 제시된 우리말을 영어로 완성하여 작문 능력 키우기

Step4 실력평가 단원별 수시평가 대비 주관식, 객관식 문제풀이

Step5 서술형 대비 학업성취도 및 수행능력평가 대비 서술형 문제풀이
교과서 구석구석 교과서에 나오는 기타 문장까지 완벽 학습

Composition

|영역별 핵심문제|

단어 및 어휘, 대화문, 문법, 독해 등 각 영역별 기출문제의 출제 유형을 분석하여 실전에 대비하고 연습할 수 있도록 문제를 배열

|단원별 예상문제|

기출문제를 분석한 후 새로운 시험 출제 경향을 더하여 새롭게 출제될 수 있는 문제를 포함하여 시험에 완벽하게 대비할 수 있도록 준비

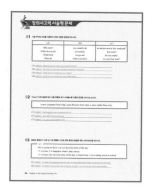

|서술형 실전 및 창의사고력 문제|

학교 시험에서 점차 늘어나는 서술형 시험에 집중 대비하고 고득점을 취득하는데 만전을 기하기 위한 학습 코너

|단원별 모의고사|

영역별, 단계별 학습을 모두 마친 후 실전 연습을 위한 모의고사

 on the textbook

교과서 파헤치기

- 단어Test1~3 영어 단어 우리말 쓰기, 우리말을 영어 단어로 쓰기, 영영풀이에 해당하는 단어와 우리말 쓰기
- 대화문Test1~2 대화문 빈칸 완성 및 전체 대화문 쓰기
- 본문Test1~5 빈칸 완성, 우리말 쓰기, 문장 배열연습, 영어 작문하기 복습 등 단계별 반복 학습을 통해 교과서 지문에 대한 완벽한 습득
- 구석구석지문Test1~2 지문 빈칸 완성 및 전문 영어로 쓰기

Contents

Lesson 5

Which Way to Go?

 의사소통 기능

- 가능성 정도 묻기
  Is it possible to visit Mirror Maze Park?
- 길 묻기
  How do I get to the restaurant?

 언어 형식

- 부정대명사 one
  Here is **one** as an example.
- 분사구문
  Looking at them closely, you may find the beauty of order and regularity.

Words & Expressions

Key Words

- **activity** [æktívəti] 명 활동
- **actually** [ǽktʃuəli] 부 실제로
- **beauty** [bjú:ti] 명 미, 아름다움
- **careful** [kέərfəl] 형 조심스러운
- **certain** [sə́:rtn] 형 어떤, 확실한
- **check** [tʃek] 동 확인하다
- **choice** [tʃɔis] 명 선택
- **closely** [klóusli] 부 자세히
- **compare** [kəmpέər] 동 비교하다
- **confusion** [kənfjú:ʒən] 명 혼란, 혼동
- **connect** [kənékt] 동 연결하다, 이어지다
- **consider** [kənsídər] 동 여기다
- **convenient** [kənví:njənt] 형 편리한
- **dead end** 막다른 길
- **decide** [disáid] 동 결정하다
- **decision** [disíʒən] 명 결정, 결심
- **difference** [dífərəns] 명 차이
- **effective** [ifékiv] 형 효과적인
- **entrance** [éntrəns] 명 입구
- **escape** [iskéip] 동 탈출하다
- **especially** [ispéʃəli] 부 특히
- **exchange** [ikstʃéindʒ] 동 교환하다
- **exit** [égzit] 명 출구
- **floor** [flɔ:r] 명 층, 바닥
- **frustrate** [frʌ́steit] 동 방해하다, 좌절시키다
- **hedge** [hedʒ] 명 산울타리

- **labyrinth** [lǽbərìnθ] 명 미궁
- **Mars** [mɑ:rz] 명 화성
- **maze** [meiz] 명 미로
- **mean** [mi:n] 동 의미하다
- **method** [méθəd] 명 방법
- **monster** [mɑ́nstər] 명 괴물
- **mythology** [miθɑ́lədʒi] 명 신화
- **notice** [nóutis] 동 주목하다, 알아차리다
- **order** [ɔ́:rdər] 명 순서, 질서
- **origin** [ɔ́:rədʒin] 명 기원
- **place** [pleis] 명 장소 동 두다
- **post office** 우체국
- **prison** [prízn] 명 감옥
- **reasonable** [rí:zənəbl] 형 (가격이) 적당한
- **regularity** [règjulǽrəti] 명 규칙성
- **reliable** [riláiəbl] 형 믿을 만한
- **remember** [rimémbər] 동 기억하다
- **schedule** [skédʒu:l] 명 스케줄
- **solution** [səlú:ʃən] 명 해결책
- **spend** [spend] 동 보내다, 쓰다
- **suggest** [səgdʒést] 동 제안하다
- **trip** [trip] 명 여행
- **unfortunately** [ənfɔ́:rtʃənətli] 부 불행하게도
- **willingly** [wíliŋli] 부 기꺼이
- **worth** [wə:rθ] 형 ~할 가치가 있는
- **yet** [jet] 부 아직

Key Expressions

- **a variety of** 다양한
- **come up with** ~을 생각해 내다
- **get out of** ~에서 나오다, 도망치다
- **get (to)** ~에 도착하다, 닿다
- **give it a try** 시도하다, 한번 해보다
- **in the order of** ~의 순서로
- **look forward to** ~을 기대하다
- **lose one's way** 길을 잃다

- **make a choice** 선택하다
- **make a decision** 결정하다
- **make a plan** 계획을 세우다
- **my pleasure** 도움이 되어 저도 기뻐요
- **set for** ~의 준비를 하다
- **That's why** ~. 그것이 ~ 한 이유이다.
- **turn around** 돌다, 돌아서다
- **Why don't you** ~? ~하는 게 어때?

Word Power

※ 서로 비슷한 뜻을 가진 어휘

- □ **actually** 실제로 – **really** 사실은
- □ **choice** 선택 – **selection** 선택
- □ **consider** 여기다 – **regard** 여기다
- □ **decide** 결정하다 – **determine** 결정하다
- □ **reasonable** 적당한 – **sensible** 합리적인

- □ **careful** 조심스러운 – **cautious** 조심스러운
- □ **closely** 자세히 – **intently** 주의 깊게
- □ **convenient** 편리한 – **handy** 편리한
- □ **prison** 감옥 – **jail** 감옥
- □ **reliable** 믿을 만한 – **dependable** 믿을 만한

※ 서로 반대의 뜻을 가진 어휘

- □ **beauty** 미, 아름다움 ↔ **ugliness** 추함
- □ **connect** 연결하다 ↔ **disconnect** 연결을 끊다
- □ **difference** 차이 ↔ **similarity** 닮은 점
- □ **order** 순서, 질서 ↔ **disorder** 무질서
- □ **reliable** 믿을 만한 ↔ **unreliable** 믿을 수 없는

- □ **careful** 조심스러운 ↔ **careless** 부주의한
- □ **convenient** 편리한 ↔ **inconvenient** 불편한
- □ **entrance** 입구 ↔ **exit** 출구
- □ **reasonable** 적당한 ↔ **unreasonable** 적절하지 못한
- □ **remember** 기억하다 ↔ **forget** 잊다

※ 동사 – 명사

- □ **act** 행동하다 – **action** 행동, **activity** 활동
- □ **compare** 비교하다 – **comparison** 비교
- □ **suggest** 제안하다 – **suggestion** 제안

- □ **choose** 선택하다 – **choice** 선택
- □ **solve** 해결하다 – **solution** 해결책

English Dictionary

- □ **connect** 연결하다, 이어지다
  - → to become joined or united or linked
    접합되거나 결합되거나 연결되다
- □ **entrance** 입구
  - → a door, gate, passage, etc. used for entering a room, building or place
    방, 건물, 장소에 들어가기 위해 사용되는 문, 통로 등
- □ **exchange** 교환하다
  - → to give things of a particular kind to each other at the same time
    동시에 서로에게 특별한 종류의 어떤 것을 주다
- □ **exit** 출구
  - → a way out of a public building or vehicle
    공공 건물이나 차량 등의 나가는 길
- □ **frustrate** 방해하다, 좌절시키다
  - → to make somebody feel annoyed or impatient because they cannot do or achieve what they want
    원하는 것을 하거나 이룰 수 없어서 짜증나거나 초조하게 느끼도록 만들다
- □ **hedge** 산울타리
  - → a row of bushes or small trees planted close together, usually along the edge of a field, garden, yard or road
    보통 들판, 정원, 마당, 도로 등의 가장자리를 따라 조밀하게 줄지어 심겨진 덤불 또는 작은 나무

- □ **labyrinth** 미궁
  - → a complicated series of paths, which it is difficult to find your way through
    통과할 길을 찾기가 어려운 일련의 복잡한 통로
- □ **maze** 미로
  - → a system of paths separated by walls or hedges built in a park or garden that is designed so that it is difficult to find your way through
    공원이나 정원에 통과할 길을 찾기가 어렵도록 설계된 벽이나 울타리에 의해 분리된 통로 시스템
- □ **mythology** 신화
  - → ancient myths in general; the ancient myths of a particular culture, society, etc.
    일반적인 고대의 신화들; 특정 문화, 사회 등의 고대 신화들
- □ **prison** 감옥
  - → a building where criminals are kept as punishment or where people accused of a crime are kept before their trial
    처벌로서 범죄자를 가두거나 재판 받기 전 범죄로 고소된 사람들이 갇히는 건물
- □ **worth** ~할 가치가 있는
  - → having a specified value
    특정한 가치를 가지고 있는

서답형

01 다음 짝지어진 단어의 관계가 같도록 빈칸에 알맞은 말을 쓰시오.

> beauty : ugliness = _____ : exit

02 다음 주어진 문장의 밑줄 친 place와 같은 의미로 쓰인 것은?

> Don't place your hand on her shoulder.

① Do you know where the meeting place is?
② My mother asked me to place the bottles in the refrigerator.
③ We're looking for the place to eat something.
④ I can't remember all the places we visited in Canada.
⑤ This would be a good place for a picnic.

중요
03 다음 문장에 공통으로 들어갈 말을 고르시오.

> • He found it hard to _____ a choice.
> • I'd like to listen to your opinion before I _____ a decision.
> • Let's _____ a plan for summer vacation.

① have　　　　② take
③ go　　　　　④ make
⑤ come

04 다음 영영풀이가 가리키는 것을 고르시오.

> a row of bushes or small trees planted close together, usually along the edge of a field, garden, yard or road

① method　　　② hedge
③ monster　　　④ prison
⑤ order

중요
05 다음 중 밑줄 친 부분의 뜻풀이가 바르지 않은 것은?

① Narcissus was a character from Greek mythology. (신화)
② What do you mean by that? (의미하다)
③ My friend willingly spends lots of money on her pet. (마지못해)
④ I need to connect the printer to the computer. (연결하다)
⑤ It's very convenient to pay with my samrtphone. (편리한)

서답형
06 다음 우리말에 맞게 빈칸에 알맞은 말을 쓰시오.

(1) 많은 사람들이 미로 공원에 기꺼이 방문하여 "계획된 혼란"을 즐긴다.
　➡ Many people _____ visit _____ parks and enjoy the "planned _____."

(2) 모든 벽이 이어져 있지 않은 경우, 이 간단한 방법은 효과가 없을지도 모른다.
　➡ When all of the walls are not _____, this simple _____ may not be _____.

(3) 미로는 벽과 방, 산울타리와 같은 많은 다양한 재료로 제작된다.
　➡ _____ are made with a _____ of different materials, like walls, rooms, and _____.

01 다음 문장의 빈칸에 들어갈 말을 〈보기〉에서 골라 쓰시오.

> 보기
> compare / decide / regularity / worth / exchange

(1) The _____ of the design gets boring after a while.

(2) The museum is certainly _____ a visit.

(3) I usually _____ the prices when I buy products.

(4) Would you _____ this blue shirt for the red one?

(5) I _____ to study English and Chinese harder.

02 다음 우리말과 일치하도록 주어진 어구를 모두 배열하여 영작하시오.

(1) 이 간단한 방법은 어떤 종류의 미로에서는 효과가 없을지도 모른다.
(may / this / mazes / not / be / in / effective / simple / types / certain / method / of)
➡ _____
_____

(2) 미궁의 기원은 그리스 신화에서 찾을 수 있다.
(the origin / the labyrinth / you / Greek / mythology / find / can / of / in)
➡ _____
_____

(3) 도착한 순서로 줄을 서 주세요.
(Please / arrival / in / of / order / up / line / the)
➡ _____
_____

03 다음 우리말에 맞게 빈칸에 알맞은 말을 쓰시오. (철자가 주어진 것도 있음.)

(1) 빠져나오기 위해서는, 당신은 단지 돌아서서 들어간 길대로 걸어 나오면 된다.
➡ To get out, you simply have to _____ _____ and walk back out the way you came in.

(2) 학교 갈 준비가 되었니?
➡ Are _____ s_____ _____ school?

(3) 방문객들은 축제에서 다양한 음식들을 즐겼다.
➡ Visitors enjoyed _____ v_____ _____ foods at the festival.

04 다음 우리말을 주어진 단어를 이용하여 영작하시오.

(1) 우리는 정말 너를 다시 보기를 기대하고 있다. (forward, really)
➡ _____

(2) 우리가 시도한 첫 번째 길은 막다른 길로 드러났다. (turned, street, dead, try)
➡ _____

(3) 지금은 우리가 결정할 때이다. (make, time, when)
➡ _____

(4) 그들은 한 달에 한 번씩 승마를 간다. (go, once, horseback riding)
➡ _____

(5) 저는 핑계를 생각해 내야만 합니다. (must, an excuse, come)
➡ _____

Conversation

① 가능성 정도 묻기

> **Is it possible to visit Mirror Maze Park?** 거울 미로 공원에 가는 것이 가능할까요?

■ 'Is it possible to ~ ?'는 '~하는 것이 가능하니?' 또는 '~해도 되니?'라는 뜻으로 어떤 일이 일어날 가능성을 묻거나 상대방의 허락을 구할 때 쓰는 표현이다. 'Is it possible'에 이어지는 'to부정사' 대신에 명사절을 사용하여 'Is it possible that+주어+동사 ~?(~한 것이 가능하니?)'가 될 수도 있다. 가능성을 나타내는 조동사를 사용하여 'Can+주어+동사원형 ~?'도 가능성을 묻거나 허가를 구하는 표현이 될 수 있다.

■ 가능성을 나타내는 형용사 'possible(가능한)' 대신 'probable(~가 있을 것 같은, 가능한), likely(~할 것 같은, ~할 것으로 예상되는)'와 같은 형용사를 사용하여 'Is it likely to ~?', 'Is it probable to ~?(~할 것 같니?)'와 같이 물어볼 수 있다. 또한 부정사 대신 명사절을 사용하여 'Is it likely that+주어+동사 ~?', 'Is it probable that+주어+동사 ~?'처럼 써도 같은 의미가 될 수 있다.

■ 가능성이 있다는 것을 표현하는 경우에는 'It is possible to ~.', 'It is likely to ~.', 'It is probable to ~.'와 같이 나타내거나 'It is possible that+주어+동사 ~.', 'It is likely that+주어+동사 ~.', 'It is probable that+주어+동사 ~.'의 형태를 써서 '~하는 것이 가능하다.'라고 할 수 있다. 'Is there any chance to/that ~?(~할 가능성이 있습니까?)'도 가능성을 묻는 표현으로 쓰일 수 있다.

가능성 정도 묻기

- Is it possible to ~ / that+주어+동사 ~?
- Is it likely to ~ / that+주어+동사 ~?
- Is it probable to ~ / that+주어+동사 ~?

핵심 Check

1. 다음 밑줄 친 우리말에 해당하는 영어 문장을 possible을 이용하여 쓰시오.

> **W:** How may I help you?
>
> **B:** Hi! I bought these shoes yesterday. <u>그것을 빨간 신발로 교환할 수 있나요?</u>
>
> **W:** Oh, actually white is really popular these days.
>
> **B:** I know, and that's why I spent a long time making the decision yesterday. But I think that red will look better on me.
>
> **W:** Okay, no problem.

➡

② 길 묻기

How do I get to the restaurant? 어떻게 그 식당에 갈 수 있나요?

■ 'How do/can I get to 장소?'는 '내가 ～에 어떻게 가나요?'라는 뜻으로 길을 물을 때 쓰는 표현이다. 이 표현은 'Could/Would you tell me the way to ～?'로 바꿔 쓸 수 있다. to는 전치사로 뒤에는 가고자 하는 장소를 명사(구)로 나타낸다. 대화 중에 장소가 언급되었을 때는 'How do/can I get there?(어떻게 거기에 갈 수 있습니까?)'라고 한다.

■ 공손하게 길을 물어볼 때는 앞에 'Excuse me.'를 붙여서 말한다. 'Excuse me. Do you know where ～ is?(～가 어디 있는지 아십니까?)', 'Excuse me. Could you show[tell] me where ～ is?(～가 어디 있는지 알려주시겠습니까?)', 'Excuse me. Do you know how to get to ～?(어떻게 ～에 가는지 아십니까?)'와 같이 물어보기도 한다.

■ 대중교통을 이용하는 경우에는 'Excuse me. What line goes to ～?(실례합니다. 몇 호선이 ～에 가나요?)', 'Excuse me, what bus goes to ～?(실례합니다. 몇 번 버스가 ～로 갑니까?)', 'Excuse me, what bus should I take to get to ～?(～에 가려면 몇 번 버스를 타야 합니까?)'와 같이 물어보기도 한다.

■ 길을 알려줄 때는 'Go straight ～ blocks.(곧장 ～ 블록을 가세요.)', 'Turn right at ～.' 또는 'Make a right turn at ～.(～에서 우회전하세요.)', 'Turn left at ～.' 또는 'Make a left turn at ～.(～에서 좌회전 하세요)'처럼 안내한다. 건물에서 '그것이 ～층에 있다.'고 할 때는 'It's on ～ floor.'라고 한다. 'You can't miss it.'은 '찾기 쉬워요.'에 해당하는 말이다.

길 묻기

- How do/can I get to 장소?
- Excuse me. Do you know where ～ is?
- Excuse me. Do you know how to get to ～?
- Excuse me. I'm looking for ～. Do you know where it is?
- Could/Would you tell me the way to ～?
- Excuse me. Could you show[tell] me where ～ is?

핵심 Check

2. 다음 밑줄 친 (A)를 대신하여 쓰기에 가장 적절한 것은?

A: (A)How do I get to City Hall?
B: Go straight for two blocks and turn left. Then go straight for about 20 meters. You can see City Hall on your right.
A: Thank you for your help.

① Could you show me City Hall?
② Could you tell me the way to City Hall?
③ Can I get to City Hall?
④ Would you tell me the way?
⑤ How can I get there?

Listen and Speak 1 A

W: How may I help you?

B: Hi! I bought these shoes yesterday. Is it possible to exchange ❶ them for the red shoes?

W: Oh, actually white is really popular ❷these days.

B: I know, and that's why I ❸spent a long time ❹making the decision yesterday. But I think that red will ❺look better on me.

W: Okay, no problem.

W: 무엇을 도와드릴까요?
B: 안녕하세요! 제가 어제 이 신발을 샀는데요. 이것을 빨간색 신발로 교환하는 것이 가능한가요?
W: 오, 사실은 하얀색이 요즘 정말 인기 있어요.
B: 저도 알아요, 그래서 제가 어제 결정하는 데 오랜 시간을 보냈어요. 하지만 빨간색이 제게 더 잘 어울릴 것 같아요.
W: 알았어요, 문제 없어요.

❶ them은 'these shoes'를 가리킨다. ❷ these days: 요즘 ❸ spend+시간+~ing: ~하는 데 시간을 보내다 ❹ make the decision: 결정하다
❺ look better on: ~에게 잘 어울리다

Check(√) True or False

(1) The boy bought the white shoes yesterday. T ☐ F ☐

(2) The woman recommended the red shoes because it looked better on the boy. T ☐ F ☐

Listen and Speak 2 A

M: Hi, do you need any help?

G: Yes, please. ❶Could you suggest a good Chinese restaurant in this building? I can't decide between the two.

M: Hmm... . ❷What about Pappa Chen's? Their food is good and the prices are ❸reasonable.

G: Sounds great! ❹How do I get to the restaurant?

M: It's on the fourth floor. You can use the elevator over there. Pappa Chen's is next to the elevator.

G: Great! Thank you very much for your help.

M: My pleasure. Enjoy your dinner.

M: 안녕하세요, 도움이 필요하신가요?
G: 네, 부탁드려요. 이 건물에서 좋은 중국 음식점을 추천해 주실 수 있나요? 두 개 중에 결정할 수가 없네요.
M: 음… 파파첸스는 어떠세요? 그곳 음식은 훌륭하고 가격이 합리적이에요.
G: 좋을 것 같은데요! 그 음식점에 어떻게 가나요?
M: 그것은 4층에 있습니다. 당신은 저기 있는 승강기를 탈 수 있고요. 파파첸스는 승강기 옆에 있습니다.
G: 아주 좋아요! 도와주셔서 정말 감사합니다.
M: 천만에요. 저녁 맛있게 드세요.

❶ 'Could you suggest ~?'는 무엇을 추천해 줄 것을 요청하는 표현으로 'Can you recommend ~?' 등으로 바꾸어 표현할 수 있다.
❷ 'What about ~?'은 '~는 어때?'를 의미하며 'How about ~?' 등으로 바꾸어 표현할 수 있다. ❸ resonable: 적당한, 합리적인 ❹ 'How do/can I get to 장소?'는 '내가 ~에 어떻게 가나요?'라는 뜻으로 길을 물을 때 쓰는 표현이며 'Could/Would you tell me the way to ~?'로 바꿔 쓸 수 있다.

Check(√) True or False

(3) The man recommends Pappa Chen's because of the good food and the reasonable prices. T ☐ F ☐

(4) The Pappa Chen's is on the opposite side of the elevator. T ☐ F ☐

Listen and Speak 1 B

G: Mom, did you decide where to visit ❶during our family trip to Jeju?

W: Almost. Come here and see the plan ❷I made.

G: It looks good. Hmm... Mom, ❸is it possible to visit Mirror Maze Park on our second day?

W: It sounds exciting, but I remember you said you wanted to go ❹horseback riding.

G: I know, but I heard the park is a lot more fun. Please ... .

W: All right. Let's change our schedule for the second day.

G: Thank you! I'm very excited about the trip.

W: It's great to hear that you're ❺looking forward to the trip.

❶ 'during+명사(구)', 'while+주어+동사'
❷ 목적격 관계대명사 that 또는 which가 생략되었다.
❸ 'is it possible to ~?'는 '~하는 것이 가능하니?' 또는 '~해도 되니?'라는 뜻으로 어떤 일이 일어날 가능성을 묻거나 상대방의 허락을 구할 때 쓰는 표현이다.
❹ horseback riding: 승마
❺ look forward to+(동)명사: ~을 기대하다, 고대하다

Listen and Speak 2 B

B: Hey, Minju, where are you?

G: Oh, Andrew, I'm coming. I'm coming.

B: Good. I was worried that you were lost.

G: I think I'm okay. What about Mason and Jian?

B: ❶They are already here at my house.

G: Good! Oh, I see the post office. ❷How do I get to your place from here?

B: You are almost here. ❸Go straight for one more block. Then you will see Kim's Bakery.

G: Kim's Bakery? Okay ... .

B: Then turn right and go straight for ❹about 100 meters.

G: Turn right and go straight ... . Okay, thanks! I'll see you soon.

❶ They는 Mason과 Jian을 가리킨다.
❷ 'How do I get to 장소?'는 '내가 ~에 어떻게 가나요?'라는 뜻으로 길을 물을 때 쓰는 표현이며 'Would you tell me the way to your place from here?'로 바꾸어 쓸 수 있다.
❸ 명령문이므로 동사로 시작한다.
❹ about은 '약, 대략'을 나타낸다.

Real Life Communication

Mina: ❶Are you all set for the trip this weekend?

Jinho, Claire, & Henry: Yes!

Mina: Good! Don't be late! We're meeting at 11 a.m. ❷in front of the clock tower.

Jinho: You got it! How do we get to the airport? I don't think we've ❸decided yet.

Henry: Jinho is right. We have two choices, bus or subway.

Claire: ❹What about the subway? It's more ❺ reliable than the bus.

Henry: Is it possible to get to Terminal 2 by subway?

Claire: Yes, I already checked.

Mina: Good. Okay, then let's take the subway.

❶ Are you all set for ~?: '~할 준비가 되었니?'를 의미한다. ❷ in front of: ~ 앞에 ❸ decide: 결정하다 ❹ 'What about ~?'은 '~하는 게 어때?'라고 제안하는 표현이다. ❺ reliable: 믿을 만한

Let's Check 1

B: What are you reading, Alice?

G: It's about the origin of the ❶labyrinth.

B: Labyrinth? Wasn't that an old ❷mythological prison to keep the half-man, half-bull monster?

G: Oh, Juwon, you know about the story.

B: Not really. I forgot the name of the monster.

G: The Minotaur. The king of Crete was angry at ❸it and put ❸it in a labyrinth.

B: Interesting! Alice, is it possible to borrow the book after you're finished with ❹it?

G: Sure, no problem. Maybe this Friday.

❶ labyrinth: 미궁 ❷ mythological: 신화적인 ❸ it은 모두 'The Minotaur'를 가리킨다. ❹ it은 'the book'을 가리킨다.

다음 우리말과 일치하도록 빈칸에 알맞은 말을 쓰시오.

Listen & Speak 1 A

W: How may I help you?

B: Hi! I bought these shoes yesterday. Is it _____ to _____ them for the red shoes?

W: Oh, actually white is really popular _____ _____.

B: I know, and that's _____ I spent a long time _____ _____ _____ yesterday. But I think that red will _____ _____ on me.

W: Okay, no problem.

Listen & Speak 1 B

G: Mom, did you _____ where to visit _____ our family trip to Jeju?

W: Almost. Come here and see the plan I made.

G: It looks good. Hmm… Mom, _____ _____ _____ to visit Mirror Maze Park on our second day?

W: It sounds _____, but I remember you said you wanted to go _____ _____.

G: I know, but I heard the park is _____ _____ more fun. Please ….

W: All right. Let's change our _____ for the second day.

G: Thank you! I'm very _____ about the trip.

W: It's great to hear that you're _____ _____ _____ the trip.

Listen & Speak 2 A

M: Hi, do you need any help?

G: Yes, please. Could you _____ a good Chinese restaurant in this building? I can't _____ between the two.

M: Hmm…. What _____ Pappa Chen's? Their food is good and the prices are _____.

G: Sounds great! How do I _____ _____ the restaurant?

M: It's on the _____ floor. You can use the elevator over there. Pappa Chen's is _____ _____ the elevator.

G: Great! Thank you very much for your help.

M: My _____. Enjoy your dinner.

W: 무엇을 도와드릴까요?
B: 안녕하세요! 제가 어제 이 신발을 샀는데요. 이것을 빨간색 신발로 교환하는 것이 가능한가요?
W: 오, 사실은 하얀색이 요즘 정말 인기 있어요.
B: 저도 알아요, 그래서 제가 어제 결정하는 데 오랜 시간을 보냈어요. 하지만 빨간색이 제게 더 잘 어울릴 것 같아요.
W: 알았어요, 문제없어요.

G: 엄마, 제주도 가족 여행 동안 어디 방문할지 정하셨어요?
W: 거의. 이리 와서 내가 만든 일정표를 보렴.
G: 좋아 보여요. 흠. 엄마, 우리 두 번째 날에 거울 미로 공원에 가는 것이 가능할까요?
W: 재미있을 거 같지만, 네가 말 타러 가고 싶다고 말한 것으로 기억하는데.
G: 저도 알아요, 근데 공원이 훨씬 더 재미있다고 들었어요. 제발….
W: 알았다. 두 번째 날 우리의 일정을 변경하자.
G: 감사합니다! 전 이번 여행에 대해 너무 신이 나요.
W: 네가 이번 여행을 고대한다니 아주 좋구나.

M: 안녕하세요, 도움이 필요하신가요?
G: 네, 부탁드려요. 이 건물에서 좋은 중국 음식점을 추천해 주실 수 있나요? 두 개 중에 결정할 수가 없네요.
M: 음… 파파첸스는 어떠세요? 그곳 음식은 훌륭하고 가격이 합리적이에요.
G: 좋을 것 같은데요! 그 음식점에 어떻게 가나요?
M: 그것은 4층에 있습니다. 당신은 저기 있는 승강기를 탈 수 있고요. 파파첸스는 승강기 옆에 있습니다.
G: 아주 좋아요! 도와주셔서 정말 감사합니다.
M: 천만에요. 저녁 맛있게 드세요.

Listen & Speak 2 B

B: Hey, Minju, where are you?

G: Oh, Andrew, I'm _____. I'm _____.

B: Good. I was _____ that you were lost.

G: I think I'm okay. What about Mason and Jian?

B: They are already here at my house.

G: Good! Oh, I see the _____ _____. _____ _____ _____ _____ _____ _____ your place from here?

B: You are almost here. _____ _____ _____ one more block. Then you will see Kim's Bakery.

G: Kim's Bakery? Okay ….

B: Then _____ _____ and _____ _____ for about 100 meters.

G: _____ _____ and _____ _____ …. Okay, thanks! I'll see you soon.

Real Life Communication

Mina: _____ _____ _____ _____ _____ _____ the trip this weekend?

Jinho, Claire, & Henry: Yes!

Mina: Good! Don't be late! We're meeting at 11 a.m. _____ _____ the clock tower.

Jinho: You _____ _____! How do we _____ the airport? I don't think we've _____ yet.

Henry: Jinho is right. We have two _____, bus or subway.

Claire: What about the subway? It's more _____ than the bus.

Henry: Is it _____ _____ get to Terminal 2 _____ _____?

Claire: Yes, I already checked.

Mina: Good. Okay, then let's _____ the subway.

Let's Check 1

B: What are you reading, Alice?

G: It's about the _____ of the _____.

B: _____? Wasn't that an old _____ _____ to keep the half-man, half-bull monster?

G: Oh, Juwon, you know about the story.

B: Not really. I forgot the name of the monster.

G: The Minotaur. The king of Crete was _____ at it and _____ it in a _____.

B: 민주야, 너 어디야?
G: 오, Andrew, 나 가고 있어. 가고 있어.
B: 좋아. 네가 길을 잃었을까봐 걱정했어.
G: 괜찮은 것 같아. Mason이랑 지안이는?
B: 그들은 우리 집에 벌써 왔지.
G: 좋아! 오, 우체국이 보여. 여기서부터 너희 집까지 어떻게 가니?
B: 거의 다 왔네. 한 블록 더 직진해. 그럼 너는 킴스 빵집이 보일 거야.
G: 킴스 빵집? 알았어… .
B: 그럼 오른쪽으로 돌아서 100m 정도 직진해.
G: 오른쪽으로 돌아서 직진이라… . 알았어, 고마워! 곧 보자.

Mina: 너희 모두 이번 주말에 여행갈 준비 됐니?
Jinho, Claire, & Henry: 응!
Mina: 좋아! 늦지 마! 우리는 시계탑 앞에서 오전 11시에 만날 거야.
Jinho: 알았어! 우리 공항까지 어떻게 가지? 우리가 아직 결정하지 않은 것 같은데.
Henry: 진호 말이 맞아. 우리는 버스랑 지하철, 두 가지 선택이 있어.
Claire: 지하철은 어때? 그것은 버스보다 더 믿을 만하잖아.
Henry: 2터미널까지 지하철로 가는 것이 가능하니?
Claire: 응, 내가 이미 확인해 봤어.
Mina: 좋아. 그래, 그럼 지하철을 타자.

B: 무엇을 읽고 있니, Alice?
G: 미궁의 기원에 관한 거야.
B: 미궁? 그건 반인반수 괴물을 가두기 위한 옛 신화 속 감옥 아니니?
G: 와, 주원아, 너 그 이야기에 대해 아는구나.
B: 그다지 잘 아는 건 아니야. 그 괴물의 이름을 잊어버렸어.
G: 미노타우루스야. 크레타의 왕이 그 괴물에 화가 나서 그것을 미궁에 가두었지.

Conversation 시험대비 기본평가

[01~02] 다음 대화를 읽고 물음에 답하시오.

Mike: Hi, do you need any help?

Sora: Yes, please. Could you suggest a good Chinese restaurant in this building? I can't decide between the two.

Mike: Hmm.... What about Pappa Chen's? Their food is good and the prices are (A)reason.

Sora: Sounds great! (B)_____

Mike: It's on the fourth floor. You can use the elevator over there. Pappa Chen's is next to the elevator.

01 위 대화의 밑줄 친 (A)를 알맞은 형으로 고치시오.

➡ _____

02 위 대화의 빈칸 (B)에 들어갈 말로 어색한 것은?

① Can I get to the restaurant?

② How do I get to the restaurant?

③ Would you tell me the way to the restaurant?

④ Do you know how to get to the restaurant?

⑤ Could you show me where the restaurant is?

[03~04] 다음 대화를 읽고 물음에 답하시오.

Mina: Are you all set for the trip this weekend?

Jinho, Claire, & Henry: Yes!

Mina: Good! Don't be late! We're meeting at 11 a.m. in front ⓐ the clock tower.

Jinho: You got it! How do we get ⓑ the airport? I don't think we've decided yet.

Henry: Jinho is right. We have two choices, bus or subway.

Claire: What about the subway? It's more reliable than the bus.

Henry: (A)(it / subway / by / is / to / to / get / possible / Terminal 2)?

Claire: Yes, I already checked.

03 위 대화의 빈칸 ⓐ와 ⓑ에 각각 알맞은 전치사를 쓰시오.

➡ ⓐ _____ ⓑ _____

04 위 대화의 괄호 (A)에 주어진 단어들을 모두 배열하여 영작하시오.

➡ _____

[01~02] 다음 대화를 읽고 물음에 답하시오.

Juwon: What are you reading, Alice?

Alice: It's about the origin of the labyrinth.

Juwon: Labyrinth? Wasn't that an old mythological prison to keep the half-man, half-bull monster?

Alice: Oh, Juwon, you know about the story.

Juwon: Not really. I forgot the name of the monster.

Alice: The Minotaur. The king of Crete was angry at it and put it in a labyrinth.

Juwon: Interesting! Alice, is it possible to borrow the book after you're finished with it?

Alice: Sure, no problem. Maybe this Friday.

서답형

01 위 대화에서 다음 영영풀이가 가리키는 것을 찾아 쓰시오.

> a building where criminals are kept as punishment or where people accused of a crime are kept before their trial

➡ _____

중요

02 위 대화의 내용과 일치하지 <u>않는</u> 것은?

① Alice는 미궁의 유래에 관한 책을 읽고 있다.

② 미궁은 반인반수 괴물을 가둬 놓기 위한 옛 신화 속의 감옥이다.

③ 미노타우루스는 반인반수 괴물이다.

④ 크레타의 왕이 괴물에게 화를 내서 괴물에 의해 감옥에 갇혔다.

⑤ 주원은 Alice가 책을 다 읽은 후 책을 빌릴 수 있을 것이다.

[03~05] 다음 대화를 읽고 물음에 답하시오.

Andrew: Hey, Minju, where are you?

Minju: Oh, Andrew, I'm coming. I'm coming.

Andrew: Good. I was ⓐ<u>worry</u> that you were lost.

Minju: I think I'm okay. What ⓑ<u>about</u> Mason and Jian?

Andrew: They are already here ⓒ<u>at</u> my house.

Minju: Good! Oh, I see the post office. How do I get ⓓ<u>to</u> your place from here?

Andrew: You are almost here. Go straight ⓔ<u>for</u> one more block. Then you will see Kim's Bakery.

Minju: Kim's Bakery? Okay … .

Andrew: Then turn right and go straight for about 100 meters.

Minju: Turn right and go straight … . Okay, thanks! I'll see you soon.

서답형

03 위 대화의 밑줄 친 ⓐ~ⓔ 중 어법상 틀린 것을 찾아 바르게 고치시오.

➡ _____

서답형

04 Where is Andrew's place? Check ✓ on the map.

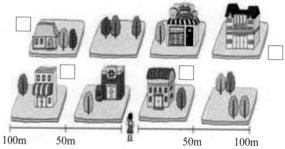

서답형

05 How can Minju get to Kim's Bakery from the post office?

➡ _____

[06~08] 다음 대화를 읽고 물음에 답하시오.

Mike: Hi, do you need any help?

Sora: Yes, please. Could you suggest a good Chinese restaurant in this building? I can't decide between the two.

Mike: Hmm.... (A)_____ Their food is good and the prices are reasonable.

Sora: Sounds great! (B)_____?

Mike: It's on the fourth floor. You can use the elevator over there. Pappa Chen's is next to the elevator.

Sora: Great! Thank you very much for your help.

Mike: My pleasure. Enjoy your dinner.

06 위 대화의 빈칸 (A)에 들어갈 말로 나머지와 의도가 <u>다른</u> 것은?

① Why don't you try Pappa Chen's?

② What about Pappa Chen's?

③ I think you should try Pappa Chen's.

④ I recommend Pappa Chen's.

⑤ I'd like to visit Pappa Chen's.

서답형
07 위 대화의 빈칸 (B)에 들어갈 말을 <보기>에 주어진 단어들을 모두 배열하여 영작하시오.

┌─── 보기 ├───
I / the / restaurant / to / how / get / do
└────────────────────────────

➡ _____

08 Where is Papa Chen's?

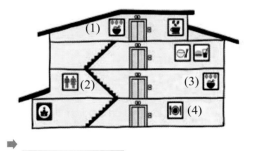

➡ _____

[09~12] 다음 대화를 읽고 물음에 답하시오.

W: How may I help you?

B: Hi! I bought these shoes yesterday. Is it possible to exchange them for the red shoes?

W: Oh, actually white is really popular these days.

B: I know, and that's why I spent a long time making the decision yesterday. But I think that red will look better on me.

W: Okay, no problem.

서답형
09 What does the boy want to do?

➡ _____

_____

서답형
10 What color is popular these days?

➡ _____

서답형
11 Why does the boy want to exchange his shoes?

➡ _____

_____

서답형
12 위 대화의 내용과 일치하도록 빈칸을 완성하시오.

I bought (A)_____ yesterday. They were so popular and I spent a long time _____. After coming back home, I thought (C)_____ _____. When I visited the shoe store and asked if I could have any chance to (D)_____ _____, I could do it. I love my red shoes now.

01 다음 대화가 자연스럽게 이어지도록 순서대로 배열하시오.

> How may I help you?

> (A) Okay, no problem.
> (B) Oh, actually white is really popular these days.
> (C) Hi! I bought these shoes yesterday. Is it possible to exchange them for the red shoes?
> (D) I know, and that's why I spent a long time making the decision yesterday. But I think that red will look better on me.

➡ _____

02 다음 대화의 내용과 일치하도록 빈칸을 완성하시오.

> **Gina:** Mom, did you decide where to visit during our family trip to Jeju?
> **Mom:** Almost. Come here and see the plan I made.
> **Gina:** It looks good. Hmm... Mom, is it possible to visit Mirror Maze Park on our second day?
> **Mom:** It sounds exciting, but I remember you said you wanted to go horseback riding.
> **Gina:** I know, but I heard the park is a lot more fun. Please … .
> **Mom:** All right. Let's change our schedule for the second day.
> **Gina:** Thank you! I'm very excited about the trip.
> **Mom:** It's great to hear that you're looking forward to the trip.

> Gina's family made a plan to visit Jeju soon. Gina and her mother talked about it. Everything looked fine, but Gina wanted to change the plan to (A)_____. Instead, she wanted to visit (B)_____ because (C)_____. Her mom decided to change their schedule for the second day, and Gina was excited about the trip.

[03~04] 다음 대화를 읽고 물음에 답하시오.

> **Mike:** Hi, do you need any help?
> **Sora:** Yes, please. Could you suggest a good Chinese restaurant in this building? I can't decide between the two.
> **Mike:** Hmm…. What about Pappa Chen's? Their food is good and the prices are reasonable.
> **Sora:** Sounds great! How do I get to the restaurant?
> **Mike:** It's on the fourth floor. You can use the elevator over there. Pappa Chen's is next to the elevator.
> **Sora:** Great! Thank you very much for your help.
> **Mike:** My pleasure. Enjoy your dinner.

03 Why does Mike recommend Pappa Chen's?

➡ _____

_____

04 How can Sora get to Pappa Chen's? Fill the blanks with suitable words.

➡ She can use _____ in the building. Pappa Chen's is _____ the elevator on _____.

Grammar

① 부정대명사 one

- Here is **one** as an example. 여기 그 예가 하나 있습니다.
- The easiest and most reliable **one** is to place a hand on one wall from the very beginning. 가장 쉽고 믿을 만한 하나는 시작 지점부터 한쪽 벽에 손을 대는 것입니다.

■ one은 앞에서 언급된 명사와 같은 종류이지만 정해지지 않은 것을 가리킬 때 쓰며, 복수는 ones이다. 형용사+one, one+관계사절 등 앞과 뒤에서 꾸며주는 말과 함께 쓸 수 있다. 특정한 것을 가리킬 때는 it을 쓴다.

- Are you **the one** who answered the phone yesterday? 당신이 어제 전화를 받은 분인가요?
- They are **the ones** who sang and danced on TV. 저들이 TV에서 노래하고 춤추던 이들이에요.
- I don't like this color. Can you show me **a blue one**? 이 색깔이 맘에 들지 않아요. 파란 색으로 보여 주시겠어요?
- A: I have lost my pen. 펜을 잃어버렸어.

  B: Do you want me to buy **one** for you? 하나 사 줄까?

  A: No, thanks. But I should find the pen as it is my lucky pen. 고맙지만 아냐. 그것은 나의 행운의 펜이기 때문에 나는 그 펜을 꼭 찾아야 해

■ 둘 중 하나를 가리킬 때 첫 번째는 one, 나머지 하나는 the other이며, 셋 중 하나를 가리킬 때 첫 번째는 one, 그 다음 하나는 another, 마지막 남은 하나는 the other이다. 또한 여러 개 중 일부는 some, 그 외에 다른 일부는 others, 나머지 전부는 the others로 쓴다.

- **One** is mine and **the other** is hers. 하나는 내 것이고, 나머지 하나는 그녀의 것이다.
- There are three buildings I like in this town. **One** is the library, **another** is the hospital, and **the other** is the City Hall. 이 마을에서 내가 좋아하는 건물이 세 개 있다. 하나는 도서관, 다른 하나는 병원, 그리고 나머지 하나는 시청이다.
- **Some** like walking, and **others** prefer running. 몇몇은 걷기를, 다른 사람들은 달리기를 더 좋아한다.
- There are balls in the box. **Some** are red and **the others** are blue. 상자 안에 공들이 있다. 몇 개는 빨간색이고, 나머지는 파란색이다.

■ 둘 중 하나를 가리킬 때는 either, 둘 모두는 both, 둘 중 어느 것도 아닐 때는 neither, 셋 이상에서 어느 것도 아닐 때는 none을 각각 사용한다.

- **Either** of the two girls likes David. 그 두 소녀들 중 하나는 David을 좋아한다.
- **Neither** of the two girls likes David. 그 두 소녀들 중 누구도 David을 좋아하지 않는다.
- **Both** of the two girls like David. 그 두 소녀들 모두 David을 좋아한다.
- **None** of the girls likes David. (셋 이상의) 그 소녀들 중 누구도 David을 좋아하지 않는다.

핵심 Check

1. 다음 괄호 안에서 알맞은 말을 고르시오.

  (1) I need a pen. Can you buy me a new (it / one)?

  (2) Which (one / either) of the two men would you like to meet?

❷ 분사구문

> • **Looking at them closely**, you may find the beauty of order and regularity. 자세히 들
> 여다보면, 여러분은 질서와 규칙성이라는 아름다움을 발견할 수 있을지도 모릅니다.

■ 분사구문은 종속접속사가 이끄는 부사절을 분사를 이용하여 간략한 부사구로 바꾼 것이며, 다음과 같은 방법으로 만든다.

1) 접속사를 생략한다. (접속사의 의미를 강조할 경우, 접속사를 남겨둘 수 있다.)
2) 주절의 주어와 같은 주어는 생략한다. (주절과 다르면 주어를 남긴다. → 독립분사구문)
3) 능동은 'V-ing' 형태로, 수동은 'Being V-ed'에서 Being을 생략한 '과거분사' 형태로 쓴다.
4) 분사구문의 부정은 not이나 never를 분사 앞에 쓴다.
5) 종속절의 시제가 주절보다 앞선 경우, 완료분사구문을 사용한다.

■ 부사구와 주절의 관계에 따라 양보, 동시동작, 이유, 시간, 조건 등의 의미로 쓰인다.

(1) 양보: **Though she is short**, she jumps the highest in my class.
   = **Being short**, she jumps the highest in my class. 비록 그녀가 작지만, 우리 반에서 가장 높이 뛴다.

(2) 동시동작(부대상황): **While he listened to the radio**, he read the report.
   = **Listening to the radio**, he read the report. 라디오를 들으며, 그는 보고서를 읽었다.

(3) 이유: **As she didn't sleep enough**, she felt tired all day.
   = **Not sleeping enough**, she felt tired all day. 잠을 충분히 못자서, 그녀는 종일 피곤했다.

(4) 시간: **When I heard the birds singing**, I felt delighted.
   = **Hearing the birds singing**, I felt delighted. 새들의 노래 소리를 들었을 때, 나는 기뻤다.

(5) 조건: **If you walk in the rain**, you'll catch a cold.
   = **Walking in the rain**, you'll catch a cold. 빗속에 걸으면 감기에 걸릴 것이다.

■ 주절과 종속절의 주어가 달라서 분사구문의 주어를 남겨 두는 것을 '독립분사구문'이라고 하며, 일반인이 주어일 경우 생략하는 것을 '비인칭 독립분사구문'이라 부른다.

(1) 독립분사구문: **As it was** rainy, he couldn't walk his dogs.
   = **It being** rainy, he couldn't walk his dogs. 비가 와서, 그는 개들을 산책시킬 수 없었다.

(2) 비인칭 독립분사구문: **generally speaking**(일반적으로 말해), **considering**(~를 고려하면)

■ 「with+목적어+분사」는 전치사 with 뒤에 나오는 목적어 입장에서의 능동/수동이 중요하다.

• Susan took a walk **with her arms folded**. (팔짱을 낀 채로)

핵심 Check

2. 다음 괄호 안에서 알맞은 말을 고르시오.

(1) With her eyes (closing / closed), Angela recalled her childhood.

(2) (Feeling / Felt) surprised, the teacher ran to the school to meet his old students.

Grammar 시험대비 기본평가

01 다음 빈칸에 들어갈 말로 알맞은 것은?

> Maria has two kitties. One is white and _____ is brown.

① another　　　　② other　　　　③ two
④ next　　　　　⑤ the other

02 다음 부사절을 분사구문으로 바꿔 쓸 때, 빈칸에 들어갈 말로 가장 적절한 것은?

> When you are in a maze, you have many choices to make.
> ➡ _____ in a maze, you have many choices to make.

① When you being　　　② You being
③ Your being　　　　　④ Having been
⑤ Being

03 다음 대화의 밑줄 친 부분 중 어법상 어색한 부분을 고르시오.

> A: How do we get to the city museum?
> B: Which ①one is better? Taking the subway or riding a bike?
> A: ②Both sound great.
> B: ③One will be convenient and ④another will be fun.
> A: Then, we should choose ⑤one with more fun.

04 다음 분사구문을 접속사가 이끄는 부사절로 만들 때, 빈칸에 알맞은 말을 써 넣으시오.

(1) Not feeling well, he couldn't go out with his friends.
　➡ As _____ _____ _____ well, he couldn't go out with his friends.

(2) Being late for school, they started to run.
　➡ Because _____ _____ _____ _____ _____, they started to run.

(3) Listening to the radio, Sean took photos.
　➡ While he _____ _____ the radio, Sean took photos.

(4) Eating much, Sarah doesn't gain any weight.
　➡ _____ _____ _____ _____, Sarah doesn't gain any weight.

 밑줄 친 부분의 용법이 나머지와 <u>다른</u> 것을 고르시오.

① <u>Being</u> interested in the magic let her become a magician.
② <u>Knowing</u> her name, I could find her seat at the conference.
③ Not <u>feeling</u> good, she left work earlier.
④ <u>Being</u> sick, Mina didn't go to school.
⑤ <u>Crossing</u> the street packed with cars, she didn't care about the traffic.

[02~03] 다음 중 어법상 옳은 것을 고르시오.

02 ① My daddy bought me a pencil but Jin took one away.
② Each of the men are going to Busan.
③ Did you buy the blue pen or the purple one?
④ I like neither coffee or coke.
⑤ I don't like the bag. I need a bigger it.

03 ① Don't knowing when to move, she asked for help.
② Being too hot, they had to cancel the race.
③ Opened the drawer, he took out a letter.
④ Being tired of running in the ground, she signed up for the gym.
⑤ Caught a cold, Mina was absent from the party.

[04~05] 다음 우리말을 어법상 알맞게 영작한 것을 고르시오.

04
두 학생 모두 장학금을 신청했지만, 누구도 받을 수 없다.

① Both students have applied for the scholarship, but anyone can get it.
② Either one of the students applied for the scholarship, but neither can get it.
③ Each students have applied for the scholarship, but both can't get it.
④ Both students have applied for the scholarship, but neither one can get it.
⑤ Both students have applied for the scholarship, but either one can get it.

수지는 눈을 감은 채 산책했다.

① Suji took a walk her eyes closing.
② Suji closed her eyes and took a walk.
③ Suji took a walk with closed her eyes.
④ Suji took a walk closed her eyes with.
⑤ Suji took a walk with her eyes closed.

서답형
06 다음 문장에서 어법상 <u>어색한</u> 단어 두 개를 찾아서 고치시오.

Tiring of taking care of infectious diseases all day long, neither she or her fellow doctor had the power to open the boxes filled with the gifts of encouragement from the citizens.

➡ _____

서답형

07 다음 그림을 보고 자연스러운 문장이 되도록 괄호 안에 주어진 단어를 바르게 배열하여 빈칸을 완성하시오.

(1) (it, from, to, reading, left, right, "evil", reads)

➡ _____,

but it becomes "live" in opposite direction.

(2) (the duck, the water, under, from, seeing)

➡ _____,

you will find its feet never stop paddling.

중요

08 다음 밑줄 친 단어의 용법이 나머지와 같지 않은 것을 고르시오.

① Sam has only small shirts. He needs a bigger <u>one</u> for the game.
② Only <u>one</u> fifth of the students answered the question correctly.
③ Charlie lost his cell phone, so he needed to buy <u>one</u>.
④ Martin broke his guitar yesterday, so his friend might lend <u>one</u> to him.
⑤ Jin sold her car and bought a used <u>one</u> from her cousin.

09 다음 각 문장에 쓰인 분사구문을 접속사를 이용한 부사절로 전환할 때, 의미상 〈보기〉와 같은 것이 <u>아닌</u> 것은?

┌─ 보기 ─┐
Being tired from the hard exercise, all the animals in the circus took a nap for an hour.
└────────┘

① Finishing the projects, Kane was able to watch the movie after a long time.
② Not knowing how much Tom liked the animals, I couldn't understand his attitude toward the cats.
③ Not having anything special to do, they just walked around the town.
④ Being old enough, you can marry without your parents' agreement now.
⑤ Living in Daegu for over 20 years, Robert still can't get the meaning of the Daegu words.

[10~12] 다음 빈칸에 알맞은 것을 고르시오.

10

┌────────────────────────────────┐
Dad bought me a laptop for my birthday, but I don't like _____ at all.
└────────────────────────────────┘

① one　　② another　　③ other
④ the other　　⑤ it

중요

11

┌────────────────────────────────┐
Cindy's dress was too old and worn to put on, so her mom would like to make new _____ for her graduation party.
└────────────────────────────────┘

① one　　② another　　③ other
④ ones　　⑤ it

12

_____ of her three children goes to a different school.

① Both   ② Each   ③ All
④ Either   ⑤ Some

[13~14] 다음 중 어법상 옳지 <u>않은</u> 문장을 고르시오.

13 ① Bill liked the pen but his girl friend broke it.
② I'm tired of always wearing the same jacket. I need to get a new one.
③ Dinner at the restaurant was excellent, but we won't order it again.
④ All of the boys want to go out.
⑤ David lost his wedding ring, so he bought a similar it.

14 ① Either of the two girls is going to do the job of guiding the customers.
② All of us know the results in the general election this week.
③ Both of them has watched the drama twice a week since March.
④ Each of the books has a great effect on children in Africa.
⑤ No one is coming to the party because of the disease.

서답형

[15~16] 우리말과 일치하도록 괄호 안에 주어진 단어들을 바르게 배열하시오.

15

또 후회하고 싶지 않았지만, 그는 경솔하게 아무에게나 투표했다. (it, to, not, again, wanting, regret), he voted for anyone at random.

➡ _____

16

마스크를 쓰지 않고 친구들과 놀았기 때문에, 그 여자가 많은 사람들에게 질병을 퍼뜨릴 가능성이 있다. (with, without, the girl, wearing, having, her friends, played, a mask), there is a possibility that she will spread the disease to many people.

➡ _____

_____

17 다음 주어진 분사구문을 접속사를 이용한 부사절로 만들 때 가장 적절한 것은?

Feeling tired, Ken didn't attend the morning soccer match.

① Although he felt tired, Ken didn't attend the morning soccer match.
② If he felt tired, Ken didn't attend the morning soccer match.
③ As soon as he felt tired, Ken didn't attend the morning soccer match.
④ As he felt tired, Ken didn't attend the morning soccer match.
⑤ Even if he felt tired, Ken didn't attend the morning soccer match.

18 다음 빈칸에 들어갈 알맞은 말을 고르시오.

The princess Elsa made a snowman called Olaf, and she decided to make many _____.

① another   ② other ones
③ one   ④ those
⑤ the others

01 다음 우리말과 일치하도록 괄호 안에 주어진 어구를 바르게 배열하여 문장을 완성하시오.

(1) Sarah는 그 디자인 샘플들 중에서 첫 번째 것을 고르고, 그 다음 하나 더 선택했지만, 어느 것도 그녀의 마음에 들지 않았다. (the first, another, Sarah, then, one, neither, but, chose)

➡ Among those design samples, _____

_____ was to her satisfaction.

(2) 이 청바지는 조금 작네요. 약간 더 큰 것을 보여 주실 수 있으세요? (slightly, a, show, you, one, me, could, bigger)

➡ These jeans are a bit small.

_____

(3) Jane은 새 바이올린이 필요하지만, 그녀는 한 대를 구입할 충분한 돈이 없다. (enough, doesn't, for, she, one, have, money)

➡ Jane needs a new violin, but

_____ .

(4) 어떤 사람들은 반려동물로 고양이를 좋아하지만, 반면에 다른 사람들은 고양이를 무서워한다. (cats, are, while, others, of, afraid)

➡ Some people like cats as pets,

_____ .

02 다음 〈보기〉에 있는 접속사를 한 번씩만 사용하여, 분사구문을 부사절로 바꾸시오. (단, 진행형 표현은 쓸 수 없다.)

┌─ 보기 ─┐
while because when if though
└─────────┘

(1) Fixing his computer, Jerry listened to the radio show.

➡ _____

(2) Having nothing to worry about, the little boy plays well with the toys.

➡ _____

(3) Looking at the mazes closely, you may find the beauty of order and regularity.

➡ _____

(4) Being sick all day long, Benny finally completed the difficult assignment.

➡ _____

03 다음 밑줄 친 부분을 부정대명사를 활용하여 어법에 맞게 고쳐 다시 쓰시오.

(1) Should Mina buy the red grapes or the green <u>those</u>?

➡ _____

(2) Frank didn't catch <u>some</u> fish in the lake last weekend.

➡ _____

_____

(3) <u>Each of the student have</u> been to Bulguksa in Gyoungju.

➡ _____

_____

(4) She has two pets and <u>it</u> is bigger than <u>another</u>.

➡ _____

_____

04 다음 그림을 보고 괄호 안의 단어를 배열하여 알맞게 영작하시오.

(1) (she, the map, the maze, stuck, calmly, in, reviewed)

➡ _____

(2) (music, cross, listening to, really, the street, it, dangerous, is, to)

➡ _____
_____

05 다음 문장에서 어법상 <u>어색한</u> 단어를 하나씩만 찾아 바르게 고치시오.

(1) Both of my cats is overweight.

➡ _____

(2) Neither of the girls are going to learn Chinese in the high school.

➡ _____

(3) Some of the islands are crowded with visitors while another are not.

➡ _____

(4) Sunny lost a lot of her dolls, so she needs to buy new one.

➡ _____

(5) Either of Mr. Brown's kids have to answer the question.

➡ _____

(6) Jason's organization will not use their material for another furniture.

➡ _____

06 다음 그림을 보고 괄호 안의 단어를 배열하여 빈칸을 알맞게 채우시오. (어법에 맞게 동사의 중복 사용 가능.)

(a honeybee, a ladybug, a spider, other, another, one, the, is)

➡ There are three insects on the spider web; _____
_____ .

07 주어진 우리말을 〈조건〉에 맞게 영작하시오.

┌── 조건 ──┐
1. 'one 또는 ones'를 사용할 것.
2. 같은 품사들이 병렬구조가 되어 순서가 크게 상관없을 때에는 주어진 단어들이 제시된 순서대로 사용할 것.
3. 접속사는 언제나 문장 중간에 넣을 것.
4. 주어진 단어를 활용하되, 괄호 안의 글자 수 조건과 시제에 맞출 것. (동사 변형 가능)

(1) 어떤 이들은 붉은 장미들을 좋아하고, 다른 이들은 흰 장미들을 좋아한다. (and, like, red, some, love, white, roses, 현재시제, 9 단어)

➡ _____

(2) Harry는 그의 컴퓨터를 팔고 새것을 하나 장만했다. (and, sell, new, Harry, his computer, purchase, a, 과거시제, 9 단어)

➡ _____

(3) 그들 중 하나가 뭔가 도움이 되는 것을 해야 한다. (have to, something, do, helpful, of, them, either, 현재시제, 9 단어)

➡ _____

Reading

Enjoy the "Planned Confusion"

Comparing the two pictures below, you can easily notice some
분사구문(= If/When you compare the two pictures below)

differences. For example, the picture on the left is called a labyrinth
수동태(~라고 불리다)

and only has an entrance. The picture on the right is called a maze and
is와 병렬 관계

has both an entrance and an exit.
both A and B: A와 B 둘 다

You can find the origin of the labyrinth in Greek mythology. It is said

to be a prison that you cannot escape. But you may notice that the
목적격 관계대명사(선행사: a prison)   명사절 접속사(notice의 목적어를 이끎)

labyrinth has only a single path. There are no dead ends. This means
뒤에 오는 명사에 수의 일치   means (that) ~

you don't have to worry about getting out of it when you enter it. If
~할 필요가 없다(= need not)   조건을 이끄는 부사절 접속사(현재시제로 미래시제를 대신함)

you follow the path all the way to the end, you will reach the center. To

get out, you simply have to turn around and walk back out the way you
to부정사의 부사적 용법 중 목적(~하기 위해서)

came in.

When you are in a maze, it's a different story. There are many choices

to make and dead ends to frustrate you. You have to keep making
to부정사의 형용사적 용법 (choices 수식)   to부정사의 형용사적 용법 (dead ends 수식)   keep Ving: 계속해서 V하다

decisions about which way to go. If you are not careful, you can easily
의문형용사+명사+to부정사(전치사의 목적어)

lose your way.

These days, mazes are often considered left-brain puzzles.
(= people often consider mazes left-brain puzzles.)

confusion: 혼란
notice: 알아차리다
labyrinth: 미궁
entrance: 입구
maze: 미로
exit: 출구
mythology: 신화
path: 통로, 길
dead end: 막다른 길
turn around: 돌아서다, 돌다
frustrate: 좌절시키다
make a decision: 결정하다
lose one's way: 길을 잃다

📎 **확인문제**

● 다음 문장이 본문의 내용과 일치하면 T, 일치하지 않으면 F를 쓰시오.

1 There are a few differences between a labyrinth and a maze. ☐

2 There is only one way to enter a labyrinth. ☐

3 Like a labyrinth, a maze also doesn't have dead ends. ☐

4 It is easy to lose your way in a maze unless you are careful. ☐

5 To get out of a labyrinth, you have to turn around and walk back out the way you

came in. ☐

Many people willingly visit maze parks and enjoy the "planned confusion." And some of them came up with their own solutions.
미로 공원에 기꺼이 방문하는 사람들을 지칭

The easiest and most reliable one is to place a hand on one wall from
= solution   to부정사의 명사적 용법(보어)
the very beginning. Then you just keep following that wall. It's like
전치사(~와 같은)
walking in a dark room. Unfortunately, this simple method may not be
추측의 조동사
effective in certain types of mazes, especially when all of the walls are not connected.

Mazes are made with a variety of different materials, like walls and
be made with: ~으로 만들어지다
rooms, hedges, bricks, mirrors, and even snow. In fact, they can also be
= mazes
printed or drawn on paper. Here is one as an example. This is called a
정해지지 않은 것 하나를 가리킬 때 쓰는 대명사(종이에 인쇄되거나 그려질 수 있는 미로를 가리킴)
number maze. You start from point A and have to go in the order of 1
→ 9 → 8 → 5 → 1 → 9 → …. Why don't you give it a try? You have
Why don't you 동사원형 (제안하는 말)   give it a try: 시험 삼아 해보다
30 seconds to escape!

Labyrinths and mazes are truly fun, but that's not the end of the story. Looking at them closely, you may find the beauty of order and
분사구문(= If/When you look at them closely)
regularity. They may also show you how creative human beings are.
labyrinths와 mazes 지칭   간접의문문(의문사+주어+동사)
If there is a maze park on your next trip, why don't you stop and take some time to enjoy it? It will surely be worth visiting!
be worth Ving: V할 가치가 있다

come up with: ~을 생각해 내다
reliable: 믿을 만한
effective: 효과적인
a variety of: 다양한
hedge: 산울타리
in the order of: ~의 순서로
escape: 탈출하다, 벗어나다
regularity: 규칙성
worth: ~할 가치가 있는

확인문제

- 다음 문장이 본문의 내용과 일치하면 T, 일치하지 <u>않으면</u> F를 쓰시오.

1 Some people succeeded in finding their own solutions to get out of a maze. ☐

2 The simple method to escape a maze works on every type of maze. ☐

3 You can enjoy mazes on paper. ☐

4 The number maze has a regular pattern. ☐

5 Labyrinths and mazes doesn't have the beauty of order and regularity. ☐

6 The writer suggests visiting a maze park. ☐

● 우리말을 참고하여 빈칸에 알맞은 말을 쓰시오.

Enjoy the "Planned Confusion"

1 _____ the two pictures _____ , you can easily _____ some _____ .

2 _____ _____ , the picture _____ _____ _____ is _____ a labyrinth and only _____ an entrance.

3 The picture _____ _____ _____ is _____ a maze and _____ _____ an entrance _____ an exit.

4 You can find _____ _____ _____ the labyrinth in Greek _____ .

5 It _____ _____ _____ _____ a prison _____ you cannot escape.

6 But you may _____ _____ the labyrinth has only _____ _____ _____ .

7 There are _____ _____ _____ .

8 This means you _____ _____ _____ _____ getting out of it when you _____ _____ .

9 If you follow the path _____ _____ _____ _____ _____ , you will reach the center.

10 _____ _____ _____ , you simply _____ _____ _____ and walk back out the way you _____ _____ .

11 When you are _____ a maze, it's a _____ story.

12 There are many choices _____ _____ and _____ to frustrate you.

13 You have to keep _____ decisions about _____ _____ _____ _____ .

14 _____ you _____ _____ _____ , you can easily _____ your way.

15 These days, mazes _____ often _____ _____ puzzles.

1 아래 두 그림을 비교하면 몇 가지 차이를 쉽게 알아차릴 수 있습니다.

2 예를 들면, 왼쪽 그림은 미궁이라 불리고 입구만 있습니다.

3 오른쪽 그림은 미로라 불리며 입구와 출구가 둘 다 있습니다.

4 미궁의 기원은 그리스 신화에서 찾을 수 있습니다.

5 그것은 여러분이 빠져나올 수 없는 감옥으로 알려져 있습니다.

6 하지만 여러분이 알아차릴 수 있듯, 미궁은 통로가 하나입니다.

7 막다른 길이 없습니다.

8 이것은 여러분이 거기에 들어갈 때 빠져나올 것을 걱정하지 않아도 된다는 것을 의미합니다.

9 통로를 따라 끝까지 가면, 여러분은 미궁의 중앙에 도착할 것입니다.

10 빠져나오기 위해서는, 여러분은 단지 돌아서 들어간 길대로 걸어 나오면 됩니다.

11 미로 안에 있을 때에는 완전히 상황이 다릅니다.

12 결정할 많은 선택지가 있고 여러분을 좌절하게 만들 막다른 길들이 있습니다.

13 어느 길로 갈지 계속 선택을 해야만 합니다.

14 조심하지 않으면 길을 잃기 쉽습니다.

15 오늘날, 미로는 흔히 좌뇌형 퍼즐로 간주됩니다.

16 Many people _____ _____ maze parks and _____ the "_____ _____."

17 And some of _____ _____ _____ _____ their own solutions.

18 The easiest and _____ _____ _____ is _____ place a hand _____ one wall from _____ _____ _____.

19 Then you just keep _____ _____ _____.

20 It's _____ _____ in a dark room.

21 _____, this simple method may not be _____ in _____ _____ of mazes, especially when all of the walls _____ _____ _____.

22 Mazes _____ _____ _____ a variety of _____ _____, like walls and rooms, _____, bricks, mirrors, _____ even snow.

23 _____ _____, they can also _____ _____ or _____ on paper.

24 _____ _____ _____ one as an example. This is _____ a number maze.

25 You start _____ point A and have to go _____ _____ of 1 → 9 → 8 → 5 → 1 → 9 → ....

26 Why don't you _____ _____ _____ _____? You have 30 seconds _____ _____!

27 Labyrinths and mazes _____ truly _____, but that's not _____ _____ of the story.

28 _____ _____ _____ closely, you may find the beauty of _____ and _____.

29 They may also show you _____ _____ _____ _____.

30 If _____ _____ a maze park on your next trip, why don't you _____ and _____ _____ _____ to enjoy it?

31 It will surely _____ _____ _____!

16 많은 사람들이 미로 공원에 기꺼이 방문하여 '계획된 혼란'을 즐깁니다.

17 그리고 그들 중 몇몇은 자기들만의 해결 방법을 찾아냈습니다.

18 가장 쉽고 믿을 만한 해결 방법은 시작 지점부터 한쪽 벽에 손을 대는 것입니다.

19 그러고는 여러분은 단지 그 벽을 계속 따라가면 됩니다.

20 이것은 마치 어두운 방을 걷는 것과 같습니다.

21 불행하게도, 이 간단한 방법은 어떤 종류의 미로에서는 특히 모든 벽이 이어져 있지는 않은 경우 효과가 없을지도 모릅니다.

22 미로는 벽과 방, 울타리, 벽돌, 거울, 심지어는 눈 등 많은 다양한 재료로 제작됩니다.

23 사실, 미로는 종이에 인쇄되거나 그려질 수도 있습니다.

24 여기 그 예가 하나 있습니다. 이것은 숫자 미로라고 불립니다.

25 여러분은 A 지점에서 출발하여 1. 9. 8. 5. 1. 9 …의 순서로 이동해야 합니다.

26 한번 시도해 보시죠? 빠져나가는 데 30초가 주어집니다!

27 미궁과 미로는 정말 재미있지만, 그것이 전부가 아닙니다.

28 자세히 들여다보면, 여러분은 질서와 규칙성이라는 아름다움을 발견할 수 있을지도 모릅니다.

29 그것들은 또한 인간이 얼마나 창조적인가를 보여줄지도 모릅니다.

30 다음 여행에 미로 공원이 있으면, 들러서 즐겨보는 것은 어떨까요?

31 분명히 들를 가치가 있을 것입니다!

● 우리말을 참고하여 본문을 영작하시오.

Enjoy the "Planned Confusion"

1 아래 두 그림을 비교하면 몇 가지 차이를 쉽게 알아차릴 수 있습니다.
➡ _____

2 예를 들면, 왼쪽 그림은 미궁이라 불리고 입구만 있습니다.
➡ _____

3 오른쪽 그림은 미로라 불리며 입구와 출구가 둘 다 있습니다.
➡ _____

4 미궁의 기원은 그리스 신화에서 찾을 수 있습니다.
➡ _____

5 그것은 여러분이 빠져나올 수 없는 감옥으로 알려져 있습니다.
➡ _____

6 하지만 여러분이 알아차릴 수 있듯, 미궁은 통로가 하나입니다.
➡ _____

7 막다른 길이 없습니다.
➡ _____

8 이것은 여러분이 거기에 들어갈 때 빠져나올 것을 걱정하지 않아도 된다는 것을 의미합니다.
➡ _____

9 통로를 따라 끝까지 가면, 여러분은 미궁의 중앙에 도착할 것입니다.
➡ _____

10 빠져나오기 위해서는, 여러분은 단지 돌아서 들어간 길대로 걸어 나오면 됩니다.
➡ _____

11 미로 안에 있을 때에는 완전히 상황이 다릅니다.
➡ _____

12 결정할 많은 선택지가 있고 여러분을 좌절하게 만들 막다른 길들이 있습니다.
➡ _____

13 어느 길로 갈지 계속 선택을 해야만 합니다.
➡ _____

14 조심하지 않으면 길을 잃기 쉽습니다.
➡ _____

15 오늘날, 미로는 흔히 좌뇌형 퍼즐로 간주됩니다.
➡ _____

16 많은 사람들이 미로 공원에 기꺼이 방문하여 '계획된 혼란'을 즐깁니다.
➡ _____

17 그리고 그들 중 몇몇은 자기들만의 해결 방법을 찾아냈습니다.
➡ _____

18 가장 쉽고 믿을 만한 해결 방법은 시작 지점부터 한쪽 벽에 손을 대는 것입니다.
➡ _____

19 그러고는 여러분은 단지 그 벽을 계속 따라가면 됩니다.
➡ _____

20 이것은 마치 어두운 방을 걷는 것과 같습니다.
➡ _____

21 불행하게도, 이 간단한 방법은 어떤 종류의 미로에서는 특히 모든 벽이 이어져 있지는 않은 경우 효과가 없을지도 모릅니다.
➡ _____
_____

22 미로는 벽과 방, 울타리, 벽돌, 거울, 심지어는 눈 등 많은 다양한 재료로 제작됩니다.
➡ _____
_____

23 사실, 미로는 종이에 인쇄되거나 그려질 수도 있습니다.
➡ _____

24 여기 그 예가 하나 있습니다. 이것은 숫자 미로라고 불립니다.
➡ _____

25 여러분은 A 지점에서 출발하여 1, 9, 8, 5, 1, 9 …의 순서로 이동해야 합니다.
➡ _____

26 한번 시도해 보시죠? 빠져나가는 데 30초가 주어집니다!
➡ _____

27 미궁과 미로는 정말 재미있지만, 그것이 전부가 아닙니다.
➡ _____

28 자세히 들여다보면, 여러분은 질서와 규칙성이라는 아름다움을 발견할 수 있을지도 모릅니다.
➡ _____

29 그것들은 또한 인간이 얼마나 창조적인가를 보여줄지도 모릅니다.
➡ _____

30 다음 여행에 미로 공원이 있으면, 들러서 즐겨보는 것은 어떨까요?
➡ _____

31 분명히 들를 가치가 있을 것입니다!
➡ _____

[01~04] 다음 글을 읽고 물음에 답하시오.

(A)_____ the two pictures below, you can easily notice some differences. For example, the picture on the left is called a labyrinth and only has an entrance. The picture on the right is called a maze and has both an entrance and an exit.

You can find the origin of the labyrinth in Greek mythology. It is said to be a prison that you cannot escape. But you may notice that the labyrinth has only a single path. There are no dead ends. This means you don't have to worry about getting out of it when you enter it. If you follow the path all the way to the end, you will reach the center. To get out, you simply have to turn around and walk back out (B)_____.

서답형
01 주어진 단어를 어법에 맞게 빈칸 (A)에 쓰시오.

> compare

➡ _____

중요
02 다음 중 빈칸 (B)에 들어갈 말로 가장 적절한 것은?

① where you come from
② to the hall a guide leads you to
③ where many people are crowded
④ the way you came in
⑤ following other people

서답형
03 다음과 같이 풀이되는 말을 위 글에서 찾아 쓰시오.

> to become aware of somebody or something

➡ _____

중요
04 다음 중 위 글의 내용과 일치하는 것은?

① A labyrinth is the same as a maze.
② There are an entrance and an exit in a labyrinth.
③ A labyrinth is a prison in Greek mythology.
④ A labyrinth has some dead ends.
⑤ A labyrinth has many paths.

[05~09] 다음 글을 읽고 물음에 답하시오.

When you are in a maze, it's a different story. There are many choices to make and dead ends to frustrate you. You have to keep making decisions about which way to go. If you are not careful, you can easily lose your way.

(A)These days, mazes are often considered left-brain puzzles. ① Many people willingly visit maze parks and enjoy (B)the "planned confusion." ② And some of them came up with their own solutions. ③ The easiest and most reliable one is to place a hand on one wall from the very beginning. ④ It's like walking in a dark room. ⑤ Unfortunately, this simple method may not be effective in certain types of mazes, especially when all of the walls are not connected.

중요
05 ①~⑤ 중 주어진 문장이 들어가기에 가장 적절한 곳은?

> Then you just keep following that wall.

①　②　③　④　⑤

06 다음 중 밑줄 친 (A)를 대신하여 쓸 수 있는 것은?

① For a long time　② Rarely
③ Nowadays　④ At last
⑤ All of a sudden

07 다음 중 (B)와 같이 표현한 이유로 가장 적절한 것은?

① Because people like to plan mazes.

② Because mazes confuse people without any plans.

③ Because mazes are planned to be solved easily.

④ Because nobody wants to be confused by some plans.

⑤ Because mazes are deliberately planned to confuse people.

서답형

08 According to the passage, what makes us frustrated? Answer in English with six words.

➡ _____

서답형

09 다음은 미로에 들어가기 전 친구에게 한 말이다. 위 글의 내용에 맞게 빈칸에 알맞은 말을 쓰시오.

_____ _____, or you will lose your way.

[10~13] 다음 글을 읽고 물음에 답하시오.

Mazes are made with a variety of different materials, like walls and rooms, hedges, bricks, mirrors, and even snow. In fact, they can also be printed or drawn on paper. Here is one as an example. This is called a number maze. You start from point A and have to go in the order of $1 \rightarrow 9 \rightarrow 8 \rightarrow 5 \rightarrow 1 \rightarrow 9 \rightarrow ....$ (A)Why don't you give it a try? You have 30 seconds to escape!

Labyrinths and mazes are truly fun, but that's not the end of the story. Looking at them closely, you may find the beauty of order and regularity. They may also show you how creative human beings are.

If there is a maze park on your next trip, why don't you stop and take some time to enjoy it? It will surely be worth visiting!

중요

10 다음 중 밑줄 친 (A)의 의미로 가장 적절한 것은?

① Why do you want to solve this maze?

② Do not try to solve the maze.

③ Why don't you try harder?

④ How about solving the maze?

⑤ Let's make some time to try harder.

11 다음 중 위 글을 읽고 답할 수 있는 것은?

① Why do people enjoy mazes?

② What can be used to make mazes?

③ How many paths are there in a maze?

④ Who invented a maze first in the world?

⑤ How many mirror mazes are there in the world?

서답형

12 글의 내용에 맞게 빈칸에 알맞은 말을 쓰시오.

Q: What is presented as an example of a printed maze?

A: _____ _____ _____ _____ as an example of a printed maze.

서답형

13 How much time is given to solve the number maze? Answer in English with a full sentence.

➡ _____

[14~18] 다음 글을 읽고 물음에 답하시오.

ⓐ[Comparing / Compared] the two pictures below, you can easily notice some differences. (A)_____, the picture on the left is called a labyrinth and only has an entrance. The picture on the right is called a maze and ⓑ[has / have] both an entrance and an exit.

You can find the origin of the labyrinth in Greek mythology. It is said to be a prison that you cannot escape. But you may notice that the labyrinth has only a single path. There are no (B)dead ends. This means you don't have to worry about getting out of it when you ⓒ [enter / enter into] it. If you follow the path all the way to the end, you will reach the center. To get out, you simply have to turn around and walk back out the way you came in.

14 다음 중 빈칸 (A)에 들어갈 말로 가장 적절한 것은?

① In other words　② For example
③ On the contrary　④ However
⑤ Therefore

15 위 글의 내용에 맞게 빈칸에 알맞은 말을 쓰시오.

Unlike _____, a maze has not only _____ but also _____.

16 다음 중 밑줄 친 (B)의 의미로 가장 적절한 것은?

① a path which is not used any more
② an end that people pursue
③ a passage where many people die
④ an other end that people usually use
⑤ a road that is closed at one end

17 ⓐ~ⓒ 중 어법상 옳은 것끼리 바르게 짝지은 것은?

① Comparing – has – enter
② Compared – has – enter
③ Comparing – has – enter into
④ Compared – have – enter into
⑤ Comparing – have – enter into

18 다음 중 위 글을 읽고 답할 수 있는 것은?

① Where can we find the origin of a maze?
② Who made a labyrinth in the mythology?
③ How many paths does a labyrinth have?
④ How can we get out of a maze easily?
⑤ What is the similarity between a maze and a labyrinth?

[19~21] 다음 글을 읽고 물음에 답하시오.

When you are in a maze, it's a different story. There are many choices to make and dead ends to frustrate you. You have to keep making decisions about which way to go. If you are not careful, you can easily lose your way.

(A) And some of them came up with their own solutions. The easiest and most reliable one is to place a hand on one wall from the very beginning. Then you just keep following that wall.

(B) These days, mazes are often considered left-brain puzzles. Many people willingly visit maze parks and enjoy the "planned confusion."

(C) It's like walking in a dark room. Unfortunately, this simple method may not be effective in certain types of mazes, especially when all of the walls are not connected.

19 자연스러운 글이 되도록 (A)~(C)를 바르게 나열한 것은?

① (A)–(C)–(B)　　② (B)–(A)–(C)
③ (B)–(C)–(A)　　④ (C)–(A)–(B)
⑤ (C)–(B)–(A)

20 다음 중 maze를 제대로 이해한 학생은?

① Andrew: I think a maze is so easy because there is only one choice to make.
② Brian: There is no need to make decisions in a maze.
③ Cindy: I think I use my right brain a lot when I enjoy a maze.
④ Dennis: Whenever I am in a maze, I am so discouraged because of many dead ends.
⑤ Erica: It's okay not to concentrate in a maze because it's easy to find my way.

서답형
21 위 글의 내용에 맞게 빈칸에 알맞은 말을 쓰시오.

Placing a hand on one wall and following the wall is effective if _____ _____.

[22~24] 다음 글을 읽고 물음에 답하시오.

Mazes are made with a variety of different materials, like walls and rooms, hedges, bricks, mirrors, and even snow. In fact, they can also be printed or drawn on paper. Here is one as an example. This is called a number maze. You start (A)_____ point A and have to go in the order of 1 → 9 → 8 → 5 → 1 → 9 → .... Why don't you give it a try? You have 30 seconds to escape!

Labyrinths and mazes are truly fun, but that's not the end of the story. Looking at (B)them closely, you may find the beauty of order and regularity. They may also show you how creative human beings are.

If there is a maze park on your next trip, why don't you stop and take some time to enjoy it? It will surely be worth visiting!

22 다음 중 빈칸 (A)에 들어가는 말과 같은 말이 들어가는 것은?

① These cups are filled _____ milk and orange juice.
② Can you please pay attention _____ my speech?
③ When did you graduate _____ university?
④ They turned _____ my proposal, so I'm depressed.
⑤ The grocery store is crowded _____ many people.

서답형
23 밑줄 친 (B)가 지칭하는 것을 위 글에서 찾아 쓰시오.

➡ _____

24 Which one is true about the passage?

① It is impossible to draw mazes on paper.
② There are few materials to make mazes.
③ The writer gives half an hour to solve the number maze.
④ We can find that the labyrinths and mazes are disorganized.
⑤ The writer thinks a maze park will be worthwhile to visit.

[01~02] 다음 글을 읽고 물음에 답하시오.

(A)If you compare the two pictures below, you can easily notice some differences. For example, the picture on the left is called a labyrinth and only has an entrance. The picture on the right is called a maze and has both an entrance and an exit.

01 밑줄 친 (A)를 대신할 수 있는 말을 쓰시오.

➡ _____

02 What do people call the thing which has only one entrance? Answer in English.

➡ _____

[03~07] 다음 글을 읽고 물음에 답하시오.

You can find the origin of the labyrinth in Greek mythology. It is said to be a prison that you cannot escape. But you may notice that the labyrinth has only a single path. There are no dead ends. This means you don't have to worry about getting out of it when you enter it. If you follow the path all the way to the end, you will reach the center. To get out, you simply have to turn around and walk back out the way you came in.

When you are in a maze, it's a different story. There are many choices to make and dead ends to frustrate you. You have to keep making decisions about which way to go. If you are not careful, you can easily lose your way.

03 Where can we find the origin of the labyrinth? Answer in English.

➡ _____

_____

04 What does it mean that the labyrinth has a single path without any dead ends? Answer in English with a full sentence.

➡ _____

_____

05 위 글의 내용에 맞게 빈칸에 알맞은 말을 쓰시오.

The labyrinth is _____ in Greek mythology, which is impossible _____. But actually it is easy to get out of it because it has only _____.

06 What can we find if we follow the path all the way to the end in a labyrinth? Answer in English with five words.

➡ _____

07 How is a maze different from a labyrinth? Fill the blank with appropriate words.

A maze is different from a labyrinth in that it has _____ and _____.

[08~11] 다음 글을 읽고 물음에 답하시오.

These days, (A)미로는 종종 좌뇌형 퍼즐로 간주됩니다. Many people willingly visit maze parks and enjoy the "planned confusion." And some of them came up with their own solutions. The easiest and most reliable (B)one is to place a hand on one wall from the very beginning. Then you just keep following that wall. It's like walking in a dark room. Unfortunately, this simple method may not be effective in certain types of mazes, especially when all of the walls are not connected.

08 주어진 단어를 활용하여 밑줄 친 우리말 (A)를 영어로 쓰시오.

> consider / often / left-brain puzzles

➡ _____

09 밑줄 친 (B)가 의미하는 것을 위 글에서 찾아 쓰시오.

➡ _____

10 According to the passage, what is the easiest and most reliable way to get out of a maze? Answer in English.

➡ _____
_____
_____

11 다음과 같이 풀이되는 말을 위 글에서 찾아 쓰시오.

> worthy of trust; worthy of being depended on

➡ _____

[12~14] 다음 글을 읽고 물음에 답하시오.

Mazes are made with a variety of different materials, like walls and rooms, hedges, bricks, mirrors, and even snow. In fact, they can also be printed or drawn on paper. Here is one as an example. This is called a number maze. You start from point A and have to go in the order of 1 → 9 → 8 → 5 → 1 → 9 → .... Why don't you give it a try? You have 30 seconds to escape!

Labyrinths and mazes are truly fun, but that's not the end of the story. Looking at them closely, you may find the beauty of order and regularity. They may also show you how creative human beings are.

If there is a maze park on your next trip, why don't you stop and take some time to enjoy it? (A)그곳은 분명히 들를 가치가 있을 것이다!

12 주어진 단어를 바르게 나열하여 밑줄 친 우리말 (A)를 영어로 쓰시오. 필요하다면 어형을 바꾸시오.

> (visit / be / surely / it / worth / will)!

➡ _____

13 What materials are used to make mazes? Answer in English with a full sentence.

➡ _____
_____
_____

14 If there is a maze park on your next trip, what does the writer suggest doing?

➡ _____
_____

Real Life Communication – C Communication Task

A: Let me ask you the first question. How do you get there?

B: I can go there by train.
교통수단 앞에 전치사 by를 쓴다.

A: Then how long does it take to get there?

B: It takes about 2 hours to get there.

A: Is it possible to get there by airplane?
=Is it likely to = Is it probably to
⋮

A: Oh, the answer is Gyeongju. Right?

해석

A: 첫 번째 질문을 할게요. 어떻게 그곳에 가나요?

B: 기차로 갈 수 있어요.

A: 그러면 그곳에 가는 데 얼마나 걸리나요?

B: 그곳에 가는 데 약 2시간 정도 걸려요.

A: 그곳에 비행기로 갈 수 있나요?
⋮

A: 오, 정답은 경주예요. 맞죠?

After You Read

Today, I went to the nearby maze park with my friends. The maze looked hard

to solve. There were many choices, and I had to keep making decisions about
to부정사의 부사적 용법: 형용사 수식   keep+Ving: 계속 V하다

which way to go. My friends said that I should just place my hand on one
의문형용사+명사+to부정사   명사절 접속사

wall from the beginning and keep following the same wall. That solution was
동사 place와 병렬 관계

simple but not very effective. I enjoyed myself very much at the park. Also, I
재귀대명사(주어와 목적어가 같을 때 사용)

found the beauty of order and regularity there and thought that human beings

are really creative.

오늘 나는 친구들과 함께 근처의 미로 공원에 갔다. 미로는 해결하기가 어려워 보였다. 선택지가 많았고 나는 어느 길로 갈지 계속해서 결정해야만 했다. 내 친구들이 내가 처음부터 벽 한쪽에 손을 얹고 계속 같은 쪽 벽을 따라가면 된다고 말했다. 그 해결 방법은 간단했지만 별로 효과적이지 않았다. 나는 미로 공원에서 매우 즐거웠다. 또한, 나는 질서와 규칙성의 아름다움을 발견했고 인간은 정말 창조적이라고 생각했다.

구문해설 • nearby: 근처의 • place: ～을 두다 • effective: 효과적인 • order: 질서 • regularity: 규칙성

Let's Write

I took a short survey about our class's preference between mountains and oceans.
take a survey = survey   between A and B: A와 B 사이에

Looking at the results, it is clear that our class prefers mountains to oceans. You
비인칭 독립분사구문(If we look ～) 가주어   접속사   prefer A to B

may wonder why our class prefers mountains. Regarding the reasons why they
의문부사(명사절)   분사전치사(= Concerning)   관계부사(형용사절)

like mountains more, I found key words like "more beautiful", "more exciting",
부사   전치사

and "lovelier."

나는 산과 바다 간의 우리 반의 선호도에 관한 간단한 설문 조사를 했다. 결과를 보면, 우리 반이 바다보다 산을 더 선호한다는 것이 명확하다. 여러분은 왜 우리 반이 산을 선호하는지 궁금할지도 모른다. 그들이 산을 더 좋아하는 이유를 보자면, 나는 "더 아름다운", "더 신나는", 그리고 "더 멋진"과 같은 핵심어를 찾았다.

구문해설 • survey: (설문) 조사 • preference: 선호도 • prefer: 선호하다 • regarding: ～에 관해서는

Words & Expressions

01 다음 짝지어진 단어의 관계가 같도록 빈칸에 알맞은 말을 쓰시오.

reasonable : _____ = reliable : unreliable

02 다음 영영풀이가 가리키는 것을 고르시오.

ancient myths in general; the ancient myths of a particular culture, society, etc.

① maze
② origin
③ regularity
④ worth
⑤ mythology

03 다음 주어진 문장의 밑줄 친 mean과 다른 의미로 쓰인 것은?

What does this sentence mean?

① The red light means that you must stop.
② Do you understand what I mean?
③ Her children mean the world to her.
④ You mean we have to start all over again?
⑤ Don't be mean over money.

04 다음 중 밑줄 친 부분의 뜻풀이가 바르지 않은 것은?

① It's not actually raining now. (사실상)
② Can you suggest a good dictionary? (추천하다)
③ Jane is a reliable friend. (믿을 만한)
④ I'll meet you at the main entrance. (출구)
⑤ You may notice that the labyrinth has only a single path. (미궁)

05 다음 문장의 빈칸에 들어갈 말을 〈보기〉에서 골라 쓰시오.

┌─ 보기 ─┐
frustrate / prison / worth / exit / reliable

(1) Oh, there's the _____! We can escape the maze.
(2) There are many choices to make and dead ends to _____ you.
(3) It is said to be a _____ that you cannot escape.
(4) It's more _____ than the bus.
(5) It will surely be _____ visiting!

06 다음 우리말에 맞게 주어진 단어를 사용하여 영작하시오.

(1) 미로를 통과했을 때, 나는 늑대 한 마리를 만났다. (when, wolf, through)
➡ _____

(2) 그들의 음식은 훌륭하고 가격이 적당하다. (good, prices)
➡ _____

Conversation

[07~08] 다음 대화를 읽고 물음에 답하시오.

W: How may I help you?
B: Hi! I bought these shoes yesterday. Is it possible to exchange them __(A)__ the red shoes?
W: Oh, actually white is really popular these days.
B: I know, and that's why I spent a long time making the decision yesterday. But I think that red will look better __(B)__ me.
W: Okay, no problem.

07 위 대화의 빈칸 (A)와 (B)에 들어갈 말로 알맞게 짝지어진 것은?

① to – for
② to – with
③ for – on
④ at – from
⑤ for – with

08 위 대화를 읽고 대답할 수 없는 것은?

① What color shoes did the boy buy?
② When did the boy buy the shoes?
③ What color is popular these days?
④ How much did the boy pay for the shoes?
⑤ Why isn't the boy satisfied with the white shoes?

[09~11] 다음 대화를 읽고 물음에 답하시오.

Gina: Mom, did you decide where to visit ⓐ during our family trip to Jeju?

Mom: Almost. Come here and see the plan I made.

Gina: It looks ⓑgood. Hmm... Mom, is it possible to visit Mirror Maze Park on our second day?

Mom: It sounds ⓒexciting, but I remember you said you wanted to go horseback riding.

Gina: I know, but I heard the park is a lot more fun. Please ....

Mom: All right. Let's change our schedule for the second day.

Gina: Thank you! I'm very ⓓexciting about the trip.

Mom: It's great to hear that you're looking ⓔ forward to the trip.

09 위 대화의 밑줄 친 ⓐ~ⓔ 중 어법상 틀린 것을 찾아 바르게 고치시오.

➡ _____

10 위 대화에서 다음 영영풀이가 나타내는 말을 찾아 쓰시오.

> a system of paths separated by walls or hedges built in a park or garden that is designed so that it is difficult to find your way through

➡ _____

11 위 대화의 내용과 일치하지 않는 것은?

① 엄마는 제주도 여행 계획을 세웠다.
② 지나는 둘째 날 거울 미로 공원 방문이 가능할지 물었다.
③ 지나는 말을 타러 가고 싶다고 엄마에게 이야기 했었다.
④ 엄마는 둘째 날 계획을 변경하였다.
⑤ 지나는 둘째 날 거울 미로 공원과 말을 타는 것을 모두 할 것이다.

12 다음 짝지어진 대화가 어색한 것을 고르시오.

① A: Is it possible to survive under the sea?
   B: Why not? All I need is a swimming mask.
② A: How do I get to the city hall?
   B: Go straight for two blocks and turn left. You can see it on your right.
③ A: Could you tell me the way to the post office?
   B: Okay! That's a great idea!
④ A: How do you get to school from your place?
   B: From my place, walk two blocks and turn right. It takes about 10 minutes.
⑤ A: How do we get to the city museum?
   B: How about taking the subway? I think it will be convenient.

[13~14] 다음 문장의 밑줄 친 부사절을 분사구문으로 바르게 바꾼 것은?

13

> If there comes a time when we can't be together, keep me in your heart. I'll stay there forever.

① Coming a time when we can't be together,
② We coming a time when we can't be together
③ If there coming a time when we can't be together,
④ There coming a time when we can't be together,
⑤ A time coming there when we can't be together,

14

> Though Ms. Kim meets a lot of people these days, she feels more lonely than before.

① Meeting a lot of people these days,
② Ms. Kim meeting a lot of people these days,
③ Ms. Kim met a lot of people these days,
④ Though Ms. Kim meeting a lot of people these days,
⑤ Meeting Ms. Kim a lot of people these days,

15 다음 중 어법상 <u>어색한</u> 문장을 <u>모두</u> 고르시오.

① Mom bought some cookies on her way home.
② Every athletes practices so hard to win a gold medal.
③ All the runners have to spend many hours at the track.
④ Tracy wondered if she could receive another when she dropped her spoon.
⑤ Dave has five big luxury cars, but I have only two small one.

16 다음 문장의 밑줄 친 부사절을 분사구문으로 알맞게 바꾼 것을 고르시오.

> As she didn't get enough scores to enter the college, Suji decided to study once more.

① As she getting not enough scores to enter the college,
② There not getting enough scores to enter the college,
③ Getting not enough scores to enter the college,
④ As getting not enough scores to enter the college,
⑤ Not getting enough scores to enter the college,

17 다음 괄호 안에서 어법상 알맞은 것을 고르시오.

(1) Either of the engineers (is / are) going to record the song today.

(2) Both of the dance teams (is / are) performing one of their best skills.

(3) (Every / Each) of the college students should complete their assignment by Friday next week.

(4) Neither of the two boys (like / likes) the soup made by Olga.

(5) This plate is dirty. Is there anyone to bring me (other / another)?

(6) Some of my apple (is / are) going to be cut for the chemical experiment.

(7) Julie can play two instruments, (neither / both) of which is a stringed one.

18 다음 밑줄 친 부분 중 어법상 어색한 것을 고르시오.

① Being tired, Chris lay down on the bed and took a rest.

② Strictly speaking, the prime minster of Japan can't make right decisions.

③ Raining all day, my friends and I stayed at home, watching movies.

④ Finding the necklace she had lost, I called Suji to come to my place.

⑤ Not having enough money, Ted couldn't buy the present for his daughter.

Reading

[19~22] 다음 글을 읽고 물음에 답하시오.

Comparing the two pictures below, you can easily notice some differences. For example, the picture on the left is called a labyrinth and only has an entrance. The picture on the right is called a maze and has both an entrance and an exit.

You can find the origin of the labyrinth in Greek mythology. It is said to be a prison that you cannot escape. But you may notice that the labyrinth has only a single path. There are no dead ends. This means you don't have to worry about getting out of it when you enter it. If you follow the path all the way to the end, you will reach the center. (A)_____, you simply have to turn around and walk back out the way you came in.

When you are in a maze, it's a different story. There are many choices (B)to make and dead ends to frustrate you. You have to keep making decisions about which way to go. If you are not careful, you can easily lose your way.

19 다음 중 빈칸 (A)에 들어갈 말로 가장 적절한 것은?

① To make out
② To find the center
③ To get out
④ To notice where you are
⑤ To know where the center is

20 다음 중 위 글을 읽고 답할 수 있는 것은?

① How many people can use a maze?
② When was the labyrinth made in Greek mythology?
③ Why does the maze have both an entrance and an exit?
④ Why does a maze make us frustrated?
⑤ What is the easy way to get out of a maze?

21 다음과 같이 풀이되는 말을 위 글에서 찾아 쓰시오.

> a road, passage, etc. that is closed at one end

➡ _____

22 다음 중 밑줄 친 (B)와 쓰임이 같은 것은?

① He went out to get some fresh air.
② June had the chance to apologize.
③ It is my job to please her.
④ She came in to find her book.
⑤ I was sad to see the news about virus.

[23~25] 다음 글을 읽고 물음에 답하시오.

Today, I went to the nearby maze park with my friends. ① The maze looked hard to solve. ② There were many choices, and I had to keep making decisions about which way to go. ③ My friends said that I should just place my hand on one wall from the beginning and keep following the same wall. ④ I enjoyed myself very much at the park. ⑤ Also, I found the beauty of order and regularity there and thought that human beings are really creative.

23 다음 중 위 글의 내용과 일치하는 것은?

① The writer went to the maze park alone.
② The maze wasn't difficult to solve.
③ The writer couldn't get out of the maze.
④ The maze made the writer ignorant of the creativeness of human beings.
⑤ The writer had the pleasure of experiencing the maze.

24 ①~⑤ 중 주어진 문장이 들어가기에 가장 적절한 곳은?

> That solution was simple but not very effective.

①   ②   ③   ④   ⑤

25 How did the maze look to the writer? Answer in English with a full sentence.

➡ _____

[26~27] 다음 글을 읽고 물음에 답하시오.

USA – Pineapple Garden Maze
If you visit Oahu, Hawaii, the Pineapple Garden Maze is a must see. It is the world's longest maze, and it attracts visitors from around the world. The maze has 11,400 native plants and covers about 5 kilometers.
England – Hampton Court Maze
The oldest hedge maze in Britain is the Hampton Court Maze. It was built in 1689. Hundreds of thousands of people visit this maze that was created during the time of William of Orange.

26 다음 중 위 글의 제목으로 가장 적절한 것은?

① Maze: an Infamous Prison
② World's Well Known Attractions
③ Famous Mazes Around the World
④ Things You Never Know about Mazes
⑤ The Origin of Mazes

27 How long is the Pineapple Garden Maze? Answer in English.

➡ _____

출제율 90%

01 다음 영영풀이가 가리키는 것을 〈보기〉에서 고르시오.

> (1) to give things of a particular kind to each other at the same time
> (2) to make somebody feel annoyed or impatient because they cannot do or achieve what they want

┤ 보기 ├
confuse, frustrate, exit, exchange

➡ (1) _____, (2) _____

출제율 95%

02 다음 우리말과 일치하도록 주어진 어구를 배열하여 완성하시오.

(1) 그는 오늘 아침 감옥에서 탈출했다.
(this / he / from / morning / the / escaped / prison)
➡ _____

(2) 그들은 그 문제를 해결하기 위해 효과적인 방법들을 생각해 내려고 노력했다.
(come / ways / the problem / with / they / up / tried to / effective / to solve)
➡ _____
_____

(3) 화성에서 생존하는 것이 가능한가?
(it / on / is / to / Mars / possible / survive)
➡ _____

(4) 그 3층으로 된 건물은 어린이를 위한 만 여권의 책을 보유하고 있다.
(three-story / building / kids / books / has / the / 10,000 / about / for)
➡ _____

[03~05] 다음 대화를 읽고 물음에 답하시오.

W: How may I help you?
B: Hi! I ⓐbought these shoes yesterday. Is it possible ⓑto exchange them for the red shoes?
W: Oh, actually white is really popular ⓒthese days.
B: I know, and that's why I spent a long time ⓓmake the decision yesterday. But I think ⓔthat red will look better on me.
W: Okay, no problem.

출제율 90%

03 위 대화의 밑줄 친 ⓐ~ⓔ 중 어법상 어색한 것을 골라 바르게 고치시오.
➡ _____

출제율 100%

04 위 대화의 여자와 남자의 관계로 적절한 것은?

① clerk – customer
② teacher – student
③ doctor – nurse
④ tourist – guide
⑤ post officer – visitor

출제율 100%

05 위 대화의 내용과 일치하지 않는 것은?

① The boy bought the shoes yesterday.
② The boy wants to exchange the shoes for the red ones.
③ The white shoes are really popular these days.
④ It took a long time for the boy to make the decision about the color.
⑤ The woman suggested the red shoes because they looked better on him.

[06~07] 다음 대화를 읽고 물음에 답하시오.

Andrew: Hey, Minju, where are you?

Minju: Oh, Andrew, I'm coming. I'm coming.

Andrew: Good. I was worried that you were lost.

Minju: I think I'm okay. What about Mason and Jian?

Andrew: They are already here at my house.

Minju: Good! Oh, I see the post office. (A)여기서부터 너희 집까지 어떻게 가니?

Andrew: You are almost here. Go straight for one more block. Then you will see Kim's Bakery.

Minju: Kim's Bakery? Okay ....

Andrew: Then turn right and go straight for about 100 meters.

Minju: Turn right and go straight .... Okay, thanks! I'll see you soon.

🖊 출제율 90%

06 밑줄 친 (A)의 우리말을 〈보기〉에 주어진 단어들을 배열하여 영작하시오.

┌─── 보기 ───┐
place / here / how / to / from / I / do / get / your
└────────┘

➡ _____

🖊 출제율 100%

07 위 대화의 내용과 일치하지 <u>않는</u> 것은?

① 민주는 Andrew네 집에 가고 있다.

② Andrew는 민주가 길을 잃었을까봐 걱정했다.

③ Mason과 지나는 이미 Andrew네 집에 도착했다.

④ 민주는 우체국에서 한 블록 더 직진하면 킴스 빵집이 보일 것이다.

⑤ 민주는 킴스 빵집에서 왼쪽으로 돌아 100미터 정도 직진하면 Andrew네 집을 찾을 수 있다.

[08~10] 다음 대화를 읽고 물음에 답하시오.

Mina: (A)너희 모두 이번 주말에 여행갈 준비됐니? (set, all, for, are)

Jinho, Claire, & Henry: Yes!

Mina: Good! Don't be late! We're meeting at 11 a.m. in front of the clock tower.

Jinho: You got it! How do we get to the airport? I don't think we've decided yet.

Henry: Jinho is right. We have two choices, bus or subway.

Claire: What about the subway? It's more reliable than the bus.

Henry: Is it possible to get to Terminal 2 by subway?

Claire: Yes, I already checked.

Mina: Good. Okay, then let's take the subway.

🖊 출제율 90%

08 위 대화의 밑줄 친 (A)의 우리말을 주어진 단어들을 사용하여 영작하시오.

➡ _____

🖊 출제율 95%

09 When and where are Mina, Jiho, Claire and Henry going to meet?

➡ _____

_____

🖊 출제율 95%

10 How will Mina, Jiho, Claire and Henry get to Terminal 2?

➡ _____

11 다음 중 빈칸에 들어갈 알맞은 말을 고르시오. *출제율 90%*

> Would you like to have _____ chocolate cookies and hot tea?

① some   ② another   ③ one
④ that   ⑤ others

12 다음 중 어법상 올바른 문장을 <u>모두</u> 고르면? *출제율 100%*

① The director winning the big awards, her fans in France felt proud of her.
② Writing too quickly, the letter had many mistakes.
③ Worked hard to review the final experiment, Sean was not able to sleep.
④ There being no pickup service, we had to walk all the way to the hotel.
⑤ Being looked a lot more elegant than before, the flowers are in bloom.

13 다음 각 문장의 부사절을 알맞은 분사구문으로 전환하여, 빈칸을 채우시오. *출제율 90%*

(1) When I went to the nearby maze park with my parents, I found the maze there looked too hard to solve.

➡ _____

I found the maze there looked too hard to solve.

(2) After they looked at the labyrinths closely, they found the beauty of order and regularity.

➡ _____

they found the beauty of order and regularity.

(3) Since Katherine had not been invited to the wedding, she stayed at home all day long.

➡ _____

Katherine stayed at home all day long.

14 다음 중 우리말과 그 영작이 어법상 바르게 짝지어지지 <u>않</u><u>은</u> 것은? *출제율 100%*

① Ben은 두 언어 모두에 흥미를 느꼈다.
→ Ben felt interested in both of the languages.
② 그 배우 두 사람 중 어느 누구도 영화에 출연한 적이 없다.
→ Neither of the actors has ever appeared in a movie.
③ 나는 장난감이 없어서 하나 갖고 싶다.
→ I have no toys, so I want to have one.
④ 우리 둘 다 클래식 음악을 좋아한다.
→ Both of us like classical music.
⑤ 나는 거리에서 세 마리의 개를 봤는데, 그것들 각각은 다른 종류였다.
→ I saw three dogs on the street, each of which were a different kind.

[15~18] 다음 글을 읽고 물음에 답하시오.

These days, mazes are often considered left-brain puzzles. Many people ①willingly visit maze parks and enjoy the "planned confusion." And some of (A)them ②came down with their own solutions. The easiest and most reliable one is to place a hand on one wall from the very beginning. Then you just keep following that wall. It's like walking ③in a dark room. Unfortunately, this simple method may not be ④effective in certain types of mazes, especially when all of the walls are not connected.

Mazes are made with a variety of different materials, like walls and rooms, hedges, bricks, mirrors, and even snow. In fact, they can also be ⑤printed or drawn on paper. Here is one as an example. This is called a number maze. You start from point A and have to go in the order of 1 → 9 → 8 → 5 → 1 → 9 → .... Why don't you give it a try? You have 30 seconds to escape!

15 ①~⑤ 중 글의 흐름상 적절하지 않은 것은?

①   ②   ③   ④   ⑤

16 다음 중 밑줄 친 (A)가 가리키는 것으로 가장 적절한 것은?

① left-brain puzzles   ② mazes
③ many people   ④ maze parks
⑤ solutions

17 다음 중 위 글의 내용과 일치하는 것은?

① There are few people who enjoy maze parks.
② It is impossible to find an easy solution to get out of a maze.
③ We can't enjoy mazes on paper.
④ People can make mazes with snow.
⑤ The number maze has no regularity.

18 What is one example of a printed maze? Answer in English.

➡ _____

[19~21] 다음 글을 읽고 물음에 답하시오.

USA – Pineapple Garden Maze
If you visit Oahu, Hawaii, the Pineapple Garden Maze is a ①must see. It is the world's longest maze, and it attracts visitors from around the world. The maze has 11,400 native plants and ②covers about 5 kilometers.

England – Hampton Court Maze
The oldest hedge maze in Britain is the Hampton Court Maze. It was built ③in 1689. Hundreds of thousands of people visit this maze that ④created during the time of William of Orange.

Italy – Labirinto di Villa Pasani
It was created in 1720 and is known as the most difficult ⑤one to solve. Part of the problem is the height of the hedges. (A)산울타리가 너무 높아서 사람들은 그 너머를 볼 수가 없다. You get a perfect view only once you've got to the center and climbed the stairs to the top of the tower.

19 다음 중 위 글을 읽고 답할 수 없는 것은?

① Where is the Pineapple Garden Maze located?
② What is the longest maze in the world?
③ When was the Hampton Court Maze built?
④ Who built the Hampton Court Maze?
⑤ What is the Labirinto di Villa Pasani known as?

20 ①~⑤ 중 어법상 바르지 않은 것은?

①   ②   ③   ④   ⑤

21 주어진 단어를 활용하여 밑줄 친 (A)의 우리말을 영어로 쓰시오.

they / so / that / over

➡ _____

[01~03] 다음 대화를 읽고 물음에 답하시오.

Gina: Mom, did you decide where to visit during our family trip to Jeju?

Mom: Almost. Come here and see the plan I made.

Gina: It looks good. Hmm... Mom, is it possible to visit Mirror Maze Park on our second day?

Mom: It sounds exciting, but I remember you said you wanted to go horseback riding.

Gina: I know, but I heard the park is a lot more fun. Please ....

Mom: All right. Let's change our schedule for the second day.

Gina: Thank you! I'm very excited about the trip.

Mom: It's great to hear that you're looking forward to the trip.

01 Where does Gina want to visit on the second day?

➡ _____

_____

02 What was the original plan on the second day?

➡ _____

03 Why does Gina want to change the schedule?

➡ _____

_____

04 다음 우리말에 맞도록 괄호 안에 주어진 어휘를 알맞게 배열하시오.

(1) 아래의 두 그림을 비교할 때, 당신은 몇 가지 차이점을 쉽게 알아차릴 수 있다. (pictures, the, below, two, comparing)

➡ _____

you can easily notice some differences.

(2) Jane은 Tom의 미로 탈출 방식을 이해하지 못했기 때문에, 그가 말한 대로 하지 않기로 결심했다. (Tom's, getting, not, the maze, out of, understanding, method of)

➡ _____

_____ Jane decided not to do as he said.

(3) 통로를 따라 끝까지 가면, 당신은 중앙에 도착할 것이다. (the path, to, through, the end, following)

➡ _____

you will reach the center.

05 다음 중에서 어법상 옳지 않은 표현이 들어간 문장을 찾아, 번호를 쓰고, 바르게 고쳐 문장을 다시 쓰시오.

① Someone having touched the doorlock of her apartment, Sam couldn't get into her place that night.

② Finding the puppy her brother had lost, Emily cried out with tears of joy.

③ Having just completed the final essay, Sam went to bed.

④ Talking with so many people for so long hours, the author got exhausted.

⑤ Anne having been infected with the virus before, she is well aware of the fear of the disease.

➡ _____

_____

06 다음 그림을 보고, 그림과 내용상 일치하는 문장을 고르시오.

① One of the animals doesn't seem to like the green food on the table.

② All are putting their hands out on the table which is full of food.

③ None of the animals is likely to pick up the carrot.

④ Every animal invited to the party seems to love eating vegetables.

⑤ Both of the rabbits have some whiskers.

*whisker: 수염

[07~10] 다음 글을 읽고 물음에 답하시오.

Comparing the two pictures below, you can easily notice some differences. For example, the picture on the left is called a labyrinth and only has an entrance. The picture on the right is called a maze and has both an entrance and an exit.

You can find the origin of the labyrinth in Greek mythology. It is said to be a prison that you cannot escape. But you may notice that the labyrinth has only a single path. There are no dead ends. This means you don't have to worry about getting out of it when you enter it. If you follow the path all the way to the end, you will reach the center. To get out, you simply have to turn around and (A)들어간 길대로 걸어 나오면 됩니다.

When you are in a maze, it's a different story. There are many choices to make and dead ends to frustrate you. You have to keep making decisions about which way to go. If you are not careful, you can easily lose your way.

07 Write the reason why you don't need to worry about getting out of the labyrinth when you enter it. Use the phrase 'It's because.'

➡ _____

_____

08 위 글의 내용에 맞게 미궁과 미로의 특징을 바르게 분류하시오.

ⓐ It has both an entrance and an exit.
ⓑ It has only a single path.
ⓒ You can find its origin in Greek mythology.
ⓓ It has many dead ends.

➡ 미궁: _____, 미로: _____

09 What happens if you are not careful in a maze? Answer in English.

➡ _____

10 주어진 단어를 바르게 나열하여 밑줄 친 우리말 (A)를 영어로 쓰시오.

in / out / the way / walk / came / back / you

➡ _____

01 다음 대화의 내용과 일치하도록 빈칸을 완성하시오.

Andrew: Hey, Minju, where are you?

Minju: Oh, Andrew, I'm coming. I'm coming.

Andrew: Good. I was worried that you were lost.

Minju: I think I'm okay. What about Mason and Jian?

Andrew: They are already here at my house.

Minju: Good! Oh, I see the post office. How do I get to your place from here?

Andrew: You are almost here. Go straight for one more block. Then you will see Kim's Bakery.

Minju: Kim's Bakery? Okay … .

Andrew: Then turn right and go straight for about 100 meters.

Minju: Turn right and go straight … . Okay, thanks! I'll see you soon.

Minju was supposed to get together at (A)_____ with Mason and Jian. When Minju was late, Andrew was worried if (B)_____. When he called her, she was near (C)_____. Andrew explained to Minju how to get to his place. He said that she should go straight for one more block and then could see (D)_____. After that, she should (E)_____.

02 다음 그림에서 자신이 원하는 휴대전화 케이스를 선택하고, 〈보기〉의 대화문 문장을 응용하여, 자신의 답변을 2개 이상 만드시오.

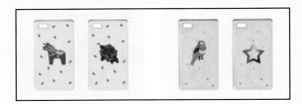

┌─ 보기 ───┐

A: What type of cell phone case would you choose?

B: I'll choose a pink one. I also like the one with a horse on it.

└──┘

(1) _____

(2) _____

(3) _____

단원별 모의고사

01 다음 짝지어진 단어의 관계가 같도록 빈칸에 알맞은 말을 쓰시오.

> act : activity = suggest : _____

02 다음 영영풀이가 가리키는 것을 고르시오.

> a door, gate, passage, etc. used for entering a room, building or place

① entrance   ② exit
③ confusion   ④ choice
⑤ labyrinth

03 다음 우리말을 주어진 단어를 이용하여 영작하시오.

(1) 우리는 미로에서 길을 잃었다. (get, in)
➡ _____

(2) 오늘의 실패에 좌절하지 마라. (failure, be)
➡ _____

(3) 우리는 믿을 만하고 열심히 일하는 사람을 찾고 있다. (look, reliable, hard-working, someone, who)
➡ _____
_____

04 다음 우리말에 맞게 빈칸에 알맞은 말을 쓰시오. (철자가 주어진 것도 있음.)

(1) 미로는 흔히 좌뇌형 퍼즐로 여겨진다.
➡ Mazes are often c_____ left-brain puzzles.

(2) 미궁은 입구만 있다.
➡ A labyrinth only has an _____.

(3) 자세히 들여다보면, 당신은 질서와 규칙성이라는 아름다움을 발견할 수 있을지도 모른다.
➡ Looking at them c_____, you may find the beauty of order and _____.

(4) 이것을 빨간색 신발로 교환하는 것이 가능한가요?
➡ Is it possible to _____ them for the red shoes?

05 다음 문장의 빈칸에 들어갈 말을 〈보기〉에서 골라 쓰시오.

> ┤ 보기 ├
>
> making decisions / a variety of / lose your way / dead ends / in the order of

(1) Mazes are made with _____ different materials.

(2) There are no _____.

(3) You start from point A and have to go _____ 1 → 2 → 3 → 4.

(4) If you are not careful, you can easily _____.

(5) You have to keep _____ about which way to go.

[06~07] 다음 대화를 읽고 물음에 답하시오.

> Juwon: What are you reading, Alice?
> Alice: It's about the origin of the labyrinth.
> Juwon: Labyrinth? Wasn't that an old mythological prison to keep the half-man, half-bull monster?
> Alice: Oh, Juwon, you know about the story.
> Juwon: Not really. I forgot the name of the monster.
> Alice: The Minotaur. The king of Crete was angry at it and put it in a labyrinth.
> Juwon: Interesting! Alice, is it possible to borrow the book after you're finished with it?
> Alice: Sure, no problem. Maybe this Friday.

06 위 대화의 내용과 일치하도록 빈칸을 완성하시오.

A labyrinth was an (A)_____
_____ to keep the half-man, half-
bull monster, named (B)_____.
It was built by (C)_____
because he was upset at it and he wanted
to lock it up in the (D)_____.

07 When can Juwon borrow the book from Alice?

➡ _____

[08~09] 다음 대화를 읽고 물음에 답하시오.

Mike: Hi, do you need any help?
Sora: (A) Yes, please. Could you suggest a
good Chinese restaurant in this building?
I can't decide between the two.
Mike: (B) Hmm.... What about Pappa Chen's?
Their food is good and the prices are
reasonable.
Sora: (C) Sounds great! How do I get to the
restaurant?
Mike: (D) Pappa Chen's is next to the elevator.
Sora: (E) Great! Thank you very much for
your help.
Mike: My pleasure. Enjoy your dinner.

08 위 대화의 (A)~(E) 중 주어진 문장이 들어가기에 적절한 곳은?

It's on the fourth floor. You can use the
elevator over there.

① (A)   ② (B)   ③ (C)   ④ (D)   ⑤ (E)

09 위 대화를 읽고 대답할 수 없는 것은?

① What does Sora ask Mike to do?
② What does Mike recommend?
③ Where is Pappa Chen's in this building?
④ How can Sora get to Pappa Chen's?
⑤ With whom will Sora go to a good
Chinese restaurant?

[10~12] 다음 대화를 읽고 물음에 답하시오.

Andrew: Hey, Minju, where are you?
Minju: Oh, Andrew, I'm coming. I'm coming.
Andrew: Good. I was worried that you were
lost.
Minju: I think I'm okay. What about Mason and
Jian?
Andrew: They are already here at my house.
Minju: Good! Oh, I see the post office. How do
I get to your place from here?
Andrew: You are almost here. Go straight for
one more block. Then you will see
Kim's Bakery.
Minju: Kim's Bakery? Okay ....
Andrew: Then turn right and go straight for
about 100 meters.
Minju: Turn right and go straight .... Okay,
thanks! I'll see you soon.

10 Why was Andrew worried about Minju?

➡ _____

11 With whom is Minju supposed to get together at Andrew's place?

➡ _____
_____

12 How does Minju get to Andrew's place from Kim's Bakery?

➡ _____
_____

13 다음 각 문장의 밑줄 친 분사구문을 부사절로 바꿀 때 어법상 어색한 것은?

① <u>Completing the important project</u>, all of his team members were rewarded.

→ After they completed the important project,

② <u>It being cloudy and chilly</u>, she went outside to see the blossoms.

→ Though it was cloudy and chilly,

③ <u>Seen from far away</u>, the high building will look like a devil's tower in the movie.

→ If it is seen from far away,

④ <u>Learning the computer language</u>, she couldn't understand the program.

→ When she learned the computer language,

⑤ <u>There being nothing to listen to</u>, I turned off the radio.

→ Since there was nothing to listen to,

[14~16] 다음 문장의 밑줄 친 부분 중 어법상 어색한 것을 고르시오.

14 ① Ben bought a big boat and his sister bought a small <u>one</u>.

② Franklin has three shirts. One is black, <u>another</u> navy, and the other sky-blue.

③ My daughter doesn't need this. Show her <u>another</u>, please.

④ Helen had two dreams. One was to see her mom, and <u>other</u> was to marry Jack.

⑤ There were a lot of stars in the sky. Some were bright, while <u>others</u> were dim.

15 ① We have no boxes to put things in, so if you have any, please lend us <u>one</u>.

② The officers required that we finish reviewing <u>all</u> of the reports.

③ He made a lot of mistakes, <u>none</u> of which is completely wrong.

④ <u>Anyone</u> interested in joining the club should contact Ms. Baker.

⑤ If you're looking for a Korean restaurant, I will let you know <u>it</u>.

16 ① <u>Being nervous</u>, the kids searched for a way to get out of the maze.

② <u>Having written quickly</u>, the book has a lot of mistakes.

③ <u>Wanting to praise him</u>, his father gave James a big hug.

④ <u>Having nothing to do</u>, the dogs sat quietly in the corner of the living room.

⑤ <u>It being stormy</u>, a ship went fishing early that morning.

17 다음 각 그림과 우리말에 맞게 주어진 단어들과 필요한 부정대명사를 추가하여, 영작하시오. (동사 변형 가능, 단어 수 조건 맞출 것)

(1) 어떤 사람들은 피자를 먹고, 또 다른 사람들은 집으로 가져간다. (it, eat, home, take, and, pizza 총 8 단어)

➡ _____

(2) 둘 다 물고기를 잡는 것에 관심이 있다.
(interested, fish, be, in, catching 총 6
단어)

➡ _____

18 다음 각 문장의 밑줄 친 부사절을 분사구문으로 바꾼 것 중 옳은 것은?

① If the hero had cut off the wrong wire, the building would have exploded.
→ Having cut off the wrong wire,

② Since Sharon went to bed earlier, she woke up at dawn.
→ Sharon going to bed earlier,

③ When it is seen from one side, the grass in the other side always looks greener.
→ Seen from one side,

④ While mom was reading a story book, the baby fell asleep.
→ Reading a story book,

⑤ As there was no umbrella, I came home without it.
→ Being no umbrella,

[19~21] 다음 글을 읽고 물음에 답하시오.

You can find the origin of the labyrinth in Greek mythology. ① It is said to be a prison that you cannot escape. ② But you may notice that the labyrinth has only a single path. ③ There are no dead ends. ④ If you follow the path all the way to the end, you will reach the center. ⑤ To get out, you simply have to turn around and walk back out the way you came in.

When you are in a maze, it's a different story. There are many choices to make and dead ends to frustrate you. You have to keep making decisions about which way to go. If you are not careful, you can easily lose your way.

19 ①~⑤ 중 주어진 문장이 들어가기에 가장 적절한 곳은?

This means you don't have to worry about getting out of it when you enter it.

①   ②   ③   ④   ⑤

20 다음 중 위 글을 읽고 답할 수 있는 것은?

① Who is the first person that made a maze?

② How many solutions are there to get out of a maze?

③ Why do we need to be careful in a maze?

④ How many dead ends are there in a maze?

⑤ Why does a labyrinth have only one path?

21 다음은 labyrinth에 들어온 친구들의 대화이다. 글의 내용에 맞게 빈칸에 알맞은 말을 쓰시오.

A: Do you know how we can reach the center?
B: Sure. Just _____
_____, and you will reach the center.

[22~25] 다음 글을 읽고 물음에 답하시오.

Mazes are made with ①a variety of different materials, ②like walls and rooms, hedges, bricks, mirrors, and even snow. In fact, ③they can also be printed or drawn on paper. Here is one as an example. This is called a number maze. You start from point A and have to go in the order of 1 → 9 → 8 → 5 → 1 → 9 → … . Why don't you give it a try? You have 30 seconds to escape!

Labyrinths and mazes are truly fun, but (A)that's not the end of the story. (B)If you look at them closely, you may find the beauty of order and regularity. They may also show you ④how creative human beings are.

⑤If there is a maze park on your next trip, why don't you stop and take some time to enjoy it? It will surely be worth visiting!

22 ①~⑤에 관한 설명으로 바르지 <u>않은</u> 것은?

① various로 바꾸어 쓸 수 있다.
② such as로 바꾸어 쓸 수 있다.
③ mazes를 지칭하는 말이다.
④ 간접의문문이므로 'how human beings are creative'로 고쳐 써야 한다.
⑤ 조건절을 이끄는 접속사이다.

23 다음 중 밑줄 친 (A)의 의미로 가장 적절한 것은?

① There is nothing in labyrinths and mazes except being fun.
② Labyrinths and mazes have something good other than being fun.
③ There are many stories related to labyrinths and mazes.
④ It is the end of the story of labyrinths and mazes.
⑤ It is hard to say that labyrinths and mazes have their own stories.

24 밑줄 친 (B)를 분사구문으로 바꿔 쓰시오.

➡ _____

25 What may you find when you look at labyrinths and mazes closely? Answer in English with a full sentence.

➡ _____

_____

26 다음 중 Labirinto di Villa Pasani에 관한 내용과 일치하지 <u>않는</u> 것은?

Italy – Labirinto di Villa Pasani
It was created in 1720 and is known as the most difficult one to solve. Part of the problem is the height of the hedges. They are so high that people can't see over them. You get a perfect view only once you've got to the center and climbed the stairs to the top of the tower.

① It is located in Italy.
② It was built in 1720.
③ People think it is the most difficult to solve.
④ There are stairs leading to the top of the tower.
⑤ The height of the hedges enables people to see over them with ease.

MEMO

To Each His Own

의사소통 기능

- 의견 묻기
  What do you think of having a concert?
- 동의하거나 이의 제기하기
  I agree. / I disagree.

언어 형식

- 'It is/was ~ that ...' 강조구문
  It is a dog **that** I want for a pet.
- 접속부사 However
  However, some people have different opinions.

Words & Expressions

Key Words

- **acronym**[ǽkrənim] 몡 두문자어
- **advice**[ædváis] 몡 충고
- **allow**[əláu] 동 허가하다
- **always**[ɔ́:lweiz] 부 항상
- **attract**[ətrǽkt] 동 마음을 끌다
- **blame**[bleim] 동 비난하다
- **captain**[kǽptən] 몡 선장, 주장
- **careful**[kéərfəl] 혱 조심하는
- **cause**[kɔːz] 동 ~을 야기하다
- **close**[klous] 혱 가까운
- **complete**[kəmplíːt] 동 완료하다
- **concert**[káːnsərt] 몡 연주회, 콘서트
- **confused**[kənfjúːzd] 혱 혼란스러워 하는
- **cousin**[kʌ́zn] 몡 사촌
- **decide**[disáid] 동 결정하다
- **destroy**[distrɔ́i] 동 파괴하다
- **easily**[íːzili] 부 쉽게
- **enough**[inʌ́f] 부 충분히
- **environment**[inváiərənmənt] 몡 환경
- **fascinate**[fǽsənèit] 동 마음을 사로잡다
- **feather**[féðər] 몡 깃털
- **festival**[féstəvəl] 몡 축제
- **flock**[flɑk] 몡 떼, 무리
- **grab**[græb] 동 붙잡다
- **grass**[græs] 몡 풀, 잔디
- **guitar**[gitáːr] 몡 기타
- **gym**[dʒim] 몡 체육관
- **harm**[hɑːrm] 동 해를 끼치다
- **however**[hauévər] 부 그러나
- **influence**[ínfluəns] 동 영향을 미치다
- **judge**[dʒʌdʒ] 동 판단하다
- **language**[lǽŋgwidʒ] 몡 언어
- **leap**[liːp] 동 뛰어오르다
- **mean**[miːn] 동 의미하다
- **mistake**[mistéik] 몡 실수
- **need**[niːd] 동 ~을 필요로 하다
- **opportunity**[àpərtjúːnəti] 몡 기회
- **opposite**[ápəzit] 몡 반대
- **proverb**[právəːrb] 몡 속담
- **quality**[kwáləti] 몡 질
- **regret**[rigrét] 동 후회하다
- **reserve**[rizə́ːrv] 동 예약하다
- **result**[rizʌ́lt] 몡 결과
- **rude**[ruːd] 혱 무례한
- **sadly**[sǽdli] 부 슬프게, 애석하게도
- **saying**[séiiŋ] 몡 속담, 격언
- **science**[sáiəns] 몡 과학
- **still**[stil] 부 아직
- **stony**[stóuni] 혱 돌이 많은
- **tool**[tuːl] 몡 도구
- **trick**[trik] 몡 속임수
- **unhealthy**[ənhélθi] 혱 건강하지 못한
- **unwise**[ənwáiz] 혱 현명하지 못한, 어리석은
- **useful**[júːsfəl] 혱 유용한, 쓸모있는
- **while**[hwail] 접 ~하는 동안
- **wisdom**[wízdəm] 몡 지혜

Key Expressions

- **ASAP (as soon as possible)** 가능한 한 빨리
- **as a result** 결과적으로
- **every now and then** 때때로, 가끔
- **find out** 발견하다
- **for example** 예를 들어
- **give it a second thought** 다시 생각해 보다
- **hand in** 제출하다
- **have a fight with ~** ~와 싸우다
- **instead of ~** 대신에
- **in a hurry** 서둘러
- **in front of** ~의 앞쪽에
- **in the end** 결국, 마침내
- **keep in touch** 연락을 취하다
- **leave ~ behind** ~을 두고 가다, 뒤에 남기다
- **make a decision** 결정하다
- **move away** 떠나다, 이사가다
- **raise money** 돈을 마련하다
- **rely on** 의존하다
- **spend time V–ing** ~하는 데 시간을 보내다
- **talk behind a person's back** 남의 험담을 하다
- **take A away from B** B로부터 A를 빼앗다
- **think over ~** 을 심사숙고하다
- **upside down** 거꾸로

Word Power

※ 서로 비슷한 뜻을 가진 어휘

- □ **agree** 동의하다 – **assent** 동의하다
- □ **close** 가까운 – **near** 가까운
- □ **enough** 충분히 – **sufficiently** 충분히
- □ **leap** 뛰어오르다 – **jump** 뛰어오르다
- □ **need** 필요로 하다 – **require** 필요로 하다

- □ **allow** 허가하다 – **permit** 허가하다
- □ **complete** 완료하다 – **finish** 끝내다
- □ **however** 그러나 – **nevertheless** 그럼에도 불구하고
- □ **mean** 의미하다 – **represent** 나타내다
- □ **opportunity** 기회 – **chance** 가능성, 기회

※ 서로 반대의 뜻을 가진 어휘

- □ **agree** 동의하다 ↔ **disagree** 동의하지 않다
- □ **rude** 무례한 ↔ **polite** 예의바른
- □ **unhealthy** 건강하지 못한 ↔ **healthy** 건강한
- □ **wisdom** 지혜 ↔ **foolishness** 어리석음

- □ **careful** 조심하는 ↔ **careless** 부주의한
- □ **sadly** 슬프게 ↔ **happily** 행복하게
- □ **unwise** 현명하지 못한 ↔ **wise** 지혜로운, 슬기로운

※ 접두사 un- → un+형용사

- □ **un-** + **attractive** → **unattractive** 매력적이지 못한
- □ **un-** + **educated** → **uneducated** 무지한
- □ **un-** + **healthy** → **unhealthy** 건강하지 못한
- □ **un-** + **usual** → **unusual** 특이한, 흔치 않은

- □ **un-** + **comfortable** → **uncomfortable** 불편한
- □ **un-** + **fortunate** → **unfortunate** 불행한
- □ **un-** + **intelligent** → **unintelligent** 우둔한
- □ **un-** + **wise** → **unwise** 현명하지 못한

※ 접미사 ly - → 형용사+ly

- □ **cheap** + **ly** → **cheaply** 저렴하게
- □ **happy** + **ly** → **happily** 행복하게
- □ **lucky** + **ly** → **luckily** 다행스럽게

- □ **easy** + **ly** → **easily** 쉽게
- □ **late** + **ly** → **lately** 최근에
- □ **quick** + **ly** → **quickly** 빨리

- □ **exact** + **ly** → **exactly** 정확히
- □ **loose** + **ly** → **loosely** 느슨하게
- □ **quiet** + **ly** → **quietly** 조용히

English Dictionary

□ **acronym** 두문자어
→ a word formed from the first letters of the words that make up the name of something
어떤 것의 이름을 구성하는 단어들의 처음 철자들로 형성된 단어

□ **agree** 동의하다
→ to have the same opinion 같은 의견을 가지다

□ **allow** 허가하다
→ to give permission 승인을 해주다

□ **become** ~이 되다
→ to come into being 생성되다

□ **careful** 조심하는
→ cautious in one's actions 행동에 신중한

□ **destroy** 파괴하다
→ to damage something so badly that it no longer exists, works, etc.
어떤 것을 매우 심하게 훼손하여 더 이상 존재하거나 작동하지 않다

□ **dull** 둔한, 따분한
→ not very lively or energetic 생기가 없거나 활동적이지 않은

□ **harm** 해를 끼치다, 손상시키다
→ to cause a person or animals physical injury, usually on purpose
보통 고의적으로 사람이나 동물이 신체적으로 해를 입게 하다

□ **influence** 영향을 미치다
→ to cause an effect on
~에 영향을 미치다

□ **leap** 뛰어오르다
→ to spring through the air from one point or position to another
한 지점 또는 위치에서 다른 지점이나 위치로 공중으로 뛰어오르다

□ **limit** 제한
→ the greatest amount, extent, or degree of something that is possible
어떤 것의 가능한 최대치의 양, 범위 또는 정도

□ **opposite** 반대
→ a person or thing that is contrary in character
성격상 상반되는 사람이나 물건

□ **regret** 후회하다
→ to feel sorrow or remorse for
슬픔이나 후회를 느끼다

□ **result** 결과
→ something that happens as a consequence
결과적으로 발생하는 것

01 접두사 un-을 붙여 반의어를 만들 수 없는 것을 고르시오.

① expensive ② attractive
③ comfortable ④ fortunate
⑤ healthy

02 밑줄 친 단어의 의미가 어색한 것을 고르시오.

① Like the saying goes, "All work and no play makes Jack a dull boy." (우둔한)
② Words of wisdom have influenced people and changed their lives in a great way. (영향을 미쳤다)
③ What does the proverb "Actions speak louder than words," mean? (속담)
④ It is the quality of time that makes people remember each other. (양)
⑤ Some say birds of a feather flock together. (깃털)

03 다음 빈칸 (A)와 (B)에 들어갈 말이 바르게 짝지어진 것은?

> • They are (A)_____ money to help flood victims.
> • Many working women rely (B)_____ relatives to help take care of their children.

  (A)   (B)
① rising on
② rising in
③ raising in
④ raising on
⑤ arising in

04 다음 제시된 단어를 사용하여 자연스러운 문장을 만들 수 없는 것은? (형태 변화 가능.)

> allow blame cause decide

① Which driver was to _____ for the accident?
② He _____ to study for the exam yesterday.
③ Don't you remember that you have to _____ in your cellphone before coming to class?
④ Please _____ me to present my apologies.
⑤ You have _____ us a lot of trouble today.

05 다음 짝지어진 단어의 관계가 〈보기〉와 같은 것끼리 짝지어진 것을 고르시오.

> ┤ 보기 ├
> allow – permit

> ⓐ rude – polite
> ⓑ wisdom – foolishness
> ⓒ rough – smooth
> ⓓ enough – sufficiently
> ⓔ agree – assent

① ⓐ, ⓑ   ② ⓐ, ⓔ
③ ⓑ, ⓒ   ④ ⓒ, ⓓ
⑤ ⓓ, ⓔ

01 다음 빈칸을 〈보기〉에 있는 어휘를 이용하여 채우시오. (각 어휘는 한 번씩만 사용 가능하며 형태 변화 가능.)

┌─── 보기 ───┐
attract   complete   grab   influence

(1) He _____ me by the arm then.
(2) The building took two years to _____.
(3) Do TV programs _____ children's behavior?
(4) What _____ me to him was his sense of humor.

02 빈칸을 주어진 영영풀이에 해당하는 말을 이용하여 채우시오.

have the same opinion

A: Cats are clean animals.
B: I _____.

03 다음 우리말에 맞도록 빈칸에 알맞은 말을 쓰시오.

(1) 나는 두문자어가 사용하기 재미있고 쉽다고 생각한다.
  ➡ I think _____ are fun and easy to use.
(2) 책의 표지로 책을 판단하지 말라.
  ➡ Don't _____ a book by its cover.
(3) 우리가 다시 생각해 보지 않고 어떤 일을 한다면 실수를 할 것이다.
  ➡ We'll make mistakes if we do something without _____ _____.
(4) 만약 우리가 시간을 들여 어떤 일을 심사숙고하지 않는다면 우리는 후회할지도 모른다.
  ➡ If we don't take time to _____ things _____, we may _____ it.

04 다음 괄호 안의 단어를 문맥에 맞게 고쳐 쓰시오.

(1) I know that smoking is _____. (healthy)
(2) I _____ get exhausted because I'm on my feet all day. (easy)

05 다음 밑줄 친 부분의 쓰임이 자연스럽지 않은 것을 찾아 고치시오.

ⓐ If you <u>will want</u>, I will buy the cap for you.
ⓑ I want to exercise every day, but I don't have <u>enough time</u>.
ⓒ Twisted proverbs make me <u>confused</u>.
ⓓ I spent my spare time <u>to draw pictures</u>.

➡ _____

06 밑줄 친 우리말과 일치하도록 주어진 단어를 이용하여 영작하시오.

(1) 연락을 취하는 것은 어려웠다.
  ➡ _____
  (keep, to, it)
(2) 쇠가 달았을 때 쳐라.
  ➡ _____
  (while, hot, strike)

Conversation

① 의견 묻기

- **What do you think of watching a movie?** 영화를 보는 것에 대해 어떻게 생각하니?
- **What do you think of eating fast food every day?** 매일 패스트푸드를 먹는 것에 대해 어떻게 생각하니?

■ "What do you think of ~?"는 '~에 대해 어떻게 생각하니?'라는 의미로 의견을 묻는 표현이며 'How do you feel about ~?', 'What is your opinion?' 등으로 바꿔 쓸 수 있다. 이에 대해 'I think/feel/believe ~.', 'It seems to me ~.', 'In my opinion, ~.' 등으로 대답할 수 있다.

의견 묻기

- What do you think of ~?
- How do you feel about ~?
- What is your opinion?

의견을 묻는 말에 대답하기

- I think/feel/believe (that) 주어+동사 ~.
- It seems to me ~.
- In my opinion[view], 주어+동사 ~.

핵심 Check

1. 다음 대화의 밑줄 친 우리말에 해당하는 적절한 영어 문장을 주어진 단어를 이용하여 완성하시오.

   G: Minju, we need a new guitar but we don't have enough money for one.
   B: What do you think of having a concert to raise money? We can introduce our new song, too.
   G: 좋은 생각이야! (idea / think / great) It will be like, "Killing two birds with one stone."
   B: That's right. Let's first make a poster for our concert.
   G: Okay.

   ➡ _____

2 동의하거나 이의 제기하기

> A: Students should wear a uniform. 학생은 교복을 입어야 해.
>
> B: I agree. / I disagree. 나도 그렇게 생각해. / 나는 그렇게 생각하지 않아.

■ 'I agree.'는 어떤 의견에 동의하는 표현이고, 'I disagree.'는 어떤 의견에 동의하지 않는 표현이다. 동의하는 다른 표현으로는 'Me, too.', 'Same here.', 'We're on the same page.' 등을 쓸 수 있고, 동의하지 않는 표현으로는 'I disagree.', 'I don't think so.', 'I'm against the idea.', 'I don't agree.' 등이 있다.

동의하기

- I agree (with you).
- Me, too.
- We're on the same page.
- You can say that again.

- I think so, too.
- Same here.
- I can't agree with you more.

동의하지 않을 때

- I disagree.
- I don't agree.
- I don't think so.
- I'm against the idea.

핵심 Check

2. 다음 우리말에 해당하는 적절한 영어 문장을 주어진 단어를 이용하여 완성하시오.

> G: Look! People are just leaving their trash behind!
>
> B: Oh, no! If we harm the environment, we'll be the ones who regret it in the end.
>
> G: 나는 네 의견에 동의해. (opinion / with / agree) Like the saying goes, "What goes around comes around."
>
> B: You're right. Let's help the earth by taking our trash with us.

➡  _____

Listen & Speak 1 A-1

B: Minju, we need a new guitar but we don't have ❶enough money for one.

G: ❷What do you think of having a concert to ❸raise money? We can introduce our new song, too.

B: What a great idea! It'll be ❹like ❺"Killing two birds with one stone."

G: That's right. Let's first make a poster for our concert.

B: Okay.

B: 민주야, 우리는 새 기타가 필요하지만 충분한 돈이 없어.

G: 너는 돈을 마련하기 위한 콘서트를 하는 것에 대해 어떻게 생각해? 우리의 신곡도 소개할 수 있어.

B: 아주 좋은 생각이야! 그건 "한 개의 돌로 두 마리의 새를 잡는 것"과 같을 거야.

G: 맞아. 우선 우리 콘서트를 위한 포스터를 만들자.

B: 그래.

❶ enough: 충분한
❷ 무언가에 대하여 상대방의 의견을 물을 때 '~에 대해 어떻게 생각해?'의 의미인 'What do you think of+(동)명사?'를 사용할 수 있다. 전치사 of 대신에 about를 쓸 수도 있다.
❸ raise money: 돈을 모으다
❹ like는 전치사로 '~와 같은'의 의미이다.
❺ Killing two birds with one stone: 한 개의 돌로 두 마리의 새를 잡는다. (일석이조)

Check(√) True or False

(1) They will raise money for making a poster. T ☐ F ☐

(2) They can't afford to buy a new guitar. T ☐ F ☐

Listen & Speak 2 A-1

B: Look! People are just ❶leaving their trash behind!

G: Oh, no! ❷If we ❸harm the environment, we'll be the ❹ones who regret it in the end.

B: ❺I agree. Like the ❻saying goes, ❼"What goes around comes around."

G: You're right. Let's help the earth ❽by taking our trash with us.

B: 봐! 사람들이 자기들의 쓰레기를 놔두고 그냥 떠나고 있어!

G: 오, 안 돼! 우리가 환경을 해치면 결국 후회하는 건 우리일 거야.

B: 나도 동의해. 속담에 '자신이 한 대로 되돌려 받는다(자업자득)'라고 하잖아.

G: 네 말이 맞아. 우리 쓰레기는 우리가 가져가서 지구를 돕자.

❶ leave ~ behind: ~을 두고 가다, 뒤에 남기다
❷ 단순 조건절에서 접속사 If는 '만일 ~라면'의 의미로 조건절을 이끌며 if 뒤에는 주어와 동사를 갖춘 절이 오게 된다. 'If+주어+동사의 현재형 ~, 주어+조동사의 현재형(will/can/may/must+동사원형 ~).'의 형태로 쓰인다.
❸ harm: 해를 끼치다
❹ one은 '(일반적인) 사람'의 뜻으로 뒤에 주격 관계대명사 who 이하가 수식하고 있다. regret: 후회하다 in the end: 결국, 마침내
❺ 'I agree.'는 '나도 동의해.'의 의미로 상대방의 의견을 동의할 때 사용하는 표현이다. 바꿔 쓸 수 있는 표현으로 'Me, too.', 'Same here.', 'We're on the same page.' 등이 있다.
❻ saying: 속담, 격언
❼ What goes around comes around.: 자신이 한 대로 되돌려 받는다(자업자득).
❽ by 동사ing: ~함으로써

Check(√) True or False

(3) The boy and the girl will leave their trash behind. T ☐ F ☐

(4) The boy agrees with what the girl says. T ☐ F ☐

Listen & Speak 1 B

W: Jacob, can you help me?

B: What is it, Mom?

W: Well, I got a message from my friend, but I don't understand ❶ what some of it means.

B: Let me see. Hmm... ASAP ❷means "as soon as possible" and HAND means "Have a nice day."

W: Oh, I see.

B: ❸What do you think of these ❹acronyms, Mom?

W: I think ❺they are ❻destroying the language. ❼What do you think?

B: ❽In my opinion, they are fun and easy ❾to use.

W: Jacob, 나 좀 도와줄 수 있니?
B: 뭔데요, 엄마?
W: 음, 내 친구한테 문자를 하나 받았는데, 이 중 일부가 무엇을 의미하는지 이해를 못하겠어.
B: 제가 볼게요, 음… ASAP는 '가능한 한 빨리'라는 의미이고, HAND는 '좋은 하루를 보내.'라는 의미예요.
W: 아, 그렇구나.
B: 이런 두문자들에 대해 어떻게 생각하세요, 엄마?
W: 난 그것들이 언어를 파괴하고 있다고 생각해. 너는 어떻게 생각하니?
B: 제 생각엔 그것들은 사용하기 재미있고 쉬운 것 같아요.

❶ understand의 목적어로 간접목적어(의문사+주어+동사)를 사용했다. it은 a message를 가리킨다. ❷ 어떤 말의 뜻이나 의미를 정의할 때에는 동사 mean을 이용해서 설명할 수 있다. ❸ 'What do you think of ~?'는 '너는 ~에 대해 어떻게 생각하니?'라는 뜻으로 상대방의 의견을 묻는 표현이다. of가 전치사이므로 뒤에 동사가 오려면 동사ing 형태의 동명사를 써야 한다. 비슷한 표현으로 'How do you feel about ~?', 'What is your opinion?' 등이 있다. ❹ acronym: 두문자어 ❺ think와 they 사이에 접속사 that이 생략되어 있다. they는 앞 문장의 acronyms(두문자들)를 의미한다. ❻ destroy: 파괴하다 ❼ 'What do you think?'로 자신의 의견에 대해 상대방이 어떻게 생각하는지 질문하고 있다. ❽ In my opinion, ~.: '제 생각엔 ~.'의 뜻으로 의견을 말할 때 사용하는 표현으로' I think that ~.'과 같은 의미이다. ❾ to use는 형용사 fun and easy 를 수식하여 '사용하기 재미있고 쉬운'으로 해석한다.

Check(√) True or False

(5) They have the same idea about the acronyms.　　T ☐ F ☐

(6) Jacob knows what ASAP and HAND mean.　　T ☐ F ☐

Let's Check 1

B: I don't think we should talk about others when they are not there.

G: ❶Why do you say that?

B: Well, I ❷had a fight with Jimin because I talked about her test results with Sam.

G: Oh, why did you do that?

B: I never thought that she would ❸find out.

G: Well, like the saying goes, ❹"Walls have ears."

B: ❺I agree. I've learned my lesson.

B: 난 다른 사람들이 자리에 없을 때 그들에 대해 이야기해서는 안 된다고 생각해.
G: 왜 그렇게 말하는 거니?
B: 음, 나는 지민이의 시험 결과에 대해서 샘과 이야기한 것 때문에 지민이랑 싸웠어.
G: 오, 너는 왜 그랬니?
B: 난 지민이가 알게 될 거라고는 전혀 생각 못했어.
G: 음, 속담에 '벽에도 귀가 있다'라고 하잖아.
B: 나도 동의해. 난 교훈을 얻었어.

❶ 'Why do you say that?'은 '왜 그렇게 말하는 거니?'라는 뜻으로 상대방에게 이유를 물을 때 사용한다. ❷ have a fight with ~: ~와 싸우다 ❸ find out: 발견하다, 찾아내다 ❹ Walls have ears.: 벽에도 귀가 있다.(낮말은 새가 듣고 밤말은 쥐가 듣는다.) ❺ 'I agree.'는 '나도 동의해.'의 의미로 상대방의 의견에 동의할 때 사용하는 표현이다.

Check(√) True or False

(7) The boy talked about Sam's test result.　　T ☐ F ☐

(8) Jimin found out that the boy talked about her test result to someone else.　　T ☐ F ☐

Listen & Speak 1 A-2

G: Dohun, what are you doing?

B: I'm watching a movie about AI robots. It's really ❶fascinating. ❷What do you think of ❸them?

G: ❹In my opinion, they will cause problems. AI robots will ❺take jobs away from people.

B: Well, I still think they are useful. There is a science festival ❻introducing AI robots. Why don't we go and ❼find out more about them?

G: Sounds good.

❶ fascinating: 대단히 흥미로운, 재미있는 ❷ 'What do you think of ~?'는 '~에 대해 어떻게 생각하니?'라는 의미로 의견을 묻는 표현이며, 'How do you feel about ~?', 'What is your opinion?' 등으로 바꿔 쓸 수 있다. ❸ them은 AI robots를 가리킨다. ❹ In my opinion은 '내 생각에는'의 의미로 자신의 의견을 말할 때 쓰는 표현이다. ❺ take A away from B: B로부터 A를 빼앗다 ❻ introducing은 현재분사로 '소개하는'으로 해석하며, 앞의 a science festival을 수식하고 있다. ❼ find out: 발견하다, 알아보다

Listen & Speak 2 A-3

G: Juwon, what's the matter?

B: Mr. Han ❶told us to hand in the art project yesterday but I still haven't finished it.

G: Well, I think you should still finish it and hand it in. Like the saying goes, ❷"Better late than never."

B: You're right and I agree. Thanks for the advice.

❶ 'tell+목적어+목적격 보어(to V)'는 '(목적어)가 ~하라고 말하다'의 의미이다. hand in: 제출하다
❷ Better late than never.: 안하는 것보다 늦는 게 낫다.

Listen & Speak 2 B

B: Yura, what are you doing?

G: I'm ❶posting my pictures on the internet. Come and ❷have a look.

B: There are so many pictures ❸that show your everyday life. Isn't it dangerous?

G: Well, my friends like my posts a lot. I think it's a good way to ❹get to know one another.

B: ❺I disagree. There might be some people who will use your pictures in a bad way.

G: Come to think of it, I should be more careful with my pictures. Thanks for your advice.

B: No problem.

❶ post: (웹사이트에 정보·사진을) 올리다, 게시하다 ❷ have a look: 살펴보다 ❸ that은 주격 관계대명사이고, that show your everyday life는 앞에 있는 명사 many pictures를 꾸며주고 있다. ❹ get to know: 알게 되다 one another: 서로 ❺ 'I disagree.'는 '나는 동의하지 않아.'의 의미로 상대방의 의견에 반대할 때 사용하는 표현으로 'I don't think so.', 'I'm against the idea.'로 바꿔 쓸 수 있다.

Real Life Communication

Claire: Jinho, what's the matter? You look upset.

Jinho: I ❶had a fight with Harry.

Claire: Why? What happened?

Jinho: We both wanted to use the same music room ❷at the same time.

Claire: I don't think there are enough music rooms ❸to practice in after school.

Jinho: I agree. ❹What do you think of ❺setting a time limit for the music rooms?

Claire: How long do you think it should be?

Jinho: I don't think ❻anyone should be allowed to use a room for more than ❼an hour a day.

Claire: I disagree. I need ❽more than an hour to practice music.

Jinho: Then how about ❾reserving a music room?

Claire: That's a good idea. Then each person will have enough time to practice.

❶ have a fight with ~: ~와 싸우다 ❷ at the same time: 동시에 ❸ to practice는 앞의 music rooms를 꾸며주는 형용사적 용법으로 사용되었다. ❹ 'What do you think of[about] ~?'는 '너는 ~에 대해 어떻게 생각하니?'라는 뜻으로 상대방의 의견을 묻는 표현이다. of가 전치사이므로 뒤에 동사가 오려면 -ing 형태의 동명사를 써야 한다. ❺ set a time limit for ~: ~의 시간 제한을 정하다 ❻ think와 anyone 사이에 접속사 that이 생략되어 있다. 'allow(허락하다)+목적어+목적격보어(to V)'의 수동태 형식으로 'be allowed to 동사원형'은 '~이 허락되다'로 해석할 수 있다. ❼ an hour a day: 하루에 1시간 a는 per(~당)의 의미이다. ❽ more than: ~보다 많이, ~ 이상 ❾ How about 동사ing?: ~하는 게 어때? (권유) reserve: 예약하다

다음 우리말과 일치하도록 빈칸에 알맞은 말을 쓰시오.

Listen & Speak 1 A

1. B: Minju, we need a new guitar _____ we don't have _____ _____ for one.

   G: What do you _____ _____ _____ a concert to _____ money? We can _____ our new song, too.

   B: What a great idea! It'll be like "_____ two birds with _____ stone."

   G: That's _____. Let's first make a _____ for our concert.

   B: Okay.

2. G: Dohun, what are you doing?

   B: I'm _____ a movie about AI robots. It's really _____. _____ _____ _____ _____ of them?

   G: In my _____, they will _____ problems. AI robots will take jobs _____ _____ people.

   B: Well, I still think they are _____. There is a science festival _____ AI robots. _____ _____ we go and find _____ more about them?

   G: Sounds good.

Listen & Speak 1 B

W: Jacob, can you help me?

B: What is it, Mom?

W: Well, I _____ _____ _____ from my friend, but I don't understand _____ _____ _____ _____ _____ _____.

B: Let me _____. Hmm... ASAP means "_____ _____ _____ _____" and HAND _____ "Have a nice day."

W: Oh, I see.

B: _____ _____ _____ _____ these _____, Mom?

W: I think they are _____ the language. What do you think?

B: _____ _____ _____, they are fun and _____ _____ _____.

해석

1. B: 민주야, 우리는 새 기타가 필요하지만 충분한 돈이 없어.
   G: 너는 돈을 마련하기 위한 콘서트를 하는 것에 대해 어떻게 생각해? 우리의 신곡도 소개할 수 있어.
   B: 아주 좋은 생각이야! 그건 "한 개의 돌로 두 마리의 새를 잡는 것"과 같을 거야.
   G: 맞아. 우선 우리 콘서트를 위한 포스터를 만들자.
   B: 그래.

2. G: 도훈아, 너 뭐 하고 있니?
   B: 나는 인공지능 로봇에 관한 영화를 보고 있어. 정말 흥미로워. 너는 그것들에 대해 어떻게 생각해?
   G: 내 생각에 그것들은 문제를 일으킬 거야. 인공지능 로봇은 사람들로부터 직업을 빼앗아 갈 거야.
   B: 글쎄, 난 여전히 그것들이 유용하다고 생각해. 인공지능 로봇들을 소개하는 과학 축제가 있어. 우리가 가서 그것들에 관해 더 알아보는 게 어때?
   G: 좋은 생각이야.

W: Jacob, 나 좀 도와줄 수 있니?
B: 뭔데요, 엄마?
W: 음, 내 친구한테 문자를 하나 받았는데, 이 중 일부가 무엇을 의미하는지 이해를 못하겠어.
B: 제가 볼게요, 음… ASAP는 '가능한 한 빨리'라는 의미이고, HAND는 '좋은 하루를 보내.'라는 의미예요.
W: 아, 그렇구나.
B: 이런 두문자들에 대해 어떻게 생각하세요, 엄마?
W: 난 그것들이 언어를 파괴하고 있다고 생각해. 너는 어떻게 생각하니?
B: 제 생각엔 그것들은 사용하기 재미있고 쉬운 것 같아요.

Listen & Speak 2 A

1. **B:** Look! People are just _____ their trash behind!

   G: Oh, no! _____ we _____ the _____, we'll be the ones who _____ it _____ _____ _____.

   B: I agree. _____ the saying goes, "_____ _____ _____ comes around."

   G: You're right. Let's help the earth by _____ our trash with us.

2. **B:** Emma, let's _____ _____ _____.

   G: What? We've only _____ _____ 30 minutes.

   B: _____ _____ _____ _____, "All work and no play makes Jack _____ _____ _____."

   G: I _____. Then let's _____ _____ _____ _____ we finish this part.

   B: Okay.

3. **G:** Juwon, what's _____ _____?

   B: Mr. Han _____ _____ _____ _____ _____ the art project yesterday but I still _____ _____ it.

   G: Well, I think you should still finish it and _____ _____ _____. Like the saying goes, "_____ _____ _____ _____."

   B: You're _____ _____ _____ _____. Thanks for the advice.

Listen & Speak 2 B

B: Yura, what are you doing?

G: I'm _____ my pictures on the internet. Come and have _____ _____.

B: There are _____ _____ _____ show your everyday life. Isn't it _____?

G: Well, my friends like my posts a lot. I think it's a good _____ _____ _____ _____ one another.

B: I disagree. There might be some _____ _____ _____ your pictures in a bad way.

G: Come to think of it, I _____ _____ _____ with my pictures. Thanks _____ your advice.

B: No problem.

해석

1. **B:** 봐! 사람들이 자기들의 쓰레기를 놔두고 그냥 떠나고 있어!

   G: 오, 안 돼! 우리가 환경을 해치면 결국 후회하는 건 우리일 거야.

   B: 나도 동의해. 속담에 '자신이 한 대로 되돌려 받는다(자업자득).'라고 하잖아.

   G: 네 말이 맞아. 우리 쓰레기는 우리가 가져가서 지구를 돕자.

2. **B:** Emma, 우리 좀 쉬자.

   G: 뭐라고? 우리 겨우 30분 동안 공부했어.

   B: 속담에 '일만 하고 놀지 않으면 바보가 된다.'라고 하잖아.

   G: 나도 동의해. 그러면 우리 이 부분을 끝내고 쉬자.

   B: 알았어.

3. **G:** 주원아, 무슨 문제 있니?

   B: 한 선생님이 미술 과제를 어제 제출하라고 하셨는데 난 아직 끝내지 못했어.

   G: 음, 나는 네가 그래도 그것을 끝내서 제출해야 한다고 생각해. 속담에 '안하는 것보다 늦는 게 낫다.'라고 하잖아.

   B: 네 말이 맞고 나도 동의해. 조언 고마워.

B: 유라야, 너 뭐 하고 있니?

G: 내 사진들을 인터넷에 올리고 있어. 와서 봐.

B: 너의 일상생활을 보여 주는 사진이 정말 많이 있네. 그거 위험하지 않니?

G: 글쎄, 내 친구들은 내 게시물들을 많이 좋아해. 난 이것이 서로 알아가는 데 좋은 방법이라고 생각해.

B: 나는 동의하지 않아. 너의 사진들을 나쁜 수단으로 이용할 일부 사람들이 있을지도 몰라.

G: 그러고 보니 나는 내 사진들에 대해 더 신중해야겠어. 충고 고마워.

B: 천만에.

Real Life Communication

Claire: Jinho, what's the matter? You look _____ .

Jinho: I _____ _____ _____ _____ Harry.

Claire: Why? What _____ ?

Jinho: We both _____ _____ _____ the same music room _____ _____ _____ _____ .

Claire: I don't think there _____ _____ _____ _____ _____ _____ in after school.

Jinho: I agree. _____ _____ _____ _____ _____ _____ _____ _____ _____ for the music rooms?

Claire: _____ _____ do you think it should be?

Jinho: I don't think anyone _____ _____ _____ _____ a room for more than an hour a day.

Claire: I disagree. I need _____ _____ _____ _____ to practice music.

Jinho: Then how _____ _____ a music room?

Claire: That's a good idea. Then each person will have _____ _____ _____ _____ .

Let's Check

1. B: I don't think _____ _____ _____ _____ _____ others _____ they are not there.

   G: _____ do you say _____ ?

   B: Well, I _____ _____ _____ _____ Jimin _____ I talked about her test _____ with Sam.

   G: Oh, why did you _____ _____ ?

   B: I _____ _____ she would find out.

   G: Well, like the saying goes, "_____ _____ _____ ."

   B: I agree. I've _____ my lesson.

2. A: I don't _____ _____ today.

   B: Then _____ _____ _____ _____ _____ _____ to eat?

   A: That's a good idea. What _____ we eat?

   B: Let's eat Chinese food. A new restaurant _____ down the street.

01 밑줄 친 부분과 바꿔 쓸 수 <u>없는</u> 것을 고르시오.

> G: Dohun, what are you doing?
>
> B: I'm watching a movie about AI robots. It's really fascinating. What do you think of them?
>
> G: <u>In my opinion, they will cause problems.</u> AI robots will take jobs away from people.

① I believe they will cause problems.

② In my view, they will cause problems.

③ I wonder if they will cause problems.

④ It seems to me that they will cause problems.

⑤ I think that they will cause problems.

02 빈칸에 알맞은 말을 고르시오.

> B: Minju, we need a new guitar but we don't have enough money for one.
>
> G: _____ We can introduce our new song, too.
>
> B: What a great idea! It'll be like "Killing two birds with one stone."
>
> G: That's right. Let's first make a poster for our concert.

① Why do you want a new guitar?

② Why don't we go and find out more about it?

③ How did you feel when you make a new song?

④ In my opinion, we should spend less money.

⑤ What do you think of having a concert to raise money?

03 밑줄 친 우리말을 주어진 단어를 이용해 영작하시오.

> G: Juwon, what's the matter?
>
> B: Mr. Han told us to hand in the art project yesterday but I still haven't finished it.
>
> G: Well, I think you should still finish it and hand it in. Like the saying goes, "Better late than never."
>
> B: <u>네 말이 맞고 나도 동의해.</u> (agree) Thanks for the advice.

➡ _____

[01~02] 다음 대화를 읽고 물음에 답하시오.

W: Jacob, can you help me?

B: What is it, Mom?

W: Well, I got a message from my friend, but I don't understand what some of it means.

B: Let me see. Hmm… ASAP means "as soon as possible" and HAND means "Have a nice day."

W: Oh, I see.

B: (A)What do you think of these acronyms, Mom?

W: I think they are destroying the language. What do you think?

B: In my opinion, they are fun and easy to use.

01 대화의 밑줄 친 (A)와 바꿔 쓸 수 있는 것을 고르시오.

① Why do you like these acronyms, Mom?

② Why did you think of these acronyms, Mom?

③ Have you ever thought of these acronyms, Mom?

④ What's your opinion about these acronyms, Mom?

⑤ What do you know about these acronyms, Mom?

02 대화의 내용과 일치하지 <u>않는</u> 것을 <u>모두</u> 고르시오.

① ASAP는 '가능한 한 빨리'를 의미한다.

② HAND는 '좋은 하루를 보내'라는 의미이다.

③ Jacob은 엄마를 돕고 있다.

④ Jacob의 엄마는 친구한테서 받은 문자 전체가 무엇을 의미하는지 전혀 이해하지 못했다.

⑤ Jacob은 두문자들이 사용하기에 재미있지만 어려운 것 같다고 생각하고 있다.

03 다음 중 짝지어진 대화가 <u>어색한</u> 것은?

① A: What do you think of my new shoes?

   B: I like them. They look great.

② A: This math test is too hard. Don't you agree?

   B: That's right. I agree with you.

③ A: Which mountain in Korea is the highest?

   B: In my opinion, Mt. Baekdu is the highest.

④ A: What do you think of shopping online?

   B: In my view, shopping online saves us a lot of time.

⑤ A: What do you think of having a pet?

   B: I agree with you.

[04~06] 다음 대화를 읽고 물음에 답하시오.

B: Look! People are just leaving their trash behind!

G: Oh, no! If we harm the environment, we'll be the ones who (A)_____ it in the end.

B: I agree. Like the saying goes, "(B)_____
_____"

G: You're right. Let's help the earth by taking our trash with us.

04 빈칸 (A)에 알맞은 말을 고르시오.

① decide   ② grab

③ regret   ④ judge

⑤ reserve

05 빈칸 (B)에 알맞은 속담을 고르시오.

① Killing two birds with one stone.

② What goes around comes around.

③ All work and no play makes Jack a dull boy.

④ Better late than never.

⑤ Walls have ears.

06 대화의 내용과 일치하지 <u>않는</u> 것을 고르시오.

① 환경을 해치는 것에 대해 소녀와 소년은 같은 생각을 가지고 있다.

② 소년은 속담을 예로 들어 환경을 해치면 자기 자신이 되돌려 받는다는 것을 말하고 있다.

③ 사람들이 쓰레기를 놔두고 떠나고 있다.

④ 소녀는 환경을 해치면 결국 후회를 할 것이라고 생각한다.

⑤ 소녀와 소년은 다른 사람들이 놓고 간 쓰레기도 가져갈 것이다.

07 다음 빈칸 (A)~(C)에 들어갈 말이 알맞게 짝지어진 것은?

> B: I don't think we should talk about others (A)_____ they are not there.
>
> G: Why do you say that?
>
> B: Well, I had a fight with Jimin (B)_____ I talked about her test results with Sam.
>
> G: Oh, why did you do that?
>
> B: I never thought that she would find out.
>
> G: Well, like the saying goes, "Walls have ears."
>
> B: (C)_____ I've learned my lesson.

① when – because – I agree.

② when – because – I don't agree.

③ because – so – I agree.

④ when – so – I think so, too.

⑤ because – because – I don't think so.

08 다음 대화의 빈칸에 들어갈 말을 〈보기〉에서 골라 순서대로 바르게 배열한 것은?

> B: Yura, what are you doing?
>
> G: _____
>
> B: _____
>
> G: _____
>
> B: _____
>
> G: Come to think of it, I should be more careful with my pictures. Thanks for your advice.
>
> B: No problem.

┌─ 보기 ─┐

(A) Well, my friends like my posts a lot. I think it's a good way to get to know one another.

(B) There are so many pictures that show your everyday life. Isn't it dangerous?

(C) I'm posting my pictures on the internet. Come and have a look.

(D) I disagree. There might be some people who will use your pictures in a bad way.

① (B) – (A) – (C) – (D)

② (B) – (C) – (A) – (D)

③ (C) – (A) – (B) – (D)

④ (C) – (B) – (A) – (D)

⑤ (C) – (D) – (B) – (A)

[01~02] 다음 대화를 읽고 물음에 답하시오.

B: Minju, we need a new guitar but we don't have enough money for one.

G: 너는 돈을 마련하기 위한 콘서트를 하는 것에 대해 어떻게 생각해? (think, raise, of, have) We can introduce our new song, too.

B: What a great idea! It'll be like "_____ _____." (one, two, stone, bird)

G: That's right. Let's first make a poster for our concert.

B: Okay.

01 밑줄 친 우리말과 일치하도록 주어진 단어를 이용해 영작하시오.

➡ _____

_____

02 빈칸에 알맞은 속담을 주어진 단어를 이용해 쓰시오.

➡ _____

[03~05] 다음 대화를 읽고 물음에 답하시오.

Claire: Jinho, what's the matter? You look upset.

Jinho: I had a fight (A)_____ Harry.

Claire: Why? What happened?

Jinho: We both wanted to use the same music room (B)_____ the same time.

Claire: I don't think there are enough music rooms to practice in after school.

Jinho: I agree. What do you think of setting a time limit for the music rooms?

Claire: How long do you think it should be?

Jinho: I don't think anyone should be allowed to use a room for more than an hour a day.

Claire: (C)_____ I need more than an hour to practice music.

Jinho: Then how about reserving a music room?

Claire: That's a good idea. Then each person will have enough time to practice.

03 빈칸 (A)와 (B)에 들어갈 전치사를 쓰시오.

➡ (A) _____ (B) _____

04 위 대화에서 다음 영영풀이에 해당하는 단어를 찾아 쓰시오.

the greatest amount, extent, or degree of something that is possible

➡ _____

05 빈칸 (C)에 들어갈 말을 〈보기〉에서 모두 골라 기호를 쓰시오.

┌ 보기 ┐
ⓐ Me, too. ⓑ I don't think so.
ⓒ I'm against the idea.
ⓓ We're on the same page.
ⓔ I agree. ⓕ I don't agree.
ⓖ Same here. ⓗ I disagree.

➡ _____

06 빈칸을 괄호 안에 주어진 단어를 알맞게 배열하여 채우시오.

A: _____?
(of, lunch, breaks, what, think, longer, you, do, having)

B: I agree with the idea. Students will have more time to eat.

Grammar

① 'It is/was ~ that ...' 강조구문

> • **It is** a dog **that** I want for a pet. 내가 애완동물로 원하는 건 개다.

■ 'It is/was ~ that ...' 형태로 It is/was와 that 사이에 강조하고 싶은 말을 넣어 강조할 수 있다.

  • **It was** a scarf **that** I gave my mom. 내가 나의 어머니께 드린 것은 바로 스카프였다.
  • **It is** the blue car **that** she will buy. 그녀가 사려고 하는 것은 바로 그 파란색 자동차이다.

■ 'It is/was ~ that ...' 구문에서 It is/was와 that 사이에 강조되는 것은 문장에서 주어, 목적어, 부사(구/절) 등이다.

  • **It was** my brother **that** took me to the mountain. 나를 그 산에 데려간 사람은 바로 나의 형이었다.
  • **It is** next week **that** I will have a concert. 내가 콘서트를 개최할 때는 바로 다음 주다.

■ 동사나 보어는 강조할 수 없다.

  • She is a genius. 그녀는 천재다. → It is a genius that she is. (✕)
  • I ate breakfast. 나는 아침을 먹었다. → It was ate that I breakfast. (✕)

■ that 대신에 강조하는 대상이 사람일 때는 who[whom], 사물일 때는 which, 장소일 때는 where, 시간 개념일 때는 when으로 바꿔 쓸 수 있다.

  • **It was** the waiter **that**[**who**] served food. 음식을 나르는 것은 바로 웨이터였다.
  • **It was** two years ago **that**[**when**] I left home. 내가 집을 떠난 것은 바로 2년 전이었다.
  • **It is** in Gyeongju **that**[**where**] we'll stay. 우리가 머무를 곳은 바로 경주이다.

■ 'It is/was ~ that ...' 강조구문을 의문문으로 바꾸고자 할 때는 be 동사를 it과 도치시킨다.

  • **It was** you **that** visited the museum yesterday. 어제 박물관을 방문한 건 바로 너였다.
    → **Was it** you **that** visited the museum yesterday? 어제 박물관을 방문한 건 바고 너였지?

■ 의문문의 의문사를 강조할 때는 'It is/was ~ that ...'을 활용하여 평서문의 형태로 바꾸고 다시 의문문의 형태로 전환한다.

  • Who broke this window?
    → It was who that boke this window. (평서문으로 전환)
    → Was it who that broke this window? (의문문의 형태로 전환)
    → Who was it that broke this window? (의문사 who를 앞으로 보냄)

핵심 Check

1. 다음 괄호 안에서 알맞은 말을 <u>모두</u> 고르시오.
   (1) It was you (who / whom / that) came up with the idea.
   (2) It was in April (that / when / where) I joined this club.

② 접속부사 However

> • **However,** some people have different opinions. 그러나 몇몇 사람들은 다른 의견을 가지고 있다.

■ However는 접속부사로 '그러나'라고 해석하고 앞 문장의 내용과 대조를 나타낼 때 사용한다. 주로 문장 앞에 오며, 문장의 맨 끝에 오기도 하며(이 경우 그 앞에 콤마를 찍는다.), 세미콜론(;)과 함께 쓰이기도 한다.

  • **However,** this is not true. 하지만, 이것은 사실이 아니다.
  • I was tired. **However,** I studied hard for the test. 나는 피곤했다. 그러나 나는 시험을 위해 열심히 공부했다.
  • Some pet cats died, **however.** 하지만 일부 애완 고양이는 죽었다.
  • He was upset. He didn't show his feelings, **however.** 그는 화가 났다. 그러나 그는 그의 감정을 보이지 않았다.
  • We wanted to arrive on time; **however,** we were delayed by traffic. 우리는 정시에 도착하고 싶었다. 하지만 교통이 막혀 지연되었다.

■ but은 등위접속사로 단어와 단어, 구와 구, 절과 절을 동등한 관계로 연결한다. however는 접속부사로 쓰이는 경우, 접속사가 아니므로 두 개의 문장을 하나로 연결할 수 없다. 다만, 앞의 문장과 논리적인 의미 관계로만 연결을 한다.

  • I have an apple **but** she has an orange. 나는 사과를 가지고 있지만 그녀는 오렌지를 가지고 있다. (절과 절 연결)
  • His manner was polite **but** cool. 그의 태도는 정중했지만 냉정했다. (단어와 단어 연결)

■ 그 밖의 접속부사(구)

  • therefore 따라서 / thus 그러므로 / consequently 따라서 / hence 이런 이유로
  • furthermore 게다가 / moreover 게다가 / in addition 더욱이 / besides 뿐만 아니라
  • nevertheless 그럼에도 불구하고 / nonetheless 그렇기는 하지만 / meanwhile 한편 / on the other had 반면에
  • otherwise 그렇지 않으면 / above all 무엇보다도 / in fact 사실은

핵심 Check

2. 다음 괄호 안에서 알맞은 단어를 고르시오.

  (1) I don't like him, (however / and) I like his songs.
  (2) We've recently bought a computer. We received it yesterday, (so / but) it didn't work.

Grammar 시험대비 기본평가

01 다음 문장에서 어법상 <u>어색한</u> 부분을 바르게 고쳐 쓰시오. <u>어색한</u> 부분이 없으면 '없음'으로 쓰시오.

(1) It is her smile who I miss the most.

_____ ➡ _____

(2) It was my bag when I lost yesterday.

_____ ➡ _____

(3) He was feeling bad. He went to work, therefore, and tried to concentrate.

_____ ➡ _____

(4) The result was satisfactory but the game was, however, far from easy.

_____

02 다음 빈칸에 알맞은 단어를 쓰시오.

We thought the figures were correct. _____, we have now discovered some errors.

03 다음 밑줄 친 ①~⑤ 중 어법상 <u>어색한</u> 곳을 고르시오.

It ①was ②last Sunday ③what Jill ④decided ⑤to go abroad.

04 다음 문장을 각 조건에 맞춰 영작하시오.

Mijin played the cello in the school auditorium.

(1) Mijin을 강조하는 'It is/was ~ that ...' 강조구문으로 쓰시오.

➡ _____

(2) the cello를 강조하는 'It is/was ~ that ...' 강조구문으로 쓰시오.

➡ _____

(3) 'in the school auditorium'을 강조하는 'It is/was ~ that ...' 강조구문으로 쓰시오.

➡ _____

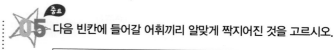
서답형

01 다음 문장에서 어법상 틀린 부분을 찾아 바르게 고쳐 쓰시오.

The workers, but, decided not to take any actions.

_____ ➡ _____

중요

02 다음 빈칸에 들어갈 말로 알맞은 것을 고르시오

It was to Kangwon-do _____ I went during my winter vacation.

① when ② where
③ how ④ what
⑤ who

03 다음 문장에서 어법상 어색한 것을 고르시오.

①There is ②Minho ③who ④has two ⑤sisters.

① There ② Minho ③ who
④ has ⑤ sisters

중요

04 다음 빈칸에 들어갈 알맞은 어휘를 고르시오.

He likes her _____ she doesn't like him.

① however ② and
③ or ④ but
⑤ therefore

중요

05 다음 빈칸에 들어갈 어휘끼리 알맞게 짝지어진 것을 고르시오.

• The hotel is great __(A)__ expensive.
• My dog loves people. __(B)__ it hates other dogs.
• I understand what you say. I cannot, __(C)__ , approve of it.

*approve of: ~을 승인하다

(A)	(B)	(C)
① but	But	but
② however	However	but
③ but	However	but
④ however	But	however
⑤ but	But	however

06 다음 중 빈칸에 들어가기에 어색한 것을 모두 고르시오.

It is _____ that lives in the wild.

① country ② Sam
③ tomorrow ④ a really big turtle
⑤ the cat

서답형

07 다음 문장의 목적어를 강조하고자 할 때, 빈칸에 적절한 어휘를 쓰시오. (that은 쓰지 말 것.)

Tom used the computer yesterday in his classroom.
→ It was the computer _____ Tom used yesterday in his classroom.

08 다음 빈칸에 들어갈 말로 알맞은 것을 고르시오.

> The trend, _____, is changing.

① that　　　　　② however
③ although　　　④ but
⑤ otherwise

09 다음 중 밑줄 친 부분이 어색한 것을 고르시오.

① Mary loves Tim. <u>Hence</u>, she doesn't want to marry him.
② You're my friend; <u>nonetheless</u>, I feel like you're taking advantage of me.
③ It would be nice to spend our vacation on the beach in Guam; <u>on the other hand</u>, it would be fun to hike the Swiss Alps.
④ Tom kept talking in the library; <u>therefore</u>, he got in trouble.
⑤ Jerry is a mouse; <u>however</u>, Jerry likes Tom which is a cat.

10 다음 우리말을 바르게 옮긴 것을 고르시오.

> 그녀는 매우 활발하다. 그러나 그녀의 여동생은 조용하고 수줍음이 많다.

① She is very active. Therefore, her sister is quiet and shy.
② She is very active. Moreover, her sister is quiet and shy.
③ She is very active. However, her sister is quiet and shy.
④ She is very active; nonetheless, her sister is quiet and shy.
⑤ She is very active. Otherwise, her sister is quiet and shy.

11 빈칸에 들어갈 말로 올바른 것은? (2개)

> It was the book _____ she bought at the bookstore.

① where　　② when　　③ who
④ that　　　⑤ which

12 다음 중 어색한 대화를 고르시오.

① A: When did you meet Sally?
　 B: It was last Friday when I met Sally.
② A: What is your favorite book?
　 B: It is *Harry Potter* what is my favorite book.
③ A: Where did you play with Sam?
　 B: It was amusement park where I played with Sam.
④ A: Who is the most important person in your life?
　 B: It is my father that is the most important person in my life.
⑤ A: Where did we meet before?
　 B: It was at music art chamber hall where we met.

서답형
13 다음 두 문장을 연결하고자 할 때 적절한 접속부사를 쓰시오.

> (1) Two old friends were happy to meet again after such a long separation.
> (2) The meeting was a strain for both of them.
>
> *strain: (~에 대한) 부담

➡ _____

서답형

14 우리말에 맞게 괄호 안의 어휘들을 배열하여 영작할 때, 주어진 지시대로 쓰시오.

(1) 5번째 단어를 쓰시오.
- 해리포터와 그의 친구들이 마법 도구를 구입한 것은 바로 그 상점에서였다. (it, his friends, at, was, the, shop, Harry Potter, and, bought, magic, where, tools)

➡ _____

(2) 2번째 단어를 쓰시오.
- 그러나 로봇은 감정이 없다. (robots, feelings, don't, however, have)

➡ _____

15 다음 중 어법상 어색한 것을 고르시오.

① It was I who met her at the airport yesterday.
② It was me that he loves.
③ It was in the hospital that I checked my health every year.
④ It is true that she is pretty.
⑤ It was his wife where John met at Lincoln College in 1925.

서답형

16 다음 그림을 보고 however와 괄호 안의 단어를 활용하여 우리말에 맞게 영작하시오.

> 서툰 일꾼이 연장 탓한다. 그러나 좋은 일꾼은 그의 연장을 탓하지 않는다. (a bad workman, a good workman, blame, tools)

➡ _____

_____

중요
17 다음 밑줄 친 it이 어법상 다른 하나를 고르시오.

① <u>It</u> was at Tim's house that she made juice yesterday.
② <u>It</u> is important that Sue exercises in the park.
③ <u>It</u> was silly that you tried to eat the cat's food.
④ <u>It</u> was strange that she didn't come to school.
⑤ <u>It</u> is certain that he will sign up for the class.

18 다음 빈칸에 공통으로 들어갈 어휘를 고르시오.

> - We'll be happy with the results of our decisions. _____, if we don't take time to think things over, we may regret it.
> - Last year, I was asked to be the captain of the school hockey team. _____, I took too much time to decide, so another friend became the captain.

① Therefore ② However ③ But
④ Besides ⑤ On the other hand

중요
19 빈칸에 들어갈 말이 바르게 짝지어진 것을 고르시오.

> _____ was in the 80's _____ lyrics reflected the poverty.
> *reflect: 반영하다 *poverty: 가난

① There, when ② It, where
③ That, that ④ It, when
⑤ There, who

01 다음 문장에서 어법상 <u>어색한</u> 곳을 찾아 바르게 고쳐 다시 쓰시오.

> Harry and his friends booked a luxury hotel. When they arrived there, it was very dirty and also smelled somewhere. Therefore, they did not complain.

➡ _____

_____

_____

_____

02 다음 중 <u>어색한</u> 문장을 골라 바르게 고쳐 쓰시오.

> (1) It was yesterday when I met him in the park.
> (2) It is Minjae what is wrong.
> (3) It is my wife where will decide it.
> (4) It's the other book which I want to read.

➡ _____

_____

03 다음 문장을 각 조건에 맞게 다시 쓰시오.

> Sara came into the cafe because of its name.

(1) 주어를 강조하는 문장으로 쓰시오.

➡ _____

_____

(2) 전치사 into의 목적어를 강조하는 문장으로 쓰시오.

➡ _____

_____

04 주어진 단어를 활용하여 〈보기 1〉과 〈보기 2〉를 연결하여 의미가 자연스러운 문장을 만드시오.

> besides   however

┤ 보기1 ├
> • She had a lot of money.
> • It was snowing and cold.
> • I don't really want to go.
> • I'm so tired.

┤ 보기2 ├
> • I'm hungry.
> • It's too late now.
> • I didn't turn on the heater.
> • She lived a simple life.

➡ (1) _____

_____

(2) _____

(3) _____

(4) _____

05 다음 문장을 목적어를 강조하는 문장으로 바꿔 쓰시오.

> I parked my motorcycle in the garage.

➡ _____

_____

06 주어진 어구를 알맞게 배열하여 문장을 완성하시오.

that / study harder / is natural / you should / than / it / for the final exam / before / to come.

➡ _____

_____

07 다음 문장을 괄호 안의 단어를 활용하여 영작할 때 빈칸을 알맞게 채우시오.

(1) 내가 여기 도착한 것은 바로 어제였다. (be, when)

➡ It _____ .

(2) 런던에 갈 사람은 바로 Jane이다. (be going to, who)

➡ It _____ .

08 다음 빈칸에 들어갈 알맞은 말을 쓰시오.

What you do is more important than what you say. So people try to do things instead of just saying something. __(A)__ , some people have different opinions. To them, __(B)__ words __(C)__ speak louder than actions.

➡ (A) _____ (B) _____ (C) _____

09 빈칸에 들어갈 어휘를 순서대로 쓰시오.

• My favorite class was psychology; _____ , I have no interest in becoming a psychologist.
• He was not unintelligent, _____ he was lazy.

10 빈칸에 들어갈 말로 (1)에는 접속사를, (2)에는 접속부사를 쓰시오.

(1) I had a close friend from elementary school _____ we went to different high schools. Now, we don't see each other anymore.
(2) I had a close cousin who moved away five years ago. _____ , I still miss her.

11 다음 〈보기〉의 접속부사를 빈칸에 알맞게 한 번씩만 쓰시오.

┤ 보기 ├
• besides • therefore • however

(1) I don't really want to see the movie. _____ , I don't have time.
(2) You are only 16. _____ , you are not eligible to drive.

*eligible: ~할 자격이 있는

(3) I'm not alone. I'm really lonely, _____ .

Proverbs Upside Down

Every now and then, words of wisdom have influenced people and changed their lives in a great way. For example, "Actions speak louder than words," means the following: what you do is more important than what you say. So people try to do things instead of just saying something. However, some people have different opinions. To them, it is words that speak louder than actions. How? They think that words can influence others to do good things. It is natural to have different ideas. Let's take a look at some other proverbs upside down.

Look before you leap: Check what is in front of you before making a decision.

I totally agree. We should always be careful before we decide to do something. Then we'll be happy with the results of our decisions. However, if we don't take time to think things over, we may regret it. Also, we'll make mistakes if we do something without giving it a second thought. As a result, it will take us more time to fix.

Posted by Suzi Kang

↳ I don't agree. Opportunities don't come often. If there is a chance, we should grab it. Or, it will be too late.

proverb: 속담
upside down: 거꾸로, 뒤집어
every now and then: 때때로, 가끔
wisdom: 지혜
influence: 영향을 미치다
instead of: ~ 대신에
leap: 뛰다
regret: 후회하다
give it a second thought: 다시 생각해 보다
opportunity: 기회
grab: 잡다

확인문제

● 다음 문장이 본문의 내용과 일치하면 T, 일치하지 않으면 F를 쓰시오.

1 Suzi Kang doesn't think that you should look before you leap. ☐

2 Suzi thinks that if you do something in a hurry, you'll make mistakes. ☐

3 Brian thinks that if there is a chance, you should grab it. ☐

4 People are not affected by words of wisdom. ☐

Last year, I was asked to be the captain of the school hockey team. However, I took too much time to decide, so another friend became the captain. Now, I regret it. As the saying goes, "Strike while the iron is hot."

another+단수 명사
접속사(~이듯이)

Posted by Brian Pearson

Out of sight, out of mind: Something is easily forgotten if it is not near us.

수동태(잊혀진다)

I agree with this saying. I had a close friend from elementary school. Sadly, we went to different middle schools. At first, we met two to three times a week. However, it was hard to keep in touch.

일주일에 두세 번(a = per)   가주어 it   진주어 to부정사

We started to spend more time with our new friends. I started thinking less and less about him and more and more about my new friends. Now, we have stopped talking or seeing each other.

= started to think
stop+Ving: V하던 것을 멈추다

Posted by Anna Brown

I disagree with your opinion. I was really close with my neighbor, Jenny. She was from America and we liked the same basketball team. We spent a lot of time watching games together.

spend time+Ving: ~하는 데 시간을 보내다

Then her family moved away three years ago. I haven't seen her since, but I still remember the times we had. I miss her more and more as time goes by. It is the quality of time that makes people remember each other.

과거시제와 함께 쓰이는 부사   그 이후로 그녀를 못 본 것이므로 현재완료
(비례) ~할수록   It is ~that 강조 구문   사역동사 make+목적어+동사원형 (목적어가 ~하게 하다)

Posted by Jaeha Park

Well, what is your opinion? There is no right or wrong answer. It is you who should decide what is best for you.

It ~ that 강조 구문(You should decide what is best for you.)

확인문제

● 다음 문장이 본문의 내용과 일치하면 T, 일치하지 <u>않으면</u> F를 쓰시오.

1 Brian became the captain of the hockey team. ☐

2 Jaeha thinks something is remembered by the quality of time. ☐

3 Brian didn't catch the chance when it was offered to him. ☐

4 Anna is getting along with the close friend from elementary school. ☐

5 Jaeha and Jenny were close friends when they were in America. ☐

---

captain: (스포츠 팀의) 주장
sight: 시야
close: 친한, 가까운
keep in touch: 연락을 취하다
disagree: 동의하지 않다
quality: 질

● 우리말을 참고하여 빈칸에 알맞은 말을 쓰시오.

Proverbs Upside Down

1 _____ _____ _____ _____, words of wisdom _____ _____ people and _____ their lives in a great way.

2 _____ _____, " _____ _____ _____ _____ _____," means the following: _____ _____ is more important _____ _____ _____ _____.

3 So people try _____ _____ _____ _____ just _____ _____.

4 _____, some people _____ different _____.

5 To them, it is _____ _____ speak _____ _____ _____. How?

6 They think _____ words can _____ _____ _____ _____ good things.

7 It is natural _____ _____ different ideas.

8 Let's _____ _____ _____ at some other proverbs _____ _____.

9 _____ _____ _____ _____: Check _____ is in front of you _____ making a decision.

10 I _____ _____. We should always _____ _____ before we _____ _____ _____ something.

11 Then we'll be happy _____ the results of our _____.

12 _____, if we _____ _____ _____ _____ things over, we may _____ it.

13 Also, we'll _____ _____ _____ we do something _____ _____ _____.

14 _____ _____ _____, it will take _____ _____ _____ _____. Posted by Suzi Kang

15 I don't agree. _____ don't _____ _____.

16 If _____ _____ _____ _____, we should _____ _____. Or, it will be _____ _____.

17 Last year, I _____ _____ the captain of the school hockey team.

속담 뒤집기

1 때때로 지혜의 말들은 사람들에게 영향을 미치고 그들의 삶을 굉장한 방향으로 바꾸었다.

2 예를 들어 '말보다 행동이 중요하다.'라는 말의 의미는 다음과 같다. 당신이 하는 것이 당신이 말하는 것보다 더 중요하다.

3 그래서 사람들은 그냥 무엇인가를 말하는 대신에 무엇인가를 하려고 노력한다.

4 그러나 몇몇 사람들은 다른 의견을 가지고 있다.

5 그들에게는 행동보다 더 중요한 것은 바로 말이다. 어떻게 그럴까?

6 그들은 말이 다른 사람들이 좋은 행동을 하는 데 영향을 미칠 수 있다고 생각한다.

7 다른 생각을 갖는 것은 자연스럽다.

8 몇 개의 다른 속담을 거꾸로 뒤집어서 살펴보자.

9 잘 생각해 보고 행동하라[돌다리도 두드려 보고 건너라]: 결정을 하기 전에 당신 앞에 있는 것이 무엇인지 확인하라.

10 나는 완전히 동의해. 우리는 무엇인가를 하기로 결정하기 전에 항상 조심해야 해.

11 그러면 우리는 우리의 결정으로 인한 결과에 행복할 거야.

12 그러나 만약 우리가 시간을 들여 어떤 일을 심사숙고하지 않는다면 우리는 후회할지도 몰라.

13 또한 우리는 다시 생각해 보지 않고 어떤 일을 한다면 실수할 거야.

14 그 결과 우리는 바로잡는 데 더 많은 시간을 들일 거야. 강수지에 의해 게시됨

15 나는 동의하지 않아. 기회는 자주 오지 않아.

16 만약 기회가 있다면 우리는 그것을 붙잡아야 해. 그렇지 않으면 너무 늦을 거야.

17 작년에 나는 학교 하키 팀의 주장이 되기를 요청받았어.

18 _____, I _____ _____ _____ time to decide, so _____ friend became the captain.

19 Now, I _____ it. As the saying goes, "_____ _____ _____ _____ _____ _____ _____." Posted by Brian Pearson

20 _____ _____ _____, _____ _____ _____ : Something is easily _____ if it is _____ _____ us.

21 I _____ _____ this _____. I had a close friend _____ elementary school.

22 Sadly, we went _____ _____ middle schools.

23 _____ _____, we met _____ _____ _____ _____ _____ _____. However, it was _____ _____ _____ _____ _____ _____.

24 We started to _____ _____ _____ with our _____ friends.

25 I started _____ _____ and _____ about him and _____ and _____ about my new friends.

26 Now, we _____ _____ _____ _____ or _____ each other. Posted by Anna Brown

27 I _____ _____ your opinion.

28 I was really _____ _____ _____ my _____, Jenny.

29 She was _____ America and we _____ _____ _____ basketball team.

30 We _____ a lot of _____ _____ games together.

31 Then _____ _____ _____ _____ three years ago.

32 I haven't _____ her since, but I still _____ the times _____ _____.

33 I miss her more and more _____ _____ _____ _____ _____.

34 _____ _____ the quality of time _____ _____ people _____ each other. Posted by Jaeha Park

35 Well, _____ is your opinion? There is _____ _____ _____ or _____ _____.

36 It is you _____ _____ _____ _____ _____ _____ for you.

---

18 그러나 나는 결정하는 데 너무 많은 시간이 걸려서 다른 친구가 주장이 되었어.

19 지금 나는 후회해. 속담에도 있듯이 '쇠가 달았을 때 두드려야 해[쇠뿔도 단김에 빼야 해].' Brian Pearson에 의해 게시됨

20 눈에서 멀어지면, 마음에서도 멀어진다: 어떤 것이 우리 가까이에 있지 않으면 쉽게 잊는다.

21 나는 이 말에 동의해. 나는 초등학교 때부터 친한 친구가 있었어.

22 아쉽게도 우리는 다른 중학교에 갔어.

23 처음에 우리는 일주일에 두세 번 만났어. 그러나 계속 연락을 하는 것은 어려웠어.

24 우리는 우리의 새로운 친구들과 더 많은 시간을 보내기 시작했어.

25 나는 그에 대해 점점 덜 생각하고 내 새로운 친구들에 대해 더욱 더 많이 생각하기 시작했어.

26 이제 우리는 서로 이야기하거나 만나지 않아. Anna Brown에 의해 게시됨

27 나는 네 의견에 동의하지 않아.

28 나는 나의 이웃 Jenny와 정말 친했어.

29 그녀는 미국에서 왔고 우리는 같은 농구 팀을 좋아했어.

30 우리는 함께 경기를 보며 많은 시간을 보냈어.

31 그런데 그녀의 가족이 3년 전에 이사 갔어.

32 나는 그 이후로 그녀를 보지 못했지만 여전히 우리가 함께했던 시간들을 기억해.

33 나는 시간이 갈수록 그녀가 점점 더 그리워.

34 사람들을 기억하게 만드는 것은 바로 시간의 질이야. 박재하에 의해 게시됨

35 당신의 의견은 무엇인가? 맞고 틀린 답은 없다.

36 당신에게 최선인 것을 결정해야 하는 사람은 바로 당신이다.

● 우리말을 참고하여 본문을 영작하시오.

Proverbs Upside Down

1 때때로 지혜의 말들은 사람들에게 영향을 미치고 그들의 삶을 굉장한 방향으로 바꾸었다.

➡ _____

➡ _____

2 예를 들어 '말보다 행동이 중요하다.'라는 말의 의미는 다음과 같다. 당신이 하는 것이 당신이 말하는 것보다 더 중요하다.

➡ _____

➡ _____

3 그래서 사람들은 그냥 무엇인가를 말하는 대신에 무엇인가를 하려고 노력한다.

➡ _____

4 그러나 몇몇 사람들은 다른 의견을 가지고 있다.

➡ _____

5 그들에게는 행동보다 더 중요한 것은 바로 말이다. 어떻게 그럴까?

➡ _____

6 그들은 말이 다른 사람들이 좋은 행동을 하는 데 영향을 미칠 수 있다고 생각한다.

➡ _____

7 다른 생각을 갖는 것은 자연스럽다.

➡ _____

8 몇 개의 다른 속담을 거꾸로 뒤집어서 살펴보자.

➡ _____

9 잘 생각해 보고 행동하라[돌다리도 두드려 보고 건너라]: 결정을 하기 전에 당신 앞에 있는 것이 무엇인지 확인하라.

➡ _____

10 나는 완전히 동의해. 우리는 무엇인가를 하기로 결정하기 전에 항상 조심해야 해.

➡ _____

11 그러면 우리는 우리의 결정으로 인한 결과에 행복할 거야.

➡ _____

12 그러나 만약 우리가 시간을 들여 어떤 일을 심사숙고하지 않는다면 우리는 후회할지도 몰라.

➡ _____

13 또한 우리는 다시 생각해 보지 않고 어떤 일을 한다면 실수할 거야.

➡ _____

14 그 결과 우리는 바로잡는 데 더 많은 시간을 들일 거야. 강수지에 의해 게시됨

➡ _____

15 나는 동의하지 않아. 기회는 자주 오지 않아.

➡ _____

16 만약 기회가 있다면 우리는 그것을 붙잡아야 해. 그렇지 않으면 너무 늦을 거야.

➡ _____

17 작년에 나는 학교 하키 팀의 주장이 되기를 요청받았어.
➡ _____

18 그러나 나는 결정하는 데 너무 많은 시간이 걸려서 다른 친구가 주장이 되었어.
➡ _____

19 지금 나는 후회해. 속담에도 있듯이 '쇠가 달았을 때 두드려야 해[쇠뿔도 단김에 빼야 해].' Brian Pearson에 의해 게시됨
➡ _____

20 눈에서 멀어지면, 마음에서도 멀어진다: 어떤 것이 우리 가까이에 있지 않으면 쉽게 잊힌다.
➡ _____

21 나는 이 말에 동의해. 나는 초등학교 때부터 친한 친구가 있었어.
➡ _____

22 아쉽게도 우리는 다른 중학교에 갔어.
➡ _____

23 처음에 우리는 일주일에 두세 번 만났어. 그러나 계속 연락을 하는 것은 어려웠어.
➡ _____

24 우리는 우리의 새로운 친구들과 더 많은 시간을 보내기 시작했어.
➡ _____

25 나는 그에 대해 점점 덜 생각하고 내 새로운 친구들에 대해 더욱 더 많이 생각하기 시작했어.
➡ _____

26 이제 우리는 서로 이야기하거나 만나지 않아. Anna Brown에 의해 게시됨
➡ _____

27 나는 네 의견에 동의하지 않아.
➡ _____

28 나는 나의 이웃 Jenny와 정말 친했어.
➡ _____

29 그녀는 미국에서 왔고 우리는 같은 농구 팀을 좋아했어.
➡ _____

30 우리는 함께 경기를 보며 많은 시간을 보냈어.
➡ _____

31 그런데 그녀의 가족이 3년 전에 이사 갔어.
➡ _____

32 나는 그 이후로 그녀를 보지 못했지만 여전히 우리가 함께했던 시간들을 기억해.
➡ _____

33 나는 시간이 갈수록 그녀가 점점 더 그리워.
➡ _____

34 사람들이 서로를 기억하게 만드는 것은 바로 시간의 질이야. 박재하에 의해 게시됨
➡ _____

35 당신의 의견은 무엇인가? 맞고 틀린 답은 없다.
➡ _____

36 당신에게 최선인 것을 결정해야 하는 사람은 바로 당신이다.
➡ _____

[01~04] 다음 글을 읽고 물음에 답하시오.

(A)Every now and then, words of wisdom have influenced people and changed their lives in a great way. For example, "Actions speak louder than words," means the following: what you do is more important than what you say. So people try to do things instead of just saying something. However, some people have different opinions. To them, it is words that speak louder than actions. How? They think that words can influence others to do good things. It is natural to have different ideas. Let's take a look at some other proverbs upside down.

01 다음 중 밑줄 친 (A)를 대신하여 쓸 수 없는 것은?

① Sometimes
② Occasionally
③ Now and then
④ From time to time
⑤ Accidentally

02 위 글을 읽고 답할 수 있는 것은?

① How many words of wisdom are there in the world?
② What do people think about words of wisdom?
③ What is it natural to have?
④ Who makes the words of wisdom?
⑤ What should we do to express our opinion?

03 다음과 같이 풀이되는 말을 위 글에서 찾아 쓰시오.

to make someone behave in a particular way

➡ _____

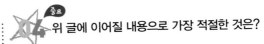

04 위 글에 이어질 내용으로 가장 적절한 것은?

① some proverbs which have influenced people's lives
② a number of people who have their own words of wisdom
③ how to make words of wisdom spread into the world
④ some sayings which have opposite meanings at a time
⑤ words that people use most in their everyday lives

[05~08] 다음 글을 읽고 물음에 답하시오.

(A)_____: Check what is in front of you before making a decision.

I totally agree. We should always be careful before we decide to do something. Then we'll be happy with the results of our decisions. However, if we don't take time to think things over, we may regret it. (B)_____, we'll make mistakes if we do something without giving it a second thought. As a result, it will take us more time to fix.　　　Posted by Suzi Kang

　⌐ I don't agree. Opportunities don't come often. If there is a chance, we should grab it. Or, it will be too late. Last year, I was asked to be the captain of the school hockey team. However, I took too much time to decide, so another friend became the captain. Now, I regret it. As the saying goes, "Strike while the iron is hot."　　Posted by Brian Pearson

05 주어진 단어를 활용하여 빈칸 (A)에 들어갈 말을 쓰시오.

(look / leap)

➡ _____

06 빈칸 (B)에 들어갈 말로 적절한 것을 <u>두 개</u> 고르시오.

① Also   ② For instance

③ Nevertheless   ④ In addition

⑤ However

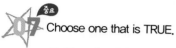

Choose one that is TRUE.

① Suzi thinks we need to grab an opportunity as soon as possible.

② Brian turned down to be the captain of the hocky team.

③ They both agree that opportunities don't come often.

④ Brian regrets becoming the captain of the school hockey team.

⑤ Suzi wants to take time to make decisions in order not to make mistakes.

서답형

08 What was Brian asked to be last year? Answer in English.

➡ _____

_____

[09~12] 다음 글을 읽고 물음에 답하시오.

Out of sight, out of mind: Something is easily forgotten if it is not near us.

I agree with this saying. I had a close friend from elementary school. (①) Sadly, we went to different middle schools. (②) At first, we met two to three times a week. (③) We started to spend more time with our new friends. (④) I started thinking less and less about him and more and more about my new friends. (⑤) Now, we have stopped talking or seeing each other.   Posted by Anna Brown

↳ I disagree with your opinion. I was really

close with my neighbor, Jenny. She was from America and we liked the same basketball team. We spent a lot of time watching games together. Then her family moved away three years ago. I haven't seen her since, but I still remember the times we had. I miss her more and more as time goes by. It is the quality of time (A)_____ makes people remember each other.   Posted by Jaeha Park

Well, what is your opinion? There is no right or wrong answer. It is you who should decide what is best for you.

09 빈칸 (A)에 들어갈 말과 <u>다른</u> 말이 들어가는 것은?

① It is a hat _____ she bought.

② It is exactly _____ I've been looking for.

③ It is music _____ Jane is interested in.

④ It was Tom _____ you were supposed to meet.

⑤ It was in September _____ Becky promised to come back.

10 ①~⑤ 중 주어진 문장이 들어가기에 가장 적절한 곳은?

> However, it was hard to keep in touch.

①   ②   ③   ④   ⑤

서답형

11 How did Jaeha spend time with Jenny? Answer in English.

➡ _____

서답형

12 Where was Jenny from?

➡ _____

[13~16] 다음 글을 읽고 물음에 답하시오.

Every now and then, ⓐwords of wisdom have ①influenced people and changed their lives in a great way.

(A) To them, it is words that speak ②louder than actions. How? They think that words can influence others to do ③good things.

(B) So people try to do things instead of just saying something. However, some people have ④different opinions.

(C) For example, "Actions speak louder than words," means the following: what you do is more important than what you say.

It is natural to have different ideas. Let's take a look at some other proverbs ⑤as it is.

서답형

13 밑줄 친 ⓐ를 대신할 수 있는 말을 위 글에서 찾아 쓰시오.

➡ _____

중요

14 자연스러운 글이 되도록 (A)~(C)를 바르게 나열한 것은?

① (A)-(C)-(B) ② (B)-(A)-(C)
③ (B)-(C)-(A) ④ (C)-(A)-(B)
⑤ (C)-(B)-(A)

15 다음 중 글의 내용을 바르게 이해한 사람은?

① A: It is hard for people to be influenced by proverbs.

② B: I think words speak louder than actions, too. So I always do something rather than say something.

③ C: It is natural for people to have similar ideas about a proverb.

④ D: There are some people who are influenced by words.

⑤ E: It is only actions that always influence people.

16 ①~⑤ 중 글의 흐름상 어색한 것은?

①   ②   ③   ④   ⑤

[17~20] 다음 글을 읽고 물음에 답하시오.

Look before you leap: Check what is in front of you before making a decision.

I totally agree. We should always be careful before we decide to do something. Then we'll be happy with the results of our decisions. However, if we don't take time to think things over, we may regret it. Also, we'll make mistakes if we do something (A)_____. As a result, it will take us more time to fix.

Posted by Suzi Kang

↳ I don't agree. Opportunities don't come often. If there is a chance, we should grab it. Or, it will be too late. Last year, I was asked to be the captain of the school hockey team. However, I took too much time to decide, so another friend became the captain. Now, I regret it. As the saying goes, "(B)Strike while the iron is hot."   Posted by Brian Pearson

17 위 글의 흐름상 빈칸 (A)에 들어갈 말로 가장 적절한 것은?

① without taking a deep breath
② with being reluctant to do it
③ without thinking about time
④ with your future in mind
⑤ without giving it a second thought

서답형

18 According to Brian, what should we do if there is a chance? Answer in English.

➡ _____

서답형

19 위 글의 내용에 맞게 빈칸에 알맞은 말을 쓰시오.

> Brian couldn't become _____ _____ because he took _____ whether or not he would accept the offer.

중요

20 밑줄 친 (B)를 대신하여 쓸 수 있는 것은?

① Birds of a feather flock together.

② Make hay while the sun shines.

③ Too many cooks spoil the broth.

④ Two heads are better than one.

⑤ Where there is a will there is a way.

[21~24] 다음 글을 읽고 물음에 답하시오.

> Out of sight, out of mind: Something is easily forgotten if it is not near us.
>
> I agree with this saying. I had a close friend from elementary school. Sadly, we went to different middle schools. At first, we met two to three times a week. However, it was hard to keep in touch. We started to spend more time with our new friends. I started thinking less and less about him and more and more about my new friends. Now, we have stopped talking or seeing each other.
>
> Posted by Anna Brown
>
> ↳ (A)_____ I was really close with my neighbor, Jenny. She was from America and we liked the same basketball team. We spent a lot of time watching games together. Then her family moved away three years ago. I haven't seen her since, but I still remember the times we had. I miss her more and more as time goes by. It is the quality of time that makes people remember each other.
>
> Posted by Jaeha Park

Well, what is your opinion? There is no right or wrong answer. It is you (B)_____ should decide what is best for you.

중요

21 빈칸 (A)에 들어갈 말로 가장 적절한 것은?

① I can't agree with you more.

② It is hard for me to disagree with you.

③ I am totally with your opinion.

④ I disagree with your opinion.

⑤ I don't disagree with you.

서답형

22 빈칸 (B)에 들어갈 말로 적절한 것을 <u>모두</u> 쓰시오.

➡ _____

23 다음 중 위 글을 읽고 답할 수 있는 것은?

① When in elementary school, how often did Anna use to meet her close friend?

② When did Anna meet her close friend for the first time?

③ Whom did Anna start thinking about when she became a middle school student?

④ How many players were there in Jaeha's hockey team?

⑤ How long did Jenny's family live in Jaeha's town?

서답형

24 According to Anna, why did Anna and her close friend grow apart from each other? Answer in English with the phrase 'It was because.'

➡ _____

_____

[01~04] 다음 글을 읽고 물음에 답하시오.

Every now and then, words of wisdom have influenced people and changed their lives in a great way. For example, "Actions speak louder than words," means the following: what you do is more important than what you say. So people try (A)_____. (a) However, some people have similar opinions. To them, it is words that speak louder than actions. How? They think that words can influence others to do good things. It is natural to have different ideas. Let's take a look at some other proverbs upside down.

01 주어진 단어를 바르게 나열하여 빈칸 (A)에 들어갈 말을 완성하시오.

(something / do / saying / to / instead / things / of / just)

➡ _____

02 밑줄 친 문장 (a)를 글의 흐름에 맞게 바르게 고쳐 쓰시오.

➡ _____

03 강조 구문을 활용하여 다음 물음에 답하시오.

Q: What can influence people and change their lives in a great way?

➡ _____

04 다음은 위 글을 요약한 것이다. 빈칸에 알맞은 말을 쓰시오.

Some people think "Actions speak louder than words." However, to others, "_____ speak louder than _____." It is natural to have _____ _____ and opinions on proverbs.

[05~08] 다음 글을 읽고 물음에 답하시오.

Look before you leap: Check what is in front of you before making a decision.

I totally agree. We should always be careful before we decide to do something. Then we'll be happy with the results of our decisions. However, if we don't take time to think things over, we may regret it. Also, we'll make mistakes if we do something without giving it a second thought. As a result, it will take us more time to fix.

Posted by Suzi Kang

ᴸ I don't agree. Opportunities don't come often. If there is a chance, we should grab it. Or, it will be too late. Last year, I was asked to be the captain of the school hockey team. However, I took too much time to decide, so another friend became the captain. Now, I regret (A)it. As the saying goes, "Strike while the iron is hot."

Posted by Brian Pearson

05 According to Suzi, why should we always be careful before we decide to do something? Use the phrase 'it's because.'

➡ _____

06 위 글의 내용에 맞게 빈칸에 알맞은 말을 쓰시오.

> Suzi thinks that deciding to do something without careful thinking will cause us to make mistakes, leading to taking _____ _____ _____ _____ them.

07 다음은 Brian이 친구에게 한 조언이다. 빈칸에 알맞은 말을 쓰시오.

> Don't hesitate to _____ _____ _____ . Take it as soon as you see it.

08 밑줄 친 (A)가 의미하는 것을 우리말로 쓰시오.

➡ _____

_____

[09~13] 다음 글을 읽고 물음에 답하시오.

> Out of sight, out of mind: (A)_____.
> I agree with this saying. I had a close friend from elementary school. Sadly, we went to ① different middle schools. At first, we ②met two to three times a week. However, it was hard to keep in touch. We started to spend more time with our new friends. I started thinking less and less about him and ③more and more about my new friends. Now, we have stopped talking or seeing each other.
> Posted by Anna Brown
> ↳ I disagree with your opinion. I was really close with my neighbor, Jenny. She was from America and we liked the same basketball team. (a)우리는 함께 경기를 보며 많은 시간을 보냈어. Then her family moved away three years ago. I haven't seen her since, but I still remember the times we had. I ④miss her more and more as time goes by. It is the quality of time that makes people ⑤forget each other. Posted by Jaeha Park
> Well, what is your opinion? There is no right or wrong answer. It is you who should decide what is best for you.

09 주어진 단어를 바르게 나열하여 빈칸 (A)에 들어갈 말을 완성하시오. 하나의 단어를 어법에 맞게 변형하시오.

> (us / forget / it / something / is / is / easily / not / if / near)

➡ _____

10 According to Anna, what was hard to do? Answer in English with a full sentence.

➡ _____

11 주어진 단어를 활용하여 밑줄 친 우리말 (a)를 영어로 쓰시오.

> (spend / a lot of / watch)

➡ _____

12 How long hasn't Jaeha seen Jenny? Answer in English with a full sentence.

➡ _____

13 ①~⑤ 중 글의 흐름상 어색한 것을 찾아 바르게 고쳐 쓰시오.

➡ _____

구석구석

After You Read B Read and Correct

Last year, I was asked to be the captain of the school soccer team. However,
<u>ask의 수동태</u> <u>접속부사</u>

I took too much time to decide, so I didn't become the captain. I think you
<u>그래서(결과)</u>

should strike while the iron is hot.
<u>~하는 동안</u>

→ I disagree with your idea. If you do something without giving it a second
<u>조건절을 이끌고 있음</u>

thought, you may regret your decision.

구문해설 • give it a second thought: 한 번 더 생각하다

작년에 나는 학교 축구팀의 주장이 되기를 요청받았어. 그러나 나는 결정하는 데 너무 많은 시간을 보내서 주장이 되지 못했어. 나는 쇠뿔도 단김에 빼야 한다고 생각해.
→ 나는 너의 생각에 동의하지 않아. 만약 네가 어떤 일을 다시 생각해 보지 않고 한다면, 너는 너의 결정을 후회할지도 몰라.

Let's Write

There is a saying that "Two heads are better than one." It means that when you
<u>두 사람의 지혜가 한 사람의 지혜보다 낫다(백지장도 맞들면 낫다)</u>

complete the work, it's helpful to have the advice or opinion of others. People
<u>가주어</u> <u>to 이하: 진주어</u>

who agree with this saying say that first, you can get great ideas from others.
<u>주격 관계대명사(people을 수식)</u>

Second, you can complete the work quickly. However, those who disagree say
<u>부사동사 complete를 수식</u> <u>앞의 내용과 대조되는 상황에 쓰임</u> <u>those who ~: ~하는 사람들</u>

that first, you can get confused with too much information. Second, you can
<u>get+형용사: ~하게 되다</u>

spend too much time before making a decision.

In my opinion, it is my own ideas that are more helpful when completing the
<u>의견을 말할 때 사용하는 표현(= I think that ~.)</u> <u>It is ~ that 강조구문</u>

work. How about you?

구문해설 • agree: 동의하다 • saying: 속담(= proverb) • complete: 완성하다 • make a decision: 결정하다

"두 사람의 지혜가 한 사람의 지혜보다 낫다."라는 속담이 있다. 이것은 일을 완성할 때 다른 사람들의 충고나 의견을 가지는 것이 도움이 된다는 것을 의미한다. 이 속담에 동의하는 사람들은 첫 번째로 다른 사람들로부터 좋은 생각을 얻을 수 있다고 말한다. 두 번째로 일을 빨리 끝낼 수 있다. 하지만 동의하지 않는 사람들은 먼저 너무 많은 정보로 혼란스럽게 될 수 있다고 말한다. 두 번째로, 결정하기 전에 많은 시간을 소비할 수 있다.
내 생각에는 일을 완성할 때, 자신의 생각을 가지는 것이 더 도움이 된다고 생각한다. 당신의 생각은 어떠한가?

Culture & Life

You can find some proverbs with similar meanings in different cultures. The
expressions may be different. However, they show the same values and thoughts.
<u>some proverbs with similar meanings in different cultures</u>

Let's read some of the proverbs and find some connections.
<u>read와 병렬 관계</u>

Turkey: The ground has ears.

Tanzania: Even the night has ears.

Kenya: He who is unable to dance says that the yard is stony.
<u>주격 관계대명사</u> <u>명사절 접속사</u>

the UK: A bad workman blames his tools.

Kenya: When elephants fight, it is the grass that gets hurt.
<u>주격 관계대명사</u>

Korea: 고래 싸움에 새우 등 터진다.

구문해설 • proverb: 속담 • similar: 유사한 • culture: 문화 • expression: 표현 • value: 가치
• connection: 연결 고리 • stony: 돌이 많은

여러분은 여러 문화에서 비슷한 속담을 찾을 수 있다. 표현은 다를지 모른다. 그러나 그들은 같은 가치와 생각들을 보여 준다. 몇몇 속담을 읽고, 연결 고리를 찾아보자.
터키 – 땅에 귀가 있다.
탄자니아 – 심지어 밤에도 귀가 있다.
케냐 – 춤을 못 추는 사람이 뜰에 돌이 많다고 말한다.
영국 – 서투른 목수가 연장만 탓한다.
케냐 – 코끼리들이 싸울 때 다치는 것은 풀이다.
한국 – 고래 싸움에 새우 등 터진다.

Words & Expressions

01 빈칸에 알맞은 단어를 고르시오.

> _____ we eat the food before he comes back, he will be mad.

① When   ② If
③ However   ④ Although
⑤ Since

02 접두사를 붙여 반의어로 만들 때 나머지 넷과 <u>다른</u> 접미사를 사용하는 것을 고르시오.

① agree   ② educated
③ intelligent   ④ usual
⑤ wise

03 다음 짝지어진 두 단어의 관계가 같도록 빈칸에 알맞은 말을 주어진 철자로 시작하여 쓰시오.

> allow : permit = chance : o_____

04 다음 빈칸에 공통으로 들어갈 말을 고르시오.

> • My best friend moved _____ when I was ten.
> • This cleaner can take dust _____ from the desk.

① in   ② into
③ for   ④ away
⑤ to

Conversation

[05~07] 다음 대화를 읽고 물음에 답하시오.

G: Dohun, what are you doing?
B: I'm watching a movie about AI robots. It's really fascinating. <u>너는 그것들에 대해 어떻게 생각해?</u> (of, what)
G: (A)_____ my opinion, they will cause problems. AI robots will take jobs (B)_____ people.
B: Well, I still think they are useful. There is a science festival introducing AI robots. Why don't we go and find (C)_____ more about them?
G: Sounds good.

05 빈칸 (A)~(C)에 알맞은 말을 〈보기〉에서 골라 쓰시오.

> ┌─ 보기 ─┐
> about at away for from in of out

➡ (A)_____   (B)_____ (2 단어)
  (C)_____

06 밑줄 친 우리말을 주어진 단어를 이용해 영작하시오.

➡ _____

07 대화의 내용과 일치하지 <u>않는</u> 것을 고르시오.

① 소녀는 인공지능 로봇이 문제가 있다고 생각한다.
② 도훈이는 영화가 흥미롭다고 생각한다.
③ 그들은 인공지능 로봇들을 소개하는 과학 축제에 갈 것이다.
④ 그들은 인공지능 로봇에 대해 같은 생각을 가지고 있다.
⑤ 도훈이는 영화를 보는 중이다.

[08~11] 다음 대화를 읽고 물음에 답하시오.

B: I don't think we should talk about others when they are not there. (①)

G: (A)_____ do you say that?

B: (②) Well, I had a fight with Jimin because I talked about her test results with Sam. (③)

G: Oh, (B)_____ did you do that?

B: (④) I never thought that she would find out.

G: Well, like the saying (C)_____, "ⓐ_____."

B: (⑤) I've learned my lesson.

08 ①~⑤ 중 주어진 문장이 들어갈 곳은?

I agree.

①   ②   ③   ④   ⑤

09 대화에서 다음 영영풀이에 해당하는 단어를 찾아 쓰시오.

something that happens as a consequence

➡ _____

10 빈칸 (A)~(C)에 들어갈 말로 알맞게 짝지어진 것은?

① What – why – means
② What – how – goes
③ Why – why – goes
④ Why – how – means
⑤ What – why – goes

11 빈칸 ⓐ에 알맞은 말을 고르시오.

① Two heads are better than one.
② Killing two birds with one stone.
③ Better late than never.
④ What goes around comes around.
⑤ Walls have ears.

12 다음 대화에서 흐름상 어색한 부분을 찾아 바르게 고치시오.

A: What do you think of having no tests at school?

B: I agree with the idea. Students will not review the lessons.

➡ _____
_____
_____

Grammar

13 빈칸에 들어갈 말로 알맞은 단어를 쓰시오.

At high tide, the water from the Adriatic Sea often rises and leaves the streets full of water. _____, I would be able to walk around the town through the raised walkways.

14 다음 강조하는 문장에서 어법상 어색한 부분을 찾아 올바른 문장으로 고쳐 쓰시오.

(1) Jessy took first place.

→ (Jessy 강조) It was Jessy that she took first place.

➡ _____

(2) My brother called me last night.

→ (last night 강조) It was last night where my brother called me.

➡ _____

(3) Jane met her staff yesterday to discuss an important matter.

→ (her staff 강조) It was her staff which Jane met yesterday to discuss an important matter.

➡ _____
_____

15 다음 중 밑줄 친 it의 성질이 다른 하나를 고르시오.

① It was this summer that you and I met for the first time.

② It was she that woke me up in the morning.

③ It was the day before yesterday that you watched TV in this living room.

④ It was you that he wanted to meet.

⑤ It was certain that he would succeed.

16 다음 중 어법상 올바른 문장을 고르시오.

① It is Rob who wants to stay with you.

② It is a sandwich what the woman is eating.

③ It is the pen when is used to write a formal letter.

④ It is the man where is listening to music.

⑤ It is the girl which I met yesterday in Jeju Island.

17 우리말을 영어로 옮길 때 (A), (B), (C)에 들어갈 말을 damage와 good을 이용하여 쓰시오.

초콜릿을 너무 많이 먹으면 당신의 치아를 손상시킬 수 있다. 그러나 약간의 초콜릿은 당신에게 좋을 수 있다.

→ Eating too much chocolate ___(A)___ . A little bit of chocolate ___(B)___ , ___(C)___ .

➡ (A) _____
(B) _____
(C) _____

18 다음 빈칸에 들어갈 단어끼리 알맞게 짝지어진 것을 고르시오.

• My brother went home _____ I did not.

• He tried hard. _____, he failed in the end.

① but, However
② but, But
③ or, But
④ or, However
⑤ however, However

19 다음 문장을 주어진 부분을 강조하고자 할 때, 어법상 어색한 것을 고르시오.

> Susan studied English in the library yesterday.

① 주어: It was Susan that studied English in the library yesterday.

② 동사: Susan did study English in the library yesterday.

③ 목적어: It was English what Susan studied in the library yesterday.

④ 장소 부사: It was in the library where Susan studied English yesterday.

⑤ 시간 부사: It was yesterday when Susan studied English in the library.

Reading

[20~23] 다음 글을 읽고 물음에 답하시오.

Every now and then, words of wisdom have influenced people and changed their lives in a great way. For example, "Actions speak louder than words," means the following: (A)_____. So people try to do things instead of just saying something. However, some people have different opinions. To (B) them, it is words that speak louder than actions. How? They think that words can influence others to do good things. It is natural to have different ideas. Let's take a look at some other proverbs upside down.

20 What can words influence others to do? Answer in English with a full sentence.

➡ _____

21 다음 중 빈칸 (A)에 들어갈 말로 가장 적절한 것은?

① saying good things to others will benefit you

② what you do is more important than what you say

③ believing only what you see can harm you from time to time

④ saying is one thing and behaving is another

⑤ we live in a world where the loudest always win.

22 다음 중 밑줄 친 (B)에 해당하는 사람이 할 말로 가장 적절한 것은?

① A: I think we should do something before saying it.

② B: We need to show people that we are actors not just speakers.

③ C: I don't want people to consider me as a talker.

④ D: Meaningful words are more influential than meaningless actions.

⑤ E: It can be said that words speak more quietly than actions.

23 위 글의 제목으로 가장 적절한 것은?

① Proverbs: The Only Logical Thought

② Sayings: Making Our Lives Comfortable

③ Looking at Proverbs in a Different Way

④ Words of Wisdom: the Most Effective Way to Persuade People

⑤ The Origin of Various Words of Wisdom in the World

[24~26] 다음 글을 읽고 물음에 답하시오.

Look before you leap: Check what is in front of you before making a decision.

I totally agree. We should always be careful before we decide to do something. Then we'll be happy with the results of our decisions. However, if we don't take time to think things over, we may regret it. Also, we'll make mistakes if we do something without giving it a second thought. (A)_____, it will take us more time to fix.   Posted by Suzi Kang

↳ I don't agree. Opportunities don't come often. If there is a chance, we should grab it. Or, it will be too late. Last year, I was asked to be the captain of the school hockey team. However, I took too much time to decide, so another friend became the captain. Now, I regret it. As the saying goes, "Strike while the iron is hot."   Posted by Brian Pearson

24 다음 중 빈칸 (A)에 들어갈 말로 가장 적절한 것은?

① On the other hand ② Nevertheless
③ For instance   ④ However
⑤ As a result

25 글의 내용과 일치하는 것은?

① Suzi wants to be as careless as she can before making decisions.
② Both students agree that they should be cautious when making decisions.
③ Brian is proud of his friend being the captain of the hockey team.
④ Brian feels sorry for taking too much time to consider accepting the offer.
⑤ Brian was asked to be the captain of the school hockey team this year.

26 According to Suzi, what should we always do before we decide to do something? Answer in English.

➡ _____

_____

[27~29] 다음 글을 읽고 물음에 답하시오.

There is a saying that "Two heads are better than one." It means that when you complete the work, it's helpful to have the advice or opinion of others. (①) People who agree with this saying say that first, you can get great ideas from others. (②) Second, you can complete the work quickly. (③) However, those who disagree say that first, you can get confused with too much information. (④) In my opinion, it is many different ideas that are more helpful when completing the work. How about you? (⑤)

27 ①~⑤ 중 주어진 문장이 들어가기에 가장 적절한 곳은?

Second, you can spend too much time before making a decision.

①   ②   ③   ④   ⑤

28 What does the writer think about getting many different ideas from others? Answer in English.

➡ _____

_____

29 Write the reason why some people disagree with the saying 'Two heads are better than one.' Use the phrase 'It is because.'

➡ _____

_____

01 출제율 90%

다음 짝지어진 단어의 관계가 같도록 빈칸에 알맞은 말을 주어진 철자로 시작하여 쓰시오.

> leap : jump = saying : p_____

02 출제율 95%

다음 빈칸 (A)와 (B)에 들어갈 말이 바르게 짝지어진 것은?

> • Text messaging enables people to (A)_____ in close contact at all times.
> • He wasn't well, so we had to (B)_____ him behind.

	(A)	(B)		(A)	(B)
①	keep	leave	②	keep	look
③	keep	turn	④	take	leave
⑤	take	turn

03 출제율 100%

다음 빈칸에 들어갈 말을 〈보기〉에서 찾아 쓰시오.

> ┤ 보기 ├
> captain   opportunity   proverb   result

(1) "Don't judge a book by its cover" is a _____.

(2) It is important not to miss any _____ in your life.

(3) This was not the _____ that I was expecting.

(4) Brian became the _____ of our music club.

04 출제율 90%

다음 영영풀이가 나타내는 말을 고르시오.

> to seize eagerly

① hold ② grab ③ force
④ crash ⑤ smash

[05~08] 다음 대화를 읽고 물음에 답하시오.

Claire: Jinho, what's the matter? You look upset.

Jinho: (①) I had a fight with Harry.

Claire: Why? What happened?

Jinho: (②) We both wanted to use the same music room at the same time.

Claire: (③) I don't think there are enough music rooms to practice in after school.

Jinho: I agree. (a)What do you think of setting a time limit for the music rooms?

Claire: (A)_____ do you think it should be?

Jinho: I don't think anyone should be allowed to use a room for more than an hour a day.

Claire: (④) I need more than an hour to practice music.

Jinho: Then how about reserving a music room?

Claire: (⑤) That's a good idea. Then each person will have enough time to practice.

05 출제율 95%

①～⑤ 중 주어진 문장이 들어갈 곳은?

> I disagree.

① ② ③ ④ ⑤

06 빈칸 (A)에 알맞은 말을 고르시오.

① Why
② What
③ How
④ How long
⑤ What time

07 대화의 밑줄 친 (a)와 바꿔 쓸 수 있는 것을 모두 고르시오.

① Why do you like setting a time limit for the music rooms?
② What do you say to setting a time limit for the music rooms?
③ When do you set a time limit for the music rooms?
④ How do you feel about setting a time limit for the music rooms?
⑤ What's your opinion about setting a time limit for the music rooms?

08 대화의 내용과 일치하지 <u>않는</u> 것을 고르시오.

① 진호와 Harry가 싸웠다.
② 진호와 Harry는 동시에 같은 음악실을 사용하기를 원했다.
③ 진호는 하루에 1시간 이상 음악실을 사용해서는 안 된다고 생각했다.
④ Harry는 음악 연습을 하려면 1시간 이상 필요하다고 생각한다.
⑤ 진호는 음악실을 예약해서 사용하는 것을 제안했다.

[09~12] 다음 대화를 읽고 물음에 답하시오.

B: Yura, what are you doing?
G: I'm posting my pictures on the internet. (①) Come and have a look.
B: There are so many pictures that show your everyday life. (②)
G: Well, my friends like my posts a lot. I think it's a good way to get to know one another. (③)
B: (A)_____ There might be some people who will use your pictures in a bad way. (④)
G: Come to think of it, I should be more careful with my pictures. Thanks for your advice. (⑤)
B: No problem.

09 ①~⑤ 중 주어진 문장이 들어갈 곳은?

Isn't it dangerous?

①   ②   ③   ④   ⑤

10 빈칸 (A)에 알맞은 말을 <u>모두</u> 고르시오

① We're on the same page.
② I disagree.
③ I'm against the idea.
④ I don't think so.
⑤ Same here.

11 대화에서 다음 영영풀이에 해당하는 단어를 찾아 쓰시오.

cautious in one's actions

➡ _____

12 대화의 내용과 일치하지 <u>않는</u> 것을 고르시오. *출제율 100%*

① The pictures which are posted on the internet show Yura's everyday life.

② Some people used her pictures in a bad way.

③ Yura will be more careful in posting her pictures on the internet.

④ Yura is posting her pictures on the internet.

⑤ Yura's friends like her posts.

13 다음 중 밑줄 친 It의 쓰임이 나머지 넷과 <u>다른</u> 하나를 고르시오. *출제율 95%*

① It is a pity that you can't join us.

② It is odd that she left so suddenly.

③ It was because I didn't study at all that I failed the English test.

④ It is not your fault that your apartment doesn't absorb sound as well as your office.

⑤ It is certain that he will pass the test.

14 다음 문장에서 어법상 어색한 곳을 찾아 바르게 고쳐 쓰시오. *출제율 90%*

(1) It is careful decisions what help you to accomplish the project.

➡ _____

_____

(2) We tried to keep in touch however it was getting harder and harder to see each other.

➡ _____

_____

(3) Jinho thinks setting a time limit is a good way to solve this problem. Therefore, Chaire disagrees with his idea because she needs enough time to practice.

➡ _____

_____

_____

_____

(4) What was Tom that saw a lion yesterday.

➡ _____

[15~19] 다음 글을 읽고 물음에 답하시오.

Out of sight, out of mind: Something is easily forgotten if it is not near us.

I ①<u>agree with</u> this saying. I had a close friend from elementary school. Sadly, we went to different middle schools. At first, we met two to three times ②<u>a week</u>. However, it was hard (A) <u>to keep in touch</u>. We started to spend more time with our new friends. I started thinking less and less about him and more and more about my new friends. Now, we have stopped ③<u>to talk or see</u> each other.   Posted by Anna Brown

└, I disagree with your opinion. I was really close with my neighbor, Jenny. She was from America and we liked the same basketball team. We spent a lot of time ④<u>watching games</u> together. Then her family moved away three years ago. I haven't seen her since, but I still remember the times we had. I miss her more and more as time goes by. It is the quality of time ⑤ <u>that</u> makes people remember each other.

Posted by Jaeha Park

Well, what is your opinion? There is no right or wrong answer. It is you who should decide what is best for you.

15 What does the underlined (A) mean?

① to touch and feel someone

② to get to know someone better

③ to make someone feel comfortable

④ to keep away from someone you know

⑤ to communicate with somebody regularly

16 ①~⑤ 중 어법상 바르지 <u>않은</u> 것은?

①　　　②　　　③　　　④　　　⑤

17 위 글의 내용과 일치하지 <u>않는</u> 부분을 두 군데 찾아 바르게 고쳐 쓰시오.

Jaeha doesn't think the saying 'Out of sight, out of mind' is right. He had a close cousin who moved away five years ago. However, he still misses her.

➡ _____

18 According to Jaeha, what makes people remember each other? Answer in English.

➡ _____

_____

19 다음 중 위 글의 내용과 일치하는 것은?

① Anna keeps seeing her close friend from elementary school.

② Anna used to see her close friend more than three times per week.

③ Jaeha spent time playing basketball with Jenny.

④ Jaeha and Jenny had the same interest in common.

⑤ Jaeha went to America to see Jenny because he missed her.

[20~22] 다음 글을 읽고 물음에 답하시오.

There is a saying that "(A)_____"
It means that when you complete the work, it's helpful to have the advice or opinion of others. People who agree with this saying say that first, you can get great ideas from others. Second, you can complete the work quickly. However, those who disagree say that first, you can get confused with too much information. Second, you can spend too much time before making a decision. In my opinion, it is many different ideas that are more helpful when completing the work. How about you?

20 빈칸 (A)에 들어갈 말로 가장 적절한 것은?

① Opposites attract.

② Even the night has ears.

③ Two heads are better than one.

④ A bad man blames his tools.

⑤ You can't teach an old dog new tricks.

21 What are two benefits of getting the advice or opinion of others? Answer in English with a full sentence.

➡ _____

_____

22 According to the writer, what is more helpful when completing the work? Answer in English.

➡ _____

_____

01 밑줄 친 우리말과 일치하도록 주어진 단어를 이용해 영작하시오.

> A: 남의 험담을 하는 것을 어떻게 생각하니?
> (of, behind, talk, think, back)
> B: I think it's rude. Remember, walls have ears.

➡ _____

_____

02 밑줄 친 문장 (A)와 같은 의미가 되도록 주어진 단어를 이용하여 쓰시오.

> W: Jacob, can you help me?
> B: What is it, Mom?
> W: Well, I got a message from my friend, but I don't understand what some of it means.
> B: Let me see. Hmm… ASAP means "as soon as possible" and HAND means "Have a nice day."
> W: Oh, I see.
> B: (A)What do you think of these acronyms?
> W: I think they are destroying the language.

➡ (feel, about)

_____

➡ (opinion, about)

_____

➡ (say, to)

_____

03 대화의 흐름상 빈칸에 들어갈 말을 주어진 단어를 이용해 영작하시오.

> B: Emma, let's take a break.
> G: What? We've only studied for 30 minutes.
> B: Like the saying goes, "All work and no play makes Jack a dull boy."
> G: _____ Then let's take a break after we finish this part.
> B: Okay.

➡ (1)_____ (agree)

(2)_____ (page)

(3)_____ (here)

04 다음 괄호 안의 어구를 이용하여 빈칸을 채우시오.

(1) 내가 프랑스에서 그 선물 파는 가게에 들렀던 것은 바로 작년 겨울방학이었다. (last winter, when, drop by)

➡ It was _____

the gift shop in France.

(2) 나는 내 학급 친구들을 위한 약간의 선물을 사고 싶었다. 그러나 나는 그것들을 고르기에 충분한 시간이 없었다. (buy, gift, however, enough)

➡ I wanted _____

_____

_____

05 〈보기〉를 참고하여 각 문장의 빈칸에 알맞은 것을 써 넣으시오.

> ┤ 보기 ├
> but,   however

(1) I am too busy these days _____ I want to watch the movie.

(2) My sister and I are going to go on a trip this weekend. After hearing our schedule, _____, my father doesn't accept our trip.

Look before you leap: Check what is in front of you before making a decision.

I totally agree. We should always be careful before we decide to do something. Then we'll be happy with the results of our decisions. However, if we don't take time to think things over, we may regret it. Also, we'll make mistakes if we do something without giving it a second thought.   (A)   a result, it will take us more time to fix.   Posted by Suzi Kang

┗, I don't agree. Opportunities don't come often. If there is a chance, we should grab it. Or, it will be too late. Last year, I was asked to be the captain of the school hockey team. However, I took too much time to decide, so another friend became the captain. Now, I regret it.   (B)   the saying goes, "Strike while the iron is hot."

Posted by Brian Pearson

06 빈칸 (A)와 (B)에 공통으로 들어갈 말을 쓰시오.

➡ _____

07 다음 중 위 글의 내용과 일치하지 <u>않는</u> 곳을 세 군데 찾아 바르게 고쳐 쓰시오.

> **Brian:** Last year, I was asked to be the captain of the school soccer team. However, I took too much time to decide, so I didn't become the captain. I think you should strike while the iron is cold.
>
> **Suzi:** I agree with your idea. If you do something without giving a second thought, you may regret your decision.

➡ _____

08 According to Brian, why should we grab opportunities? Answer in English and use the phrase 'It's because.'

➡ _____

Every now and then, words of wisdom have influenced people and changed their lives in a great way. For example, "Actions speak louder than words," means the following: what you do is more important than what you say. So people try to do things instead of just saying something. However, some people have different opinions. To them, it is words that speak louder than actions. How? They think that words can influence others to do good things. (A)다른 생각을 갖는 것은 자연스럽다. Let's take a look at some other proverbs upside down.

09 주어진 단어를 활용하여 밑줄 친 우리말 (A)를 영어로 쓰시오.

(it / idea)

➡ _____

10 What does the proverb "Actions speak louder than words," mean? Answer in English.

➡ _____

_____

01 다음 역사적 사실을 보고 각 문제에서 제시한 단어를 활용하여 의문문을 만들고, 그에 적절한 답을 강조 구문으로 쓰시오.

who	Admiral Yi Sun-shin	Martin Luther King	Steve Jobs	Pixar
when	in 1592	in 1963	in 1979	in 1995
what	fought against Japan	delivered a speech	founded Apple Company	produced the first 3D computer animated feature film *Toy Story*

> (1) when 사용. 제시 단어: Admiral Yi Sun-shin
> (2) who 사용. 제시 단어: deliver a speech
> (3) what 사용. 제시 단어: Steve Jobs, founded
> (4) which company 사용. 제시 단어: produce

(1) _____

(2) _____

(3) _____

(4) _____

02 다음 속담에 대한 찬반 의견을 참고하여 글쓴이의 의견을 완성하시오.

> Two heads are better than one.
>
> **Agree:** get great ideas from others, complete the work quickly
>
> **Disagree:** get confused with too much information, spend too much time before making a decision
>
> **Q:** Which do you think is helpful when completing the work?
>
> **A:** I think having many different ideas is more helpful when completing the work.

> There is a saying that "_____" It means that when you complete the work, it's helpful to have the advice or opinion of others. People who agree with this saying say that first, you can _____. Second, you can _____. However, those who disagree say that first, you can _____. Second, you can _____. In my opinion, it is _____ that _____. How about you?

단원별 모의고사

01 다음 빈칸에 공통으로 들어갈 전치사를 고르시오.

> • We were _____ a hurry, so we had to have a quick snack.
> • We decided not to buy it _____ the end.

① on ② at ③ in
④ for ⑤ from

02 다음 빈칸에 알맞은 단어를 〈보기〉에서 골라 쓰시오.

> ┌─ 보기 ─┐
> behind down in over

(1) There was no time to think it _____.
(2) Let's keep _____ touch next year.
(3) Let's take a look at some other proverbs upside _____.
(4) Make sure you don't leave trash _____.

03 빈칸에 들어갈 말로 알맞은 것을 고르시오.

> A good workman doesn't _____ his tools.

① judge ② leap ③ blame
④ harm ⑤ strike

04 다음 우리말에 맞도록 빈칸에 알맞은 말을 쓰시오. (철자가 주어진 경우 주어진 철자로 시작할 것.)

(1) 우리가 환경에 해를 끼치면 결국 후회하는 건 우리일 것이다.
➡ If we _____ the environment, we'll be the ones who _____ it in the end.

(2) 기회는 자주 오지 않는다.
➡ O_____ don't come often.

(3) 반대되는 사람들에게 끌린다.
➡ _____ attract.

(4) 사람들은 그냥 무엇인가를 말하는 대신에 무엇인가를 하려고 노력한다.
➡ People try to do things _____ of just saying something.

05 빈칸 ⓐ~ⓔ에 들어가지 <u>않는</u> 말을 고르시오.

> Claire: Jinho, what's the matter? You look upset.
> Jinho: I had a fight with Harry.
> Claire: Why? What happened?
> Jinho: We both wanted to use the music room at the ⓐ_____ time.
> Claire: I don't think there are ⓑ_____ music rooms to practice in after school.
> Jinho: I agree. What do you think of ⓒ_____ a time limit for the music rooms?
> Claire: How long do you think it should be?
> Jinho: I don't think anyone should ⓓ_____ to use a room for more than an hour a day.
> Claire: I disagree. I need ⓔ_____ than an hour to practice music.
> Jinho: Then how about reserving a music room?
> Claire: That's a good idea. Then each person will have enough time to practice.

① setting ② less ③ same
④ enough ⑤ be allowed

[06~09] 다음 대화를 읽고 물음에 답하시오.

> W: Jacob, can you help me?
> B: What is it, Mom? (①)
> W: Well, I got a message from my friend. (②)
> B: Let me see. Hmm⋯ ASAP means "as soon as possible" and HAND means "Have a nice day." (③)
> W: Oh, I see.
> B: (④) What do you think of these (A)_____, Mom?
> W: I think they are destroying the language. (⑤) What do you think?
> B: (B)제 생각엔 그것들은 사용하기 재미있고 쉬운 것 같아요. (opinion, fun, easy, use)

06 ①~⑤ 중 주어진 문장이 들어갈 곳은?

> However, I don't understand what some of it means.

① ② ③ ④ ⑤

07 대화의 흐름상 빈칸 (A)에 들어갈 단어를 주어진 철자로 시작하여 쓰시오.

➡ a_____

08 위 대화에서 다음 영영풀이에 해당하는 단어를 찾아 쓰시오.

> to damage something so badly that it no longer exists, works, etc.

➡ _____

09 밑줄 친 우리말 (B)와 일치하도록 주어진 단어를 이용하여 영작하시오.

➡ _____

[10~11] 다음 대화를 읽고 물음에 답하시오.

> B: Look! People are just leaving their trash (A)_____!
> G: Oh, no! If we harm the environment, we'll be the ones who regret it (B)_____ the end.
> B: I agree. Like the saying goes, "What goes around comes around."
> G: You're right. Let's help the earth (C)_____.

10 빈칸 (A)와 (B)에 알맞은 말을 쓰시오.

➡ (A) _____ (B) _____

11 빈칸 (C)에 알맞은 말을 고르시오.

① by leaving our trash behind
② by relying on it
③ by having less time to do it
④ by taking our trash with us
⑤ by using it in a bad way

12 다음 중 어법상 어색한 것은?

① Was it the music store that you dropped by yesterday?
② Was it last year when we planned our travel?
③ Were it you that failed the physics exam?
④ Was it you and I that were elected on the influential people in the school?
⑤ Was it at the amusement park where you met your family?

13 지난 토요일 가족과 즐거운 시간을 보낸 Suji의 가족 사진이다. 빈칸에 들어갈 단어끼리 바르게 짝지어진 것을 고르시오.

• It was the guitar (A) I played sitting on a chair.

• It was a cat (B) is sitting on my grandmother's lap.

• We had a great time last Sunday. (C) , my older sister couldn't join.

	(A)	(B)	(C)
①	that	who	But
②	which	that	However
③	that	which	But
④	which	what	However
⑤	that	what	But

14 괄호 안의 단어를 활용하여 우리말에 맞게 영작하시오.

(1) 회의가 6시간 전에 개최됐다. 그러나 아직 진행 중이다. (conference, hold, in progress)

　➡ _____

　_____

(2) Suji가 어제 저녁 공원에서 먹었던 것은 바로 치즈피자였다. (which, eat)

　➡ _____

　_____

15 의문사를 강조하는 'it is ∼ that ...' 구문의 의문문을 만들고자 한다. 각 단계에 알맞은 답을 쓰시오.

> When did he leave Busan?

(1) 주어진 문장을 평서문으로 바꾸시오.

　➡ _____

(2) (1)의 문장을 강조구문으로 바꾸시오.

　➡ _____

(3) (2)의 문장을 의문문으로 바꾸시오.

　➡ _____

(4) 의문사 when을 앞으로 보내어 의문문으로 쓰시오.

　➡ _____

16 다음 각 문장을 괄호 안의 단어를 배열하여 문장을 완성할 때, 주어진 지시대로 쓰시오.

(1) 5번째 단어를 쓰시오.

• 그녀가 그녀의 편지를 보낸 것은 바로 너의 집이었다. (that, your house, it, sent, she, letter, was, her, to)

　➡ _____

(2) 7번째 단어를 쓰시오.

• 사람들이 서로를 기억하게 만드는 것은 바로 시간의 질이야. (other, is, quality, it, the, of, people, each, makes, remember, time, that).

　➡ _____

[17~20] 다음 글을 읽고 물음에 답하시오.

Look before you leap: (A)_____
I totally agree. We should always be careful before we decide to do something. Then we'll be ①happy with the results of our decisions. However, if we don't take time ②to think things over, we may ③regret it. Also, we'll make mistakes if we do something without giving it a second thought. As a result, it will take us more

time to fix.   Posted by Suzi Kang
└, I don't agree. Opportunities don't come often. If there is a chance, we should ④ignore it. Or, it will be too late. Last year, I was asked to be the captain of the school hockey team. However, I took too much time to decide, so __(B)__ friend became the captain. Now, I ⑤regret it. As the saying goes, "Strike while the iron is hot."
            Posted by Brian Pearson

17 주어진 어구를 바르게 배열하여 빈칸 (A)에 들어갈 말을 쓰시오.

(making / in front of / a decision / what / check / is / you / before)

➡ _____

_____

18 ①~⑤ 중 글의 흐름상 어색한 것은?

①   ②   ③   ④   ⑤

19 다음 중 수지의 주장과 맞는 속담은?

① The icing on the cake.
② Laughter is the best medicine.
③ Haste makes waste.
④ Talking on the wall.
⑤ A friend in need is a friend indeed.

20 다음 중 빈칸 (B)에 알맞은 것은?

① one   ② some
③ other   ④ another
⑤ the other

[21~24] 다음 글을 읽고 물음에 답하시오.

I was really close with my neighbor, Jenny. (①) She was from America and we liked the same basketball team. (②) We spent a lot of time watching games together. (③) I haven't seen her since, but I still remember the times we had. Unlike the saying "_____," I miss her more and more as time goes by. (④) It is the quality of time that makes people remember each other. (⑤)
            Posted by Jaeha Park

21 빈칸 (A)에 들어갈 말로 가장 적절한 것은?

① Every Jack has Jill
② Out of sight, out of mind
③ Well begun is half done
④ It never rains but it pours
⑤ Heaven helps those who help themselves

22 ①~⑤ 중 주어진 문장이 들어가기에 가장 적절한 곳은?

Then her family moved away three years ago.

①   ②   ③   ④   ⑤

Homes Everywhere

 의사소통 기능

- 바람·소원 표현하기
  I wish I could live on the water.
- 상상하여 말하기
  What would you do if you lived in Alaska?

언어 형식

- 가정법 과거
  If I lived in a pueblo, **I would climb** up a ladder to enter my house.

- 5형식 동사 keep / make
  They would **keep me cool** in summer and **warm** in winter.

Words & Expressions

Key Words

- **appear** [əpíər] 동 보이다, 나타나다
- **cave** [keiv] 명 동굴
- **colorful** [kʌ́lərfəl] 형 형형색색의
- **earth** [ə:rθ] 명 흙
- **enter** [éntər] 동 ~에 들어가다
- **everywhere** [évriwer] 부 모든 곳에, 어디나
- **family name** 성(姓)
- **flat** [flæt] 형 평평한
- **floating** [flóutiŋ] 형 떠다니는
- **hidden** [hídn] 형 숨겨진
- **house** [hauz] 동 수용하다
- **however** [hauévər] 부 그러나, 하지만
- **huge** [hju:dʒ] 형 거대한, 굉장히 큰
- **imagine** [imǽdʒin] 동 상상하다
- **install** [instɔ́:l] 동 설치하다
- **invader** [invéidər] 명 침략자
- **invisible** [invízəbl] 형 눈에 보이지 않는, 투명한
- **island** [áilənd] 명 섬
- **jungle** [dʒʌ́ŋgl] 명 밀림, 정글
- **ladder** [lǽdər] 명 사다리
- **like** [laik] 전 ~와 같은
- **millionaire** [mìljənéər] 명 백만장자
- **mostly** [móustli] 부 주로, 일반적으로
- **opening** [óupəniŋ] 명 구멍
- **pole** [poul] 명 기둥, 막대기
- **raised** [reizd] 형 높이 올린
- **rise** [reiz] 동 오르다, 올라가다
- **roof** [ru:f] 명 지붕
- **share** [ʃɛər] 동 공유하다
- **sometimes** [sʌ́mtàimz] 부 때때로, 가끔
- **store** [stɔ:r] 동 저장하다, 보관하다
- **straw** [strɔ:] 명 짚, 지푸라기
- **surface** [sə́:rfis] 명 표면, 지면, 수면
- **support** [səpɔ́:rt] 동 지탱하다, 떠받치다
- **swampy** [swámpi] 형 습지의
- **take** [teik] 동 ~을 타다
- **thick** [θik] 형 두꺼운, 살찐
- **tide** [taid] 명 조수, 흐름
- **travel** [trǽvəl] 동 여행하다, 이동하다
- **unwelcome** [ənwélkəm] 형 반갑지 않은
- **usually** [júːʒuəli] 부 보통, 대개
- **Venetian** [vəníːʃən] 명 베니스 사람
- **village** [vílidʒ] 명 마을, 촌락
- **walkway** [wɔ́:kwei] 명 통로
- **wheel** [hwi:l] 명 바퀴
- **wooden** [wúdn] 형 나무로 된

Key Expressions

- **all day** 하루 종일
- **all over the world** 세계 곳곳에
- **at high tide** 만조에
- **be known as** ~로 알려지다
- **be made up of** ~로 구성되다, ~로 만들어지다
- **be used for** ~로 사용되다
- **climb up** ~에 올라가다
- **come over** 들르다
- **for a while** 당분간, 잠시 동안
- **full of** ~로 가득 찬
- **go sledding** 썰매 타러 가다
- **hand down** ~을 물려주다
- **live in** ~에 살다, ~에 거주하다
- **make sense** 이치에 맞다
- **more than** ~ 이상의
- **one of** ~ 중 하나
- **on top of** ~ 위에
- **on weekends** 주말마다
- **pull A up** A를 당겨 올리다
- **stop A from ~ing** A가 ~하지 못하게 막다
- **take a look** 보다
- **upside down** 거꾸로 된, 뒤집힌
- **up to** ~까지
- **walk around** 돌아다니다
- **What is it ~ like?** ~은 어때?

Word Power

※ 서로 비슷한 뜻을 가진 어휘

- □ **appear** 나타나다 – **show up** 나타나다
- □ **hidden** 숨겨진 – **concealed** 숨겨진, 가려진
- □ **store** 저장하다, 보관하다 – **save** 모으다, 저축하다
- □ **travel** 여행하다, 이동하다 – **wander** 유랑하다, 방랑하다

- □ **earth** 흙 – **soil** 토양, 흙
- □ **huge** 거대한, 굉장히 큰 – **enormous** 거대한, 막대한
- □ **support** 지탱하다, 떠받치다 – **sustain** 지탱하다, 떠받치다

※ 서로 반대의 뜻을 가진 어휘

- □ **appear** 보이다, 나타나다 ↔ **disappear** 사라지다
- □ **enter** ~에 들어가다 ↔ **exit** 나가다, 퇴거하다
- □ **huge** 거대한, 굉장히 큰 ↔ **tiny** 매우 작은
- □ **invisible** 눈에 보이지 않는, 투명한 ↔ **visible** 눈에 보이는
- □ **thick** 두꺼운 ↔ **thin** 얇은

- □ **colorful** 형형색색의 ↔ **colorless** 색이 없는
- □ **flat** 평평한 ↔ **uneven** 울퉁불퉁한, 평탄하지 않은
- □ **install** 설치하다 ↔ **remove** 제거하다
- □ **rise** 오르다, 올라가다 ↔ **descend** 내려가다, 내려오다
- □ **unwelcome** 반갑지 않은 ↔ **welcome** 환영하는, 반가운

※ 형용사(adjective) vs 부사(adverb)

- □ **early** 이른 – **early** 이르게
- □ **far** 먼 – **far** 멀리
- □ **good** 좋은, 착한 – **well** 좋게, 제대로
- □ **high** 높은 – **high** 높이
- □ **long** 긴 – **long** 길게

- □ **enough** 충분한 – **enough** 충분히
- □ **fast** 빠른 – **fast** 빠르게
- □ **hard** 단단한, 어려운 – **hard** 열심히, 강력하게
- □ **late** 늦은 – **late** 늦게
- □ **well** 건강한, 적절한 – **well** 제대로, 완전히, 잘

English Dictionary

- □ **cave** 동굴
  - → a large hole in the side of a hill or under the ground
    언덕의 한 측면이나 땅의 아래에 있는 큰 구멍
- □ **flat** 평평한
  - → level, with no high hills or other raised parts
    언덕이나 다른 높이 올라 있는 곳이 없는, 평평한
- □ **house** 수용하다
  - → to provide a place for somebody to live
    어떤 사람에게 살 곳을 제공하다
- □ **millionaire** 백만장자
  - → a person who has a million pounds, dollars, etc.; a very rich person
    백만 달러나 백만 파운드를 갖고 있는 사람; 매우 부자인 사람
- □ **install** 설치하다
  - → to fix equipment or furniture into position so that it can be used
    장비나 가구를 사용할 수 있도록 제자리에 고정시키다
- □ **invisible** 눈에 보이지 않는, 투명한
  - → impossible to see 볼 수 없는
- □ **opening** 구멍
  - → a space or hole that somebody or something can pass through
    어떤 사람이나 사물이 지나갈 수 있는 공간이나 구멍
- □ **store** 저장하다, 보관하다
  - → to put something that is not being used in a place where it can be kept safely
    사용하지 않고 있는 어떤 사물을 안전하게 있을 수 있는 곳에 넣다
- □ **support** 지탱하다, 떠받치다
  - → to hold somebody or something in position; to prevent somebody or something from falling
    어떤 사람이나 사물을 제자리에 대다; 어떤 사람이나 사물이 떨어지는 것을 막다
- □ **swampy** 습지의
  - → very wet or covered with water land in which plants, trees, etc. are growing
    식물이나 나무 등이 자라는 매우 습하고 물로 덮인 땅
- □ **tide** 조수
  - → the regular upward and downward movement of the level of the ocean that is caused by the pull of the sun and the moon on Earth
    지구 위에 있는 태양과 달의 인력에 의해 발생하는 바다 수면 높이의 정기적인 상하 움직임
- □ **walkway** 통로
  - → a passage or path for walking along, often outside and raised above the ground
    종종 밖이나 지면에서 올라와 있는 통행을 위한 길

서답형
01 다음 짝지어진 단어의 관계가 같도록 빈칸에 알맞은 말을 쓰시오.

> hidden – concealed = store : _____

02 다음 영영풀이가 가리키는 것을 고르시오.

> level, with no high hills or other raised parts

① flat
② uneven
③ visible
④ high
⑤ ground

중요
03 다음 중 밑줄 친 부분의 뜻풀이가 바르지 않은 것은?

① My name will appear at the front of the book. (나타나다, 보이다)
② Some plastic bags were floating in the beach. (떠다니는)
③ The surface of the moon is pitted with craters. (표면)
④ Would you take this to the post office for me? (~을 타다)
⑤ They crush the strawberry with a heavy wooden press. (나무로 된)

서답형
04 다음 우리말을 주어진 어휘를 이용하여 영작하시오.

(1) 그 정부는 달갑지 않은 교육 정책을 고집하고 있다. (unwelcome, persist in)
➡ _____
_____

(2) 아기를 안고 있을 때 머리를 떠받치는 것은 중요하다. (support, hold)
➡ _____
_____

(3) 그녀는 연세가 거의 100세이시고 주로 방에만 계신다. (nearly, mostly, keep)
➡ _____
_____

서답형
05 다음 문장의 빈칸에 들어갈 말을 〈보기〉에서 골라 쓰시오.

> 보기
> come over / all day / climb up / known as / on weekends

(1) The construction workers sawed and hammered _____.
(2) Rain, snow and hail are collectively _____ precipitation.
(3) Why don't you _____ to Korea this summer?

06 다음 문장의 빈칸 (A)와 (B)에 각각 공통으로 들어갈 말로 바르게 짝지어진 것은?

> • They could hand __(A)__ those privileges to their children.
> • The box I ordered was left upside __(A)__ in the hallway.
> • He tried to stop himself __(B)__ crying out in front of people.
> • There is nothing to prevent us __(B)__ going there.

① over – from
② over – to
③ down – out
④ down – to
⑤ down – from

01 다음 주어진 영영풀이에 맞는 단어를 쓰시오.

> to fix equipment or furniture into position so that it can be used

➡ _____

02 다음 짝지어진 단어의 관계가 같도록 빈칸에 알맞은 말을 쓰시오.

> enter : exit = appear : _____

03 다음 문장의 빈칸에 들어갈 말을 〈보기〉에서 골라 쓰시오.

> ┤ 보기 ├
> make sense / on top of / more than /
> pull up / walk around

(1) Jane used to like to _____ in bare feet.

(2) Can you open the doors while I _____ the shades?

(3) This sentence doesn't _____ at all .

04 다음 우리말에 맞게 빈칸에 알맞은 말을 쓰시오.

> 우리 할머니는 돌아가시기 전에 그녀의 보석들을 물려주셨다.

➡ My grandmother had _____ her jewels before she passed away.

05 다음 우리말과 일치하도록 주어진 어구를 모두 배열하여 영작하시오.

(1) 나는 왜 그들이 떠나고 싶어 하는지 짐작이 안 된다.

(why / I / leave / imagine / they / want to / cannot)

➡ _____

(2) 신도시들이 서울의 과잉 인구를 수용하기 위해 만들어졌다.

(house / to / were / Seoul's / designed / over-population / new towns)

➡ _____
_____

(3) 정원에서 놀고 있는 아이들은 오늘 행복해 보인다.

(in the garden / the children / appear / today / playing / happy)

➡ _____
_____

06 다음 우리말에 맞게 주어진 단어를 사용하여 영작하시오.

(1) 베를린에서는 많은 사람들이 보통 자전거를 타고 출근한다. (usually)

➡ _____

(2) 난 종종 혼자 있는 것을 좋아한다. (often, on my own)

➡ _____

(3) 내가 주말에 주로 하는 것은 독서이다. (mostly, during)

➡ _____

Conversation

① 바람·소원 표현하기

A: Can you have dinner with me today?
B: I wish I could, but I have to go home early today.

■ 'I wish I could~.'는 '내가 ~하면 좋겠다.'라는 뜻으로, 바람이나 소원을 나타내는 표현이다. I wish 뒤에는 사실과 반대되거나 가능성이 거의 없는 일이 온다. 만약 가능성이 있거나 결과를 아직 모르는 것을 희망할 때는 I hope를 쓴다.

■ I wish 뒤에는 could를 이용해 현재 사실과 반대되는 내용, 혹은 가능성이 없는 일을 가정한다.
  • I wish I could live on the water.
    = I want to live on the water, but I can't.
  • I wish I could travel for the rest of my life.
    = I want to travel for the rest of my life, but I can't.

■ 더 알아볼 표현 I hope ~
'I hope ~'는 'I wish I could ~'와 달리 실현 가능성이 있거나 가능성이 높은 상황에서 사용한다.
  • I hope I don't have to work late tomorrow. 나는 내일 늦게까지 일하지 않았으면 좋겠다.
  • I hope you can finish your homework in time. 네가 네 숙제를 제시간에 끝낼 수 있기를 바라.

핵심 Check

1. 다음 대화의 빈칸에 알맞은 것은?

> A: What's the matter?
> B: My computer is so slow. _____ a new computer.

① I hope I could have　　② I want I can have

③ I wish I have　　④ I wish I can have

⑤ I wish I could have

2 상상하여 말하기

> A: What would you do if you became the president of your country? 네가 너희 나라의 대통령이 된다면 어떻게 하겠니?
>
> B: I would make a law to protect the environment. 나는 환경을 보호하는 법을 만들 거야.

- 'What would you do if ~?'는 '만약 ~라면 너는 어떻게 하겠니?'라는 뜻으로 상상하여 말하는 표현이다.

- 비슷한 표현으로 'Suppose ~', 'What if ~?' 등을 쓸 수 있다.
  - What would you do if you lived in Alaska?
  - Suppose you lived in Alaska.
  - What if you live in Alaska?

- 가정법 과거
  가정법 과거는 현재 사실에 반대되는 상황을 가정할 때 쓰인다.
  What would you do if you won a million dollars? 백만 달러를 얻게 된다면 뭘 할 거니?
  → If I won a million dollars, I would buy a house and a car. 내가 백만 달러를 얻게 된다면, 나는 집과 자동차를 살 거야.
  → 현재에는 백만 달러가 없지만 생기는 상황을 가정하는 내용이다.

핵심 Check

2. 다음 대화의 괄호 (A)와 (B)에서 알맞은 것을 고르시오.

> A: What would you do if you (A)[have / could have] a magical power?
>
> B: I (B)[turn / would turn] back time, then I would be able to time-travel.

Listen and Speak 2 B

G: Dohun, we need to start our project on our dream country ❶to visit.

B: That's right. Which country do you want to visit, Emma?

G: ❷In my case, I want to visit Spain.

B: ❸What would you do if you visited Spain?

G: ❹I'm interested in buildings. So I would go see La Sagrada Familia.

B: Isn't ❺that the church Antoni Gaudí designed?

G: Yes, it is. ❻It would be interesting to see ❼how his design was inspired by nature.

B: Hmm... ❽How about *Gaudí and Spain* as the title for our project?

G: I love it!

G: 도훈아, 우리가 방문하고 싶은 꿈꾸는 나라에 대한 프로젝트를 시작해야 돼.

B: 맞아. Emma, 너는 어느 나라를 방문하고 싶니?

G: 내 경우에는 스페인에 가 보고 싶어.

B: 스페인에 가게 되면 뭘 할 건데?

G: 나는 건물들에 관심이 있어. 그래서 나는 La Sagrada Familia에 가 볼 거야.

B: 그 성당은 Antoni Gaudí가 디자인한 교회 아니니?

G: 응, 맞아. 그의 디자인이 어떻게 자연에서 영감을 얻었는지 보면 흥미로울 거야.

B: 흠… '가우디와 스페인'을 우리 프로젝트 제목으로 하는 건 어떠니?

G: 아주 좋아!

❶ to부정사의 형용사적 용법으로 our dream country를 꾸며 준다. ❷ In my case 내 경우에는 ❸ '만약 ~라면 너는 어떻게 하겠니?'라는 뜻으로 상상하여 말하는 표현이다. ❹ be interested in ~에 관심이 있다 ❺ 이때 대명사 that은 앞서 언급한 La Sagrada Familia를 가리킨다. ❻ 가주어 it ~ to 구문이 사용되었으며, 뒤에 나오는 to부정사 구문이 진주어이다. ❼ 의문사 how를 사용한 간접의문문이다. ❽ 상대방에게 무언가를 제안할 때 쓸 수 있는 표현으로, 'Why don't we ~?'로 대체할 수 있다.

Check(√) True or False

(1) Emma's dream country to visit is Spain.　　　　　　　　　　　　T ☐ F ☐

(2) Dohun is not interested in visiting Spain.　　　　　　　　　　　T ☐ F ☐

Real Life Communication A

Jinho: I think ❶living in a jungle would be really exciting. Don't you think so?

Claire: But there are some dangerous animals in the jungle, Jinho.

Jinho: I know. But the jungle ❷is full of adventure. ❸I wish I could live there.

Claire: ❹What would you do if you lived in the jungle?

Jinho: I would explore ❺it. Maybe I could make some animal friends.

Claire: Then where would you sleep? In a cave?

Jinho: No, I would stay in a tree house. Then I would be safe from dangerous animals.

Claire: ❻That makes sense.

Jinho: 내 생각엔 정글에서 사는 건 정말 신날 거야. 그렇게 생각하지 않니?

Claire: 근데 진호야, 정글에는 몇몇 위험한 동물들이 있어.

Jinho: 나도 알아. 하지만 정글은 모험으로 가득하잖아. 내가 거기서 살 수 있다면 좋을 텐데.

Claire: 정글에서 산다면 뭘 할 건데?

Jinho: 난 정글을 탐험할 거야. 아마도 동물 친구들도 좀 만들 수 있겠지.

Claire: 그러면 어디서 잠을 잘 건데? 동굴에서?

Jinho: 아니, 나무로 만든 집에서 지낼 거야. 그러면 위험한 동물들한테서 안전해지겠지.

Claire: 그건 말이 되네.

❶ 동명사 구문으로 주어로 사용되었다. ❷ be full of ~로 가득 차 있다 ❸ 'I wish I could ~.'는 '내가 ~하면 좋겠다.'라는 뜻으로, 바람이나 소원을 나타내는 표현이다. ❹ 비슷한 표현으로 'Suppose ~', 'What if ~?' 등을 쓸 수 있다. ❺ 대명사 it은 the jungle을 가리킨다. ❻ 대명사 That은 Jinho가 말한 앞 문장 전체를 가리킨다.

Check(√) True or False

(3) Jinho thinks it would be great to live in a jungle.　　　　　　　　T ☐ F ☐

(4) Claire believes that it would be dangerous in the jungle due to some animals.　T ☐ F ☐

Listen and Speak 1 A

G: ❶Have you heard from Julia? She's traveling in Turkey, right?

B: Yes, she sent me some pictures. Do you want to see ❷them?

G: Yes, please.

B: Okay, ❸take a look.

G: Oh, look at those cave houses! ❹They look so unique, don't they? ❺I wish I could try living there.

B: I like those balloons. ❻They look so beautiful!

G: I think Turkey is a wonderful place ❼to visit. ❽I hope to visit there some day.

B: Me too!

❶ 상대방에게 무엇을 해본 적이 있냐고 물을 때 현재완료 용법을 사용할 수 있다. ❷ 대명사 them은 앞서 언급된 some pictures를 가리킨다. ❸ take a look 보다 ❹ 대명사 They는 앞서 언급한 those cave houses를 가리킨다. ❺ '내가 ~하면 좋겠다'라는 뜻으로, 바람이나 소원을 나타내는 표현이다. I wish 뒤에는 사실과 반대되거나 가능성이 거의 없는 일이 온다. ❻ 대명사 They는 those balloons를 가리킨다. ❼ to부정사의 형용사적 용법으로 사용되었다. ❽ 가능성이 있거나 결과를 아직 모르는 것을 희망할 때는 I hope를 쓴다.

Listen and Speak 1 B

B: Will ❶it snow today?

G: I have no idea. Why are you waiting for snow, Taeho?

B: I got a new sled for my birthday. ❷I can't wait to ❸test it out.

G: ❹Let me check the weather. Umm, there will be no snow ❺for a while.

B: ❻I wish I could live in Alaska. Then I could go sledding all day!

G: ❼No kidding! Alaska is a very cold place.

B: I think ❽it would be fun. I want to build a snow house and stay there on vacation.

G: Living in a snow house sounds fun!

❶ 날씨를 이야기할 때는 대명사 it이 사용된다. ❷ I can't wait to ~. 빨리 ~하고 싶다. ❸ test out 시험해 보다 ❹ 동사 let은 목적보어로 동사원형을 취한다. ❺ for a while 잠시 동안, 한동안 ❻ '내가 ~하면 좋겠다'라는 뜻으로, 바람이나 소원을 나타내는 표현이다. ❼ 무엇이 사실임을 강조하거나 남이 방금 한 말에 동의를 표할 때, 혹은 상대방이 한 말이 사실인지를 물을 때 쓴다. ❽ 대명사 it은 B가 앞서 말했던 알래스카에 가서 사는 것(to live in Alaska)을 가리킨다.

Listen and Speak 1 C

A: Look at these houses. ❶They look very natural.

B: Wow, ❷I wish I could ❸try living here!

A: Which house would you most like to live in?

B: I wish I could live in the stone house. ❹It looks very strong.

❶ 대명사 They는 앞 문장의 these houses를 가리킨다. ❷ I wish 뒤에는 사실과 반대되거나 가능성이 거의 없는 일이 온다. ❸ try ~ing 시험삼아 ~해 보다 ❹ 대명사 It은 앞 문장의 the stone house를 가리킨다.

Listen and Speak 2 A - 1

B: This is my ❶dream house, Alice. What do you think?

G: Oh, the house has wheels! Is ❷it a kind of car?

B: Yes, ❸it can move like a car.

G: So ❹what would you do if you lived in that house?

B: ❺I would travel to many places with my family.

G: That sounds cool.

❶ dream 꿈에서나 가능할 듯한 완벽한 것 ❷ 대명사 it은 the house with wheels를 가리킨다. ❸ 앞서 가리킨 집을 의미한다. ❹ '만약 ~라면 너는 어떻게 하겠니?'라는 뜻으로 상상하여 말하는 표현이다. ❺ 'What would you do if ~?'라는 질문에 대답할 때에는 'I would ~'라고 말한다.

Listen and Speak 2 A - 2

G: What would you do ❶if you became a millionaire, Juwon?

B: I would build my own house.

G: ❷What kind of house would you build?

B: I would build a house ❸that is completely covered with mirrors.

G: Why?

B: The mirrors would make the house almost ❹invisible. Wouldn't that be cool?

G: ❺That would be cool!

❶ 현재 사실과 반대되는 내용을 가정하고 있으므로 가정법 과거 문장을 쓴다. ❷ What kind of ~ 어떤 종류의 ~ ❸ 접속사 that으로 사용되었다. ❹ invisible 보이지 않는 ❺ 대명사 That은 앞서 언급된 문장. '집을 거울로 꾸며 눈에 거의 보이지 않는 것'을 의미한다.

 Listen and Speak 2 A - 3

G: Look. The house in this picture is ❶upside down.

B: That's ❷interesting. Does anybody live there?

G: No, it would not be easy to live ❸there because the inside is also upside down.

B: Really? But I want to ❹try living there.

G: What would you do if you lived in that house?

B: I would walk upside down ❺like Spider-Man. I could also see things differently.

❶ upside down 거꾸로 된 ❷ interesting 흥미롭게 하는 ❸ there는 the house in the picture를 가리킨다. ❹ try ~ing 시험삼아 ~해 보다 ❺ like ~처럼

 Listen and Speak 2 C

A: ❶What would you do if you could have a magical power?

B: I would ❷turn into a bird. Then I would ❸ be able to fly freely in the sky.

A: That's cool.

❶ 비슷한 표현으로 'Suppose ~', 'What if ~?' 등을 쓸 수 있다. ❷ turn into ~ ~로 변하다 ❸ be able to ~할 수 있다

 Real Life Communication B

A: ❶I wish I could stay in a house on the water during my vacation.

B: What would you do if you were ❷there?

A: I would ❸go swimming every day. I would also ❹go fishing.

B: That sounds fun.

❶ I wish 뒤에는 could를 이용해 현재 사실과 반대되는 내용, 혹은 가능성이 없는 일을 가정한다. ❷ there는 앞선 문장에서 언급된 'a house on the water'를 가리킨다. ❸ go swimming 수영하러 가다 ❹ go fishing 낚시하러 가다

 Let's Check 1

B: This is my dream house. What do you think, Alice?

G: Oh, it's in the deep sea. ❶It looks so unique. So, ❷what would you do if you lived in that house?

B: ❸I have an interest in deep sea animals. So I would ❹explore the deep sea and find some unique sea animals.

G: That sounds cool!

❶ 대명사 It은 B's dream house in the deep sea를 가리킨다. ❷ 'What would you do if ~?'는 '만약 ~라면 너는 어떻게 하겠니?'라는 뜻으로 상상하여 말하는 표현이다. ❸ have an interest in ~에 관심이 있다 ❹ explore 탐험하다

 Let's Check 2

A: ❶What's the matter?

B: My computer is so slow. ❷I wish I could have a new computer.

❶ '무슨 일이니?'라는 의미로 What's wrong?으로 대체할 수 있다. ❷ I wish 뒤에는 could를 이용해 현재 사실과 반대되는 내용. 혹은 가능성이 없는 일을 가정한다.

● 다음 우리말과 일치하도록 빈칸에 알맞은 말을 쓰시오.

Listen and Speak 1 A

G: _____ you heard from Julia? She's _____ in Turkey, right?

B: Yes, she sent me some pictures. Do you _____ to _____ them?

G: Yes, please.

B: Okay, _____ a look.

G: Oh, look at those cave houses! They look so _____, don't they? I wish I could try _____ there.

B: I like _____ balloons. They look so beautiful!

G: I think Turkey is a wonderful place _____ visit. I _____ to visit there _____ _____ .

B: Me _____!

Listen and Speak 1 B

B: Will _____ snow today?

G: I have no idea. _____ are you _____ _____ snow, Taeho?

B: I got a new sled for my birthday. I can't _____ to test it _____ .

G: Let me _____ the weather. Umm, there will be no snow for a while.

B: I wish I could live in Alaska. Then I _____ go sledding all day!

G: No _____! Alaska is a very cold _____ .

B: I think it would be fun. I want to _____ a snow house and _____ there on _____ .

G: _____ in a snow house _____ fun!

Listen and Speak 1 C

A: Look at _____ houses. They look very _____ .

B: Wow, I wish I could _____ living here.

A: _____ house would you _____ like to _____ _____ ?

B: I wish I could live in the stone house. It looks very _____ .

Listen and Speak 2 A-1

B: This is my dream house, Alice. _____ do you think?

G: Oh, the house has wheels! Is it a _____ of car?

B: Yes, it can move _____ a car.

G: So _____ would you do if you _____ in that house?

B: I would _____ to many places with my family.

G: That sounds _____ .

해석

G Julia한테서 소식 들었니? 그 애는 터키에서 여행 중이잖아, 맞지?

B 응, Julia가 나한테 사진 몇 장을 보내 왔어. 사진 보고 싶니?

G 응, 보고 싶어.

B 알겠어, 봐.

G 오, 저 동굴 집 좀 봐! 정말 특이하다. 그렇지 않니? 난 그곳에서 살아 봤으면 좋겠어.

B 난 저 열기구가 마음에 들어. 매우 아름다워 보여!

G 내 생각엔 터키가 방문하기에 정말 멋진 곳 같아. 언제 한 번 방문해 보고 싶다.

B 나도 그래!

B: 오늘 눈이 오는 거니?

G: 나도 모르겠어. 태호야, 왜 눈을 기다리는 거니?

B: 내 생일 선물로 새 썰매를 받았거든. 그거 빨리 시험해 보고 싶어.

G: 날씨 좀 확인해 볼게. 음, 당분간은 눈 소식이 없을 거야.

B: 알래스카에 살면 좋을 텐데! 그럼 온종일 썰매를 타러 갈 수 있을 텐데!

G: 말도 안 돼! 알래스카는 정말 추운 곳이야.

B: 내 생각엔 정말 즐거울 것 같아. 눈으로 집을 짓고 방학 때 그곳에서 지내고 싶어.

G: 눈으로 만든 집에 사는 건 재미있을 것 같아!

A: 이 집들 좀 봐. 매우 자연 그대로인 것 같아.

B: 우와, 이곳에 살아 봤으면 좋겠어.

A: 어느 집에서 가장 살아보고 싶니?

B: 돌로 만든 집에서 살아 보면 좋을 텐데. 매우 튼튼해 보여.

B: 이게 내 꿈의 집이야, Alice. 어떻게 생각하니?

G: 와, 바퀴가 달린 집이라니! 자동차의 일종이니?

B: 응, 자동차처럼 움직일 수 있어.

G: 그래서 그 집에서 살게 되면 뭘 할 거니?

B: 나는 가족들이랑 많은 곳을 여행할 거야.

G: 정말 신나게 들린다.

Listen and Speak 2 A-2

G: What would you do if you _____ a millionaire, Juwon?

B: I would _____ my own house.

G: What _____ of house would you _____?

B: I would build a house that is completely _____ with mirrors.

G: Why?

B: The _____ would make the house almost _____. Wouldn't that be cool?

G: That _____ be cool!

Listen and Speak 2 A-3

G: Look. The house in this picture is _____ down.

B: That's _____. Does anybody live there?

G: No, it would not be _____ to live there because the inside is also _____ _____.

B: Really? But I want to try living there.

G: _____ would you do if you lived in that house?

B: I would walk upside down _____ Spider-Man. I could also see things _____.

Listen and Speak 2 B

G: Dohun, we _____ to start our project on our dream country to _____.

B: That's right. _____ country do you want to visit, Emma?

G: In my _____, I want to visit Spain.

B: What _____ you do if you _____ Spain?

G: I'm _____ in buildings. So I would go see La Sagrada Familia.

B: Isn't _____ the church Antoni Gaudi _____?

G: Yes, it is. It would be interesting to see _____ his design was _____ by nature.

B: Hmm... . _____ about *Gaudí and Spain* as the title for our project?

G: I love it!

Listen and Speak 2 C

A: _____ would you do if you could have a magical power?

B: I would _____ _____ a bird. Then I would be _____ _____ _____ freely in the sky.

A: That's cool.

해석

G: 주원아, 백만장자가 되면 뭘 할 거니?

B: 나는 나만의 집을 지을 거야.

G: 어떤 집을 짓고 싶은데?

B: 나는 거울로 완전히 덮인 집을 지을 거야.

G: 왜?

B: 그 거울들이 집을 거의 안 보이게 만들어줄 거야. 멋지지 않니?

G: 그건 멋질 거야!

G: 봐, 이 사진에 있는 집은 거꾸로 되어 있어.

B: 흥미로운데. 그 집에 누가 사는 건가?

G: 아니, 내부도 거꾸로 되어 있으니까 그곳에서 살기는 쉽지 않을 거야.

B: 정말? 하지만 나는 그곳에서 살아 보고 싶어.

G: 저 집에 살게 된다면 너는 뭘 할 거니?

B: 나는 스파이더맨처럼 거꾸로 걸어다닐 거야. 난 또한 사물을 다르게 볼 수 있을 거야.

G: 도훈아, 우리가 방문하고 싶은 꿈꾸는 나라에 대한 프로젝트를 시작해야 돼.

B: 맞아. Emma, 너는 어느 나라를 방문하고 싶니?

G: 내 경우에는 스페인에 가 보고 싶어.

B: 스페인에 가게 되면 뭘 할 건데?

G: 나는 건물들에 관심이 있어. 그래서 나는 La Sagrada Familia에 가 볼 거야.

B: 그 성당은 Antoni Gaudi가 디자인한 교회 아니니?

G: 응, 맞아. 그의 디자인이 어떻게 자연에서 영감을 얻었는지 보면 흥미로울 거야.

B: 흠… '가우디와 스페인'을 우리 프로젝트 제목으로 하는 건 어때?

G: 아주 좋아!

A: 마법의 힘을 갖게 된다면 너는 무엇을 할 거니?

B: 난 새로 변할 거야. 그러면 하늘을 자유롭게 날 수 있겠지.

A: 그거 멋있다.

Real Life Communication A

Jinho: I think _____ in a jungle would be really _____. Don't you think so?

Claire: But there are _____ dangerous animals in the jungle, Jinho.

Jinho: I know. But the jungle is _____ of adventure. I wish I _____ _____ there.

Claire: What _____ you do if you _____ in the jungle?

Jinho: I would _____ it. Maybe I could make some animal friends.

Claire: Then _____ would you sleep? In a _____?

Jinho: No, I would stay in a tree house. _____ I would be safe from _____ _____.

Claire: That _____ sense.

Real Life Communication B

A: I wish I could _____ in a house on the water _____ my vacation.

B: What _____ you do if you _____ there?

A: I would go swimming _____ _____. I would also go _____.

B: That _____ fun.

Let's Check 1

B: _____ is my dream house. _____ do you think, Alice?

G: Oh, it's in the deep sea. It looks so _____. So, what would you do if you _____ in that house?

B: I have an _____ in _____ _____ animals. So I would _____ the deep sea and find some _____ sea animals.

G: _____ sounds cool!

Let's Check 2

A: What's the _____?

B: My computer is so slow. I wish I could _____ a new computer.

[01~02] 다음 대화를 읽고 물음에 답하시오.

> G: Have you heard from Julia? She's traveling in Turkey, right?
> B: Yes, she sent me some pictures. Do you want to see them?
> G: Yes, please.
> B: Okay, take a look.
> G: Oh, look at those cave houses! They look so unique, don't they? (A) 난 그곳에서 살아 보면 좋을 텐데. (try)
> B: I like those balloons. They look so beautiful!
> G: I think Turkey is a wonderful place to visit. I hope to visit there some day.
> B: Me too!

01 위 대화의 밑줄 친 (A)의 우리말을 주어진 단어를 이용하여 영작하시오. (7 words)

➡ _____

02 위 대화를 읽고 대답할 수 <u>없는</u> 것은?

① Who is traveling in Turkey?
② Who received photos from Julia?
③ What kind of houses are there in Turkey?
④ When is G planning to visit Turkey?
⑤ Who wants to visit Turkey?

[03~04] 다음 대화를 읽고 물음에 답하시오.

> A: Look at these houses. They look very natural.
> B: Wow, _____(A)_____ try living here.
> A: Which house would you most like to live in?
> B: _____(B)_____ live in the stone house. It looks very strong.

03 위 대화의 빈칸 (A)와 (B)에 공통으로 들어갈 말을 쓰시오. (4 words)

➡ _____

04 What kind of house does B want most to live in? (9 words)

➡ _____

[01~03] 다음 대화를 읽고 물음에 답하시오.

G: Dohun, we need to start our project on our dream country ⓐto visit.

B: That's right. ⓑWhich country do you want to visit, Emma?

G: ⓒIn my case, I want to visit Spain.

B: (A) 네가 스페인을 방문한다면 뭘 할 거니?

G: I'm interested in buildings. So I ⓓwould go see La Sagrada Familia.

B: Isn't that the church Antoni Gaudí designed?

G: Yes, it is. It would be ⓔinterested to see how his design was inspired by nature.

B: Hmm... How about *Gaudí and Spain* as the title for our project?

G: I love it!

서답형

01 위 대화의 밑줄 친 ⓐ~ⓔ 중 흐름상 어색한 것을 찾아 바르게 고치시오.

➡ _____

서답형

02 위 대화의 밑줄 친 (A)를 영작하시오. (8 words)

➡ _____

서답형

03 위 대화에서 주어진 영영풀이가 가리키는 단어를 찾아 쓰시오.

> to give someone an idea for a book, film, product, etc.

➡ _____

[04~06] 다음 대화를 읽고 물음에 답하시오.

B: This is my dream house, Alice. What do you think?

G: Oh, the house has wheels! Is it a kind of car?

B: Yes, it can move like a car.

G: So what would you do if you (A)[lived / have lived] in that house?

B: I (B)[will travel / would travel] to many places with my family.

G: That sounds cool.

서답형

04 위 대화의 괄호 (A)와 (B)에서 알맞은 것을 고르시오.

➡ (A) _____ (B) _____

중요

05 위 대화를 읽고 대답할 수 없는 것은?

① What kind of house is B's dream house?

② What does B's dream house include?

③ What can B's dream house move like?

④ Where is the conversation taking place?

⑤ What does G think about B's dream house?

06 위 대화의 주제로 가장 적절한 것은?

① 꿈에 그리던 집에 대한 상상

② 자동차로 만든 집에 대한 상상

③ 가족과의 여행에 대한 상상

④ 특별한 바퀴가 달린 자동차에 대한 상상

⑤ 꿈 속에서 본 집에 대한 상상

[07~09] 다음 대화를 읽고 물음에 답하시오.

> Jinho: I think living in a jungle would be really exciting. Don't you think so?
>
> Claire: ① But there are some dangerous animals in the jungle, Jinho.
>
> Jinho: I know. ② But the jungle is full of adventure. ③ I wish I could live there.
>
> Claire: What would you do if you lived in the jungle?
>
> Jinho: ④ Maybe I could make some animal friends.
>
> Claire: Then where would you sleep? In a cave?
>
> Jinho: No, I would stay in a tree house. ⑤ (A) <u>그러면 나는 위험한 동물들로부터 안전할 거야.</u>
>
> Claire: That makes sense.

07 위 대화의 ①~⑤ 중 주어진 문장이 들어가기에 가장 적절한 곳은?

> I would explore it.

①   ②   ③   ④   ⑤

08 위 대화의 내용과 일치하지 <u>않는</u> 것은?

① Jinho believes living in a jungle will be exciting.

② Claire thinks living in a jungle can be dangerous.

③ All jungles are full of exciting adventures.

④ Jinho thinks he could make some animal friends in the jungle.

⑤ Jinho would stay in a tree house for protection.

서답형

09 위 대화의 밑줄 친 (A)의 우리말을 영작하시오.

➡ _____

10 다음 중 짝지어진 대화가 <u>어색한</u> 것을 고르시오.

① A: What would you do if you visited Spain?

   B: I would go see La Sagrada Familia.

② A: What if you won a lottery?

   B: I'll travel all over the world.

③ A: What would you do if you had only a day left to live?

   B: I would visit my family and spend time with them.

④ A: What would you do if you lived in a desert?

   B: I would ride a camel.

⑤ A: What would you do if your friends told you their secrets?

   B: I would tell no one about it.

서답형

11 다음 대화의 밑줄 친 우리말에 맞게 주어진 단어를 바르게 나열하시오.

> A: <u>마법의 힘을 갖게 된다면 너는 뭘 할 거니?</u>
> (could / a magical power / you / if / do / what / you / have / would)
>
> B: I would turn into a bird. Then I would be able to fly freely in the sky.

➡ _____

[01~02] 다음 대화를 읽고 물음에 답하시오.

G: What would you do if you became a millionaire, Juwon?

B: (A)나는 나만의 집을 지을 거야.

G: What kind of house would you build?

B: I would build a house that is completely covered with mirrors.

G: Why?

B: The mirrors would make the house almost invisible. Wouldn't that be cool?

G: That would be cool!

중요

01 위 대화의 밑줄 친 (A)의 우리말에 맞게 영작하시오.

➡ _____

02 What would B cover his dream house completely with? (9 words)

➡ _____

_____

서답형

03 다음 대화의 밑줄 친 우리말을 영작하시오. (8 words)

A: What's the matter?

B: My computer is so slow. 내가 새 컴퓨터를 갖고 있다면 좋을 텐데.

➡ _____

[04~05] 다음 대화를 읽고 물음에 답하시오.

A: I wish I could stay in a house on the water during my vacation.

B: (A)네가 거기에 있다면 무엇을 할 거니? (what, be)

A: I would go swimming every day. I would also go fishing.

B: That sounds fun.

04 위 대화의 밑줄 친 (A)의 우리말을 주어진 단어를 이용해 영어로 옮기시오.

➡ _____

05 What are the two things A would do in a house on the water? (7 words)

➡ _____

[06~07] 다음 대화를 읽고 물음에 답하시오.

G: Look. The house in this picture is upside down.

B: That's interesting. Does anybody live there?

G: No, it would not be easy to live there because the inside is also upside down.

B: Really? But I want to try living there.

G: What would you do if you lived in that house?

B: I would walk upside down like Spider-Man. I could also see things differently.

06 What are G and B talking about? (10 words)

➡ _____

_____

07 What would B do if he lived in the house that is upside down? (9 words)

➡ _____

_____

Grammar

① 가정법 과거: 'If+주어+동사 과거형 ~, 주어+would/could+동사원형 …'

> • **If** I **lived** in a pueblo, I **would climb** up a ladder to enter my house. 내가 만약 푸에
> 블로에 산다면, 집에 들어가기 위해 사다리를 오를 텐데.
> • **If** I **lived** in a house with a garden, I **would plant** many flowers in it. 내가 정원이
> 있는 집에 산다면, 나는 정원에 많은 꽃을 심을 텐데.

■ 가정법 과거: 현재 사실을 반대로 가정 또는 실현 가능성이 없는 일을 가정할 때 쓰이며, '**If**+주어+**동
사 과거형** ~, 주어+**would/could**+**동사원형** …' 형태로, '만약 ~라면 …할 텐데'의 뜻이다.

   • **If** I **have** her number, I **will call** her. 내게 그녀의 전화번호가 있다면, 그녀에게 전화할 것이다. (조건문, 가능성이 유)
   • **If** I **had** her number, I **would call** her. 내게 그녀의 전화번호가 있다면, 그녀에게 전화할 텐데. (가정법)
     = **As** I **don't have** her number, **I can't call** her. 내게 그녀의 전화번호가 없어서, 전화할 수 없다. (직설법)
   • **If** Jane **were** here, she **would help** me. Jane이 여기 있다면, 그녀가 나를 도울 텐데.

■ 가정법 과거완료: 일어난 과거 사실을 반대로 가정할 때 쓰이며, '**If**+주어+**had**+**과거분사** ~, 주어
+**would/could**+**have**+**과거분사** …'의 형태이다.

   • **If** Peter **had played** the music, they **would have respected** him. Peter가 그 음악을 연주했더라면, 그들은 그
   를 존경했을 텐데.

■ '**I wish**' 가정법은 현재 사실에 반대되는 소망 또는 현재 사실에 대한 유감을 나타낸다.

   • **I wish** I **were** a world famous director. 내가 세계적으로 유명한 감독이라면 좋을 텐데.
     = **I'm sorry that** I'**m not** a world famous director. (직설법)

■ 가정법의 다양한 표현들로 직설법의 의미를 나타낼 수 있다.

   • **As** there **is** a gondola, we **can** go to school. 곤돌라가 있어서, 우리는 학교에 갈 수 있다. (직설법)
   → **If** there **were no** gondola, we **couldn't go** to school. 곤돌라가 없다면, 우리는 학교에 갈 수 없을 텐데. (가정법)
   → **Were** there **no** gondola, we **couldn't go** to school. (If 생략 후 도치)
   → **Without a** gondola, we **couldn't go** to school. (Without = But for)
   → **If it were not for** a gondola, we **couldn't go** to school.
   → **Were it not for** a gondola, we **couldn't go** to school. (If 생략 후 도치)

핵심 Check

1. 다음 우리말에 맞게 괄호 안의 어휘를 바르게 배열하여 빈칸을 채우시오.
   (1) 내가 로봇이라면, 그녀의 말을 들을 텐데. (a robot, I, listen, were, would, her, to)
      ➡ If I _____.
   (2) 돈이 좀 있으면, 서울에 아파트를 살 텐데. (if, an apartment, money, buy, Seoul,
      would, had, some, I, in)
      ➡ I _____.

❷ 5형식 동사 keep / make

> • They would **keep me cool** in summer and **warm** in winter. 그것들은 나를 여름에는 시원하게, 겨울에는 따뜻하게 유지해 줄 것이다.
>
> • Staying home all day **makes Tim and Julie bored**. 하루 종일 집에 있는 것이 Tim과 Julie를 지루하게 만든다.

- **5형식 문장의 기본 형태(목적보어의 종류)**
  - Anthony **made** Tommy **an actor**. (명사) Anthony는 Tommy를 배우로 만들었다.
  - The noise **made** our learning **difficult**. (형용사) 그 소음은 우리의 학습을 어렵게 만들었다.
  - Your friends **want** you **to clean the room**. (to부정사) 네 친구들은 네가 방을 청소길 원한다.
  - The song **made** me **cry**. (원형부정사) 그 노래는 나를 울게 만들었다.
  - They **saw** Mina **singing a song**. (현재분사) 그들은 Mina가 노래를 부르고 있는 것을 보았다.

- **동사 keep과 make의 5형식 예문과 목적보어의 종류**
  - These gloves **keep** my hands **warm**. 이 장갑은 내 손을 따뜻하게 유지시킨다. (형용사)
  - I **kept** Peter **waiting**. 나는 Peter를 계속 기다리게 했다. (현재분사: 능동)
  - He **kept** his face **hidden**. 그는 자신의 얼굴을 숨긴 채로 있었다. (과거분사: 수동)
  - Kate **made** her son **a lawyer**. Kate는 그녀의 아들을 변호사로 만들었다. (명사)
  - The song always **makes** me **happy**. 그 노래는 항상 나를 행복하게 만든다. (형용사)
  - Sad movies **make** me **cry**. 슬픈 영화는 나를 울게 한다. (원형부정사)

- **그 외 5형식에 쓰는 동사들과 목적보어**
  - (1) have, get
    - The manager **had** the car **ready** by tomorrow. 매니저가 내일까지 차를 준비시켰다. (형용사)
    - I **had** my brother **repair** my car. 나는 오빠에게 내 차를 수리하도록 부탁했다. (원형부정사)
    - The professor **had** the report **printed**. 교수님이 보고서를 인쇄되도록 시켰다. (과거분사)
    - I **got** Mike **to fix** the machine. 나는 Mike가 기계를 고치게 했다. (to부정사)
    - Sumi **got** the car **washed**. 수미가 세차를 시켰다. (과거분사)

  - (2) leave, find
    - Mike **left** the door **open**. Mike는 문을 열어 두었다. (형용사)
    - You **left** the work half **done**. 당신은 일을 반만 해 놓았다. (과거분사)
    - I **found** the water **run[running]**. 나는 물이 흐르는 것을 발견했다. (원형부정사/현재분사)

핵심 Check

2. 다음 괄호 안에서 알맞은 말을 고르시오.

(1) Jay kept her cat (walking / walk) across the garden.

(2) The neighbor kept the door (closing / closed) during her holiday.

01 다음 각 가정법 문장에서 어법상 <u>어색한</u> 단어를 한 개씩 찾아 고치시오.

(1) If I live in Venice, I could take a gondola.

_____ ➡ _____

(2) If the gondola had wings, we can fly in the sky.

_____ ➡ _____

(3) It would be nice if my neighbor calls me to come over for tea.

_____ ➡ _____

(4) I will be able to walk around if the town had raised walkways.

_____ ➡ _____

02 다음 중 어법상 <u>어색한</u> 문장을 고르시오.

① The show program made him a super star.
② The lady made her three sons politicians.
③ My grandparents called me of Puppy Ducky.
④ The participants found the experiment exciting.
⑤ Please keep your hands clean when you touch the tools.

03 다음 빈칸에 들어갈 말로 알맞은 것은?

> If there _____ *vaporetto*, a water bus, I would travel from island to island.

① can be ② is ③ have been
④ were ⑤ has been

04 다음 각 문장의 빈칸에 공통으로 들어갈 말로 알맞은 것은?

> • The suspect _____ her face covered and hidden.
> • The dry weather and strong wind _____ the wildfire burning.
> • Your support _____ him from committing a crime.
> • The doctors always _____ their hands clean.

① got ② let ③ had
④ took ⑤ kept

★ 01 다음 문장의 빈칸 (A)~(C)에 들어갈 말로 가장 적절한 것은?

> • If I (A)_____ a lot of meney, I could buy the car.
> • If it were not for his advice, the president (B)_____ not win many votes.
> • If the movie (C)_____ earlier, Jim would come and get me out of the cinema.

	(A)	(B)	(C)
①	had	would	starts
②	have had	could	starts
③	have had	could	will start
④	had	would	started
⑤	have	could	started

02 다음 밑줄 친 부분과 쓰임이 같은 것을 모두 고르면?

> Going sledding in the snow <u>made</u> Tom and Sophie excited.

① The college students <u>made</u> a reading club and volunteered at the public library in the town.

② The wives of the coaches <u>made</u> the players a meal which was good for their health and athletic ability.

③ The vocal coaches and the producer at the competition show <u>made</u> the little girl a world famous singer.

④ Problems that seemed impossible to solve at that time <u>made</u> those people gathering at the square even stronger.

⑤ My father <u>made</u> a real cheeseburger for me and my best friend Jenny.

[03~06] 다음 우리말과 일치하도록 괄호 안에 주어진 단어들을 바르게 배열하시오.

03

> 그들은 침입자들로부터 자신을 안전하게 지키기 위해서 그곳에서 살기로 결정했다.
> → They decided to live there (invaders, from, to, themselves, safe, keep).

➡ They decided to live there _____ _____.

04

> 한 건물 안에서 함께 사는 것은 그들을 안전하게 지켜준다.
> → (them, safe, in, living, building, together, one, keeps).

➡ _____

05

> 비가 오면, 우리는 수영장에 갈 수 없을 텐데.
> → If (could, the swimming pool, go, we, it, to, rained, not).

➡ If _____.

06

> 토루에 산다면, 나는 항상 집에서 함께 놀 친구들이 있을 텐데.
> → If I lived in a tulou, I (with, would, have, to, always, friends, play) at home.

➡ If I lived in a tulou, I _____ _____ at home.

17 다음 중 같은 뜻을 가진 문장끼리 짝지어진 것은?

① She would invite me every weekend and enjoy swimming with me if she lived in a house with a swimming pool.
   = She didn't live in a house with a swimming pool, so she wouldn't invite me every weekend to enjoy swimming.

② Sean could write a letter to the director of the film if he knew her address in Seoul.
   = Sean can't write a letter to the director of the film though he knows her address in Seoul.

③ If my grandmother could walk faster than usual, she would arrive soon at the hospital.
   = My grandmother can't walk faster than usual, so she won't arrive at the hospital.

④ If it rained now, Jefferson would stay in his office.
   = It rains now, so Jefferson will stay in his office.

⑤ If the kids had seen the bus coming, they would not have got hurt in the accident.
   = The kids didn't see the bus coming, but they couldn't get hurt in the accident.

[08~09] 다음 우리말을 어법상 알맞게 영작한 것을 고르시오.

08

> 헬멧을 착용하는 것은 오토바이 운전자들을 안전하게 지켜준다.

① Wearing a helmet keeps motorbike drivers safely from accidents.

② Wearing a helmet keeps motorbike drivers safe from accidents.

③ Wearing helmets safely keep motorbike drivers from accidents.

④ Wearing helmets safely keeps motorbike drivers into accidents.

⑤ Wearing a helmet keeps safe for motorbike drivers from accidents.

09

> 겨울에 얇은 옷을 여러 겹으로 입는 것은 우리의 몸을 따뜻하게 유지해 주고, 우리가 활동하기 더 편하게 만들어 준다.

① Putting on layers of thin clothes in winter keep our bodies warm and makes us more active.

② Putting on thin layers of clothes in winter keeps our bodies warmly and makes us more active.

③ Putting on layers of thin clothes in winter keeps our bodies warm and makes us more actively.

④ Putting on layers of thin clothes in winter keeps our bodies warm and make us more active.

⑤ Putting on layers of thin clothes in winter keeps our bodies warm and makes us more active.

서답형
10 다음 가정법 과거 문장에서 어법상 어색한 부분을 찾아서 고치시오. (2곳)

> If you lived in a desert and have no one to live with, what will you do?

➡ _____

[11~12] 다음 주어진 문장들 중 문장의 구조적 형식이 <u>다른</u> 하나는?

11 ① People in that town always call the poor boy a fool.

② They left the baby alone in the forest where monkeys and wolves lived.

③ The physical education teacher made his students run faster.

④ The princess helped the maids wash the dishes used at the party.

⑤ The old woman in the country made them traditional Korean food.

12 ① He always keeps the door open.

② The way he proposed will keep your bag from getting stolen.

③ All the animals in the jungle saw Tarzan enter the cave.

④ The passenger got the porter to carry the baggage.

⑤ She found the man wearing black clothes disappearing into the dark.

[13~14] 다음은 각각 가정법 과거 형식의 문장들이다. 어법상 옳은 것을 고르시오.

13 ① If Miranda has the ticket, she could take the bus on her way to New York.

② If I knew the truth, I would tell it to you.

③ I wish the new house will provide the comfort to the guests from Mexico.

④ If the tourists had seen the vaporetto, a water bus, they can travel on it.

⑤ I wish the villagers know the answer to the problem of the polluted river.

14 ① If the lady is in Beijing, she could join her sister's graduation.

② If the robots had AI, they won't do the bad thing to human officers.

③ If it were not for the tie she bought me, I would not be able to pass the interview.

④ My younger brother could have got hurt, if the driver didn't pull up the bus immediately.

⑤ If the fish know the way to the river where they were born, they could go up against the stream.

15 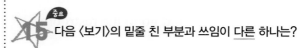 다음 〈보기〉의 밑줄 친 부분과 쓰임이 <u>다른</u> 하나는?

> ┤ 보기 ├
>
> I <u>could</u> climb up a ladder to get in my house if I lived in a *pueblo* in New Mexico.

① I wish I <u>could</u> memorize as many poems as possible.

② The dogs and cats <u>could</u> get free lunch if the old lady bought their food at Ball Mart.

③ If the witnesses knew the motorbike's number, they <u>could</u> report to the judge.

④ Were it not for Sheryl's help, Peterson <u>could</u> not finish his science assignment.

⑤ <u>Could</u> you bring him a glass of apple juice after the game?

01 다음 각 가정법 문장에서 어법상 어색한 단어를 한 개씩 찾아 바르게 고치시오. (고친 부분은 두 단어라도 상관 없음.)

(1) Without a ladder, people won't be able to enter their *pueblos*.

　➡ _____

(2) If your house has a flat roof, you could sometimes sleep up on the roof under the moon.

　➡ _____

(3) I wish I will live in a different house in a different country.

　➡ _____

(4) If it were not for the houses on the water, people in Venice will not be able to keep themselves safe from invaders.

　➡ _____

(5) Suji would be late for the art class yesterday if her car had been broken.

　➡ _____

(6) If the physics teacher were in the boy's situation, she will understand how urgently he should go to the restroom.

　➡ _____

(7) I wish the round houses in China can house more than 50 families.

　➡ _____

02 다음 우리말과 일치하도록 괄호 안에 주어진 단어들을 바르게 배열하여 문장을 완성하시오.

(1) 그 나무 기둥들이 지금까지 베니스를 지탱해 준다. (wooden, Venice, support, poles, those)

　➡ _____ to this day.

(2) 그 두꺼운 벽들이 여름에는 사람들을 시원하게, 겨울에는 따뜻하게 유지해 줄 것이다. (warm, cool, keep, in summer, people, and, would, walls)

　➡ The thick _____ _____ in winter.

(3) 중국의 어떤 사람들은 커다란 둥근 건물을 그들의 집으로 만들었다. (building, a, house, made, their, huge, round)

　➡ Some people in China _____ _____ .

(4) 수상 버스는 섬에서 섬으로 여행하는 것을 더욱 편하게 만들어 준다. (easier, makes, from, to, it, travel, island, water bus)

　➡ A _____ _____ to island.

03 다음 〈보기〉의 문장과 같은 뜻이 되도록 괄호 안에 주어진 조건에 맞게 빈칸을 채우시오.

> Without many wooden poles in the ground, Venice would be very different.

(1) _____ many wooden poles in the ground, Venice would be very different. (it, be동사 활용, 5 단어)

(2) _____ wooden poles in the ground, Venice would be very different. (there, no 활용, 4 단어)

(3) _____ many wooden poles in the ground, Venice would be very different. (it, be동사 활용, 4 단어)

(4) _____ , Venice isn't very different. (직설법, there, 접속사 as 활용, 9 단어)

04 다음 주어진 문장과 뜻이 같도록 빈칸을 알맞게 채우시오. (11 단어)

> As Matthew doesn't live in a house with a soccer field, he can't invite his friends to play soccer after school.
> → If Matthew _____
> _____ his friends to play soccer after school.

05 다음 〈보기〉와 같이 우리말에 맞게 괄호 안에 주어진 단어들을 활용하여 빈칸에 들어갈 알맞은 말을 채워 넣으시오.

> ┌─ 보기 ┐
> They wanted to <u>keep themselves safe from</u> invaders. 그들은 침입자들로부터 자신들을 안전하게 지키기를 원했다. (safe, from, them)

(1) Staying home all day long _____
_____ _____. 하루 종일 집에 머물러 있는 것은 그들을 지루하게 만들었다. (bore)

(2) The visitors _____ _____ _____
_____ _____ in the woods. 그 방문객들은 숲에서 코알라들이 잎들을 먹고 있는 것을 보았다. (the koalas, see, leaf, eat)

(3) Brian and his friends _____ _____
_____ _____ _____ their parents.
Brian과 그의 친구들은 그들의 부모님이 그들의 이름을 부르는 것을 들었다. (call, name, hear, by)

(4) The swampy surface _____ _____
_____ _____ _____ _____
_____ their homes. 늪지 표면은 그들이 자기들의 집을 짓는 것을 어렵게 만들었다. (for, to, make, build)

[06~07] 다음 그림을 보고, 그림과 괄호 안에 주어진 단어를 활용하여 우리말에 맞게 빈칸을 채우시오.

06

stone house

> 내가 돌 집에 산다면, 태풍도 그 집을 흔들 수 없을 텐데. (the typhoon, shake)
> ➡ If _____
> _____.
> (가정법 과거, If 제외 총 11 단어)

07

My house is made of earth.

> 흙으로 만든 집에 사는 것은 우리를 여름에 시원하게 유지해 준다. (keep, cool, make, live, earth)
> ➡ _____
> _____ in summer.
> (동명사 주어, 5형식 문장, in summer 제외 총 10 단어)

08 다음 직설법 문장을 가정법으로 고치시오.

(1) As there is no food left, the homeless man will work today.
➡ _____
_____

(2) Since he is not strong enough, he will exercise at the gym every day.
➡ _____
_____

If I Lived There

Different people live in different houses. Some use ladders to enter their houses. Others live in houses on the water. And others share their houses with many people. Imagine you live in one of these houses. How would that change your life?

Pueblos in New Mexico, USA

If I lived in a *pueblo*, I would climb up a ladder to enter my house. There's a hidden opening on top of the house. If unwelcome visitors appeared, I would pull the ladder up to stop them from entering. The thick walls are made of earth, straw, and water. They would keep me cool in summer and warm in winter. The house has a flat roof. I would sometimes sleep up on the roof under the moon and stars.

Houses on Water in Venice, Italy

If I lived in Venice, I would take a gondola to school every morning. Venice has 118 small islands. On weekends, I would travel from island to island by a *vaporetto*, a water bus. At high tide, the water from the Adriatic Sea often rises and leaves the streets full of water. However, I would be able to walk around the town through the raised walkways.

ladder: 사다리
enter: ～로 들어가다
unwelcome: 반갑지 않은
appear: 나타나다
pull up: 끌어올리다
earth: 흙
tide: 조수
walkway: 통로

📎 **확인문제**

● 다음 문장이 본문의 내용과 일치하면 T, 일치하지 <u>않으면</u> F를 쓰시오.

1 By pulling the ladder up, people living in a *pueblo* protect themselves. ☐

2 The walkways in Venice are raised because the streets are always full of water. ☐

3 A gondola is a water bus in Venice. ☐

Venice is known as the "floating city." In Venice, there are many colorful houses on the water. You may wonder how and why they built 간접의문문(의문사+주어+동사) the houses on the water. The old Venetians decided to live there to keep themselves safe from invaders. But it was not easy for them to 재귀대명사의 재귀적 용법(주어와 목적어가 같을 때 목적어로 재귀대명사 사용)   to부정사의 의미상 주어 build their homes on this swampy surface. So they installed more than 진주어 10 million wooden poles in the ground. It is these wooden poles that It ~ that 강조구문('These wooden poles support Venice to this day.'에서 주어 강조) support Venice to this day.

Tulou in Fujian, China

If I lived in a *tulou*, a huge round house in Fujian, China, I would always have friends at home to play with. I would sometimes hear my to부정사의 형용사적 용법(friends 수식) neighbor calling me to come over for tea or dinner. In a *tulou*, there are 지각동사+목적어+Ving: 목적어가 V하는 것을 듣다 usually three to five floors. The first floor is used for cooking and eating. ~을 위해 사용된다 And people store food and tools on the second floor. Do you wonder where I would sleep? My bedroom would be on the third or fourth floor. 간접의문문(의문사+주어+동사)

A *tulou* is like a village. The people living in a *tulou* mostly have the 현재분사(the people 수식) same family name. Some large *tulou* can house up to 50 families. They ~까지 work together and share many things. Living together in one building 동명사 주어(~하는 것) keeps them safe. 동명사 주어는 단수 취급

Homes are everywhere. But they are different all over the world. What is your home like?

---

invader: 침략자
swampy: 습지의
install: 설치하다, 장착하다
support: 지지하다, 지탱하다
come over: 들르다
store: 저장하다
family name: 성
house: 수용하다
up to: ~까지

📎 **확인문제**

● 다음 문장이 본문의 내용과 일치하면 T, 일치하지 <u>않으면</u> F를 쓰시오.

1 The old Venetians invaded the islands and kept living there. ☐

2 It was on the swampy surface that the old Venetians built their houses. ☐

3 More than 10 billion wooden poles are still in the ground. ☐

4 A *tulou* is a small house which can house up to about five families. ☐

5 A *tulou* has usually three to five floors. ☐

6 Friends gather together to live in a *tulou* so they have different family names. ☐

● 우리말을 참고하여 빈칸에 알맞은 말을 쓰시오.

1 Different people _____ _____ different houses.

2 Some _____ _____ _____ _____ _____ _____ _____ .
Others _____ _____ houses _____ the water.

3 And _____ _____ their houses _____ many people.

4 _____ you _____ _____ one of these houses. How would _____ _____ your life?

Pueblos in New Mexico, USA

5 If I _____ _____ a *pueblo*, I _____ _____ up a ladder _____ _____ _____ house.

6 There's a _____ _____ on top of the house.

7 _____ unwelcome visitors _____ , I _____ _____ the ladder _____ _____ _____ them _____ entering.

8 The thick walls _____ _____ _____ earth, straw, and water.

9 They would _____ _____ _____ in summer and _____ in winter.

10 The house has _____ _____ _____ . I would sometimes _____ _____ _____ _____ _____ under the moon and stars.

Houses on Water in Venice, Italy

11 If I _____ _____ Venice, I _____ _____ _____ to school every morning.

12 Venice _____ 118 small _____ . _____ _____ , I would travel _____ _____ _____ _____ by a *vaporetto*, a water bus.

13 At high tide, the water _____ the Adriatic Sea often _____ and _____ the streets _____ _____ _____ .

14 _____ , I would _____ the town through the raised walkways.

15 Venice _____ _____ the " _____ city."

1 다양한 사람들이 다양한 집에서 살고 있습니다.

2 어떤 사람들은 집에 들어가기 위해 사다리를 이용합니다. 다른 사람들은 물 위에 있는 집에서 살고 있습니다.

3 그리고 또 다른 사람들은 많은 사람들과 함께 집을 공유합니다.

4 여러분이 이 집들 중 하나에 산다고 상상해 보세요. 여러분의 삶은 어떻게 바뀔까요?

푸에블로 – 미국 뉴멕시코

5 내가 만약 푸에블로에 산다면, 나는 집에 들어가기 위해 사다리를 오를 것이다.

6 집 꼭대기에는 숨겨진 구멍이 있다.

7 반갑지 않은 방문객이 나타난다면 나는 사다리를 끌어올려 그들이 들어오지 못하게 할 것이다.

8 두꺼운 벽은 흙, 지푸라기, 물로 만들어져 있다.

9 그것들은 여름에는 시원하게, 겨울에는 따뜻하게 유지시켜 준다.

10 집에는 평평한 지붕이 있다. 때때로 나는 달과 별들 아래의 지붕 위에서 잠을 잘 것이다.

물 위에 있는 집 – 이탈리아 베니스

11 내가 만약 베니스에 산다면, 나는 매일 아침 곤돌라를 타고 학교에 갈 것이다.

12 베니스는 **118**개의 작은 섬이 있다. 주말마다 나는 수상 버스인 바포레토를 타고 이 섬 저 섬을 여행할 것이다.

13 조수가 높을 때에는 아드리아 해의 물이 자주 범람하고 거리는 물로 가득 찬다.

14 그러나 나는 돌출되어 있는 통로로 도심 주변을 걸어다닐 수 있을 것이다.

15 베니스는 '떠다니는 도시'로 알려져 있다.

16 In Venice, _____ _____ many _____ on the water.

17 You may wonder _____ and _____ _____ _____ _____ _____ _____ the water.

18 The old Venetians _____ _____ _____ _____ _____ to keep _____ _____ _____ invaders.

19 But it was not easy _____ _____ _____ _____ their homes on this _____ surface.

20 So they _____ more than 10 million _____ in the ground.

21 It is these _____ _____ that _____ Venice _____ this day.

Tulou in Fujian, China

22 If I _____ in a *tulou*, a huge round house in Fujian, China, I _____ always _____ _____ at home _____ _____ _____.

23 I would sometimes _____ my neighbor _____ _____ _____ for tea or dinner.

24 In a *tulou*, there _____ usually _____ _____ _____ _____.

25 The first floor _____ _____ cooking and eating.

26 And people _____ _____ and _____ _____ the second floor.

27 Do you wonder _____ _____ _____ _____? My bedroom _____ _____ _____ the third or fourth floor.

28 A *tulou* is _____ a village. The people _____ _____ a *tulou* mostly _____ the same family name.

29 Some large *tulou* _____ _____ _____ _____ 50 families. They _____ _____ and _____ many things.

30 _____ together in one building _____ _____ _____.

31 Homes are everywhere. But they are _____ _____ _____. _____ is your home _____?

16 베니스에는 물 위에 있는 색색의 건물들이 많다.

17 여러분은 어떻게, 그리고 왜 그들이 물 위에 집을 지었는지 궁금할 것이다.

18 옛 베니스 사람들은 침략자들로부터 자신들을 안전하게 지키기 위해 그곳에 살기로 결정했다.

19 하지만 그들이 이 습지 위에 집을 짓는 것은 쉽지가 않았다.

20 그래서 그들은 땅에 천만 개 이상의 나무 기둥을 설치했다.

21 이 나무 기둥들이 바로 지금까지 베니스를 지탱해 주고 있는 것이다.

토루 - 중국 푸젠

22 내가 만약 거대하고 둥그런 집인 중국 푸젠의 토루(tulou)에 산다면, 나는 항상 집에 함께 놀 친구들이 있을 것이다.

23 때때로 나의 이웃이 차를 마시거나 저녁 식사를 하러 집에 들르라고 나를 부르는 소리를 듣게 될 것이다.

24 토루는 대개 3층에서 5층으로 되어 있다.

25 1층은 요리하고 식사하는 데에 사용된다.

26 그리고 사람들은 2층에 식량과 도구를 보관한다.

27 내가 어디에서 잠을 잘지 궁금한가? 내 침실은 3층이나 4층에 있을 것이다.

28 토루는 마을과 같다. 토루에 사는 사람들은 대부분 같은 성(姓)을 가지고 있다.

29 몇몇 큰 토루는 50가구까지 수용할 수 있다. 그들은 함께 일하고 많은 것을 공유한다.

30 한 건물에 함께 사는 것은 그들을 안전하게 지켜 준다.

31 집은 어디에나 있습니다. 그러나 전 세계의 집은 모두 다릅니다. 여러분의 집은 어떤가요?

● 우리말을 참고하여 본문을 영작하시오.

1 다양한 사람들이 다양한 집에서 살고 있습니다.
➡ _____

2 어떤 사람들은 집에 들어가기 위해 사다리를 이용합니다. 다른 사람들은 물 위에 있는 집에서 살고 있습니다.
➡ _____

3 그리고 또 다른 사람들은 많은 사람들과 함께 집을 공유합니다.
➡ _____

4 여러분이 이 집들 중 하나에 산다고 상상해 보세요. 여러분의 삶은 어떻게 바뀔까요?
➡ _____

Pueblos in New Mexico, USA

5 내가 만약 푸에블로에 산다면, 나는 집에 들어가기 위해 사다리를 오를 것이다.
➡ _____

6 집 꼭대기에는 숨겨진 구멍이 있다.
➡ _____

7 반갑지 않은 방문객이 나타난다면 나는 사다리를 끌어올려 그들이 들어오지 못하게 할 것이다.
➡ _____

8 두꺼운 벽은 흙, 지푸라기, 물로 만들어져 있다.
➡ _____

9 그것들은 여름에는 시원하게, 겨울에는 따뜻하게 유지시켜 준다.
➡ _____

10 집에는 평평한 지붕이 있다. 때때로 나는 달과 별들 아래의 지붕 위에서 잠을 잘 것이다.
➡ _____

Houses on Water in Venice, Italy

11 내가 만약 베니스에 산다면, 나는 매일 아침 곤돌라를 타고 학교에 갈 것이다.
➡ _____

12 베니스는 118개의 작은 섬이 있다. 주말마다 나는 수상 버스인 바포레토를 타고 이 섬 저 섬을 여행할 것이다.
➡ _____

13 조수가 높을 때에는 아드리아 해의 물이 자주 범람하고 거리는 물로 가득 찬다.
➡ _____

14 그러나 나는 돌출되어 있는 통로로 도심 주변을 걸어다닐 수 있을 것이다.
➡ _____

15 베니스는 '떠다니는 도시'로 알려져 있다.
➡ _____

16 베니스에는 물 위에 있는 색색의 건물들이 많다.
➡ _____

17 여러분은 어떻게, 그리고 왜 그들이 물 위에 집을 지었는지 궁금할 것이다.
➡ _____

18 옛 베니스 사람들은 침략자들로부터 자신들을 안전하게 지키기 위해 그곳에 살기로 결정했다.
➡ _____

19 하지만 그들이 이 습지 위에 집을 짓는 것은 쉽지가 않았다.
➡ _____

20 그래서 그들은 땅에 천만 개 이상의 나무 기둥을 설치했다.
➡ _____

21 이 나무 기둥들이 바로 지금까지 베니스를 지탱해 주고 있는 것이다.
➡ _____

Tulou **in Fujian, China**

22 내가 만약 거대하고 둥그런 집인 중국 푸젠의 토루(*tulou*)에 산다면, 나는 항상 집에 함께 놀 친구들이 있을 것이다.
➡ _____

23 때때로 나의 이웃이 차를 마시거나 저녁 식사를 하러 집에 들르라고 나를 부르는 소리를 듣게 될 것이다.
➡ _____

24 토루는 대개 3층에서 5층으로 되어 있다.
➡ _____

25 1층은 요리하고 식사하는 데에 사용된다.
➡ _____

26 그리고 사람들은 2층에 식량과 도구를 보관한다.
➡ _____

27 내가 어디에서 잠을 잘지 궁금한가? 내 침실은 3층이나 4층에 있을 것이다.
➡ _____

28 토루는 마을과 같다. 토루에 사는 사람들은 대부분 같은 성(姓)을 가지고 있다.
➡ _____

29 몇몇 큰 토루는 50가구까지 수용할 수 있다. 그들은 함께 일하고 많은 것을 공유한다.
➡ _____

30 한 건물에 함께 사는 것은 그들을 안전하게 지켜 준다.
➡ _____

31 집은 어디에나 있습니다. 그러나 전 세계의 집은 모두 다릅니다. 여러분의 집은 어떤가요?
➡ _____

[01~04] 다음 글을 읽고 물음에 답하시오.

(A)_____ Some use ladders to enter their houses. Others live in houses on the water. And others share their houses with many people. Imagine you live in one of these houses. How would that change your life?

***Pueblos* in New Mexico, USA**

If I lived in a *pueblo*, I would climb up a ladder to enter my house. (①) There's a hidden opening on top of the house. (②) If unwelcome visitors appeared, I would pull the ladder up to stop them from entering. (③) The thick walls are made of earth, straw, and water. (④) The house has a flat roof. (⑤) I would sometimes sleep up on the roof under the moon and stars.

01 다음 중 빈칸 (A)에 들어갈 말로 가장 적절한 것은?

① Different people live various lives.
② Different people live in different houses.
③ There are many kinds of people in the world.
④ People build their houses with various materials.
⑤ There are many people who own many houses.

02 ①~⑤ 중 주어진 문장이 들어가기에 가장 적절한 곳은?

They would keep me cool in summer and warm in winter.

①   ②   ③   ④   ⑤

03 Choose one that is TRUE.

① It is hard to find *pueblos* in New Mexico.
② People who live in *pueblos* enter the house through the door.
③ *Pueblos* have pointy roofs.
④ *Pueblos* have walls which are made of only earth.
⑤ By pulling up ladders, people living in *pueblos* can aviod unwanted guests.

04 서답형 What would the writer do on the roof of the house? Answer in English.

➡ _____

_____

[05~08] 다음 글을 읽고 물음에 답하시오.

Houses on Water in Venice, Italy

If I lived in Venice, I would take a gondola to school every morning. Venice has 118 small islands. On weekends, I would travel from island to island by a vaporetto, a water bus. At high tide, the water from the Adriatic Sea often rises and leaves the streets full of water. (A)_____, I would be able to walk around the town through the raised walkways.

Venice is known as the "floating city." In Venice, there are many colorful houses on the water. You may wonder how and why they built the houses on the water. The old Venetians decided to live there to keep themselves safe from invaders. But it was not easy for them to build their homes on this swampy surface. So they installed more than 10 million wooden poles in the ground. It is these wooden poles that support Venice to this day.

05 빈칸 (A)에 들어갈 말로 가장 적절한 것은?

① For instance ② However
③ That is ④ Therefore
⑤ In addition

서답형
06 다음과 같이 풀이되는 말을 위 글에서 찾아 쓰시오.

always very wet

➡ _____

서답형
07 When you are in Venice, what are there on the water? Answer in English.

➡ _____

08 중요 다음 중 위 글을 읽고 답할 수 있는 것은?

① How long would it take to go to school by gondola?
② What happens in Venice when it is at low tide?
③ Who first invented a *vaporetto* in Venice?
④ Who named Venice "floating city?"
⑤ What supports Venice to this day?

[09~12] 다음 글을 읽고 물음에 답하시오.

Tulou in Fujian, China

If I lived in a *Tulou*, a huge round house in Fujian, China, I would always have friends at home to play with. I would sometimes hear my neighbor calling me to come over for tea or dinner. In a *Tulou*, there are usually three to five floors. The first floor is used for cooking and eating. And people store food and tools on the second floor. Do you wonder where I would sleep? My bedroom would be on the third or fourth floor.

A *tulou* is like (A)_____. The people living in a *tulou* mostly have the same family name. Some large *tulou* can house up to 50 families. They work together and share many things. Living together in one building keeps them safe.

Homes are everywhere. But they are different all over the world. What is your home like?

09 중요 글의 흐름상 빈칸 (A)에 들어갈 말로 가장 적절한 것은?

① a city ② a church
③ a village ④ a tomb
⑤ a bedroom

서답형
10 What is a *tulou*? Answer in English with a full sentence.

➡ _____

11 중요 What is TRUE about a *tulou*?

① It has only one floor.
② It houses only five families.
③ It can't store food.
④ It can't keep people safe.
⑤ People living there share many things.

서답형
12 If the writer lived in a tulou, where would he or she sleep? Answer in English with a full sentence.

➡ _____

[13~16] 다음 글을 읽고 물음에 답하시오.

Different people live in ①different houses. Some use ladders to enter their houses. Others live in houses on the water. And others share their houses with many people. Imagine you live in one of these houses. How would (A) that change your life?

***Pueblos* in New Mexico, USA**

If I lived in a *pueblo*, I would ②climb up a ladder to enter my house. There's a hidden opening on top of the house. If ③welcome visitors appeared, I would pull the ladder up to stop them from entering. The thick walls are made of earth, straw, and water. They would keep me ④cool in summer and warm in winter. The house has a ⑤flat roof. I would sometimes sleep up on the roof under the moon and stars.

13 ①~⑤ 중 글의 흐름상 어색한 것은?

①   ②   ③   ④   ⑤

14 다음 중 밑줄 친 (A)의 의미로 가장 적절한 것은?

① building different houses
② sharing a house with many people
③ leaving your house to live your life on your own
④ living in one of the houses mentioned above
⑤ living in a *pueblo* to live a different life from yours

15 What is there on top of a *pueblo*? Answer in English.

➡ _____

16 다음 중 푸에블로를 바르게 소개하고 있는 사람은?

① Semin: You can enjoy the house because it has a beautiful garden leading to the house.
② Yena: You'd better learn how to use a rope to enter the house.
③ Penny: You can experience the house only in Mexico.
④ David: Sleep up on the roof and enjoy the fantastic moon and stars.
⑤ Emma: The structure of the house welcome anyone who wants to come in.

[17~21] 다음 글을 읽고 물음에 답하시오.

Houses on Water in Venice, Italy

If I lived in Venice, I would take a gondola to school every morning. Venice has 118 small islands. On weekends, I would travel from island to island by a *vaporetto*, a water bus. At high tide, the water from the Adriatic Sea often rises and leaves the streets full of water. However, I would be able to walk around the town through the raised walkways.

(A) But it was not easy for them to build their homes on this swampy surface.

(B) Venice is known as the "floating city." In Venice, there are many colorful houses on the water.

(C) So they installed more than 10 million wooden poles in the ground. It is these wooden poles that support Venice to this day.

(D) You may wonder how and why they built the houses on the water. The old Venetians decided to live there to keep ⓐthemselves safe from invaders.

17 자연스러운 글이 되도록 (A)~(D)를 바르게 나열하시오.

➡ _____

서답형

18 What is a *vaporetto*? Answer in English with a full sentence.

➡ _____

서답형

19 다음 중 글의 내용과 일치하지 <u>않는</u> 부분을 찾아 바르게 고쳐 쓰시오.

> Building their homes on wetland was not an easy work to do for the old Venetians. But they made many poles made of steel and had them support Venice.

➡ _____

20 중요
Why are the streets full of water at high tide?

① Because of many water buses
② Due to lots of visitors
③ Owing to swampy land
④ Due to lowered walkways
⑤ Because at high tide, the water from the Adriatic Sea often rises

21 밑줄 친 @와 쓰임이 같은 것은?

① The man made the pasta <u>himself</u>.
② Please seat <u>yourself</u> on the chair.
③ The mayor <u>herself</u> attended the meeting.
④ He showed the picture to me <u>himself</u>.
⑤ Did they take the pictures <u>themselves</u>?

[22~25] 다음 글을 읽고 물음에 답하시오.

Tulou in Fujian, China

If I lived in a *tulou*, a huge round house in Fujian, China, I would always have friends at home to play with. (①) I would sometimes hear my neighbor (A)_____ me to come over for tea or dinner. (②) In a *tulou*, there are usually three to five floors. (③) The first floor is used for cooking and eating. (④) And

people store food and tools on the second floor. (⑤) My bedroom would be on the third or fourth floor.

A *tulou* is like a village. The people living in a *tulou* mostly have the same family name. Some large *tulou* can house up to 50 families. They work together and share many things. Living together in one building keeps them safe.

Homes are everywhere. But they are different all over the world. What is your home like?

22 동사 call을 어법에 맞게 빈칸 (A)에 쓰시오.

➡ _____

23 중요
①~⑤ 중 주어진 문장이 들어가기에 가장 적절한 곳은?

> Do you wonder where I would sleep?

①   ②   ③   ④   ⑤

24 중요
Choose one that is TRUE.

① A *tulou* is a small square house.
② A *tulou* is one of traditional houses in China.
③ It is almost impossible to hear someone call your name in a *tulou*.
④ A *tulou* has up to five floors.
⑤ You have to cook outside when living in a *tulou*.

서답형

25 How many families can some large *tulous* house? Answer in English with a full sentence.

➡ _____

[01~05] 다음 글을 읽고 물음에 답하시오.

Different people live in different houses. Some use ladders to enter their houses. Others live in houses on the water. And others share their houses with many people. Imagine you live in one of these houses. How would that change your life?

Pueblos in New Mexico, USA

If I lived in a *pueblo*, I would climb up a ladder to enter my house. There's a hidden opening on top of the house. If unwelcome visitors appeared, I would pull the ladder up to stop them from entering. The thick walls are made of earth, straw, and water. They would keep me cool in summer and warm in winter. The house has a flat roof. I would sometimes sleep up on the roof under the moon and stars.

01 What do some people have to use to enter their houses? Answer in English.

➡ _____

_____

02 ⭐중요 What would the writer do if unwelcome visitors appeared? Answer in English with a full sentence.

➡ _____

_____

03 What are the thick walls made of? Answer in English.

➡ _____

_____

04 ⭐중요 Why is it possible to sleep on the roof of the house, *pueblo*? Answer in English and use the word 'because.'

➡ _____

_____

05 다음과 같이 풀이되는 말을 위 글에서 찾아 쓰시오.

a device used for climbing that has two long pieces of wood, metal, or rope with a series of steps between them

➡ _____

[06~09] 다음 글을 읽고 물음에 답하시오.

Houses on Water in Venice, Italy

If I (A)_____ in Venice, I would take a gondola to school every morning. Venice has 118 small islands. On weekends, I would travel from island to island by a va poretto, a water bus. At high tide, the water from the Adriatic Sea often rises and leaves the streets full of water. However, I would be able to walk around the town through the raised walkways.

Venice is known as the "floating city." In Venice, there are many colorful houses on the water. You may wonder how and why they built the houses on the water. The old Venetians decided to live there to keep themselves safe from invaders. But it was not easy for them to build their homes on this swampy surface. So they installed more than 10 million wooden poles in the ground. It is these wooden poles that support Venice to this day.

06 빈칸 (A)에 동사 live를 어법에 맞게 쓰시오.

➡ _____

07 What would the writer do on weekends? Answer in English.

➡ _____

_____

08 What is Venice known as? Answer in English with a full sentence.

➡ _____

09 다음 중 위 글의 내용과 일치하지 <u>않는</u> 곳을 한 군데 찾아 바르게 고쳐 쓰시오.

> Venice is the city which was built on a swampy surface. The old Venetians wanted to be safe from themselves, so they made the city with lots of wooden poles.

➡ _____

[10~12] 다음 글을 읽고 물음에 답하시오.

Tulou in Fujian, China

If I lived in a *tulou*, a huge round house in Fujian, China, I would always have friends at home to play with. I would sometimes hear my neighbor calling me to come over for tea or dinner. In a *tulou*, there are usually three to five floors. The first floor is used for cooking and eating. And people store food and tools on the second floor. (A)내가 어디에서 잠을 잘지 궁금한가? My bedroom would be on the third or fourth floor.

A *tulou* is like a village. The people living in a *tulou* mostly have the same family name. Some large *tulou* can house up to 50 families. They work together and share many things. Living together in one building keeps them safe.

Homes are everywhere. But (B)they are different all over the world. What is your home like?

10 주어진 단어를 바르게 나열하여 밑줄 친 우리말 (A)를 영어로 쓰시오.

> (wonder / sleep / do / would / where / you / I)

➡ _____

11 밑줄 친 (B)가 가리키는 것을 우리말로 쓰시오.

➡ _____

12 위 글을 바탕으로 중국의 토루를 소개하는 글을 완성하시오.

> Do you want to share your house with many people? Why don't you visit a *tulou* in Fujian, China? In a *tulou*, people with _____ live in one building together. They work together and _____. There are usually three to five floors. The first floor is for _____. The second floor is used to _____. The third or fourth floor is used for _____.

Let's Write

When you visit Korea, you might wonder where you can stay. Why don't you
〔간접의문문(의문사+주어+동사)〕 〔Why don't you 동사 ~?: 권유 표현〕
stay in a *hanok*? A *hanok* is a traditional Korean house.

If you stayed in a *hanok*, you would sleep on the floor because there are no
〔가정법 과거(현재와 반대)〕 〔조동사 과거형+원형〕 〔there are+복수 주어〕
beds. *Hanok* houses are mostly built with natural materials such as wood,
〔부사(주로)〕 〔be built with 재료〕 〔= like〕
stone, straw, paper, and earth. These materials help you keep your skin
〔help+목적어+목적보어((to) 동사원형)〕
healthy. In the cold winter, the warm *ondol* floors heat your body. The doors in
hanok are covered with thin paper. They help keep you cool in summer.
〔= help to keep you cool〕

〔구문해설〕 • **natural material**: 천연 재료 • **straw**: 밀짚, 지푸라기

여러분이 한국을 방문할 때, 어디에서 머물지 궁금할 것입니다. 한옥에서 머물러 보면 어떨까요? 한옥은 한국의 전통 가옥입니다. 만약 여러분이 한옥에서 지낸다면, 여러분은 침대가 없기 때문에 바닥에서 잠을 자게 될 것입니다. 한옥 집은 대개 나무, 돌, 지푸라기, 종이, 흙과 같은 천연 재료로 지어져 있습니다. 이 재료들은 여러분의 피부를 건강하게 유지하도록 도와줍니다. 추운 겨울에는 따뜻한 온돌 바닥이 여러분의 몸을 데워줍니다. 한옥 문들은 얇은 종이로 덮여 있습니다. 그 문들은 여름에 여러분이 시원하게 지내도록 도와줍니다.

Culture & Life

If you walked down a street in the village of the Ndebele in South Africa, you
〔가정법 과거 (If+주어+과거동사, 주어+조동사의 과거형+동사원형)〕
would see houses with many unique patterns and styles. Each house tells a
〔each+단수 명사: 단수 취급〕
different story. Some stories might be about neighbors' babies. Others express
personal opinions. A long time ago, the Ndebele were at war with the Boers.
〔be at war: 전쟁을 치르다〕
When the Boers invaded their land, the Ndebele painted their houses with many
colorful symbols. So, their enemies couldn't understand what they were secretly
〔관계대명사(the thing which)〕
communicating to each other. The symbols expressed feelings such as sadness.

Those symbols were handed down from mothers to daughters. And they have kept
〔from A to B: A에서 B로〕 〔5형식 동사(keep+목적어+목적격보어)〕
their traditions alive.

〔구문해설〕 • **unique**: 독특한, 고유한 • **express**: 표현하다 • **opinion**: 의견 • **invade**: 침범하다
• **communicate**: 의사소통하다

남아프리카 은데벨레족 마을의 거리를 걸어가다 보면, 많은 독특한 모양과 양식의 집들을 보게 될 것이다. 각각의 집들은 서로 다른 이야기를 한다. 어떤 이야기들은 이웃 아이들에 관한 것일지 모른다. 또 다른 이야기들은 개인적인 의견을 표현한다. 오래전, 은데벨레족은 보어인과 전쟁을 치렀다. 보어인들이 그들의 땅을 침략했을 때, 은데벨레족은 여러 색의 상징으로 집을 칠했다. 그래서 적들은 그들이 비밀리에 주고받는 의사소통을 이해하지 못했다. 이러한 상징들은 슬픔과 같은 감정들을 표현했다. 그 상징들은 엄마들에게서 딸들에게로 전해져 왔다. 그리고 그들은 자신들의 전통이 계속 살아 있도록 유지해 왔다.

01 다음 짝지어진 단어의 관계가 〈보기〉와 같도록 빈칸에 알맞은 말을 쓰시오.

┌─ 보기 ┤
light – heavy
└─

(1) welcome – _____
(2) visible – _____

02 다음 중 밑줄 친 부분의 뜻풀이가 바르지 <u>않은</u> 것은?

① There is a narrow <u>walkway</u> next to the school. (통로)
② <u>Travel</u> expenses will be paid by the company. (여행하다, 이동하다)
③ You cannot make bricks without <u>straw</u>. (짚, 지푸라기)
④ When water levels <u>rise</u>, flooding results. (오르다, 올라가다)
⑤ The country has been regarded as an <u>invader</u> in the Middle East. (침략자)

03 다음 주어진 문장의 밑줄 친 take와 같은 의미로 쓰인 것은?

I used to <u>take</u> a cab every morning not to be late for school.

① When did you <u>take</u> your driving test?
② Virginia is planning to <u>take</u> a computer course.
③ Can I <u>take</u> a bus going to City Hall from here?
④ Most hotels are willing to <u>take</u> credit cards.
⑤ Getting a paper cut doesn't <u>take</u> a long time to heal.

04 다음 우리말을 주어진 어구를 이용하여 영작하시오.

당신이 하는 말은 비논리적이다. (what, make sense, 7 words)

➡ _____

[05~06] 다음 대화를 읽고 물음에 답하시오.

A: (A)I wish I could stay in a house on the water during my vacation.
B: _____(B)_____ if you were there?
A: I would go swimming every day. I would also go fishing.
B: That sounds fun.

05 위 대화의 밑줄 친 (A)의 의도로 가장 적절한 것은?

① 상상력 표현하기 ② 소원 표현하기
③ 감정 표현하기 ④ 의견 표현하기
⑤ 선호 표현하기

06 위 대화의 빈칸 (B)에 들어갈 말로 가장 적절한 것은?

① What would you do
② Which would you do
③ What could you do
④ Which could you do
⑤ What will you do

[07~08] 다음 대화를 읽고 물음에 답하시오.

B: This is my dream house. What do you think, Alice?
(A) That sounds cool!
(B) Oh, it's in the deep sea. It looks so unique. So, what would you do if you lived in that house?
(C) I have an interest in deep sea animals. So I would explore the deep sea and find some unique sea animals.

07 위 대화가 자연스럽게 이어지도록 (A)~(C)의 순서를 배열하시오.

➡ _____

08 다음 중 위 대화를 읽고 대답할 수 있는 질문은?

① Why did B make the dream house?
② In what country is B's dream house located?
③ How was B's dream house built?
④ When is B planning to go to the dream house?
⑤ What would B find around the dream house?

[09~11] 다음 대화를 읽고 물음에 답하시오.

Jinho: I think living in a jungle would be really exciting. Don't you think so?
Claire: But there are some dangerous animals in the jungle, Jinho.
Jinho: I know. (A)그렇지만 정글은 모험으로 가득 차 있잖아. I wish I could live there.
Claire: (B)What would you do if you lived in the jungle?
Jinho: I would explore (C)it. Maybe I could make some animal friends.

09 위 대화의 밑줄 친 (A)의 우리말을 영작하시오.

➡ _____

10 다음 중 위 대화의 밑줄 친 (B)와 바꿔 쓸 수 있는 것은?

① I should say you live in the jungle.
② What if you lived in the jungle?
③ Why don't you live in the jungle?
④ What about living in the jungle?
⑤ Have you ever imagined that you lived in the jungle?

11 위 대화의 밑줄 친 (B)it이 가리키는 것을 찾아 쓰시오.

➡ _____

Grammar

12 다음 주어진 문장과 가장 가까운 의미를 가진 문장을 고르시오.

Living together in one building keeps us safe from invaders or thieves.

① When we lived together in one building, we were safe from invaders or thieves.
② We live together in one building, which makes us safe from invaders or thieves.
③ If we lived together in one building, we would be safe from invaders or thieves.
④ We live together in one building to feel safe from invaders or thieves.
⑤ We live together in one building because of the threat from invaders or thieves.

[13~14] 다음 가정법으로 주어진 우리말에 맞게 괄호 안에 주어진 어구를 어법상 적절한 형태로 바꿔 배열하고, 직설법 문장으로도 바꾸시오.

13

수영장이 있는 집에 산다면, 나는 매일 수영을 즐길 텐데. (in, with, a swimming pool, a house, I, I, live, will, enjoy)

➡ (1) If _____

_____ swimming every day.

(2) 직설법: As _____

_____

swimming every day.

14

땅 속에 이 나무 기둥들을 설치하지 않았더라면, 그들은 베니스에서 살 수 없었을 텐데. (in the ground, can't, install, this, live, not, have, wooden poles, they)

➡ (1) If they _____

_____

in Venice.

(2) 직설법: As _____

_____

in Venice.

[15~16] 다음 중 어법상 어색한 문장을 고르시오.

15 ① If Junsik told what his friends did to the teacher, they would be punished.

② If Mina put that dress on, she would not look like a poor girl.

③ If Inho got up earlier, he could get there on time.

④ If my neighbor didn't fail to catch the bus that morning, he would not have been late for work.

⑤ If Smith were the boss, he could change the company's policy.

16 ① The housewives at the meeting made their husbands impressed by the gifts.

② The audience at the preview found the movie very touching.

③ The teacher kept the noisy boys raised their hands until the end of class.

④ Studying mathematics alone made me feel disappointed with myself.

⑤ The ice box helped keep the vegetables fresh longer than I thought.

17 다음 우리말을 영작할 때, 어법상 옳지 않은 문장을 모두 고르시오.

나무 기둥들이 없다면, 그 도시는 사람이 살 수 없을 텐데.

① Without wooden poles, people couldn't have lived in the city.

② If there were no wooden poles, people could not live in the city.

③ If it were not for wooden poles, people could not live in the city.

④ Were it not for wooden poles, people could not live in the city.

⑤ If there are no wooden poles, people could not live in the city.

Reading

[18~20] 다음 글을 읽고 물음에 답하시오.

Different people live ①in different houses. Some use ladders ②to enter into their houses. Others live in houses ③on the water. And others share their houses with many people. Imagine you live in one of these houses. How would that change your life?

***Pueblos* in New Mexico, USA**

If I lived in a *pueblo*, I would climb up a ladder to enter my house. There's a hidden opening on top of the house. If unwelcome visitors appeared, I would pull the ladder up to stop them from entering. The thick walls ④are made of earth, straw, and water. They would keep me cool in summer and warm in winter. The house has a flat roof. I ⑤would sometimes sleep up on the roof under the moon and stars.

18 ①~⑤ 중 어법상 바르지 않은 것은?

①   ②   ③   ④   ⑤

19 What is the passage mainly talking about?

① different people living different lives
② different ways to build houses
③ various houses in the world
④ how to get to an agreement among people
⑤ the special building method in the world

20 According to the passage, what does a *pueblo* have on top of the house?

➡ _____

_____

[21~24] 다음 글을 읽고 물음에 답하시오.

Houses on Water in Venice, Italy

If I lived in Venice, I would take a gondola to school every morning. Venice has 118 small islands. On weekends, I would travel from island to island by a vaporetto, a water bus. At high tide, the water from the Adriatic Sea often rises and leaves the streets full of water. However, I would be able to walk around the town through the raised walkways.

Venice is known (A)_____ the "floating city." (①) In Venice, there are many colorful houses on the water. (②) The old Venetians decided to live there to keep themselves safe from invaders. (③) But it was not easy for them to build their homes on this swampy surface. (④) So they installed more than 10 million wooden poles in the ground. (⑤) It is these wooden poles that support Venice to this day.

21 다음 중 빈칸 (A)에 들어갈 말과 같은 말이 들어가는 것은?

① I'm not in the mood _____ watching a movie.
② You should be ashamed _____ what you said to her.
③ Using chopsticks is related _____ their culture.
④ We regarded her _____ our leader.
⑤ Why was she absent _____ school the other day?

22 ①~⑤ 중 주어진 문장이 들어가기에 가장 적절한 곳은?

> You may wonder how and why they built the houses on the water.

①   ②   ③   ④   ⑤

23 위 글의 내용을 바르게 이해한 사람은?

① A: It must be really fun to take a gondola to work every morning.
② B: I didn't know that Venice has so many big islands.
③ C: It is really amazing that people built many colorful houses under the water.
④ D: It is shameful that there is no water bus in Venice.
⑤ E: It is surprising that over ten million poles that support Venice to this day was made of wood.

24 What would make it possible for the writer to walk around the town at high tide? Answer in English.

➡ _____

_____

[25~27] 다음 글을 읽고 물음에 답하시오.

When you visit Korea, you might wonder where you can stay. Why don't you stay in a *hanok*? A *hanok* is a traditional Korean house. If you stayed in a *hanok*, you would sleep on the floor because there are no beds. *Hanok* houses are mostly built with natural materials such as wood, stone, straw, paper, and earth. These materials help you keep your skin healthy. In the cold winter, the warm *ondol* floors heat your body. The doors in *hanok* are covered with thin paper. They help keep you cool in summer.

25 Write the reason why you would sleep on the floor if you stayed in a *hanok*. Answer in English.

➡ _____

26 According to the passage, what heats your body in the cold winter? Answer in English.

➡ _____

_____

27 다음 중 위 글을 읽고 답할 수 있는 것은?

① How long did it take to build a *hanok*?
② What are traditional clothes of Korea?
③ How many people are needed to build a *hanok*?
④ With what are *hanok* houses mostly built?
⑤ With what are floors inside *hanok* covered?

출제율 90%

01 다음 영영풀이가 가리키는 것을 고르시오.

> to provide a place for somebody to live

① appear ② house
③ enter ④ install
⑤ relax

출제율 100%

02 다음 〈보기〉에서 알맞은 단어를 골라 문장을 완성하시오.

> ┌─ 보기 ─┐
> for a while / live in / on weekends / up to
> / take a look

(1) Now forget the details and _____ at the big picture.

(2) I am so exhausted because I have to work even _____.

(3) We lived on the outskirts of New York _____.

[03~05] 다음 대화를 읽고 물음에 답하시오.

B: Will it snow today?

G: I have no idea. Why are you waiting for snow, Taeho?

B: I got a new sled for my birthday. (A)

G: Let me check the weather. Umm, there will be no snow for a while.

B: I wish I could live in Alaska. Then I could go sledding all day!

G: No kidding! Alaska is a very cold place.

B: I think it would be fun. I want to build a snow house and stay there on vacation.

G: Living in a snow house sounds fun!

출제율 95%

03 위 대화의 빈칸 (A)에 들어갈 말로 가장 적절한 것은?

① I can't wait to receive another present.
② I can't wait to test it out.
③ I can't wait to make a sled for myself.
④ I can't wait to clean it up.
⑤ I can't wait to check the weather.

출제율 90%

04 What would B do if he lived in Alaska? (11 words)

➡ _____

_____

출제율 100%

05 다음 중 위 대화의 내용과 일치하지 않는 것은?

① G does not know whether it will snow or not today.
② A snow sled was given to B as a birthday gift.
③ It will snow for a while today.
④ B wants to live in Alaska and go sledding.
⑤ G thinks it's exciting to live in a snow house.

[06~07] 다음 대화를 읽고 물음에 답하시오.

G: Have you heard from Julia? She's traveling in Turkey, right? (①)

B: Yes, she sent me some pictures. Do you want to see (A)them? (②)

G: Yes, please.

B: Okay, take a look. (③)

G: Oh, look at those cave houses! (B)They look so unique, don't they? (④) I wish I could try living there.

B: I like those balloons. (⑤)

G: I think Turkey is a wonderful place to visit. I hope to visit (C)there someday.

B: Me too!

06 위 대화의 ①~⑤ 중 다음 주어진 문장이 들어갈 가장 적절한 곳은?

> They look so beautiful!

①   ②   ③   ④   ⑤

07 위 대화의 밑줄 친 (A)~(C)가 가리키는 것을 영어로 쓰시오.

➡ (A) _____

   (B) _____

   (C) _____

08 다음 가정법 문장들 중 어법상 옳은 것을 고르시오.

① If the lady were not so hungry, she can share her lunch with the man.

② April will feel sad if her boyfriend left her alone in the cinema.

③ All the students in her school would feel proud if Yuna wins the gold medal in the Olympics.

④ What would they do if they lived in a huge building as one family?

⑤ If it had not been for the thick walls, the people living in the pueblo would feel cold in winter.

09 다음 각 빈칸에 공통으로 들어갈 단어 중 나머지 넷과 성격이 다른 하나는?

① Dancing with the puppies _____ the girl so happy that she couldn't believe it was real.

② Karl _____ his mother upset as he forgot to lock the door.

③ Jordan _____ the government take action about the pollution of the river.

④ The heating system _____ the people inside the building feel warm and cozy.

⑤ The author _____ an impressive story that everybody loved.

[10~11] 다음 주어진 우리말을 어법에 맞게 바르게 영작한 것은?

10

> 어머니가 아프지 않으셔서 우리들과 함께 제주도로 여행을 가실 수 있으면 좋을 텐데. (그러나 어머니가 아프시다.)

① I wish we were not sick and could go to the Jeju island with my mom.

② I wish my mom were not sick and could go to the Jeju island with us.

③ I wish my mom were not sick and couldn't go to the Jeju island with us.

④ My mom wishes we were not sick and could go to the Jeju island with us.

⑤ I wish my mom is not sick and can go to the Jeju island with us.

11

> 비가 심하게 오지 않았다면, 강물이 넘치지 않았을 텐데. (그러나 비가 너무 심하게 왔다).

① If it had not rained heavily, the river wouldn't have overflowed.

② If it had not rained heavily, the river wouldn't overflow.

③ Had it not rained heavily, the river would not overflow.

④ Didn't it rain heavily, the river would not be overflowed.

⑤ If it rained not heavily, the river would not have overflowed.

[12~13] 다음 문장의 밑줄 친 부분이 어법상 어색한 것은?

출제율 100%

12
① The smile on the baby boy made his parents happy and <u>relieved</u>.
② My sisters always keep their room <u>clean</u>.
③ The movie we saw last night made almost all the people <u>sleep</u>.
④ The police officers kept the little girl <u>safely</u> from the gangsters.
⑤ These clothes would keep the poor kids in the village <u>warm</u>.

출제율 95%

13
① The medicine that the doctor in the clinic prescribed will make you <u>sleepy</u>.
② The kittens I saw at the animal hospital made me <u>excited</u>.
③ The new refrigerator her father brought home can't keep the fruit <u>fresh</u>.
④ Each of the birds on the trees is keeping their eggs <u>warm</u>.
⑤ The collections in this museum make the visitors <u>interesting</u> in ancient Korean arts.

출제율 95%

14 다음 우리말을 괄호 안에 주어진 어구를 활용하여 조건에 맞게 영작하시오.

> 반갑지 않은 방문객이 나타난다면, 나는 사다리를 끌어올려 그들이 들어오지 못하게 할 텐데.
> (appear, pull up, stop, will, enter, the ladder, unwelcome visitors, from. If로 시작하는 가정법, 단어 변형 가능, 총 15 단어로 할 것.)

➡ _____
_____

출제율 95%

15 다음 중 각 문장의 밑줄 친 부분의 쓰임이 같은 것끼리 묶인 것을 고르시오.

> ⓐ The star chef, Mr. Baek, <u>made</u> the kids special food to encourage their lives.
> ⓑ Please do your best not to <u>make</u> your loved ones disappointed.
> ⓒ The principal <u>made</u> the teachers clean the way to the school.
> ⓓ The ladies in the club wanted to <u>make</u> the singer world famous.
> ⓔ Susan persuaded Jack to <u>make</u> a decision to help them.
> ⓕ My grandmother used to <u>make</u> me and my brother the sweet potato pizza.
> ⓖ Generally speaking, the cloudy weather <u>makes</u> people depressed.

① ⓐ, ⓒ, ⓓ, ⓔ
② ⓐ, ⓒ, ⓕ, ⓖ
③ ⓐ, ⓔ, ⓕ, ⓖ
④ ⓑ, ⓒ ⓓ, ⓖ
⑤ ⓑ, ⓒ, ⓔ, ⓖ

[16~19] 다음 글을 읽고 물음에 답하시오.

Tulou in Fujian, China

If I ①<u>lived</u> in a *tulou*, a huge round house in Fujian, China, I would always have friends at home ②<u>to play</u>. I would sometimes hear my neighbor calling me ③<u>to come</u> over for tea or dinner. In a *tulou*, there are usually three to five floors. The first floor is used for cooking and eating. And people store food and tools on the second floor. Do you wonder where I would sleep? My bedroom would be on the third or fourth floor.

A *tulou* is like a village. The people ④<u>living</u> in a *tulou* mostly have the same family name. Some large *tulou* can house ⑤<u>up to</u> 50 families. They work together and share many things. Living together in one building keeps them safe.

✎ 출제율 100%

16 위 글의 제목으로 가장 적절한 것은?

① A *Tulou*: the Only Traditional House in China
② A Single-person House for Chinese People
③ A *Tulou*: A Community House in Fujian
④ A *Tulou*: A Huge Royal House in Fujian
⑤ The World's Famous House: *Tulous*

✎ 출제율 95%

17 ①~⑤ 중 어법상 바르지 <u>않은</u> 것은?

①   ②   ③   ④   ⑤

✎ 출제율 100%

18 Choose one that is TRUE.

① *Tulous* are found everywhere in China.
② It would be hard to find friends in a *tulou*.
③ Sleeping rooms are on the same floor as a cooking room in a *tulou*.
④ To store food and tools in a *tulou* would not be easy.
⑤ It would be easy to hear neighbors call someone's name in a *tulou*.

✎ 출제율 90%

19 How many floors does a *tulou* usually have? Answer in English with a full sentence.

➡ _____

[20~23] 다음 글을 읽고 물음에 답하시오.

If you (A)_____ down a street in the village of the Ndebele in South Africa, you would see houses with many unique patterns and styles. Each house tells a different story. Some stories might be about neighbors' babies. Others express personal opinions.

A long time ago, the Ndebele were at war with the Boers. When the Boers invaded their land, the Ndebele painted their houses with many colorful symbols. So, their enemies couldn't understand what they were secretly communicating to each other. The symbols expressed feelings such as sadness. Those symbols were handed down from mothers to daughters. And they have kept their traditions alive.

✎ 출제율 95%

20 빈칸 (A)에 들어갈 말로 가장 적절한 것은?

① walk   ② will walk
③ have walked   ④ walked
⑤ had walked

✎ 출제율 90%

21 Write the reason why the Boers couldn't understand what the Ndebele were secretly communicating to each other. Use the phrase 'It was because.'

➡ _____

_____

✎ 출제율 90%

22 What did the symbols express? Answer in English.

➡ _____

✎ 출제율 100%

23 Choose one that is NOT true.

① The passage is about the stories of the Ndebele and their houses.
② The village of the Ndebele can be found in South Africa.
③ The houses in the village have many ordinary patterns and styles.
④ Each house in the village has their own stories.
⑤ Some houses in the village express personal opinions.

[01~02] 다음 대화를 읽고 물음에 답하시오.

B: This is my dream house, Alice. What do you think?

G: Oh, the house has wheels! Is it a kind of car?

B: Yes, it can move like a car.

G: So what would you do if you lived in that house?

B: I would travel to many places with my family.

G: That sounds cool.

01 Describe B's dream house in English. (Include two features.)

➡ _____

02 What would B do if he lived in his dream house? (9 words)

➡ _____

03 다음 그림을 보고 자연스러운 문장이 되도록 괄호 안에 주어진 단어를 바르게 배열하여 빈칸을 완성하시오.

(1)

➡ Living together in one _____ _____ comfortable. (the people, building, and, safe, keeps)

(2)

➡ The old Venetians installed more than 10 million wooden _____ _____. (make, support, poles, to, Venice, them)

04 다음 중에서 틀린 문장을 찾아 기호를 쓰고, 바르게 고쳐 문장을 다시 쓰시오.

① If the scientists were awarded for the discovery, their books would be sold even better.

② If the engineer made the flying taxi, I would use it as I go to work.

③ If the girl got up earlier, she wouldn't miss the bus.

④ If the officer knew the driver, he won't give her a ticket.

⑤ If the patient had put on the sunscreen, his skin would not have burned.

➡ _____
_____
_____

[05~06] 아래 각 두 문장을 가정법의 한 문장으로 합치되, 주어진 단어로 시작하시오.

05

• Andrew doesn't know the title of the song.

• He can't sing it at the school festival.

➡ If _____
_____.

06

> • I'm sorry that my sisters are not nice.
> • I want them to be as nice as Abigail.

➡ I _____ .

[07~08] 다음 글을 읽고 물음에 답하시오.

Different people live in different houses. Some use ladders to enter their houses. (A) The others live in houses on the water. And others share their houses with many people. (B)여러분이 이 집들 중 하나에 산다고 상상해 보세요. How would that change your life?

07 밑줄 친 (A)에서 어법상 틀린 것을 바르게 고쳐 다시 쓰시오.

➡ _____

08 주어진 단어를 바르게 나열하여 밑줄 친 우리말 (B)를 영어로 쓰시오.

(these / you / one / imagine / of / in / houses / live)

➡ _____

[09~10] 다음 글을 읽고 물음에 답하시오.

Tulou in Fujian, China

If I lived in a *tulou*, a huge round house in Fujian, China, I would always have friends at home to play with. I would sometimes hear my neighbor calling me to come over for tea or dinner. In a *tulou*, there are usually three to five floors. The first floor is used for cooking and eating. And people store food and tools on the second floor. Do you wonder where I would sleep? My bedroom would be on the third or fourth floor.

A *tulou* is like a village. The people living in a *tulou* mostly have the same family name. Some large *tulou* can house up to 50 families. They work together and share many things. Living together in one building keeps them safe.

09 According to the passage, what would the writer hear if she or he lived in a *tulou*? Answer in English.

➡ _____
_____

10 What do the people living in a *tulou* mostly have? Answer in English.

➡ _____
_____

창의사고력 서술형 문제

01 다음 그림을 보고, 바다 속의 집에서 살면 무엇을 하고 싶은지 자유롭게 가정법 과거 시제를 사용하여 빈칸을 채우시오.

(1) If I lived in a house under the sea, _____.
(2) If I lived in a house under the sea, _____.
(3) If I lived in a house under the sea, _____.

02 다음 대화를 읽고 Juwon의 일기를 완성하시오.

G: What would you do if you became a millionaire, Juwon?

B: I would build my own house.

G: What kind of house would you build?

B: I would build a house that is completely covered with mirrors.

G: Why?

B: The mirrors would make the house almost invisible. Wouldn't that be cool?

G: That would be cool!

Recently, I was having a chat with my friend. She asked me what I _____ if I became a millionaire. I told her that I _____ my own house that is completely _____ mirrors. I've always thought that the mirrors would make the house almost _____, and I think it's really cool.

단원별 모의고사

01 다음 영영풀이가 가리키는 것은?

> the regular upward and downward movement of the level of the ocean that is caused by the pull of the sun and the moon on Earth

① surface   ② stream   ③ wave
④ earth   ⑤ tide

02 다음 빈칸에 알맞은 단어를 고르시오.

> happy : happily = high : _____

① high   ② highly
③ highness   ④ higher
⑤ highest

03 다음 우리말에 맞게 빈칸에 알맞은 말을 쓰시오.

> 교실에서 컴퓨터들은 게임을 위해 사용되어서는 안 된다.
> ➡ In the classroom, the computers should not _____ games.

[04~05] 다음 대화를 읽고 물음에 답하시오.

B: ⓐWill it snow today?
G: I have no idea. Why are you ⓑwaiting for snow, Taeho?
B: I got a new sled for my birthday. I can't wait to ⓒtest out it.
G: Let me ⓓcheck the weather. Umm, there will be no snow for a while.
B: (A)알래스카에 살 수 있다면 좋을 텐데! Then I could go sledding all day!
G: No kidding! Alaska is a very cold place.

B: I think it ⓔwould be fun. I want to build a snow house and stay there on vacation.
G: Living in a snow house sounds fun!

04 위 대화의 밑줄 친 (A)의 우리말을 주어진 단어를 사용하여 영작하시오. (wish, 7 words)

➡ _____

05 위 대화의 밑줄 친 ⓐ~ⓔ 중 어법상 어색한 것을 골라 바르게 고치시오.

➡ _____

[06~07] 다음 대화를 읽고 물음에 답하시오.

G: Look. ①The house in this picture is upside down.
B: That's interesting. ②Does anybody live there?
G: ③No, it would not be easy to live there because the inside is also upside down.
B: Really? But I want to try living there. ④I have wanted to live alone.
G: What (A)[would / could] you do if you (B)[lived / have lived] in that house?
B: I would walk upside down like Spider-Man. ⑤I could also see things differently.

06 밑줄 친 문장 ①~⑤ 중에서 전체 흐름과 관계 없는 문장은?

①   ②   ③   ④   ⑤

07 위 대화의 괄호 (A)와 (B)에서 알맞은 말을 고르시오.

➡ (A) _____ (B) _____

08 다음 대화의 밑줄 친 부분의 의도로 가장 적절한 것은?

> A: What's the matter?
> B: My computer is so slow. I wish I could have a new computer.

① 질문하기   ② 불만 토로하기
③ 의견 묻기   ④ 바람 표현하기
⑤ 상상력 표현하기

[09~11] 다음 대화를 읽고 물음에 답하시오.

> G: Dohun, we need to start our project on our dream country to visit.
> B: That's right. Which country do you want to visit, Emma?
> G: In my case, I want to visit Spain.
> B: What would you do if you visited Spain?
> G: I'm interested in buildings. (A)그래서 난 La Sagrada Familia를 보러 갈 거야.
> B: Isn't that the church Antoni Gaudí designed?
> G: Yes, it is. (B)It would be interesting to see how his design was inspired by nature.
> B: Hmm… How about *Gaudí and Spain* _(C)_ the title for our project?
> G: I love it!

09 위 대화의 밑줄 친 (A)의 우리말을 주어진 단어를 이용하여 영작하시오. (go, 8 words)

➡ _____

10 위 대화의 밑줄 친 (B)It이 가리키는 것을 찾아 쓰시오.

➡ _____

11 위 대화의 빈칸 (C)에 적절한 것은?

① as   ② for
③ from   ④ at
⑤ with

12 다음 대화를 읽고 빈칸에 알맞은 말을 쓰시오.

> A: _____ you could have a magical power?
> B: I would turn into a bird. Then I would be able to fly freely in the sky.
> A: That's cool.

[13~15] 다음 중 밑줄 친 부분의 쓰임이 나머지와 다른 것은?

13 ① The staff and makeup artists will make them look like the real idol singers.
② The teacher majoring in literature will make your report better for the review.
③ The drummer at the concert will make their songs more rhythmical for the beat.
④ The students at the cooking class will make you delicious bread.
⑤ Will the researchers make me nervous by asking some embarrassing requests?

14 ① Thomas had no idea <u>if</u> the rumor about the war would turn out true.

② <u>If</u> he were not ill, he would come to Ann's birthday party.

③ The employees in the company wouldn't go out to have lunch <u>if</u> it started raining.

④ The little girl would call her mom <u>if</u> she needed any help.

⑤ The athlete would get a full scholarship to the college <u>if</u> he won the championship medal.

15 ① The new clothes that his mother bought him <u>made</u> him look great.

② The smiles on my daughters' faces <u>make</u> me a superman.

③ The music with touching lyrics always <u>make</u> her encouraged to carry on.

④ My uncle in the college lab <u>made</u> me a fantastic figure of a dinosaur.

⑤ Eating too much junk food can <u>make</u> the little kids sick.

[16~17] 다음 중 〈보기〉의 밑줄 친 단어와 쓰임이 같은 것은?

16

> ┤ 보기 ├
>
> Dennis <u>would</u> meet the girl from Canada if his friend Sean asked him to guide her.

① My parents <u>would</u> go on a picnic to the park when I wasn't born.

② The members of the soccer club <u>would</u> like to have the steak for the party.

③ The CEO of the company <u>would</u> hire the person if she improved her skills.

④ <u>Would</u> you find me the ring I had been wearing before I took a shower?

⑤ The English teacher said that I <u>would</u> get the scholarship next year.

17

> ┤ 보기 ├
>
> The old Venetians decided to live in Venice to <u>keep</u> themselves safe from invaders.

① Please send out the photocopies and <u>keep</u> the original with you.

② You should <u>keep</u> your answers as simple as possible.

③ The poor family could not <u>keep</u> up the monthly payment for their house.

④ The politicians have failed to <u>keep</u> their election promises.

⑤ The museum has <u>kept</u> the visitors from taking pictures of its pictures.

18 다음 중 〈보기〉의 문장과 의미가 가장 가까운 것을 고르시오.

> ┤ 보기 ├
>
> If Choo were in good condition, he would make twice as many home runs as any other players

① As Choo was in good condition, he made twice as many home runs as any other player.

② As Choo isn't in good condition, he didn't make twice as many home runs as any other player.

③ Though Choo was not in good condition, he made twice as many home runs as any other player.

④ As Choo is not in good condition, he doesn't make twice as many home runs as any other player.

⑤ As Choo was not in good condition, he didn't make twice as many home runs as any other player.

19 다음 중 내용상 〈보기〉의 밑줄 친 부분과 바꿔 쓸 수 <u>없는</u> 것은?

> ┌ 보기 ┐
>
> <u>If it were not for a gondola</u>, the Venetians could not go around as freely as they want.

① Were it not for a gondola,

② Without a gondola,

③ Had it not been for a gondola,

④ But for a gondola,

⑤ If there were no gondola,

20 다음 〈보기〉의 문장들 중에서 어법상 <u>어색한</u> 것을 <u>모두</u> 고르면?

> ┌ 보기 ┐
>
> ⓐ The thick walls made of earth, straw, and water would keep me cool in summer and warm in winter.
>
> ⓑ The flat roof which a *pueblo* has makes it possible for me to sleep up on the roof under the moon and stars.
>
> ⓒ The raised walkways in Venice keep me walk around the town every day.
>
> ⓓ The old Venetians decided to live in Venice to keep themselves safely from invaders.
>
> ⓔ Those wooden poles that they installed have kept Venice to stand strong to this day.
>
> ⓕ Living in a huge round building makes me able to hear my neighbor calling me to come over for tea or dinner.
>
> ⓖ At high tide, the water from the Adriatic Sea often rises and leaves the streets full of water.
>
> ⓗ Living together in one building allows them be safe from the outsiders.

① ⓐ, ⓑ, ⓕ, ⓖ ② ⓐ, ⓒ, ⓓ, ⓖ

③ ⓒ, ⓓ, ⓔ, ⓗ ④ ⓑ, ⓒ, ⓔ, ⓖ

⑤ ⓒ, ⓓ, ⓕ, ⓗ

21 다음 우리말을 주어진 조건에 맞게 영작하시오.

> 내가 오직 사다리를 사용해야 집에 들어갈 수 있다면, 그것은 재미있을 텐데.
> (can, will, use, ladders, a house, enter, by, fun. If로 시작, 어휘 변형 가능, 총 14 단어로 할 것)

➡ _____

_____

[22~27] 다음 글을 읽고 물음에 답하시오.

> **Houses on Water in Venice, Italy**
>
> If I lived in Venice, I would take a gondola to school every morning. Venice has 118 small islands. On weekends, I would travel from island to island by a vaporetto, a water bus. At high tide, the water from the Adriatic Sea often rises and leaves the streets full of water. However, I would be able to walk around the town through the raised walkways.
>
> Venice is known as the "(A)_____." (①) In Venice, there are many colorful houses on the water. (②) You may wonder how and why they built the houses on the water. (③) The old Venetians decided to live there to keep themselves safe from invaders. (④) But it was not easy for them to build their homes on this swampy surface. (⑤) (B)<u>It is these wooden poles that support Venice to this day</u>

22 글의 흐름상 빈칸 (A)에 들어갈 말로 가장 적절한 것은?

① drowning boat ② forgotten city

③ man-made tower ④ floating city

⑤ city of the conqueror

23 ①~⑤ 중 주어진 문장이 들어가기에 가장 적절한 곳은?

So they installed more than 10 million wooden poles in the ground.

①　　②　　③　　④　　⑤

24 What happens in Venice when it is at high tide? Answer in English.

➡ _____

_____

25 Choose one that is NOT true.

① A gondola is taken in order to go to school in Venice.

② Thanks to a water bus called a *vaporetto*, it is possible to travel between islands.

③ There are over 118 small islands in Venice.

④ The raised walkways make it possible for people in Venice to walk around.

⑤ The things that support Venice to this day are the wooden poles made by the old Venetians.

26 Write the reason why the old Venetians decided to live in Venice. Answer in English.

➡ _____

_____

27 다음 중 밑줄 친 (B)의 문법적 특징과 다른 하나는?

① It was in the library that I saw him.

② It was her husband that stole the money.

③ It is my car that is parked in front of the restaurant.

④ It is surprising that she didn't mention about the issue.

⑤ It is New York that I want to live in.

[28~29] 다음 글을 읽고 물음에 답하시오.

Tulou in Fujian, China

If I lived in a *tulou*, a huge round house in Fujian, China, I would always have friends at home to play with. I would sometimes hear my neighbor calling me to come over for tea or dinner. In a *tulou*, there are usually three ⓐ _____ five floors. The first floor is used ⓑ _____ cooking and eating. And people store food and tools on the second floor. Do you wonder where I would sleep? My bedroom would be on the third or fourth floor.

A *tulou* is like a village. The people living in a *tulou* mostly have the same family name. Some large *tulou* can house up to 50 families. They work together and share many things. Living together in one building keeps them safe.

28 위 글의 ⓐ, ⓑ에 들어갈 전치사를 쓰시오.

➡ ⓐ _____, ⓑ _____

29 What keeps people living in a *tulou* safe? Answer in English.

➡ _____

_____

MEMO

Lesson 8

Behind the Numbers

🎤 의사소통 기능

- 상술하기
  Five out of twenty-five students don't have pets.
  Over sixty percent of the students voted for her.
- 이해 점검하기
  Do you see what I mean?

🎤 언어 형식

- too ~ to ...
  It's **too** hard **to** read and draw graphs.

- No one ...
  No one needs graphs in real life.

교과서
Words & Expressions

Key Words

- **adventure** [ədvéntʃər] 명 모험
- **anyway** [éniwèi] 부 게다가, 어쨌든
- **arrow** [ǽrou] 명 화살
- **article** [áːrtikl] 명 글, 기사
- **break** [breik] 동 고장 내다
- **celebrate** [séləbrèit] 동 기념하다
- **chase** [tʃeis] 동 뒤쫓다
- **claim** [kleim] 동 주장하다
- **class president** 학급 반장
- **count** [kaunt] 동 (수를) 세다
- **courageous** [kəréidʒəs] 형 용감한
- **election** [ilékʃən] 명 선거
- **enough** [inʌ́f] 형 충분한
- **equal** [íːkwəl] 동 같다
- **facial** [féiʃəl] 형 얼굴의
- **favorite** [féivərit] 형 매우 좋아하는
- **graph** [ɡræf] 명 그래프
- **greedy** [ɡríːdi] 형 탐욕스러운, 욕심 많은
- **helpful** [hélpfəl] 형 도움이 되는
- **importance** [impɔ́ːrtəns] 명 중요성
- **lastly** [lǽstli] 부 마지막으로
- **leaf** [liːf] 명 잎, 나뭇잎, 풀잎
- **lucky** [lʌ́ki] 형 행운의
- **match** [mætʃ] 동 일치하다
- **matter** [mǽtər] 동 중요하다
- **midnight** [mídnait] 명 자정
- **minus** [máinəs] 전 ~을 뺀

- **muscle** [mʌ́sl] 명 근육
- **noon** [nuːn] 명 정오
- **novel** [návəl] 명 소설
- **percent** [pərsént] 명 퍼센트, 백분
- **picnic** [píknik] 명 소풍
- **pie chart** 원 그래프
- **poisonous** [pɔ́izənəs] 형 독이 있는
- **realize** [ríːəlàiz] 동 깨닫다
- **reason** [ríːzn] 명 이유
- **repeat** [ripíːt] 동 반복하다, 따라 말하다
- **represent** [rèprizént] 동 나타내다
- **result** [rizʌ́lt] 명 결과
- **salty** [sɔ́ːlti] 형 짭짤한
- **science-fiction** 형 공상과학의
- **snack** [snæk] 명 간식
- **shout** [ʃaut] 동 외치다, 소리치다
- **soldier** [sóuldʒər] 명 군인, 병사
- **solution** [səlúːʃən] 명 해결책
- **struggle** [strʌ́gl] 동 투쟁하다, 분투하다
- **suddenly** [sʌ́dnli] 부 갑자기
- **sum** [sʌm] 명 계산, 총계
- **survey** [sərvéi] 동 설문조사하다
- **tax** [tæks] 명 세금
- **typewriter** [táipraitər] 명 타자기
- **vote** [vout] 동 투표하다
- **wave** [weiv] 동 손을 흔들다
- **weather report** 일기 예보

Key Expressions

- **be about to** 막 ~하려고 하다
- **be proud of** ~을 자랑스러워하다
- **be regarded as** ~로 여겨지다
- **be related to** ~와 연관되어 있다
- **be worried about** ~에 대해 걱정하다
- **between A and B** A와 B 사이에
- **get back** 되찾다
- **get inside** 들어가다
- **get off** 내리다
- **hide up** 잠복하다
- **in other words** 다시 말하면

- **look back** 뒤돌아보다
- **look up** 올려보다
- **not ~ anymore** 더 이상 ~ 않다
- **one by one** 하나씩
- **pick up** 집어들다
- **pull A onto B** A를 B로 끌어올리다
- **put down** 내려놓다
- **read oneself to sleep** 읽다가 잠들다
- **run for** 출마하다
- **take A to B** A를 B에 데려가다
- **walk out** 걸어나가다

Word Power

※ 서로 비슷한 뜻을 가진 어휘
- chase 뒤쫓다 – pursue 추적하다
- equal 같다 – match 일치하다
- poisonous 독이 있는 – toxic 유독성의
- struggle 고군분투하다 – strive 애쓰다

- claim 주장하다 – insist 주장하다
- novel 소설 – fiction 소설
- represent 나타내다 – express 나타내다
- tax 세금 – duty 세금, 의무

※ 서로 반대의 뜻을 가진 어휘
- courageous 용감한 ↔ cowardly 겁이 많은
- lastly 마지막으로 ↔ firstly 첫째로
- midnight 자정 ↔ midday 정오

- greedy 탐욕스러운, 욕심 많은 ↔ generous 아끼지 않는, 후한
- lucky 행운의 ↔ unlucky 불행의

※ 접미사 –tion, 동사+tion
- act + -tion → action 행동
- compete + -tion → competition 경쟁
- educate + -tion → education 교육
- infect + -tion → infection 감염, 전염병
- situate + -tion → situation 상황

- calculate + -tion → calculation 계산
- correct + -tion → correction 정정, 수정
- examinate + -tion → examination 시험, 검토
- inform + -tion → information 정보
- solve + -tion → solution 해결책

※ 접미사 –y, 명사+y
- blood + -y → bloody 피투성이의
- fun + -y → funny 재미있는
- risk + -y → risky 위험한
- shine + -y → shiny 빛나는

- dust + -y → dusty 먼지투성이인
- greed + -y → greedy 탐욕스러운
- salt + -y → salty 짭짤한
- thirst + -y → thirsty 갈증이 나는

English Dictionary

- article 글, 기사
  → a piece of writing appearing in a newspaper
  신문에 나오는 글
- celebrate 기념하다
  → to take part in special enjoyable activities in order to show that a particular occasion is important
  특정한 행사가 중요하다는 것을 보여주기 위해 특별하고 즐거운 활동에 참여하다
- greedy 탐욕스러운, 욕심 많은
  → wanting a lot more food, money, etc. than you need
  필요한 것보다 더 많은 돈이나 음식 등을 원하는
- novel 소설
  → a long written story about characters and events that have been invented by the writer
  작가에 의해 지어진 등장인물과 사건에 대한 긴 이야기
- poisonous 독이 있는
  → containing poison
  독을 가지고 있는

- realize 깨닫다
  → to understand clearly
  명확하게 이해하다
- represent 나타내다
  → to express by some symbol or character
  어떤 상징이나 특징으로 표현하다
- sum 총계, 계산
  → the total of two or more numbers or quantities, determined by mathematical process
  수학적 과정에 의해 결정되는 둘 또는 그 이상의 숫자 혹은 수량의 전체
- tax 세금
  → an amount of money that you have to pay to the government so that it can pay for public services
  정부가 공공 서비스에 대한 지불을 하도록 정부에 내야 하는 돈
- wave 손을 흔들다
  → to signal in greeting, by raising the hand and moving the fingers
  손을 들고 손가락을 움직여 인사로 신호하다

01 문장의 빈칸에 공통으로 들어갈 말로 가장 알맞은 것은?

> • Did you read the _____ about the plastic island?
> • Plastic _____ s, like shampoo bottles, can be recycled, but they must be clean.

① object　　　　② result
③ poem　　　　④ article
⑤ novel

02 주어진 〈영영풀이〉를 읽고 빈칸에 알맞은 단어를 쓰시오.

> Each theme _____ the history and culture of the Joseon era.

> to express by some symbol or character

03 다음 빈칸에 들어갈 말이 바르게 짝지어진 것은?

> (A) I'm writing an article about students' favorite snacks. I'm _____ their health.
> (B) I will _____ the President in the election next year.

	(A)	(B)
①	related to	run for
②	related to	put down
③	worried about	run for
④	worried about	get back
⑤	put down	get back

04 다음 중 짝지어진 단어의 관계가 <u>다른</u> 것은?

① claim – insist
② equal – match
③ struggle – strive
④ novel – fiction
⑤ courageous – cowardly

[05~06] 다음 설명에 해당하는 단어를 고르시오.

05
> an amount of money that you have to pay to the government so that it can pay for public services

① tax　　　　② sum
③ fee　　　　④ cost
⑤ fare

06
> a long written story about characters and events that have been invented by the writer

① election　　　　② novel
③ typewriter　　　④ graph
⑤ science-fiction

07 다음 우리말에 맞게 주어진 단어를 활용하여 세 단어를 쓰시오.

> Jane은 이 반짝이는 장식품들을 하나씩 만듭니다. (one)

➡ Jane makes these shiny ornaments _____.

01 다음 빈칸에 들어갈 말을 〈보기〉에서 찾아 쓰시오. (필요하면 어형을 변화시킬 것)

┤ 보기 ├

adventure   celebrate   elect   face

(1) Chimpanzees can express its feelings through _____ expressions and sounds.

(2) In fact, Valentine's Day is _____ in most parts of the world.

(3) We just had an _____ for class presidents at school.

(4) These sports give people a chance to feel thrills from high speeds or _____.

02 다음 문장의 빈칸에 공통으로 들어갈 단어를 철자 s로 시작하여 쓰시오.

- Government is the best _____ for giving money to people who need it.
- They added different herbs and flowers to scent the _____.
- We need to find a better _____ to the conflict.

03 다음 우리말과 같은 표현이 되도록 문장의 빈칸을 채우시오.

(1) 참가자들은 단어를 듣고 그 단어를 반복했습니다.
➡ Participants listened to the words and then _____ the words back.

(2) 영화 속에서, 몇몇 계약직 노동자들은 그들의 인권을 지키려고 고군분투한다.
➡ In the movie, some contract workers _____ to preserve their human rights.

(3) 돈은 종종 사람들을 탐욕스럽고 이기적으로 만든다.
➡ Money often makes people _____ and selfish.

(4) 서로의 차이가 정말 중요하긴 하지만 서로가 같은 인간이라는 점이 더 중요하다.
➡ Our differences do _____, but our common humanity _____ more.

04 영영풀이에 해당하는 단어를 〈보기〉에서 찾아 첫 번째 빈칸에 쓰고, 두 번째 빈칸에는 우리말 뜻을 쓰시오.

┤ 보기 ├

wave   greedy   celebrate   sum

(1) _____: to take part in special enjoyable activities in order to show that a particular occasion is important: _____

(2) _____: to signal in greeting, by raising the hand and moving the fingers: _____

(3) _____: the total of two or more numbers or quantities, determined by mathematical process: _____

(4) _____: wanting a lot more food, money, etc. than you need: _____

Conversation

① 상술하기

- **Five out of twenty students chose science-fiction books.** 20명의 학생들 중 5명이 공상 과학 책을 선택했다.

- **Two out of twenty students chose history books.** 20명의 학생들 중 2명이 역사책을 선택했다.

■ 'X out of Y'는 'Y 중에 X'라는 뜻으로 전체 Y 중에 X가 차지하는 비중을 나타낼 때 쓰는 표현이며, X와 Y는 숫자를 가리킨다. 전체 중 일부가 차지하는 비율을 나타낼 때는 퍼센트(percent)를 사용하여 나타낼 수도 있다.

- **A:** What can you tell from the pie chart? (원그래프에서 무엇을 알 수 있니?)

  B: Five out of twenty students like action movies. That is twenty-five percent of total. (20명의 학생들 중 5명이 액션 영화를 좋아해. 그것의 전체의 25%야.)

핵심 Check

1. 다음 빈칸에 공통으로 알맞은 어구를 쓰시오.

> **A:** What is this graph about?
>
> **B:** I did a survey on the kinds of pets my classmates have.
>
> **A:** What were the results?
>
> **B:** Twenty _____ twenty-five students have pets. Only five _____ twenty-five students don't have pets.

2 이해 점검하기

> • **Do you see what I mean?** 내 말이 무슨 뜻인지 알겠어?

■ 'Do you see what I mean?'은 '내 말이 무슨 뜻인지 알겠어?'라는 뜻으로 상대방에게 어떤 상황에 대해 그것을 이해했는지 묻는 표현이다.

■ 같은 표현으로는 'Do you get what I mean?', 'Do you understand?', 'Do you follow me?' 등으로 바꿔서 표현할 수 있으며, 이에 대해 'Yes, I get it.', 'No, I don't understand.' 등으로 대답할 수 있다.

A: I surveyed 100 students and the results show that eighty percent of the students liked pizza and fried chicken for snacks. Do you see what I mean? (100명의 학생들을 조사했는데, 80%의 학생들이 간식으로 피자와 후라이드 치킨을 좋아한다는 결과가 나왔어. 내 말이 무슨 뜻인지 알겠어?)

B: Students really like fast food. What else did they like? (학생들이 정말 패스트푸드를 좋아하는구나. 그리고 또 뭘 좋아했는데?)

A: Twelve percent of the students chose chocolate cake as their favorite. (12%의 학생들이 초콜릿 케이크를 가장 좋아한다고 뽑았어.)

B: Wow, students should really try to eat healthier snacks! (우와, 학생들은 더 건강한 간식을 먹어야겠다!)

핵심 Check

2. 다음 우리말을 주어진 단어를 이용하여 영작하시오.

> B: My brother broke my computer. I'm so angry.
> G: Well, It takes a lot of muscles to look angry, but only a few to smile. Do you see what I mean?
> B: 응, 이해했어.(get) I guess it's not good to stay angry for a long time.
> G: That's right. Remember, it's always better to smile.

➡ _____

Conversation 교과서 대화문 익히기

Listen & Speak 1 A

B: Minju, ❶what is this graph about?

G: I did a survey on the kinds of pets ❷my classmates have.

B: What were the results?

G: ❸Eighty percent of the students have pets. ❹Only five out of twenty-five students don't have pets.

B: What kind of pets do they have?

G: Well, ten students have dogs and three students have cats.

B: ❺What about the rest?

G: Seven students have fish.

B: 민주야, 이 그래프는 무엇에 관한 거야?

G: 나는 우리 반 친구들이 가지고 있는 애완동물의 종류에 대해 설문 조사했어.

B: 결과가 어땠어?

G: 학생들의 80%가 애완동물을 가지고 있어. 25명의 학생들 중 5명만 애완동물이 없어.

B: 그들은 어떤 종류의 애완동물을 가지고 있니?

G: 음. 10명은 개, 3명은 고양이를 가지고 있어.

B: 나머지는?

G: 7명은 물고기를 가지고 있어.

❶ 'what ~ about?'은 '~는 무엇에 관한 거니?'로 해석한다.
❷ 목적격 관계대명사 'that/which'가 생략되어 있는 관계대명사절로 선행사 'pets'를 수식하는 역할을 한다.
❸ 주어가 'percent'일 때는 'of' 뒤의 명사에 동사 수를 일치시킨다. 'the students'가 복수 명사이므로 동사는 'have'를 사용한다.
❹ 'X out of Y'는 'Y 중에 X'라는 뜻으로 전체 Y 중에 X가 차지하는 비중을 나타낼 때 쓰는 표현이다.
❺ 'What about+명사?'는 '~은 어때?'라는 표현이고, 'the rest'는 '나머지'의 뜻이다. 'rest'가 '휴식'을 의미할 때는 'the'를 사용하지 않는다.

Check(√) True or False

(1) Minju surveyed on the kinds of pets her classmates have. T ☐ F ☐

(2) Only eight out of twenty-five students don't have pets. T ☐ F ☐

Listen & Speak 2 A

B: Emma, ❶can you help me with this math problem?

G: Sure, what is it?

B: You have to move one stick ❷to make this sum right. How could four minus five equal six?

G: Oh, it's simple. You need to move one of the sticks in number four to make it eleven. ❸Do you see what I mean?

B: Yes, now I see what you mean. Eleven minus five equals six. How clever!

G: ❹Thinking outside the box can be helpful sometimes.

B: Emma, 이 수학 문제 좀 도와줄래?

G: 물론이지. 뭔데?

B: 이 계산이 맞도록 너는 한 개의 막대기를 옮겨야 해. 어떻게 4빼기 5가 6이 되지?

G: 오, 이건 간단해. 너는 숫자 4를 11로 만들기 위해 막대기 하나를 옮기면 돼. 무슨 말인지 알겠니?

B: 응. 이제 네 말이 무슨 뜻인지 알겠어. 11 빼기 5는 6이지. 너 정말 똑똑하구나!

G: 틀 밖에서 생각하는 것은 때때로 도움이 될 수 있지.

❶ 'help A with B'는 'A가 B하는 것을 돕다'라는 의미이다.
❷ 부정사의 부사적 용법 중 '목적'을 나타내는 용법으로 'in order to, so as to'로 바꾸어 쓸 수 있다.
❸ 'Do you see what I mean?'은 '내 말이 무슨 뜻인지 알겠어?'라는 뜻으로 상대방에게 어떤 상황에 대해 그것을 이해했는지 묻는 표현이다. 'Do you get what I mean?', 'Do you understand?' 등으로 바꿔서 표현할 수 있다.
❹ 'Thinking'은 동명사 주어로 사용되었다. 'think outside the box'는 '새로운 사고를 하다, 틀에서 벗어나 생각하다'라는 의미이다.

Check(√) True or False

(3) They need to move a stick to make the number four into eleven. T ☐ F ☐

(4) The boy thinks Emma is very clever. T ☐ F ☐

Listen & Speak 1 B

M: Mason, how was the election?

B: It was bad. I didn't win.

M: ❶How come?

B: Yura won. Over sixty percent of the students ❷voted for her.

M: Well, ❸you tried your best and that's what matters.

B: I guess so. I have learned many things ❹ while running for class president.

M: I'm really proud of you.

B: Thanks, Dad.

❶ 왜(Why?)'의 의미를 가진다. 'How come you didn't win?'의 줄임말이다.
❷ 'vote for'는 '~에게 투표하다'의 의미이다.
❸ 'try one's best'는 '최선을 다하다'라는 의미이고, 'what matters'는 보어 자리에 사용된 명사절로 'what'은 '관계대명사'로 '~인 것'의 의미이다.
❹ 'while+-ing'는 '~하는 동안'의 의미이다.

Listen & Speak 2 B

B: Jian, ❶what's the matter? You look upset.

G: My brother broke my computer. I'm so angry.

B: ❷I'm sorry to hear that, but your facial muscles must be tired.

G: What do you mean?

B: Well, ❸it takes a lot of muscles to look angry, but ❹only a few to smile. Do you see what I mean?

G: Oh, I get it. I guess ❺it's not good to stay angry for a long time.

B: That's right. Remember, ❻it's always better to smile!

❶ 상대방이 뭔가에 불만족하거나 실망하고 있는 것을 보고 그 이유를 물을 때 사용하는 표현이다.
❷ 유감이나 동정을 표현하는 말로 '안 됐구나.'의 의미이다.
❸ 'It takes+목적어+to부정사 ~' 형태로 '~하는 데 …을 필요로 하다'라는 의미이다.
❹ '(it takes) only a few muscles to smile.'에서 중복되는 말을 생략한 형태이다.
❺ 가주어(it) ~ 진주어(to stay angry) 구문이다.
❻ 가주어(it) ~ 진주어(to smile) 구문이다.

Real Life Communication

Mina: Henry, what are you doing?

Henry: I'm writing an article about students' favorite snacks. ❶I'm worried about their health.

Mina: Why?

Henry: Well, I surveyed 100 students and the results show ❷that eighty percent of the students liked pizza and fried chicken for snacks. ❸Do you see what I mean?

Mina: Oh, ❹I get it. Students really like fast food. ❺What else did they like?

Henry: Twelve percent of the students chose chocolate cake ❻as their favorite.

Mina: Wow, students should really try to eat healthier snacks!

❶ 'be worried about ~'은 '~에 관해 걱정하다'라는 의미이다.
❷ 'that'은 동사 'show'의 목적어를 이끄는 접속사이다.
❸ 'Do you see[know] what I mean?'은 '내 말이 무슨 뜻인지 알겠어?'라는 뜻으로 상대방에게 어떤 상황에 대해 그것을 이해했는지 묻는 표현이다.
❹ '이해했다'라는 뜻으로 'I understand.'와 같은 표현이다.
❺ 'else'는 '그 밖의, 다른'의 뜻을 가진 부사로 의문대명사 뒤에 위치한다.
❻ 'as'는 '전치사로 사용되었다.

Let's Check ❶

B: These days, you don't need paper tickets ❶ to watch a movie or go to a concert. You just need to store your ticket in your cell phone. Then show the ticket on your phone's screen before you go in. ❷You don't need to go through the trouble of printing out tickets. Do you see what I mean?

❶ to부정사의 부사적 용법 중 '목적'으로 '~하기 위해'의 의미로 사용되었다.
❷ 'don't need to V'는 '~할 필요없다'라는 의미로 'don't have to', 'need not'으로 바꾸어 쓸 수 있다.

● 다음 우리말과 일치하도록 빈칸에 알맞은 말을 쓰시오.

Listen & Speak 1 A

B: Minju, what is this _____ about?

G: I did a _____ on the _____ of pets my classmates have.

B: What were the _____?

G: Eighty _____ of the students have pets. Only five _____ _____ twenty-five students don't have pets.

B: _____ _____ _____ pets do they have?

G: Well, ten students have dogs and three students have cats.

B: What about _____ _____?

G: Seven students have _____.

Listen & Speak 1 B

M: Mason, how was the _____?

B: It was _____. I didn't _____.

M: _____ _____?

B: Yura won. _____ sixty percent of the students voted for her.

M: Well, you tried _____ _____ and that's _____ _____.

B: I _____ so. I have learned many things while _____ _____ class _____.

M: I'm really _____ _____ you.

B: Thanks, Dad.

Listen & Speak 2 A

B: Emma, can you _____ me _____ this math problem?

G: Sure, what is it?

B: You _____ _____ move one stick _____ _____ this _____ right. _____ could four _____ five _____ six?

G: Oh, it's simple. You _____ _____ move one of the _____ in number four _____ _____ it eleven. Do you see _____ _____ _____?

B: Yes, now I see _____ you mean. Eleven _____ five equals six. _____ clever!

G: _____ _____ _____ _____ can be _____ sometimes.

Listen & Speak 2 B

B: Jian, what's _____ _____? You _____ _____.

G: My brother _____ my computer. I'm so angry.

B: _____ _____ _____ _____ that, but your _____ muscles must _____ _____.

G: _____ _____ _____ _____?

B: Well, it _____ a lot of _____ _____ _____ angry, but only _____ _____ to smile. Do you see _____ I mean?

G: Oh, I _____ it. I guess it's not good _____ _____ angry _____ _____ _____ _____.

B: That's right. Remember, _____ always better _____ _____!

Real Life Communication

Mina: Henry, what are you doing?

Henry: I'm writing an _____ about students' _____ _____. I'_____ _____ _____ their health.

Mina: Why?

Henry: Well, I _____ 100 students and the _____ show that _____ _____ of the students liked pizza and fried chicken for snacks. _____ _____ what I mean?

Mina: Oh, _____ _____ _____. Students really like fast food. _____ _____ did they like?

Henry: _____ of the students _____ chocolate cake as their _____.

Mina: Wow, students should really _____ _____ eat _____ snacks!

Let's Check

B: _____ _____, you don't need _____ _____ to watch a movie or go to a concert. You just need to _____ your ticket _____ your cell phone. Then _____ the ticket on your phone's _____ before you _____ _____. You _____ _____ _____ _____ the _____ of _____ out tickets. Do you see _____ _____?

B: 지안아, 무슨 문제 있니? 너 속상해 보여.

G: 내 남동생이 내 컴퓨터를 고장 냈어. 정말 화나.

B: 그렇다니 유감이지만, 너의 얼굴 근육은 피곤할 거야.

G: 무슨 뜻이니?

B: 음, 화난 표정을 지을 때는 많은 근육이 필요하지만, 웃을 때는 몇 개의 근육만 필요하거든. 무슨 말인지 알겠어?

G: 오, 이해했어. 오랫동안 화난 상태로 있으면 좋지 않겠구나.

B: 맞아. 기억해, 웃는 게 항상 더 낫다는 것을 말이야!

미나: Henry, 너 뭐 하고 있니?

Henry: 난 학생들이 가장 좋아하는 간식에 관한 기사를 쓰고 있어. 나는 그들의 건강이 걱정 돼.

미나: 왜?

Henry: 음, 난 100명의 학생들에게 설문 조사를 했고, 학생들의 80%가 간식으로 피자나 프라이드치킨을 좋아한다는 결과가 나왔어. 무슨 뜻인지 알겠니?

미나: 아, 알겠어. 학생들은 패스트푸드를 정말 좋아하지. 그들은 또 어떤 것을 좋아했니?

Henry: 학생들의 12%가 가장 좋아하는 것으로 초콜릿 케이크를 골랐어.

미나: 와우, 학생들은 더 건강한 간식을 먹도록 정말로 노력해야겠다!

B: 요즘에, 당신은 영화를 보거나 공연장에 가기 위해 종이 티켓이 필요하지 않습니다. 당신은 단지 당신의 휴대전화에 티켓을 저장하면 됩니다. 그리고 나서 입장하기 전에 휴대전화 화면 위의 티켓을 보여줍니다. 당신은 번거롭게 티켓을 출력할 필요가 없습니다. 무슨 뜻인지 아시겠어요?

01 우리말에 맞도록 주어진 단어를 이용하여 영어로 쓰시오.

> 내 말이 무슨 뜻인지 알겠어? (see / what)

➡ _____

02 다음 대화의 빈칸에 들어갈 말로 알맞지 <u>않은</u> 것은?

> A: How could five plus three equal six?
> B: Why don't you move the stick in number five to make it three? _____
> A: Do you mean the one on the top left?
> B: That's right.

① Do you get what I mean?
② Do you understand?
③ Do you get it?
④ Did you move the stick?
⑤ Do you get the point?

03 다음 대화의 빈칸에 들어갈 말로 알맞은 것은?

> M: Mason, how was the election?
> B: It was bad. I didn't win.
> M: _____
> B: Yura won. Over sixty percent of the students voted for her.
> M: Well, you tried your best and that's what matters.
> B: I guess so.

① What about you?
② How come?
③ What do you think of the result of the election?
④ Are you satisfied with the result of the election?
⑤ How do you like the election?

[01~02] 다음 대화를 읽고 물음에 답하시오.

> Mina: Henry, what are you doing?
>
> Henry: I'm writing an article about students' favorite snacks. (A)_____
>
> Mina: Why?
>
> Henry: Well, I surveyed 100 students and the results show that eighty percent of the students liked pizza and fried chicken for snacks. Do you see what I mean?
>
> Mina: Oh, I get it. Students really like fast food. What else did they like?
>
> Henry: Twelve percent of the students chose chocolate cake as their favorite.
>
> Mina: Wow, students should really try to eat healthier snacks!

01 위 대화의 빈칸 (A)에 들어갈 말로 알맞은 것을 고르시오.

① I had trouble writing the article.

② I'm happy with the result of the survey.

③ I'm worried about their health.

④ I'm not satisfied with the article.

⑤ I think most students are more worried about their health than any other thing.

02 위 대화의 내용과 일치하지 <u>않는</u> 것은?

① Henry is writing an article about students' favorite snacks.

② The results show that 80 percent of the students liked pizza and fried chicken for snacks.

③ Most students like fast food.

④ Twelve students surveyed liked chocolate cake.

⑤ We can know most students eat healthier snacks.

03 다음 두 사람의 대화가 <u>어색한</u> 것은?

① A: What is your favorite type of movie?

B: My favorite type of movie is a romance movie.

② A: We should have more tennis classes for after-school classes.

B: What makes you say that?

③ A: Do you think we can go on a picnic on Wednesday?

B: I don't think so. Wednesday will be too cold to go on a picnic.

④ A: Do you see what I mean?

B: Oh, I've seen it before.

⑤ A: What can you tell from the chart?

B: Forty percent of the students liked red.

04 다음 대화의 밑줄 친 (a)~(e) 중 어휘의 쓰임이 <u>어색한</u> 것은?

> B: Jian, what's the matter? You (a)<u>look upset</u>.
>
> G: My brother broke my computer. I'm so angry.
>
> B: I'm (b)<u>sorry</u> to hear that, but your facial muscles must be (c)<u>relaxed</u>.
>
> G: What do you mean?
>
> B: Well, it takes (d)<u>a lot of muscles</u> to look angry, but only a few to smile. Do you see what I mean?
>
> G: Oh, I get it. I guess it's not good (e)<u>to stay angry</u> for a long time.
>
> B: That's right. Remember, it's always better to smile!

① (a)   ② (b)   ③ (c)   ④ (d)   ⑤ (e)

중요
05 대화의 ①~⑤ 중 도표의 내용과 일치하지 <u>않는</u> 것은?

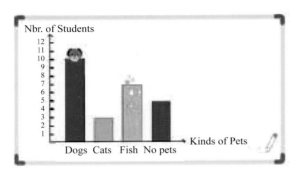

Nbr. of Students

Kinds of Pets

Dogs Cats Fish No pets

B: Minju, what is this graph about?

G: ①I did a survey on the kinds of pets my classmates have.

B: What were the results?

G: ②Eighty percent of the students don't have pets. ③Only five out of twenty-five students don't have pets.

B: What kind of pets do they have?

G: Well, ④ten students have dogs and three students have cats.

B: What about the rest?

G: ⑤Seven students have fish.

①   ②   ③   ④   ⑤

06 다음 대화의 (A)~(D)를 알맞은 순서로 배열한 것은?

(A) Look at the pie chart. Seventy percent of the students said that they wanted to learn tennis. Do you see what I mean?

(B) Oh, I see.

(C) We should have more tennis classes for after-school classes.

(D) What makes you say that?

① (A)–(C)–(B)–(D)   ② (B)–(A)–(D)–(C)

③ (C)–(B)–(A)–(D)   ④ (C)–(D)–(A)–(B)

⑤ (D)–(C)–(A)–(B)

[07~08] 다음 대화를 읽고 물음에 답하시오.

B: Emma, can you help me with this math problem?

G: Sure, what is it?

B: You have to move one stick to make this sum right. (a)<u>어떻게 4빼기 5가 6이 되지?</u>
(minus / how / four / five / six / could / equal)

G: Oh, it's simple. You need to move one of the sticks in number four (A)_____.
Do you see what I mean?

B: Yes, now I see what you mean. Eleven minus five equals six. How clever!

G: Thinking outside the box can be helpful sometimes.

중요
07 위 대화의 빈칸 (A)에 들어갈 말로 알맞은 것은?

① to equal six

② to make it eleven

③ to help me with this math problem

④ to make it five

⑤ to think outside the box

서답형

08 위 대화의 밑줄 친 우리말 (a)에 맞게 주어진 단어를 알맞은 순서로 배열하시오.

➡ _____

09 다음 글의 밑줄 친 (a)~(e) 중 어휘의 쓰임이 <u>어색한</u> 것은?

These days, you don't need (a)<u>paper tickets</u> to watch a movie or go to a concert. You just need to (b)<u>store</u> your ticket in your cell phone. Then show the ticket (c)<u>on your phone's screen</u> before you go in. You (d)<u>need to</u> go through the trouble of printing out tickets. Do you see (e)<u>what I mean</u>?

① (a)   ② (b)   ③ (c)   ④ (d)   ⑤ (e)

[01~02] 다음 대화를 읽고 물음에 답하시오.

Mina: Henry, what are you doing?

Henry: I'm writing an article about students' favorite snacks. I'm worried about their health.

Mina: Why?

Henry: Well, I surveyed 100 students and the results show that eighty percent of the students liked pizza and fried chicken for snacks. (A)_____

Mina: Oh, I get it. Students really like fast food. What else did they like?

Henry: Twelve percent of the students chose chocolate cake as their favorite.

Mina: Wow, students should really try to eat healthier snacks!

01 위 대화를 읽고 다음 질문에 대한 답을 조건에 맞게 영어로 쓰시오.

┤ 조건 ├
- 대명사 'them'을 이용할 것.
- 4 단어로 쓸 것.

Q: How many students liked pizza and fried chicken for snacks?

➡ _____

02 위 대화의 흐름상 빈칸 (A)에 들어갈 말을 〈조건〉에 맞게 영어로 쓰시오.

┤ 조건 ├
- 이해했는지 확인하는 표현을 쓸 것.
- 'see'와 'what'을 이용할 것.

➡ _____

03 다음 원 그래프에 맞게 대화의 빈칸을 완성하시오.

Favorite Type of Movie

Total number of students: 20

A: What can you tell from the pie chart?

B: Six _____ twenty students like _____. That is _____ the total. And _____ twenty students like scary movies. That is _____ of the total.

04 다음 그림을 참고하여 대화의 흐름상 의미가 통하도록 주어진 단어를 알맞은 순서대로 빈칸에 배열하시오.

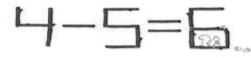

B: Emma, can you help me with this math problem?

G: Sure, what is it?

B: You have to move one stick to make this sum right. How could four minus five equal six?

G: Oh, it's simple. _____ Do you get what I mean?

B: Yes, now I see what you mean. Eleven minus five equals six. How clever!

(move / one of / eleven / the / in number / sticks / four / to make / it)

➡ You need to _____

_____.

Grammar

1 too 형용사/부사 to 동사원형

- It's **too** hard **to read** and **draw** graphs. 그래프를 읽고 그리는 것은 너무 어려워.

■ 'too 형용사/부사 to부정사'의 형태로 '너무 ~해서 …할 수 없다'로 해석하고 'so 형용사/부사 that 주어 can't.'로 바꿔 쓸 수 있다.
- The house looked **too** scary for me **to go** in. 그 집은 너무 무서워 보여서 나는 들어갈 수 없었다.
  = The house looked **so** scary **that** I **couldn't** go in.

■ to부정사의 의미상 주어는 'for+목적격'의 형태로 따로 나타내 주어야 한다.
- The bed is too heavy **for me** to lift. 그 침대는 내가 들기에 너무 무겁다.
- The problem is too difficult **for me** to solve. 그 문제는 너무 어려워서 나는 풀지 못한다.

■ 'too ~ to …' 구문에서 주어와 to부정사의 목적어가 일치하는 경우, 목적어를 쓰지 않는다.
- The soup is too hot to eat it. (✗)
  → The soup is too hot to eat. 그 수프는 먹기에 너무 뜨겁다.
cf. 'too ~ to …' 구문을 'so ~ that …' 구문으로 바꿀 경우, 생략된 목적어를 that절에 명시해야 한다.
- The laptop was **too** expensive for me **to buy**. 그 노트북은 너무 비싸서 내가 살 수가 없었다.
  → The laptop was **so** expensive **that** I couldn't buy **it**. 그 노트북은 너무 비싸서 나는 그것을 살 수 없었다.

■ '형용사/부사 enough to 부정사(= so 형/부 that 주어 can 동사원형)'는 '~할 만큼 충분히 …하다'라는 뜻을 갖는다.
- She is tall **enough to** be a volleyball player. 그녀는 배구 선수가 되기에 충분히 키가 크다.
  = She is **so** tall **that** she can be a volleyball player.
*'enough 명사 to동사원형'은 '~할 만큼 충분한 명사'로 해석한다.
ex. We don't have **enough** time **to do** that. 우리는 그것을 할 충분한 시간을 가지고 있지 않다.

핵심 Check

1. 다음 괄호 안에서 알맞은 말을 고르시오.
   (1) The weather is (to / too / so) cold (to / too / that) go for a swim.
   (2) There are (too / enough) chairs to sit on.
   (3) It is too late (to / for) him to get the operation.
   (4) I was stupid (too / enough) to believe him.

186 Lesson 8. Behind the Numbers

② No one ...

> • **No one** needs graphs in real life. 아무도 실제 생활에서는 그래프가 필요하지 않아.

- 'No one ...'은 문장의 시제가 현재인 경우 'No one + 단수동사' 형태로 쓰고 '아무도 ... 않다'라는 의미이다.
  - **No one** goes out in this hot weather. 아무도 이 더운 날씨에 나가지 않는다.
  - **No one** was outside the building when it rained. 비가 왔을 때 아무도 건물 밖에 있지 않았다.

- 'No one ...'은 none, nobody, nothing 등과 같이 문장 전체를 부정한다.
  - **No one** wears a uniform outside of school. 학교 밖에서 어느 누구도 교복을 입지 않는다.
    = **Nobody** wears a uniform outside of school.
  - **None** of us is entirely blameless in this matter. 우리들 중 이 문제에 대해 전적으로 떳떳한 사람은 아무도 없어.

  *none of 단수명사+단수 동사
  *none of 복수명사+단수/복수 동사
  - **Nothing** could weaken his resolve to continue. 그 무엇도 계속하겠다는 그의 결심을 약화시키지 못했다.

- 문장 앞에 Not이 붙는 경우는 전체 부정이 아니라 부분 부정이다.
  - **Not** every man can sing well. (부분 부정) 모든 사람이 노래를 잘할 수 있는 것은 아니다.
  - **No** man can sing well. (전체 부정) 노래를 잘할 수 있는 사람이 없습니다.

- none, nothing이 but과 함께 쓰이면(nothing but) '오직'이란 뜻이 된다.
  - **Nothing but** a miracle can save her now. 이제 오직 기적만이 그녀를 구할 수 있다.

핵심 Check

2. 다음 괄호 안에서 알맞은 단어를 고르시오.

(1) No one (is / are) cooking in the kitchen.

(2) No one (comes / come) to a party without a present.

3. 다음 문장과 같은 의미가 되도록 빈칸에 알맞은 말을 한 단어로 쓰시오.

> No one can replace you. = _____ can replace you.

01 다음 문장에서 어법상 <u>어색한</u> 부분을 바르게 고쳐 쓰시오. 어색한 부분이 없으면 '없음'으로 쓰시오.

(1) None of the teachers has pointed that out to the students.

_____ ➡ _____

(2) Not everyone believe fortunetellers.

_____ ➡ _____

(3) I'm too tired to studying.

_____ ➡ _____

(4) The bread is too dry to eat it.

_____ ➡ _____

02 괄호 안의 단어를 활용하여 빈칸에 어법상 알맞게 쓰시오.

None of my advice _____(seem) to have penetrated his thick skull.

*penetrate 관통하다

03 다음 밑줄 친 ①~⑤ 중 어법상 <u>어색한</u> 것을 고르시오.

The dishwasher is ①<u>too</u> heavy ②<u>for</u> ③<u>me</u> ④<u>to</u> lift ⑤<u>it</u>.

04 다음 문장과 같은 뜻이 되도록 괄호 안의 단어를 활용하여 다시 쓰시오.

(1) I slept too late to get up early. (so)

➡ _____

(2) He was wise enough to accept the offer. (so)

➡ _____

(3) The box was too heavy for me to lift. (so)

➡ _____

(4) The problem was so difficult that I couldn't solve it. (too)

➡ _____

(5) She was so lucky that she could be chosen for the team.

➡ _____

서답형
01 다음 문장에서 어법상 틀린 부분을 찾아 바르게 고쳐 쓰시오.

> The tea is so hot for me to drink.

_____ ➡ _____

02 다음 빈칸에 들어갈 말로 알맞은 것을 고르시오.

> The car is too expensive _____ him to buy.

① to   ② for   ③ of
④ that   ⑤ so

03 다음 문장에서 어법상 어색한 것을 고르시오.

> Fortunately, ①no one ②were in the house ③when ④the fire ⑤broke out.

① no one   ② were
③ when   ④ the fire
⑤ broke out

04 우리말에 맞게 영작할 때 빈칸에 들어갈 어휘로 알맞은 것을 고르시오.

> 공자는 "모든 것이 저만의 아름다움을 지니고 있으나 모든 이가 그것을 볼 수는 없다."고 말했다.
> → Confucius said, "Everything has its beauty but _____ everyone sees it."

① not   ② no
③ none   ④ all
⑤ some

05 우리말에 맞게 영작할 때, 빈칸에 들어갈 말로 바르게 짝지어 진 것을 고르시오.

> • 여기에서는 한 번도 무슨 일이 생기는 법이 없다.
> → ___(A)___ ever happens here.
> • 모든 사람들이 그 게들을 못마땅하게 여기지는 않습니다.
> → ___(B)___ is angry about the crabs.
> • 주변에 다른 사람은 아무도 없었다.
> → There ___(C)___ no one else around.

	(A)	(B)	(C)
①	Not everyone	None of you	were
②	No one	None of you	was
③	Nothing	None of you	were
④	Nothing	Not everyone	was
⑤	Nothing	Not everyone	were

06 다음 빈칸에 들어갈 알맞은 말을 모두 고르시오.

> None of the passengers _____ badly hurt.

① to be   ② being   ③ be
④ are   ⑤ were

07 다음 빈칸에 들어갈 말로 적절하지 않은 것을 고르시오.

> This book is too difficult for _____ to read.

① you   ② him   ③ me
④ her   ⑤ I

08 다음 중 어법상 어색한 것을 고르시오.

> ①The joke ②is ③too rude ④to repeat ⑤ it.

① The joke   ② is
③ too   ④ to repeat
⑤ it

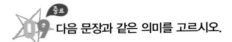 다음 문장과 같은 의미를 고르시오.

> None of the groups knew each other.

① Everyone in the groups knew each other.
② Not everyone in the groups knew each other.
③ Some in the groups knew each other, and the others in the groups didn't know each other.
④ No one in the groups knew each other.
⑤ Some in the groups knew each other, others in the groups didn't know each other, and still others were new members.

서답형
10 두 문장이 같은 뜻이 되도록 빈칸에 알맞은 말을 쓰시오.

> These shoes are too small for me to wear.
> = These shoes are _____ small _____
>   I can't wear _____.

11 다음 우리말을 옮긴 것으로 알맞은 것을 고르시오.

> 네 환상을 깨고 싶진 않지만 모든 사람들이 너처럼 정직하지는 않아.

① I hate to break your fantasy, but not everyone is as honest as you.
② I hate to break your fantasy, but no one is as honest as you.
③ I don't want to break your fantasy, but no one is as honest as you.
④ I want to break your fantasy, but not everyone is as honest as you.
⑤ I want to break your fantasy, but no one is as honest as you.

12 다음 중 어법상 어색한 것을 고르시오.

> She was ①too ②shy ③to ④asking anyone ⑤for help.

① too   ② shy   ③ to
④ asking   ⑤ for

13 다음 문장과 같은 의미를 갖는 문장을 고르시오.

> It's warm enough for us to eat outside.

① It's so warm that we can't eat outside.
② It's warm but we can't eat outside.
③ It's not warm enough to eat outside.
④ It's so cool that we can eat outside.
⑤ It's so warm that we can eat outside.

14 우리말을 참고하여 빈칸에 들어갈 어휘끼리 짝지어진 것을 고르시오.

> 전선이 소켓에 닿을 정도로 긴가요?
> → _____ the cable long _____ reach the socket?

① Is, so that
② Is, enough to
③ Are, so that
④ Are, enough to
⑤ Is, so as to

15 다음 중 어법상 <u>어색한</u> 것을 고르시오.

① We were amazed to find that no one were hurt.
② No one ever died of a broken heart.
③ No one has ever questioned her judgement.
④ No one has yet been chosen for the main role.
⑤ It soon became apparent that no one was going to come.

16 빈칸에 들어갈 적절한 말을 고르시오.

> Not everyone _____ that this new trend is good for Asian cinema.

① thought
② think
③ thinks
④ thinking
⑤ to think

17 빈칸에 들어갈 적절한 말을 고르시오.

> Make sure that no one _____ about this.

① finds out
② founds
③ founded
④ discovered
⑤ discover

18 우리말에 맞게 괄호 안의 단어를 활용하여 영작할 때,

(1) 3번째 단어를 쓰시오.
• 내 일에 신경쓰지 마. (it, none, business)
➡ _____

(2) 1번째 단어를 쓰시오.
• 모든 사람이 똑같이 생각하는 것은 아니다. (everyone, alike)
➡ _____

(3) 6번째 단어를 쓰시오.
• 눈이 너무 많이 쌓여 그는 걸을 수가 없었다. (deep, to walk)
➡ _____

19 다음 중 어법상 <u>어색한</u> 것을 <u>모두</u> 고르시오.

① Is it too much to ask for being a little quiet?
② Is it too late to cancel my order?
③ It is too late of them to put it off now.
④ It was too stormy to sail that night.
⑤ The sale prices were too good to miss them.

20 빈칸에 들어갈 알맞은 단어끼리 짝지어진 것을 고르시오.

> Death is more universal than life; __(A)__ dies but __(B)__ lives.

	(A)	(B)
①	not everyone	everyone
②	no one	not everyone
③	everyone	no one
④	no one	everyone
⑤	everyone	not everyone

01 다음 문장에서 어법상 <u>어색한</u> 것을 찾아 바르게 고쳐 다시 쓰시오.

> No one were supposed to know about it.

➡ _____

02 다음 (A) 문장을 (B)처럼 고쳤을 때 어법상 <u>어색한</u> 부분을 찾아 바르게 고치시오.

> (A) I'm too frightened to ask him now.
> (B) I'm so frightened that he can't ask me now.

➡ _____

03 주어진 철자로 시작하여 빈칸에 들어갈 알맞은 말을 순서대로 쓰시오.

> (1) Korea will be too small f_____ you to work.
>   당신에게 한국은 활동하는 데 너무 좁습니다.
> (2) N_____ one knows for sure what happened.
>   무슨 일이 있었는지 아무도 확실히 모른다.

04 다음 우리말에 맞게 괄호 안의 단어를 활용하여 영작하시오.

(1) 그 기계는 너무 위험해서 사람들이 다룰 수 없다.

➡ (so, handle) _____

_____

(2) 그 상점은 사람들이 너무 많아서 둘러볼 수 없다. (too, around, crowded)

➡ _____

05 〈보기〉에 주어진 어휘를 이용하여 영작하시오.

> ┤ 보기 ├
> • could have predicted
> • it   • final   • lately
> • outcome   • be well   • enough
> • has been   • well

(1) 어느 누구도 그 최종 결과를 예측할 수 없었을 것이다.

➡ _____

(2) 모든 사람이 그 최종 결과를 예측할 수는 없었을 것이다.

➡ _____

(3) 그녀는 최근에 외출을 할 정도로 몸이 좋아졌다.

➡ _____

(4) 그녀가 여행을 할 정도로 건강한가요?

➡ _____

06 우리말에 맞게 괄호의 단어를 활용하여 영작하시오.

(1) 그는 자동차 한 대를 충분히 들어올릴 정도로 힘이 세요. (lift, enough)

➡ _____

(2) 그 음식은 그의 공복을 채우기에 충분하지 못했다. (hunger, enough)

➡ _____

(3) 그녀는 책장 꼭대기까지 닿을 수 있을 정도로 키가 크다. (reach, so)

➡ _____
_____

07 다음 각 문장과 같은 의미가 되도록 괄호 안의 단어를 활용하여 문장을 다시 쓰시오.

(1) No one parked their car in the garage. (nobody)

(2) Not everyone parked their car in the garage. (some, others)

➡ (1) _____
(2) _____
_____

08 〈보기〉의 단어 중 하나를 제외하고 모두 활용하여 우리말에 맞게 영작하시오.

보기
문이 너무 뻑뻑해서 열리지 않는다.
(it, door, is, the, too, to, open, stiff)

➡ _____

09 빈칸에 공통으로 들어갈 2 단어를 쓰시오.

(1) 자본주의를 싫어하는 사람도 있고 PC를 싫어하는 사람도 있다. 그러나 PC를 좋아하는 사람 중에 마이크로소프트 사를 싫어하는 사람은 없다.

➡ There are people who don't like capitalism, and people who don't like PCs. But there's _____ who likes the PC who doesn't like Microsoft. (Bill Gates)

(2) 모두가 비슷한 생각을 한다는 것은, 아무도 생각하고 있지 않다는 말이다.

➡ When all think alike, _____ thinks very much. (Albert Einstein)

10 우리말을 참고하여 빈칸에 들어갈 알맞은 말을 쓰시오.

• 너무 어두워서 나는 책을 읽을 수가 없다.
➡ It is too dark for me to _____ books.

11 다음 문장을 괄호 안의 단어를 활용하여 영작할 때 빈칸을 알맞게 채우시오.

(1) 거리에는 한 사람도 보이지 않았다. (no)
➡ _____ seen on the street.

(2) 나는 케이크를 만들기에 충분한 설탕이 없다. (enough)
➡ I don't have _____ a cake.

(3) 우리는 쇼핑을 가기에 충분한 시간이 없다. (enough)
➡ There isn't _____ go shopping.

(4) 그는 너무 피곤해서 올라갈 수 없었다. (so, climb up)
➡ He was _____.

Do Graphs Matter, Pascal?

Pascal was doing his math homework in his room. He was struggling
with graphs.
<small>= He had hard time with graphs.</small>

"It's too hard to read and draw graphs. Why do I need these anyway?
<small>too ~ to V: 너무 ~해서 V할 수 없는</small>
No one needs graphs in real life." He put down his pen and picked
<small>No one ~: 아무도 ~ 않는   과거시제(put–put–put)</small>
up his favorite book, *Robin Hood*. He decided to read himself to sleep.
When he was about to open the book, he heard a voice. He looked up
<small>be about to V: 막 V하려고 하다</small>
from the book to see who was talking. He couldn't believe his eyes. It
<small>to부정사의 부사적 용법(~하기 위해서) 간접의문문(의문사+주어+동사): see의 목적어</small>
was his dog, Manny, who was talking!
"Close your eyes and repeat after me. *Cogito ergo sum*," said Manny.
"You can talk?"
"Just repeat! *Cogito ergo sum*."
Pascal closed his eyes and repeated the words. Suddenly, he heard
men shouting. When he opened his eyes, he saw soldiers on horses.
<small>지각동사+목적어+Ving: 목적어가 V하는 것을 듣다</small>
They were chasing a man with arrows in his hand. The man saw Pascal
and shouted.
"It's too dangerous for you to stand there. Come on." The man pulled
<small>to부정사의 의미상 주어</small>
Pascal onto his horse and rode into the woods.
When they arrived at a house, the man stopped and got off his horse.
"Hello, my name is Robin Hood."
"Wow! Are you the Robin Hood from the book?"
"No, I'm the Robin Hood of Sherwood Forest. Who are you and why
are you here?"
"My name is Pascal. I don't know why I'm here, but there must be a
<small>간접의문문(의문사+주어+동사): know의 목적어   ~임에 틀림없다</small>
reason. You saved me from the soldiers. Thank you so much. Is there
anything I can do for you?"

<small>
graph: 그래프, 도표
matter: 중요하다
struggle: 고군분투하다, 몸부림치다
read oneself to sleep: 읽다가 잠들다
repeat: 반복하다
shout: 소리치다
soldier: 병사, 군인
chase: 뒤쫓다, 추적하다
arrow: 화살
reason: 이유
</small>

📎 **확인문제**

● 다음 문장이 본문의 내용과 일치하면 T, 일치하지 않으면 F를 쓰시오.

1 Pascal was fond of drawing graphs. ☐

2 Pascal wasn't surprised that Manny was talking to him. ☐

3 Robin wondered why Pascal was there. ☐

"Well, can you help us get back the money that the king took from the
목적격 관계대명사(선행사는 the money)
people? He taxed them too much. He is too greedy to share with the
앞 문장의 the people 지칭
people, so they don't have enough money to buy food.
                                       to부정사의 형용사적 용법(money 수식)
I want to help them get their money back. However, there are many
          help+목적어+(to) V: 목적어가 V하도록 돕다
soldiers in the tower, so no one can get inside."
                              전체 부정(누구도 ~하지 않는)
"Hmm… I think I have a solution. But first, can you take me to the
tower? I need to count the number of soldiers."
                            the number of+복수명사: ~의 수
Robin and Pascal hid up in a tree and counted the soldiers one by one.
"There are five soldiers from midnight to six in the morning. Next,
                          from A to B: A 에서 B까지
there are three soldiers until noon, and then there are eight soldiers
until six in the evening. Lastly, there are twelve soldiers until midnight.
So, you should go inside between six in the morning and noon."
                            between A and B: A와 B 사이에
"What? I don't get it."
Pascal thought for a moment. 'Hmm… A graph might make this
                                                    추측의 조동사
easier to understand.'
to부정사의 부사적 용법(정도의 형용사 수식)
Pascal drew a graph and showed it to Robin.
"Look, the most dangerous time is between six in the evening and
midnight. Four times more soldiers work at that time than from six in
             (숫자) times (비교급) than …: …보다 (숫자) 배 더 (비교급) ~한
the morning until noon. Do you see what I mean?"
                                  = understand
"Aha! I get it now. Thank you so much, Pascal!"
"You're welcome. Now I realize the importance of graphs. No one
can say that we don't need them anymore."
명사절 접속사(say의 목적어를 이끔)
Pascal walked out of the woods. When he looked back, he saw Robin

Hood waving at him. Pascal waved back and said to himself, "It was a
지각동사+목적어+Ving: 목적어가 V하는 것을 보다   재귀대명사의 재귀적 용법
great adventure. How do I go back? Oh, I know. I should say the words
Cogito ergo sum!"

get back: 되찾다
tax: 세금을 부과하다
greedy: 탐욕스러운
enough: 충분한
solution: 해결책
count: 수를 세다
one by one: 하나씩
midnight: 자정
noon: 정오
realize: 깨닫다
look back: 뒤돌아보다
wave: (손 등을) 흔들다
adventure: 모험

 확인문제

● 다음 문장이 본문의 내용과 일치하면 T, 일치하지 않으면 F를 쓰시오.

1   Pascal counted the soldiers in order to know when to go into the tower. ☐

2   The king taxed the people too much, so people didn't have enough money. ☐

● 우리말을 참고하여 빈칸에 알맞은 말을 쓰시오.

1 Pascal _____ _____ _____ _____ in his room. He was _____ _____ graphs.

2 "It's _____ _____ _____ _____ and _____ graphs. Why do I need _____ anyway? No one _____ _____ in real life."

3 He _____ _____ his pen and _____ _____ his favorite book, *Robin Hood*.

4 He _____ _____ _____ _____ to sleep. When he _____ _____ _____ _____ the book, he heard a voice.

5 He _____ _____ _____ the book _____ _____ _____ _____ _____.

6 He couldn't believe his eyes. It was his dog, Manny, _____ _____ talking!

7 "_____ your eyes and _____ _____ me. *Cogito ergo sum*," said Manny.

8 "_____ _____ _____ _____?" "Just _____! *Cogito ergo sum*."

9 Pascal closed his eyes and _____ _____ _____. Suddenly, he _____ men _____.

10 _____ he opened his eyes, he saw soldiers _____ _____.

11 They were _____ a man _____ in his hand. The man saw Pascal and _____.

12 "_____ too dangerous _____ there. Come on."

13 The man _____ Pascal onto his horse and _____ into the woods.

14 When they _____ _____ a house, the man _____ and _____ _____ his horse.

15 "Hello, _____ _____ _____ Robin Hood."

16 "Wow! Are you _____ _____ _____ the book?"

17 "No, I'm the Robin Hood of Sherwood Forest. _____ _____ _____ and why _____ _____ here?"

18 "My name is Pascal. I don't know _____ _____ _____, but there _____ _____ a reason. You _____ me _____ the soldiers. Thank you so much. _____ _____ I can do _____ you?"

19 "Well, can you help us _____ _____ the money _____ the king _____ from the people? He _____ _____ too much.

20 He is _____ _____ _____ with the people, so they don't have _____ _____ _____ food.

21 I want to _____ _____ _____ their money _____. _____, there are many soldiers in the tower, so _____ _____ _____ _____ inside."

22 "Hmm… I think I have a solution. But first, can you _____ _____ _____ _____ _____ _____? I need to _____ _____ _____ soldiers."

23 Robin and Pascal _____ _____ in a tree and _____ the soldiers _____ _____ _____.

24 "_____ _____ five soldiers _____ midnight _____ six in the morning.

25 Next, there are _____ _____ _____ _____, and then there are _____ _____ _____ six in the evening.

26 _____, there are twelve soldiers _____ midnight. So, you should _____ _____ _____ six in the morning _____ _____."

27 "What? I _____ _____ _____."

28 Pascal thought for a moment. 'Hmm… A graph _____ _____ _____ _____ _____ _____ understand.'

29 Pascal _____ a graph and _____ _____ to Robin.

30 "Look, _____ _____ _____ _____ _____ is between six in the evening and midnight.

31 _____ _____ _____ _____ _____ work at that time _____ from six in the morning until noon. Do you see _____ _____ _____?"

32 "Aha! I _____ _____ now. Thank you _____ _____, Pascal!"

33 "You're welcome. Now I _____ _____ _____ _____ _____ _____. No one can say _____ we don't need _____ anymore."

34 Pascal _____ _____ the woods. When he _____ _____, he saw Robin Hood _____ at him.

35 Pascal _____ _____ and said to _____, "It was a great _____. How _____ _____ _____ _____ _____? Oh, I know. I _____ _____ the words *Cogito ergo sum*!"

---

19 "음, 우리가 왕이 사람들에게서 가져간 돈을 되찾는 것을 도와줄 수 있니? 그는 그들에게 세금을 너무 많이 부과했어.

20 그는 너무 탐욕스러워서 사람들과 나누지 않아. 그래서 그들은 음식을 살 충분한 돈이 없어.

21 나는 그들의 돈을 다시 찾을 수 있도록 돕고 싶어. 하지만 탑 안에 병사들이 많아서 아무도 들어갈 수 없어."

22 "흠… 제게 해결책이 있는 것 같아요. 그러나 우선 저를 탑에 데려가 주실 수 있나요? 저는 병사들의 수를 세야 해요."

23 로빈과 파스칼은 나무에 숨어서 병사들의 수를 한 명씩 세었습니다.

24 "자정부터 새벽 여섯 시까지는 다섯 명의 병사들이 있어요.

25 그다음, 정오까지는 세 명의 병사들이 있고, 오후 여섯 시까지는 여덟 명의 병사들이 있어요.

26 마지막으로, 자정까지는 열두 명의 병사들이 있어요. 그래서 당신은 새벽 여섯 시에서 정오 사이에 들어가야 해요."

27 "뭐라고? 나는 이해하지 못했어."

28 파스칼은 잠시 생각에 잠겼습니다. '흠…그래프가 이것을 이해하는 것을 쉽게 해 줄지도 몰라.'

29 파스칼은 그래프를 그려서 그것을 로빈에게 보여주었습니다.

30 "보세요, 가장 위험한 시간은 저녁 여섯 시에서 자정까지예요.

31 오전 여섯 시부터 정오까지보다 그 시간에 네 배나 더 많은 병사들이 일해요. 제 말이 무슨 뜻인지 아시겠어요?"

32 "아하! 이제 이해했어. 너무 고마워, 파스칼!"

33 "천만에요. 이제 저는 그래프의 중요성을 깨달았어요. 아무도 그래프가 더 이상 필요 없다고 말할 수 없을 거예요."

34 파스칼은 숲에서 걸어 나왔습니다. 그가 뒤돌아봤을 때, 그는 로빈 후드가 그에게 손을 흔들고 있는 것을 보았습니다.

35 파스칼은 손을 흔들어 답하고 혼잣말을 했습니다. "정말 멋진 모험이었어. 나는 어떻게 돌아가지? 오, 알겠어. 나는 코기토 에르고 숨이라는 말을 해야 해!"

● **우리말을 참고하여 본문을 영작하시오.**

1 파스칼은 그의 방에서 수학 숙제를 하고 있었습니다. 그는 그래프 문제에 고군분투하고 있었습니다.
➡ _____

2 "그래프를 읽고 그리는 것은 너무 어려워. 게다가 내가 왜 그래프가 필요하겠어? 아무도 실제 생활에서는 그래프가 필요하지 않아."
➡ _____
_____

3 그는 그의 펜을 내려놓고, 그가 가장 좋아하는 책, '로빈 후드'를 집어 들었습니다.
➡ _____

4 그는 책을 읽으며 잠들기로 했습니다. 그가 책을 펴려고 할 때, 그는 목소리를 들었습니다.
➡ _____

5 누가 말하고 있는지 보기 위해 그는 책에서 눈을 들어 올려다보았습니다.
➡ _____

6 그는 그의 눈을 믿을 수 없었습니다. 말하는 것은 바로 자신의 개, Manny였습니다!
➡ _____

7 "눈을 감고 내 말을 따라 말하세요. *코기토 에르고 숨.*" Manny가 말했습니다.
➡ _____

8 "너는 말할 수 있니?" "그냥 따라 하세요! *코기토 에르고 숨.*"
➡ _____

9 파스칼은 그의 눈을 감고 그 단어들을 따라 말했습니다. 갑자기 그는 남자들이 소리치는 것을 들었습니다.
➡ _____

10 그가 눈을 떴을 때, 그는 말을 탄 병사들을 보았습니다.
➡ _____

11 그들은 손에 화살을 든 남자를 뒤쫓고 있었습니다. 그 남자는 파스칼을 보고 소리쳤습니다.
➡ _____

12 "네가 거기 서 있는 것은 너무 위험해. 이리 와."
➡ _____

13 그 남자는 파스칼을 그의 말에 올려 태우고 숲으로 말을 몰았습니다.
➡ _____

14 그들이 한 집 앞에 이르렀을 때, 그 남자는 멈추고 말에서 내렸습니다.
➡ _____

15 "안녕, 내 이름은 로빈 후드야."
➡ _____

16 "와우! 당신이 책 속의 로빈 후드인가요?"
➡ _____

17 "아니, 나는 셔우드 숲의 로빈 후드야. 너는 누구이고 왜 여기에 있니?"
➡ _____

18 "제 이름은 파스칼이에요. 저는 제가 왜 여기 있는지 모르지만 이유가 분명 있을 거예요. 당신은 저를 병사들로부터 구해줬어요. 정말 감사드려요. 제가 당신을 위해 할 수 있는 것이 있을까요?"
➡ _____
_____

19 "음, 우리가 왕이 사람들에게서 가져간 돈을 되찾는 것을 도와줄 수 있니? 그는 그들에게 세금을 너무 많이 부과했어.

➡ _____

20 그는 너무 탐욕스러워서 사람들과 나누지 않아. 그래서 그들은 음식을 살 충분한 돈이 없어.

➡ _____

21 나는 그들의 돈을 다시 찾을 수 있도록 돕고 싶어. 하지만 탑 안에 병사들이 많아서 아무도 들어갈 수 없어."

➡ _____

22 "흠… 제게 해결책이 있는 것 같아요. 그러나 우선 저를 탑에 데려가 주실 수 있나요? 저는 병사들의 수를 세야 해요."

➡ _____

23 로빈과 파스칼은 나무에 숨어서 병사들의 수를 한 명씩 세었습니다.

➡ _____

24 "자정부터 새벽 여섯 시까지는 다섯 명의 병사들이 있어요.

➡ _____

25 그다음, 정오까지는 세 명의 병사들이 있고, 오후 여섯 시까지는 여덟 명의 병사들이 있어요.

➡ _____

26 마지막으로, 자정까지는 열두 명의 병사들이 있어요. 그래서 당신은 새벽 여섯 시에서 정오 사이에 들어가야 해요."

➡ _____

27 "뭐라고? 나는 이해하지 못했어."

28 파스칼은 잠시 생각에 잠겼습니다. '흠… 그래프가 이것을 이해하는 것을 쉽게 해 줄지도 몰라.'

➡ _____

29 파스칼은 그래프를 그려서 그것을 로빈에게 보여주었습니다.

➡ _____

30 "보세요, 가장 위험한 시간은 저녁 여섯 시에서 자정까지예요.

➡ _____

31 오전 여섯 시부터 정오까지보다 그 시간에 네 배나 더 많은 병사들이 일해요. 제 말이 무슨 뜻인지 아시겠어요?"

➡ _____

32 "아하! 이제 이해했어. 너무 고마워, 파스칼!"

➡ _____

33 "천만에요. 이제 저는 그래프의 중요성을 깨달았어요. 아무도 그래프가 더 이상 필요 없다고 말할 수 없을 거예요."

➡ _____

34 파스칼은 숲에서 걸어 나왔습니다. 그가 뒤돌아봤을 때, 그는 로빈 후드가 그에게 손을 흔들고 있는 것을 보았습니다.

➡ _____

35 파스칼은 손을 흔들어 답하고 혼잣말을 했습니다. "정말 멋진 모험이었어. 나는 어떻게 돌아가지? 오, 알겠어. 나는 코기토 에르고 숨이라는 말을 해야 해!"

➡ _____

[01~03] 다음 글을 읽고 물음에 답하시오.

Pascal was doing his math homework in his room. He was struggling with graphs.

"It's too hard to read and draw graphs. Why do I need these anyway? No one needs graphs in real life." (①) He put down his pen and picked up his favorite book, *Robin Hood*. (②) He decided to read himself to sleep. (③) He looked up from the book to see who was talking. (④) He couldn't believe his eyes. It was his dog, Manny, who was talking! (⑤)

"Close your eyes and repeat after me. *Cogito ergo sum*," said Manny.

"You can talk?"

"Just repeat! *Cogito ergo sum.*"

Pascal closed his eyes and repeated the words.

01 (①)~(⑤) 중 주어진 문장이 들어가기에 가장 적절한 곳은?

> When he was about to open the book, he heard a voice.

① ② ③ ④ ⑤

서답형
02 다음과 같이 풀이되는 말을 위 글에서 찾아 쓰시오.

> to say or write something again or more than once

➡ _____

03 다음 중 위 글을 읽고 답할 수 있는 것은?

① Why was Pascal studying math?
② How long did Pascal live with Manny?
③ Why does Pascal like *Robin Hood*?
④ What did Manny tell Pascal to do?
⑤ What does '*Cogito ergo sum*' mean?

[04~06] 다음 글을 읽고 물음에 답하시오.

"No, I'm the Robin Hood of Sherwood Forest. (A)_____"

"My name is Pascal. I don't know why I'm here, but there must be a reason. You saved me from the soldiers. Thank you so much. Is there anything I can do for you?"

"Well, can you help us get back the money that the king took from the people? He taxed them too much. He is too greedy to share with the people, so they don't have enough money to buy food. I want to help them get their money back. (B)_____, there are many soldiers in the tower, so no one can get inside."

"Hmm... I think I have a solution. But first, can you take me to the tower? I need to count the number of soldiers."

04 빈칸 (A)에 들어갈 말로 가장 적절한 것은?

① What brings you here again?
② Who are you and when did you arrive?
③ How come you came alone?
④ What can I do for you here?
⑤ Who are you and why are you here?

05 빈칸 (B)에 들어갈 말로 가장 적절한 것은?

① Therefore ② Nevertheless
③ As a result ④ However
⑤ Moreover

서답형
06 To where does Pascal want Robin to take him? Answer in English.

➡ _____

[07~09] 다음 글을 읽고 물음에 답하시오.

Suddenly, Pascal heard men shouting. When ①he opened his eyes, ②he saw soldiers on horses. They were chasing a man with arrows in his hand. The man saw ③Pascal and shouted.

"It's too dangerous for ④you to stand there. Come on." The man pulled Pascal onto ⑤his horse and rode into the woods.

When they arrived at a house, the man stopped and got off his horse.

"Hello, my name is Robin Hood."

"Wow! Are you the Robin Hood from the book?"

07 밑줄 친 ①~⑤ 중 가리키는 대상이 다른 하나는?

①   ②   ③   ④   ⑤

08 다음 중 위 글에서 찾아볼 수 있는 장면은?

① Pascal with arrows in his hand
② Pascal shouting at some men
③ Soldiers chasing Pascal on horses
④ Robin Hood running out of the woods
⑤ Robin Hood being chased by soldiers

서답형
09 What did Robin Hood do when he arrived at a house with Pascal? Answer in English.

➡ _____

_____

[10~12] 다음 글을 읽고 물음에 답하시오.

Robin and Pascal hid up in a tree and counted the soldiers one by one.

"There are five soldiers from midnight to six

in the morning. Next, there are three soldiers until noon, and then there are eight soldiers until six in the evening. Lastly, there are twelve soldiers until midnight. So, you should ①go inside between six in the morning and noon."

"What? I don't get it."

Pascal thought for a moment. 'Hmm... A graph might make this ②easier to understand.'

Pascal ③drew a graph and showed it to Robin.

"Look, ④the safest time is between six in the evening and midnight. Four times more soldiers work at that time than from six in the morning until noon. Do you see what I mean?"

"Aha! I get it now. Thank you so much, Pascal!"

"You're welcome. Now I realize the importance of graphs. No one can say that we ⑤don't need them anymore."

Pascal walked out of the woods. When he looked back, he saw Robin Hood waving at him. Pascal waved back and said to himself, "It was a great adventure. How do I go back? Oh, I know. I should say the words *Cogito ergo sum!*"

10 밑줄 친 ①~⑤ 중 글의 흐름상 어색한 것은?

①   ②   ③   ④   ⑤

11 위 글의 내용과 일치하는 것은?

① Robin understood what Pascal said at once.
② Pascal made Robin count the soldiers alone.
③ Pascal realized the importance of graphs.
④ Robin couldn't understand the graph.
⑤ Pascal couldn't figure out when to enter the tower.

서답형

12 When Pascal looked back, what did he see? Answer in English with seven words.

➡ _____

[13~15] 다음 글을 읽고 물음에 답하시오.

Pascal was doing his math homework in his room. He was struggling with graphs.

"It's too hard to read and draw graphs. Why do I need these anyway? No one needs graphs in real life." He put down his pen and picked up his favorite book, *Robin Hood*. He decided to read himself to sleep. When he was about to open the book, he heard a voice. He looked up from the book to see who was talking. He couldn't believe his eyes. It was his dog, Manny, who was talking!

"Close your eyes and repeat after me. *Cogito ergo sum*," said Manny.

"You can talk?"

"Just repeat! *Cogito ergo sum*."

Pascal closed his eyes and repeated the words.

서답형

13 What was Pascal doing in his room? Answer in English.

➡ _____

14 What did Pascal think about graphs?

① He thought they were very useful.

② He thought they were interesting.

③ He thought they made lives difficult.

④ He thought they were not necessary.

⑤ He thought they were informative.

15 Choose one that is TRUE.

① Pascal drew graphs with ease.

② Pascal had a friend named Manny.

③ Pascal heard a voice while reading.

④ Pascal did what Manny told him to do.

⑤ Pascal wasn't interested in who was talking to him.

[16~19] 다음 글을 읽고 물음에 답하시오.

Suddenly, he heard men shouting. When he opened his eyes, he saw soldiers on horses. They were chasing a man with arrows in his hand. The man saw Pascal and shouted.

"It's too dangerous for you to stand there. Come on." The man pulled Pascal onto his horse and rode into the woods.

When they arrived at a house, the man stopped and got off his horse.

"Hello, my name is Robin Hood."

"Wow! Are you the Robin Hood from the book?"

"No, I'm the Robin Hood of Sherwood Forest. Who are you and why are you here?"

"My name is Pascal. I don't know why I'm here, but there ⓐmust be a reason. You saved me from the soldiers. Thank you so much. Is there anything I can do for you?"

"Well, can you help us get back the money that the king took from the people? He taxed them too much. He is too (A)_____ to share with the people, so they don't have enough money to buy food. I want to help them get their money back. However, there are many soldiers in the tower, so no one can get inside."

16 위 글의 흐름상 빈칸 (A)에 들어갈 말로 가장 적절한 것은?

① generous   ② indifferent

③ anxious   ④ boring

⑤ greedy

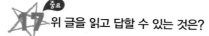 위 글을 읽고 답할 수 있는 것은?

① Why were the men chasing Robin?

② How long did it take to get to the house?

③ What made Pascal go there?

④ How many men were chasing Robin?

⑤ Why did Robin pull Pascal onto his horse?

18 밑줄 친 @와 쓰임이 같은 것은?

① His new novel is a <u>must</u> for them.

② All visitors <u>must</u> write their names.

③ You <u>must</u> read this book for yourself.

④ They <u>must</u> keep quiet in the library.

⑤ He <u>must</u> be brave to help you in that situation.

서답형
19 What does Robin want to do to help people? Answer in English.

➡ _____

[20~23] 다음 글을 읽고 물음에 답하시오.

"Hmm... I think I have a solution. But first, can you take me to the tower? I need to count the number of soldiers."

Robin and Pascal hid up in a tree and counted the soldiers one by one.

"There are five soldiers from midnight to six in the morning. Next, there are three soldiers until noon, and then there are eight soldiers until six in the evening. Lastly, there are twelve soldiers until midnight. So, you should go inside (A)_____."

"What? I don't get it."

Pascal thought for a moment. 'Hmm... A graph might make (B)this easier to understand.'

Pascal drew a graph and showed it to Robin.

"Look, the most dangerous time is between six in the evening and midnight. Four times more soldiers work at that time than from six in the morning until noon. Do you see what I mean?"

"Aha! I get it now. Thank you so much, Pascal!"

"You're welcome. Now I realize the importance of graphs. No one can say that we don't need them anymore."

Pascal walked out of the woods. When he looked back, he saw Robin Hood waving at him. Pascal waved back and said to himself, "It was a great adventure. How do I go back? Oh, I know. I should say the words *Cogito ergo sum*!"

20 위 글의 흐름상 빈칸 (A)에 들어갈 말로 가장 적절한 것은?

① anytime you want to go inside

② except six in the morning and noon

③ between noon and in the evening

④ between six in the morning and noon

⑤ between midnight and in the evening

서답형
21 밑줄 친 (B)의 의미를 우리말로 쓰시오.

➡ _____

서답형
22 What did Pascal realize? Answer in English.

➡ _____

23 Choose one that is TRUE.

① Pascal couldn't draw a graph for Robin.

② Five soldiers work after morning.

③ Pascal wasn't helpful for Robin.

④ Robin didn't know Pascal was leaving.

⑤ Pascal thought the experience adventurous.

[01~04] 다음 글을 읽고 물음에 답하시오.

Pascal was doing his math homework in his room. (A)He was struggling with graphs.

"It's too hard to read and draw graphs. Why do I need these anyway? No one needs graphs in real life." He put down his pen and picked up his favorite book, *Robin Hood*. He decided to read himself to sleep. When he was about to open the book, he heard a voice. He looked up from the book to see who was talking. He couldn't believe his eyes. It was his dog, Manny, who was talking!

"Close your eyes and repeat after me. *Cogito ergo sum*," said Manny.

"You can talk?"

"Just repeat! *Cogito ergo sum*."

Pascal closed his eyes and repeated the words.

01 주어진 어구를 활용하여 밑줄 친 (A)와 같은 의미의 문장을 쓰시오.

(have / hard time)

➡ _____

02 What did Pascal do after putting down his pen? Answer in English.

➡ _____

03 Write the reason why Pascal couldn't believe his eyes when he looked up from the book. Use the phrase 'It was because.'

➡ _____

04 When Pascal was about to open the book, what happened? Answer in English.

➡ _____
_____

[05~09] 다음 글을 읽고 물음에 답하시오.

Suddenly, Pascal heard men shouting. When he opened his eyes, he saw soldiers on horses. They were chasing a man with arrows in his hand. The man saw Pascal and shouted.

"It's too dangerous for you to stand there. Come on." The man pulled Pascal onto his horse and rode into the woods.

When they arrived at a house, the man stopped and got off his horse.

"Hello, my name is Robin Hood."

"Wow! Are you the Robin Hood from the book?"

"No, I'm the Robin Hood of Sherwood Forest. Who are you and why are you here?"

"My name is Pascal. I don't know why I'm here, but there must be a reason. You saved me from the soldiers. Thank you so much. Is there anything I can do for you?"

"Well, can you help us get back the money that the king took from the people? He taxed them too much. He is too greedy to share with the people, so they don't have enough money to buy food. I want to help them get their money back. However, there are many soldiers in the tower, so no one can get inside."

"Hmm... I think I have a solution. But first, can you take me to the tower? I need to count the number of soldiers."

05 What did Pascal see when he opened his eyes? Answer in English.

➡ _____

★06 What did Robin have in his hand? Answer in English.

➡ _____

07 Write the reason why the people don't have enough money to buy food. Use the phrase 'It was because.'

➡ _____

_____

08 다음은 위 글의 내용을 요약한 것이다. 빈칸에 알맞은 말을 쓰시오.

Robin Hood met Pascal in the middle of a chase from soldiers. He and Pascal rode into _____. After they got off at a safe place, Robin Hood explained to Pascal that the greedy king was overtaxing the people and asked Pascal to help him _____.

09 Write the reason why no one can get inside the tower. Use the phrase 'It was because.'

➡ _____

_____

[10~13] 다음 글을 읽고 물음에 답하시오.

Robin and Pascal hid up in a tree and counted the soldiers one by one.

"There are five soldiers from midnight to six in the morning. Next, there are three soldiers until noon, and then there are eight soldiers until six in the evening. Lastly, there are twelve soldiers until midnight. So, you should go inside between six in the morning and noon."

"What? I don't get it."

Pascal thought for a moment. 'Hmm... A graph might make this easier to understand.'

Pascal drew a graph and showed it to Robin.

"Look, the most dangerous time is between six in the evening and midnight. Four times more soldiers work at that time than from six in the morning until noon. Do you see what I mean?"

"Aha! I get it now. Thank you so much, Pascal!"

"You're welcome. Now I realize the importance of graphs. No one can say that we don't need them anymore."

Pascal walked out of the woods. When he looked back, he saw Robin Hood waving at him. Pascal waved back and said to himself, "It was a great adventure. How do I go back? Oh, I know. I should say the words *Cogito ergo sum*!"

10 What did Robin and Pascal do when hiding up in a tree? Answer in English.

➡ _____

11 How many soldiers are there from midnight to noon? Answer in English.

➡ _____

12 What did Pascal use to make Robin understood? Answer in English.

➡ _____

13 What did Pascal see when he looked back? Answer in English.

➡ _____

Communication Task

I did a survey on the books we want for our school library.
<small>'the books'를 선행사로 하는 목적격 관계대명사 that/which가 생략되어 있다.</small>

The result says that thirteen out of twenty students chose novels.
<small>'say'의 목적어를 이끄는 접속사   ~ 중에서</small>

That is sixty-five percent of the total. Five out of twenty students chose

science-fiction books. However, only two out of twenty students chose history

books. From this survey result, I think the school library should get more
<small>동사 'think'의 목적어를 이끄는 접속사 'that'이 생략되어 있다.</small>

novels. Do you see what I mean?

구문해설 • **survey**: 조사 • **result**: 결과 • **choose**: 선택하다 • **total**: 총계

해석

나는 우리 학교 도서관에 필요한 책들을 조사했다. 그 결과 20명 중 13명이 소설을 선택하였다. 이는 전체의 65퍼센트이다. 20명 중 5명은 공상 과학 책을 선택했다. 그러나 20명 중 2명만이 역사책을 선택했다. 이러한 조사 결과를 통해 학교 도서관은 더 많은 소설을 구해야 한다고 생각한다. 무슨 뜻인지 알겠니?

Before You Read B Look and Write

Book Club: Your Reviews

Title: *Robin Hood*

Topic of the book: It's about a man who struggles to help people from the
<small>선행사 주격 관계대명사   to부정사의 부사적 용법</small>

greedy king.

My favorite character: My favorite character is Robin Hood because he shoots
<small>이유를 나타내는 접속사 (절과 절을 연결)</small>

arrows better than soldiers.

My opinion of the book: It's bad to tax too much.
<small>명사적 용법</small>

After all, not money but people matter the most.
<small>not A but B A가 아니라 B   주어가 people이므로 복수 동사</small>

구문해설 • **struggle**: 분투하다, 투쟁하다 • **greedy**: 욕심 많은 • **tax**: 세금 • **after all**: 결국 • **matter**: 중요하다

책 동아리: 너의 후기들
제목: 로빈 후드
책의 주제: 욕심 많은 왕으로부터 사람을 구하려 고군분투하는 한 남자의 이야기이다.
내가 가장 좋아하는 등장인물: 병사들보다 화살을 더 잘 쏘기 때문에 내가 가장 좋아하는 등장인물은 로빈 후드이다.
책에 대한 나의 논평: 세금을 너무 많이 부과하는 것은 나쁘다. 결국, 돈이 아니라 사람이 가장 중요하다.

Let's Write

Look at the survey result on "Who is your favorite character?" Fifteen out of thirty
<small>~에 관한   out of: ~ 중에서</small>

students chose Hong Gildong. In other words, fifty percent of the students chose
<small>다시 말해서</small>

the character. I think it's because the character is courageous. Next, nine students
<small>it's because+이유</small>

chose Kongiwi and six students chose Robin Hood. No one chose Nolbu. Maybe

it's because the character is too greedy to be liked by others.
<small>too ~ to V: 너무 ~해서 V할 수 없는</small>

구문해설 • **survey**: 설문조사 • **result**: 결과 • **courageous**: 용기 있는

'당신이 가장 좋아하는 등장인물은 누구입니까?'라는 설문 조사 결과를 보자. 30명의 학생들 중 15명이 홍길동을 선택했다. 다시 말하면, 학생들 중 50퍼센트가 그 등장인물을 선택했다. 내 생각에 그것은 그 등장인물이 용감하기 때문이다. 그다음에 9명의 학생들이 콩쥐를 선택했고, 6명의 학생들이 로빈 후드를 선택했다. 아무도 놀부를 선택하지 않았다. 아마도 그것은 그 등장인물이 다른 사람들이 좋아하기에 너무 탐욕스럽기 때문일 것이다

Words & Expressions

01 다음 주어진 두 단어의 관계가 같도록 빈칸에 알맞은 단어를 쓰시오.

> represent – express : fiction – _____

02 다음 문장의 빈칸 (A)와 (B)에 들어갈 어휘가 바르게 짝지어진 것은?

> • Nobel Prizes are (A)_____ the highest form of recognition in the world.
> • I was just (B)_____ ask you the same thing.

① worried about – about to
② worried about – due to
③ looked up – going to
④ regarded as – about to
⑤ regarded as – related to

[03~04] 다음 영영풀이에 해당하는 것을 고르시오.

03

> a piece of body tissue that helps you to move a particular part of the body

① picnic   ② muscle
③ result   ④ limb
⑤ cell

04

> a thin stick with a sharp point at one end, which is shot from a bow

① survey   ② shout
③ tax   ④ solution
⑤ arrow

05 문장의 흐름에 맞게 빈칸을 두 단어로 채우시오.

> Some people try to get on the subway before others _____.

06 다음 밑줄 친 부분의 뜻이 잘못된 것은?

① The child chased after the bird. (뒤쫓았다)
② Believe it or not, many people claim to have seen a UFO. (주장하다)
③ Can you count the eggs in the basket? (수를 세다)
④ These salty foods have become an indispensable part of our lives! (소금)
⑤ I realized how hard the work was. (깨달았다)

Conversation

07 다음 대화의 빈칸 (A)에 들어갈 말로 알맞은 것은?

> M: Mason, how was the election?
> B: It was bad. I didn't win.
> M: How come?
> B: Yura won. Over sixty percent of the students voted for her.
> M: Well, you tried your best and that's what matters.
> B: I guess so. I have learned many things (A)_____.
> M: I'm really proud of you.
> B: Thanks, Dad.

① while running with her
② while running the election
③ while running for class president
④ while running a race
⑤ while running for class

08

다음 그림에 맞게 대화의 빈칸에 문제의 해결 방법으로 알맞은 말을 고르시오.

Move one stick to make this sum right.

A: How could six plus two equal eleven?
B: Why don't you move the stick in number six to make it nine? Do you see what I mean?
A: _____
B: That's right.

① Do you mean the one on the bottom left?
② Do you mean the one on the top right?
③ Do you mean the one on the bottom right?
④ Do you mean the one on the top left?
⑤ Do you mean the one on the middle?

[09~10] 다음 대화를 읽고 물음에 답하시오.

Mina: Henry, what are you doing?
Henry: I'm writing an article about students' favorite snacks. (①) I'm worried about their health. (②)
Mina: Why?
Henry: Well, I surveyed 100 students and the results show that sixty percent of the students liked pizza and twenty percent of the students liked fried chicken for snacks. In other words, most students liked fried chicken more than any other snack. (③)
Mina: Oh, I get it. Students really like fast food. What else did they like? (④)
Henry: Twelve percent of the students chose chocolate cake as their favorite. (⑤)
Mina: Wow, students should really try to eat healthier snacks!

09

위 대화에서 다음 도표와 다른 문장을 찾아 바르게 고치시오. (문장 전체를 바르게 고쳐 쓰시오.)

Favorite Snacks

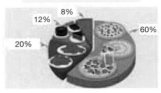

➡ _____

10

위 대화의 (①)~(⑤) 중 주어진 문장이 들어갈 위치로 알맞은 것은?

Do you see what I mean?

①   ②   ③   ④   ⑤

11

다음 대화를 읽고 답할 수 없는 질문은?

B: Jian, what's the matter? You look upset.
G: My brother broke my computer. I'm so angry.
B: I'm sorry to hear that, but your facial muscles must be tired.
G: What do you mean?
B: Well, it takes a lot of muscles to look angry, but only a few to smile. Do you see what I mean?
G: Oh, I get it. I guess it's not good to stay angry for a long time.
B: That's right. Remember, it's always better to smile!

① What made Jian angry?
② How did the boy feel about Jian's matter?
③ Why does it take only a few facial muscles to smile?
④ Does Jian see what the boy means?
⑤ Why is it always better to smile?

12 우리말에 맞게 주어진 단어를 활용하여 영작하시오.

(1) 난 혼자 가기 너무 무서워. (scared, too, on my own)

➡ _____

(2) 난 바빠서 숨 돌릴 틈도 없다. (to, take a rest)

➡ _____

(3) 그는 너무 정직해서 거짓말을 못한다. (so, honest, tell)

➡ _____

(4) 승객과 승무원은 아무도 다치지 않았다. (none, injured)

➡ _____

13 각 문장과 같은 의미의 문장을 쓰시오.

(1) They were brave enough to face the strong enemy.

➡ _____
_____

(2) He is clever enough to solve the riddle.

➡ _____

14 다음 중 어법상 올바른 문장을 고르시오.

① No one are wearing a uniform.
② No one swims in the sea.
③ No one were happy with the news.
④ No one carry a bag with them.
⑤ No one correct him when he is wrong.

15 다음 문장을 바꿔 쓸 때 어색한 것을 고르시오.

① It was warm enough for her children to play outside.
　→ It was so warm that her children could play outside.
② I was too hungry to walk.
　→ I was so hungry that I couldn't walk.
③ She is rich enough to help the poor.
　→ She is so rich that she can help the poor.
④ The toy was so expensive that I couldn't buy it.
　→ The toy was expensive enough for me to buy.
⑤ He behaved so kindly that I thanked him.
　→ He behaved kindly enough for me to thank.

16 어법상 어색한 것을 바르게 고쳐 문장을 다시 쓰시오.

> This chance is too good to miss it.

➡ _____

17 다음 중 문장 전환이 어색한 것을 고르시오.

① Minji is so short that she can't get on the ride.
　→ Minji is too short to get on the ride.
② The cat is so old that she can't climb up the tree.
　→ The cat is too old to climb up the tree.
③ The dog is too big to get inside the box.
　→ The dog is so big that he can get inside the box.
④ Jake is too weak to lift the boxes.
　→ Jake is so weak that he can't lift the boxes.
⑤ The problem was too difficult for me to write.
　→ The problem was so difficult that I couldn't solve it.

Reading

[18~20] 다음 글을 읽고 물음에 답하시오.

Pascal was doing his math homework in his room. He was struggling (A)_____ graphs.

"It's too hard to read and draw graphs. (①) Why do I need these anyway? No one needs graphs in real life." (②) He put down his pen and picked up his favorite book, *Robin Hood*. (③) He decided to read himself to sleep. When he was about to open the book, he heard a voice. (④) He couldn't believe his eyes. (⑤) It was his dog, Manny, who was talking!

"Close your eyes and repeat after me. *Cogito ergo sum*," said Manny.

"You can talk?"

"Just repeat! *Cogito ergo sum*."

Pascal closed his eyes and repeated the words.

18 빈칸 (A)에 들어갈 말과 같은 말이 들어가는 것은?

① You may refer _____ your notes.
② Her job is mainly concerned _____ sales.
③ The book is well organized in terms _____ plot.
④ Drought may result _____ the shortened snow season.
⑤ Their goal is to bring _____ peace in people.

19 (①)~(⑤) 중 주어진 문장이 들어가기에 가장 적절한 곳은?

He looked up from the book to see who was talking.

①   ②   ③   ④   ⑤

20 Choose one that is not TRUE.

① Pascal had difficult time studying graphs.
② Pascal thought graphs were not needed in real life.
③ Pascal's favorite book was *Robin Hood*.
④ Pascal was surprised to see his dog talking to him.
⑤ Pascal repeated what Manny said with his eyes open.

[21~23] 다음 글을 읽고 물음에 답하시오.

When they arrived at a house, the man stopped and ①got off his horse.

"Hello, my name is Robin Hood."

"Wow! Are you the Robin Hood from the book?"

"No, I'm the Robin Hood of Sherwood Forest. Who are you and why are you here?"

"My name is Pascal. I don't know why I'm here, but there must be a reason. You ②saved me from the soldiers. Thank you so much. Is there anything I can do for you?"

"Well, can you help us ③get back the money that the king took from the people? He taxed them too much. He is too ④greedy to share with the people, so they don't have enough money (A)to buy food. I want to help them get their money back. However, there are many soldiers in the tower, so no one can get inside."

"Hmm... I think I have a solution. But first, can you take me to the tower? I need to count ⑤a number of soldiers."

21 밑줄 친 ①~⑤ 중 글의 흐름상 어색한 것은?

①   ②   ③   ④   ⑤

22 밑줄 친 (A)와 쓰임이 같은 것은?

① It was nice to talk with her.
② Is there any chance to meet him?
③ They kept running to escape.
④ He ordered me to get some water.
⑤ She must be upset to hear the news.

23 What did Robin ask Pascal? Answer in English and use the word 'if.'

➡ _____

_____

24 위 글의 제목으로 가장 적절한 것은?

① Seven: World's Common Lucky Number
② Various Meanings That Numbers Have in the World
③ The Meanings of Different Numbers in Different Cultures
④ What Makes People in the World Think Number Has Meanings?
⑤ The Meanings of Certain Numbers in Korea

25 밑줄 친 (A)가 의미하는 것을 위 글에서 찾아 쓰시오.

➡ _____

26 Choose one that is TRUE.

① The number 7 is considered a lucky number all around the world.
② There exists a day for ghosts in China.
③ People in Western don't like the number 13 including Italian.
④ St. Anthony prayed for lost things or people.
⑤ Chinese see the number 4 as a lucky number.

[24~26] 다음 글을 읽고 물음에 답하시오.

What kinds of numbers are thought to be lucky or unlucky? Do you think it is similar around the world?

Usually, the number 7 is a lucky number in countries like England, the USA, and France. However, a lucky number in one country can be unlucky in another. Chinese people think 7 is unlucky because July or "the seventh month" is often thought of as a month for ghosts.

Many people in Western countries don't like the number 13. There are even scary movies about Friday the 13th. However, in Italy, the number is related to a good person, St. Anthony. He prayed for lost things or people. Now, people celebrate the day he died, June 13th.

How about the number 4? In Germany, the number is regarded as lucky because it matches the number of leaves on a four-leaf clover. However, in China, the sound of the word for the number 4 is similar to (A)that of the Chinese word for death.

출제율 90%

01 다음 짝지어진 단어의 관계가 같도록 빈칸에 알맞은 말을 쓰시오.

> greedy – generous : midday – _____

출제율 90%

02 다음 영영풀이에 해당하는 단어는?

> a piece of writing appearing in a newspaper

① suggestion　② lesson
③ novel　④ article
⑤ cartoon

[03~04] 다음 대화를 읽고 물음에 답하시오.

B: Emma, can you help me with this math problem?
G: Sure, what is it?
B: You have to (a)move one stick to make this sum (b)right. How could four minus five equal six?
G: Oh, it's simple. You need to move one of the sticks in number (c)five to make it eleven. Do you see what I mean?
B: Yes, now I see what you mean. Eleven minus five (d)equals six. How clever!
G: Thinking outside the box can be (e)helpful sometimes.

출제율 100%

03 위 그림을 참고하여 대화의 밑줄 친 (a)~(e) 중, 어휘의 쓰임이 어색한 것은?

① (a)　② (b)　③ (c)　④ (d)　⑤ (e)

출제율 100%

04 위 대화의 내용과 일치하지 않는 것은?

① The boy asks Emma to help him with the math problem.
② To make this sum right, Emma has to move one stick.
③ Emma thinks the solution of this math problem is simple.
④ The boy thinks Emma is very clever.
⑤ The boy doesn't understand what Emma means.

출제율 95%

05 다음 대화의 밑줄 친 (a)~(e) 중, 어법상 어색한 것은?

> B: Minju, (a)what is this graph about?
> G: I did a survey on the kinds of (b)pets my classmates have.
> B: What were the results?
> G: Eighty percent of the students (c)have pets. Only five out of twenty-five students (d)doesn't have pets.
> B: What kind of pets do they have?
> G: Well, ten students have dogs and three students have cats.
> B: (e)What about the rest?
> G: Seven students have fish.

① (a)　② (b)　③ (c)　④ (d)　⑤ (e)

[06~07] 다음 대화를 읽고 물음에 답하시오.

M: Mason, how was the election?
B: It was bad. I didn't win.
M: (A)How come?
B: Yura won. Over sixty percent of the students voted for her.
M: Well, you tried your best and that's what matters.

B: I guess so. I have learned many things while running for class president.

M: I'm really proud of you.

B: Thanks, Dad.

출제율 90%

06 대화의 밑줄 친 (A)를 완전한 문장으로 쓰시오.

➡ _____

출제율 95%

07 위 대화에서 다음 〈영영풀이〉가 설명하는 단어를 찾아 쓰시오.

> to compete as a candidate in an election

➡ _____

[08~09] 다음 대화를 읽고 물음에 답하시오.

Mina: Henry, what are you doing?

Henry: I'm writing an article about students' favorite snacks. I'm worried about their health.

Mina: Why?

Henry: Well, I surveyed 100 students and the results show that eighty percent of the students liked pizza and fried chicken for snacks. (A)Do you see what I mean?

Mina: Oh, I get it. Students really like fast food. What else did they like?

Henry: Twelve percent of the students chose chocolate cake as their favorite.

Mina: Wow, students should really try to eat healthier snacks!

출제율 100%

08 위 대화를 읽고 답할 수 <u>없는</u> 질문은?

① What are they talking about?

② How many students did Henry survey?

③ According to the survey, do the students often eat healthy snacks?

④ What percent of the students chose chocolate cake?

⑤ How many kinds of snacks can the students eat in this survey?

출제율 90%

09 위 대화의 밑줄 친 (A)와 같은 의미를 가진 문장이 되도록 get 을 활용하여 영작하시오.

➡ _____

출제율 95%

10 다음 대화의 (A)와 (B)의 우리말에 맞게 주어진 단어를 이용하여 영작하시오.

B: Jian, what's the matter? You look upset.

G: My brother broke my computer. I'm so angry.

B: I'm sorry to hear that, but your facial muscles must be tired.

G: What do you mean?

B: Well, (A)화난 표정을 지을 때는 많은 근육이 필요해(take, a lot of, look), but only a few to smile. Do you see what I mean?

G: Oh, I get it. I guess (B)오랫동안 화난 상태로 있으면 좋지 않아(it, stay, for).

B: That's right. Remember, it's always better to smile!

➡ (A) _____

(B) _____

11 다음 도표를 보고 '~ percent of ...' 표현을 사용하여 아래 질문에 2가지 사실을 상술하는 답을 쓰시오.

Favorite Color

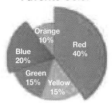

Q: What can you tell from the chart?

➡ (1) _____

(2) _____

12 빈칸에 공통으로 들어갈 두 단어를 쓰시오.

- _____ likes the same cars, clothes, or music. (모두가 같은 자동차, 옷, 음악을 좋아하는 것은 아니다.)
- _____ agrees with the use of CCTV in schools. (모든 사람이 학교에서의 CCTV 사용에 대해 찬성하는 것은 아니다.)
- _____ can afford to own their own apartment or house. (모든 사람이 자신의 아파트나 집을 장만할 수 있는 건 아니다.)

13 괄호 안에 주어진 어휘를 이용하여 다음 문장과 같은 의미를 지닌 문장을 쓰시오.

(1) Nobody was at home. (no)
➡ _____

(2) Nobody has told me about the new rules. (no)
➡ _____

(3) Some are able to join these active groups. Others aren't. (everyone)
➡ _____

(4) Some people seem to be happy. Others don't. (everyone)
➡ _____

14 다음 문장을 too를 이용하여 바꿔 쓰시오.

(1) He was so young that he can't understand it.
➡ _____

(2) Alex was so shy that he couldn't talk to her.
➡ _____

(3) The manual was so complicated that he couldn't understand it.
➡ _____
_____

[15~19] 다음 글을 읽고 물음에 답하시오.

Robin and Pascal hid up in a tree and counted the soldiers one by one.

"There are five soldiers from midnight to six in the morning. Next, there are three soldiers until noon, and then there are eight soldiers until six in the evening. Lastly, there are twelve soldiers until midnight. So, you should go inside between six in the morning and noon."

"What? (A)I don't get it."

Pascal thought for a moment. 'Hmm... A graph might make this easier to understand.'

Pascal drew a graph and showed it to Robin.

"Look, the most dangerous time is between six in the evening and midnight. Four times more soldiers work at that time than from six in the morning until noon. Do you see what I mean?"

"Aha! I get it now. Thank you so much, Pascal!"

"You're welcome. Now I realize the importance of graphs. No one can say that we don't need them anymore."

Pascal walked out of the woods. When he looked back, he saw Robin Hood ⓐ_____ at him. Pascal ⓑ_____ back and said to himself, "It was a great adventure. How do I go back? Oh, I know. I should say the words *Cogito ergo sum*!"

출제율 90%

15 빈칸 ⓐ와 ⓑ에 동사 wave를 어법에 맞게 각각 쓰시오.

➡ ⓐ _____, ⓑ _____

출제율 100%

16 밑줄 친 (A)를 대신하여 쓸 수 있는 것은?

① I don't know what to do.
② I don't understand what you say.
③ I can't believe what you said.
④ I want more information from you.
⑤ I don't make you understood.

출제율 90%

17 How many soldiers work from six in the evening to midnight? Answer in English.

➡ _____
_____

출제율 95%

18 When Pascal drew a graph and showed it to Robin, what happened?

① He needed more information.
② He drew it as Pascal did.
③ He kept asking about it.
④ He thought it was not helpful.
⑤ He understood it right away.

출제율 100%

19 위 글을 읽고 답할 수 있는 것은?

① Why did Robin want to go inside?
② How many soldiers are there inside?
③ What does *Cogito ergo sum* mean?
④ Why did they count the soldiers?
⑤ How many hours did a soldier work a day?

[20~22] 다음 글을 읽고 물음에 답하시오.

Look at the survey result on "Who is your favorite character?" Fifteen out of thirty students chose Hong Gildong. (A)_____, fifty percent of the students chose the character. I think it's because the character is courageous. Next nine students chose Kongiwi and six students chose Robin Hood. No one chose Nolbu. Maybe it's because the character is too greedy to be liked by others.

출제율 95%

20 빈칸 (A)에 들어갈 말로 가장 적절한 것은?

① For instance
② In other words
③ Nevertheless
④ On the other hand
⑤ However

출제율 90%

21 How many characters were there for students to choose? Answer in English.

➡ _____

출제율 100%

22 Choose one that is NOT true.

① Thirty students took part in the survey.
② Half of the students chose Hong Gildong as their favorite character.
③ Six students chose Robin Hood.
④ Kongiwi was chosen by thirty percent of students.
⑤ Nolbu was chosen due to his greediness.

01 다음 대화의 밑줄 친 부분에서 잘못된 것을 바르게 고쳐 쓰시오.

Mina: Henry, what are you doing?

Henry: I'm writing an article about students' favorite snacks. (A)I'm worry about their health.

Mina: Why?

Henry: Well, I surveyed 100 students and the results show that eighty percent of the students liked pizza and fried chicken for snacks. (B) Do you see that I mean?

Mina: Oh, I get it. Students really like fast food. What else did they like?

Henry: Twelve percent of the students chose chocolate cake as their favorite.

Mina: Wow, students should really try to eat healthier snacks!

➡ (A) _____

(B) _____

02 다음 우리말에 맞게 괄호 안에 주어진 어휘를 활용하여 빈칸을 채우시오.

(1) 너의 옷은 나에게 맞을 만큼 충분히 크다. (big, fit)

➡ Your clothes are _____ .

(2) 그들은 골고루 돌아갈 만큼 충분한 음식이 있다. (go)

➡ They have _____ around.

(3) 나에게 음료수를 사 줄 만큼 충분한 돈을 갖고 있니? (buy, a drink)

➡ Have you got _____
_____ ?

03 다음 도표를 보고 대화의 빈칸을 완성하시오.

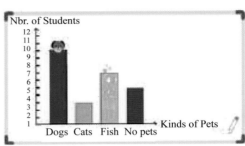

B: Minju, what is this graph (1)_____?

G: I did a survey on the kinds of (2)_____ my classmates have.

B: What were the results?

G: Eighty percent of the students have pets. Only (3)_____ twenty-five students don't have pets.

B: What kind of pets do they have?

G: Well, (4)_____ have dogs and three students have cats.

B: What about the rest?

G: Seven students have (5)_____ .

04 우리말에 맞게 주어진 단어를 활용하여 알맞게 영작하시오.

(1) Covid-19에도 불구하고 모든 사람이 마스크를 쓰는 것은 아닙니다. (despite, everyone)

➡ _____

(2) 이번 장마철에는 폭우로 인해 거리를 걷는 사람이 없었습니다. (no, rainy season, due to)

➡ _____
_____

(3) 대유행(pandemic)이 너무 심해서 Berlin으로 여행할 수 없습니다. (severe)

[1] so, that 활용 ➡ _____
_____

[2] too, to 활용 ➡ _____
_____

Robin and Pascal hid up in a tree and counted the soldiers one by one.

"There are five soldiers from midnight to six in the morning. Next, there are three soldiers until noon, and then there are eight soldiers until six in the evening. Lastly, there are twelve soldiers until midnight. So, you should go inside between six in the morning and noon."

"What? I don't get it."

Pascal thought for a moment. 'Hmm... A graph might make this easier to understand.' Pascal drew a graph and showed it to Robin.

"Look, the most dangerous time is between six in the evening and midnight. Four times more soldiers work at that time than from six in the morning until noon. Do you see what I mean?"

"Aha! I get it now. Thank you so much, Pascal!"

"You're welcome. Now I realize the importance of graphs. No one can say that we don't need them anymore."

Pascal walked out of the woods. When he looked back, (A)_____. Pascal waved back and said to himself, "It was a great adventure. How do I go back? Oh, I know. I should say the words *Cogito ergo sum*!"

05 주어진 단어를 바르게 배열하여 빈칸 (A)에 들어갈 말을 쓰시오. 필요하다면 어형을 바꾸시오.

(he / him / Robin Hood / see / wave / at)

➡ _____

06 According to Pascal, when was the most dangerous time? Answer in English.

➡ _____

07 How many times more soldiers worked during the most dangerous time compared to six in the morning until noon? Answer in English with a full sentence.

➡ _____

_____

08 Why did Pascal draw a graph? Answer by using the words below.

(a graph / to / make / easier / for / to / understand)

➡ _____

_____

[09~10] 다음 글을 읽고 물음에 답하시오.

Look at the survey result on "Who is your favorite character?" Fifteen out of thirty students chose Hong Gildong. In other words, fifty percent of the students chose the character. I think it's because the character is courageous. Next nine students chose Kongiwi and six students chose Robin Hood. No one chose Nolbu. Maybe it's because (A)the character is too greedy to be liked by others.

09 주어진 단어를 사용하여 밑줄 친 문장 (A)와 같은 의미의 문장을 쓰시오.

(so / that)

➡ _____

_____

10 What percent of students chose Robin Hood? Answer in English.

➡ _____

01 주어진 도표를 보고 'X out of Y'와 '~ percent of ...'를 이용하여 빈칸을 완성하시오.

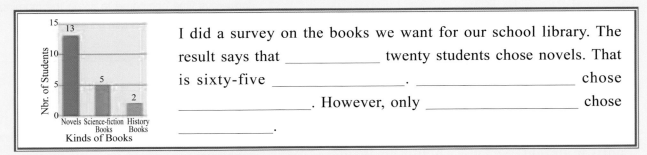

I did a survey on the books we want for our school library. The result says that ＿＿＿＿＿ twenty students chose novels. That is sixty-five ＿＿＿＿＿＿＿. ＿＿＿＿＿＿＿＿ chose ＿＿＿＿＿＿＿. However, only ＿＿＿＿＿＿＿ chose ＿＿＿＿＿.

02 다음 그래프를 참고하여 각 문항에 알맞은 퍼센트(%)를 계산한 후 가능한 문장을 쓰시오.

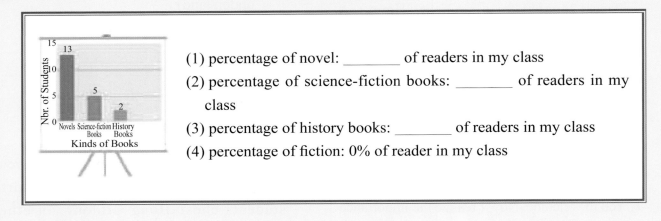

(1) percentage of novel: ＿＿＿＿ of readers in my class

(2) percentage of science-fiction books: ＿＿＿＿ of readers in my class

(3) percentage of history books: ＿＿＿＿ of readers in my class

(4) percentage of fiction: 0% of reader in my class

03 다음 그래프를 보고 그래프를 설명하는 글을 완성하시오.

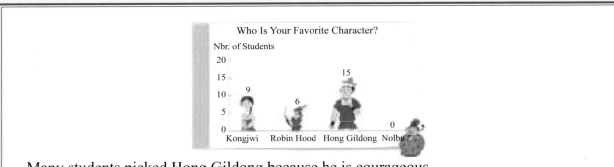

Many students picked Hong Gildong because he is courageous.
No one picked Nolbu. I think it's because he is too greedy.

Look at the survey result on "Who is your favorite character?" ＿＿＿＿ out of thirty students chose ＿＿＿＿. In other words, ＿＿＿＿ percent of the students chose the character. I think it's because the character is ＿＿＿＿. Next, ＿＿＿＿ students chose ＿＿＿＿ and ＿＿＿＿ students chose ＿＿＿＿. No one chose ＿＿＿＿. Maybe it's because the character is ＿＿＿＿ liked by others.

단원별 모의고사

01 다음 단어에 대한 영어 설명이 <u>어색한</u> 것은?

① realize: to understand or become aware of a particular fact or situation

② midnight: 12 o'clock at night

③ solution: a way of solving a problem or dealing with a difficult situation

④ count: to calculate the total number of people, things, etc.

⑤ greedy: having a lot of money or valuable possessions

02 다음 짝지어진 단어의 관계가 같도록 빈칸에 알맞은 말을 쓰시오.

> lucky – unlucky : firstly – _____

03 다음 중 짝지어진 대화가 <u>어색한</u> 것은?

① A: Do you see what I mean?
   B: No, I don't understand.

② A: Can you help me with this math problem?
   B: Sure, what is it?

③ A: What's the matter? You look upset.
   B: I'm sorry to hear that.

④ A: What kind of pets do they have?
   B: Well, ten students have dogs and three students have cats.

⑤ A: We should have more tennis classes for after-school classes.
   B: What makes you say that?

04 다음 영영풀이에 해당하는 어구를 고르시오.

> used to introduce an explanation that is simpler than the one given earlier

① therefore   ② moreover

③ in the end   ④ in other words

⑤ however

05 다음 대화의 밑줄 친 (a)~(e)에 대한 설명 중 <u>잘못된</u> 것은?

> Mina: Henry, what are you doing?
>
> Henry: I'm writing an article about students' favorite snacks. (a)I'm worried about their health.
>
> Mina: (b)Why?
>
> Henry: Well, I surveyed 100 students and the results show that (c)eighty percent of the students liked pizza and fried chicken for snacks. (d)Do you see what I mean?
>
> Mina: Oh, I get it. Students really like fast food. What else did they like?
>
> Henry: (e)Twelve percent of the students chose chocolate cake as their favorite.
>
> Mina: Wow, students should really try to eat healthier snacks!

① (a): 그들의 건강에 대해 걱정한다는 의미이다.

② (b): 'How come?'이나 'What makes you say that?'으로 바꾸어 쓸 수 있다.

③ (c): 'eighty out of one hundred students'로 바꾸어 쓸 수 있다.

④ (d): '내 말이 무슨 뜻인지 알겠어?'라는 뜻으로 'What do you mean?'으로 바꾸어 쓸 수 있다.

⑤ (e): 그 학생들 중 12퍼센트라는 의미이다.

06 다음 대화의 우리말을 <조건>에 맞게 영작하시오.

> B: Emma, can you help me with this math problem?
> G: Sure, what is it?
> B: You have to move one stick to make this sum right. How could four minus five equal six?
> G: Oh, it's simple. You need to move one of the sticks in number four to make it eleven. Do you see what I mean?
> B: Yes, now I see what you mean. Eleven minus five equals six. How clever!
> G: 틀 밖에서 생각하는 것은 때때로 도움이 될 수 있지.

> ┤ 조건 ├
> • 동명사를 이용할 것.
> • 빈도부사는 문장 끝에 쓸 것.
> • 'outside, box, helpful'을 사용할 것.

➡ _____

[07~08] 다음 대화를 읽고 물음에 답하시오.

> B: Jian, what's the matter? You look upset.
> G: My brother broke my computer. I'm so angry.
> B: I'm sorry to hear that, but your facial muscles must be tired.
> G: What do you mean?
> B: Well, it takes a lot of muscles to look angry, but (A)only a few to smile. Do you see what I mean?
> G: Oh, I get it. I guess it's not good to stay angry for a long time.
> B: That's right. Remember, it's always better to smile!

07 밑줄 친 (A)를 생략되지 않은 문장으로 다시 쓰시오.

> ┤ 조건 ├
> 'muscles'를 추가하여 8 단어로 쓸 것.

➡ _____

08 위 대화를 읽고 다음 문장의 빈칸에 알맞은 말을 넣어 Jian에게 조언하는 말을 완성하시오.

> It takes a lot of _____ to look angry, but you don't need a lot to _____. So don't stay _____ for a long time.

09 다음 글의 밑줄 친 어구의 뜻이 잘못된 것은?

> These days, you (a)don't need paper tickets to watch a movie or go to a concert. You just need to (b)store your ticket in your cell phone. Then show the ticket (c)on your phone's screen before you go in. You (d)don't need to (e)go through the trouble of printing out tickets. Do you see what I mean?

① (a): 종이 티켓이 필요하지 않다
② (b): 티켓을 저장하다
③ (c): 휴대전화 화면 위의
④ (d): ~해서는 안 된다
⑤ (e): 번거롭게 티켓을 출력하다

10 괄호 안의 단어를 활용하여 우리말에 맞게 영작하시오.

(1) 당신은 너무 커서 이 자전거를 탈 수 없어요. (too, big)

➡ _____

(2) John의 아들은 너무 똑똑해서 친구들과 어울릴 수 없어요. (smart, too, hang out with)

➡ _____

(3) 이 커피는 너무 써서 마실 수가 없어요. (bitter, too)

➡ _____

(4) 이 애플파이는 너무 맛있어서 사지 않을 수가 없어. (so, buy, stop, delicious)

➡ _____

_____

(5) 이 밧줄은 너무 두꺼워서 가위로 자를 수가 없습니다. (too, cut)

➡ _____

(3) 모든 사람이 그걸 살 여유가 되는 건 아니다.
→ Not everyone can afford it.

➡ _____

(4) 창문을 좀 닫아 주시겠어요?
→ Would you be kind enough closing the window?

➡ _____

11 다음 빈칸에 들어갈 어휘로 적절치 <u>않은</u> 것을 <u>모두</u> 고르시오.

> It was too cold for us to _____ outside.

① go
② going
③ swim
④ swimming
⑤ do some activities

12 다음 중 어법상 <u>어색한</u> 것을 <u>모두</u> 고르시오.

① He had so much work that he could rest.
② The container was too heavy for him to lift it.
③ He is too slow to catch up with others.
④ His voice is too small to be heard.
⑤ The problem was too hard for her to solve.

14 다음 그래프의 해석이 <u>잘못된</u> 것을 고르시오.

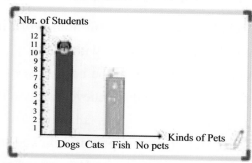

① Most students have dogs.
② Not everyone has pets.
③ No one has cats.
④ About 40% of my classmates raise fish.
⑤ Everyone has pets.

13 다음 각 문장에서 어법상 <u>어색한</u> 곳을 바르게 고쳐 다시 쓰시오. (어색한 곳이 없을 경우, '없음'으로 쓸 것.)

(1) 신입 사원 중 사실 눈에 띄는 인물이 없다.
→ No one really stand out among new recruits.

➡ _____

(2) 따라서 아무도 그 고릴라들을 도울 수 없다.
→ Therefore, nobody are able to help the gorillas.

➡ _____

15 다음 각 문장을 괄호 안의 단어를 배열하여 문장을 완성할 때,

(1) 3번째 단어를 쓰시오.
• 모든 사람이 다 그렇게 생각하는 것은 아니다.
(like, not, thinks, that, everyone)

➡ _____

(2) 6번째 단어를 쓰시오.
• 그녀는 상황이 자기가 견디기에 너무 힘들다고 말했다. (to, deal, situation, said, the, too, for, stressful, her, she, was)

➡ _____

(3) 7번째 단어를 쓰시오.

• 나는 너무 배가 불러서 더 이상 먹을 수 없다.
(more, I, full, that, I, am, can't, so, eat)

➡ _____

(4) 10번째 단어를 쓰시오.

• 그 돌은 너무 무거워서 그가 그것을 옮길 수
없었다. (stone, heavy, couldn't, it, that,
the, was, move, so, he)

➡ _____

18 밑줄 친 ①~⑤ 중 어법상 바르지 않은 것은?

①   ②   ③   ④   ⑤

[16~18] 다음 글을 읽고 물음에 답하시오.

Pascal was doing his math homework in his room. He was ①struggling with graphs.

(A) He looked up from the book to see ②who was talking. He couldn't believe his eyes. It was his dog, Manny, who ③was talking!

(B) He put down his pen and picked up his favorite book, *Robin Hood*. He decided to read ④himself to sleep. When he was about to ⑤ opening the book, he heard a voice.

(C) "It's too hard to read and draw graphs. Why do I need these anyway? No one needs graphs in real life."

[19~25] 다음 글을 읽고 물음에 답하시오.

Suddenly, he heard men shouting. When he opened his eyes, he saw ①soldiers on horses. They were chasing a man with ②arrows in his hand. The man saw Pascal and shouted.

"(A)네가 거기 서 있는 것은 너무 위험해. Come on." The man pulled Pascal onto his horse and rode into the woods.

When they arrived at a house, the man stopped and got ___(B)___ his horse.

"Hello, my name is Robin Hood."

"Wow! Are you the Robin Hood from the book?"

"No, I'm the Robin Hood of Sherwood Forest. Who are you and why are you here?"

"My name is Pascal. I don't know why I'm here, but there must be a ③reason. You saved me from the soldiers. Thank you so much. Is there anything I can do for you?"

"Well, can you help us get back the money that the king took from the people? He taxed them too much. He is too ④greedy to share with the people, so they don't have ⑤enough money to buy food. I want to help them get their money back. However, there are many soldiers in the tower, so no one can get inside."

"Hmm... I think I have a solution. But first, can you take me to the tower? I need to count the number of soldiers."

16 자연스러운 글이 되도록 (A)~(C)를 바르게 나열하시오.

➡ _____

17 다음 중 위 글을 읽고 답할 수 없는 것은?

① What was Pascal's favorite book?

② When did Pascal hear a voice?

③ What was too hard for Pascal to do?

④ Why was Pascal surprised?

⑤ How long did Pascal do his homework?

19 밑줄 친 우리말 (A)를 다음 〈조건〉에 맞게 영어로 쓰시오.

┌─ 조건 ─┐
가주어 It과 진주어 to부정사를 이용할 것.
└────────┘

➡ _____

20 위 글의 빈칸 (B)에 알맞은 것은?

① on   ② off   ③ into
④ from   ⑤ with

21 What were the soldiers chasing? Answer in English.

➡ _____

_____

22 다음 중 ①~⑤에 해당하는 영영풀이가 <u>아닌</u> 것은?

① a member of an army, especially one who is not an officer

② a thin stick with a sharp point at one end, which is shot from a bow

③ an explanation for something that has happened or that somebody has done

④ giving more of something, especially money, than is usual or expected

⑤ as many or as much as somebody needs or wants

23 로빈의 성품을 잘 묘사하는 단어를 <u>두 개</u> 고르시오.

① just   ② mindless   ③ brave
④ cowardly   ⑤ thoughtless

24 Choose one that is NOT true.

① Robin Hood had arrows in his hand.

② Rohin Hood rode into the woods with Pascal.

③ The tower was protected by many soldiers.

④ The soldiers kept chasing Robin until they found him in the woods.

⑤ The king was greedy enough to tax people too much.

25 Write the reason why Pascal wanted Robin to take him to the tower. Use the phrase 'It was because.'

➡ _____

_____

MEMO

MEMO

MEMO

MEMO

Middle School 3-2
학교시험 완벽 대비

2학기 전과정

적중100 plus

영어 기출문제집

영어 중 3

지학 | 민찬규

Best Collection

내용문의 중등영어발전소 적중100 편집부 TEL 070-4416-3636

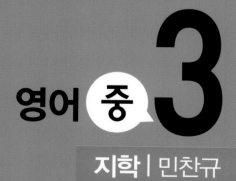

INSIGHT
on the textbook

교과서 파헤치기

영어 기출 문제집

적중100 plus
2학기 전과정

영어 중 3

지학 | 민찬규

INSIGHT
on the textbook
교과서 파헤치기

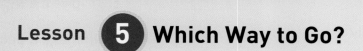

※ 다음 영어를 우리말로 쓰시오.

01	decision	_____
02	difference	_____
03	especially	_____
04	convenient	_____
05	dead end	_____
06	frustrate	_____
07	hedge	_____
08	beauty	_____
09	origin	_____
10	solution	_____
11	confusion	_____
12	compare	_____
13	unfortunately	_____
14	maze	_____
15	labyrinth	_____
16	actually	_____
17	willingly	_____
18	connect	_____
19	worth	_____
20	monster	_____
21	closely	_____

22	consider	_____
23	suggest	_____
24	exchange	_____
25	prison	_____
26	reasonable	_____
27	effective	_____
28	mythology	_____
29	escape	_____
30	regularity	_____
31	entrance	_____
32	reliable	_____
33	choice	_____
34	exit	_____
35	get out of	_____
36	look forward to	_____
37	give it a try	_____
38	make a decision	_____
39	turn around	_____
40	lose one's way	_____
41	a variety of	_____
42	come up with	_____
43	make a choice	_____

※ 다음 우리말을 영어로 쓰시오.

01 혼란, 혼동 _____

02 미, 아름다움 _____

03 믿을 만한 _____

04 결정하다 _____

05 제안하다 _____

06 자세히 _____

07 괴물 _____

08 탈출하다 _____

09 층, 바닥 _____

10 조심스러운 _____

11 방해하다, 좌절시키다 _____

12 출구 _____

13 신화 _____

14 선택 _____

15 편리한 _____

16 산울타리 _____

17 여기다 _____

18 미궁 _____

19 미로 _____

20 차이 _____

21 입구 _____

22 주목하다, 알아차리다 _____

23 출구 _____

24 감옥 _____

25 연결하다, 이어지다 _____

26 순서, 질서 _____

27 (가격이) 적당한 _____

28 결정, 결심 _____

29 규칙성 _____

30 불행하게도 _____

31 해결책 _____

32 기꺼이 _____

33 비교하다 _____

34 효과적인 _____

35 다양한 _____

36 ~에서 나오다, 도망치다 _____

37 선택하다 _____

38 돌다, 돌아서다 _____

39 ~을 기대하다 _____

40 시도하다, 한번 해보다 _____

41 ~을 생각해 내다 _____

42 결정하다 _____

43 길을 잃다 _____

※ 다음 영영풀이에 알맞은 단어를 <보기>에서 골라 쓴 후, 우리말 뜻을 쓰시오.

1 _____ : a way out of a public building or vehicle: _____

2 _____ : having a specified value: _____

3 _____ : to become joined or united or linked: _____

4 _____ : the point or place where something begins or is created: _____

5 _____ : the act of picking or deciding between two or more possibilities:

_____

6 _____ : a door, gate, passage, etc. used for entering a room, building or place:

_____

7 _____ : the quality that makes one person or thing unlike another: _____

8 _____ : to give things of a particular kind to each other at the same time:

_____

9 _____ : a complicated series of paths, which it is difficult to find your way through:

_____

10 _____ : ancient myths in general; the ancient myths of a particular culture, society,

etc.: _____

11 _____ : to get away from a place where you have been kept as a prisoner or not

allowed to leave: _____

12 _____ : a building where criminals are kept as punishment or where people accused

of a crime are kept before their trial: _____

13 _____ : a situation in which people are uncertain about what to do or are unable

to understand something clearly: _____

14 _____ : to make somebody feel annoyed or impatient because they cannot do or

achieve what they want: _____

15 _____ : a row of bushes or small trees planted close together, usually along the

edge of a field, garden, yard or road: _____

16 _____ : a system of paths separated by walls or hedges built in a park or garden

that is designed so that it is difficult to find your way through: _____

보기			
frustrate	maze	connect	mythology
labyrinth	confusion	difference	choice
hedge	escape	exit	origin
prison	worth	exchange	entrance

대화문 Test

※ 다음 우리말과 일치하도록 빈칸에 알맞은 말을 쓰시오.

Listen & Speak 1 A

W: How may I help you?

B: Hi! I _____ these shoes yesterday. Is it _____ to _____ them for the red shoes?

W: Oh, actually white is really _____ _____ _____.

B: I know, and that's _____ I spent a long time _____ _____ _____ yesterday. But I think that red will _____ _____ me.

W: Okay, no _____.

W: 무엇을 도와드릴까요?

B: 안녕하세요! 제가 어제 이 신발을 샀는데요. 이것을 빨간색 신발로 교환하는 것이 가능한가요?

W: 오, 사실은 하얀색이 요즘 정말 인기 있어요.

B: 저도 알아요, 그래서 제가 어제 결정하는 데 오랜 시간을 보냈어요. 하지만 빨간색이 제게 더 잘 어울릴 것 같아요.

W: 알았어요, 문제없어요.

Listen & Speak 1 B

G: Mom, did you _____ where _____ _____ _____ our family trip to Jeju?

W: Almost. Come here and see the _____ _____ _____.

G: It looks good. Hmm… Mom, _____ _____ _____ to visit Mirror Maze Park _____ our second day?

W: It sounds _____, but I remember you said you wanted to go _____ _____.

G: I know, but I heard the park is _____ _____ more fun. Please ….

W: All right. _____ _____ our _____ for the second day.

G: Thank you! I'm very _____ about the trip.

W: It's great to hear that you're _____ _____ _____ the trip.

G: 엄마, 제주도 가족 여행 동안 어디 방문할지 정하셨어요?

W: 거의. 이리 와서 내가 만든 일정표를 보렴.

G: 좋아 보여요. 흠. 엄마, 우리 두 번째 날에 거울 미로 공원에 가는 것이 가능할까요?

W: 재미있을 거 같지만, 네가 말 타러 가고 싶다고 말한 것으로 기억하는데.

G: 저도 알아요, 근데 공원이 훨씬 더 재미있다고 들었어요. 제발….

W: 알았다. 두 번째 날 우리의 일정을 변경하자.

G: 감사합니다! 전 이번 여행에 대해 너무 신이 나요.

W: 네가 이번 여행을 고대한다니 아주 좋구나.

Listen & Speak 2 A

M: Hi, do you _____ any _____?

G: Yes, please. Could you _____ a good Chinese restaurant in this building? I can't _____ _____ the two.

M: Hmm…. What _____ Pappa Chen's? Their food is good and the prices are _____.

G: Sounds great! How do I _____ _____ the restaurant?

M: It's on the _____ _____. You can use the elevator _____ _____. Pappa Chen's is _____ _____ the elevator.

G: Great! Thank you very much _____ your _____.

M: My _____. Enjoy your dinner.

M: 안녕하세요, 도움이 필요하신가요?

G: 네, 부탁드려요. 이 건물에서 좋은 중국 음식점을 추천해 주실 수 있나요? 두 개 중에 결정할 수가 없네요.

M: 음… 파파첸스는 어떠세요? 그곳 음식은 훌륭하고 가격이 합리적이에요.

G: 좋을 것 같은데요! 그 음식점에 어떻게 가나요?

M: 그것은 4층에 있습니다. 당신은 저기 있는 승강기를 탈 수 있고요. 파파첸스는 승강기 옆에 있습니다.

G: 아주 좋아요! 도와주셔서 정말 감사합니다.

M: 천만에요. 저녁 맛있게 드세요.

Listen & Speak 2 B

B: Hey, Minju, where are you?

G: Oh, Andrew, I'm _____. I'm _____.

B: Good. I was _____ that you were _____.

G: I think I'm okay. _____ _____ Mason and Jian?

B: They are already here at my house.

G: Good! Oh, I see the _____ _____. _____ _____ _____ _____ _____ your place from here?

B: You are almost here. _____ _____ _____ one more block. Then you will see Kim's Bakery.

G: Kim's Bakery? Okay ....

B: Then _____ _____ and _____ _____ for about 100 meters.

G: _____ _____ and _____ _____ .... Okay, thanks! I'll see you soon.

B: 민주야, 너 어디야?
G: 오, Andrew, 나 가고 있어. 가고 있어.
B: 좋아. 네가 길을 잃었을까봐 걱정했어.
G: 괜찮은 것 같아. Mason이랑 지안이는?
B: 그들은 우리 집에 벌써 왔지.
G: 좋아! 오, 우체국이 보여. 여기서부터 너희 집까지 어떻게 가니?
B: 거의 다 왔네. 한 블록 더 직진해. 그럼 너는 킴스 빵집이 보일 거야.
G: 킴스 빵집? 알았어… .
B: 그럼 오른쪽으로 돌아서 100m 정도 직진해.
G: 오른쪽으로 돌아서 직진이라… . 알았어, 고마워! 곧 보자.

Real Life Communication

Mina: _____ _____ _____ _____ _____ the trip this weekend?

Jinho, Claire, & Henry: Yes!

Mina: Good! Don't _____ _____! We're meeting at 11 a.m. _____ _____ _____ the clock tower.

Jinho: You _____ _____! How do we _____ _____ the airport? I don't think we've _____ yet.

Henry: Jinho is right. We have two _____, bus or _____.

Claire: What about the subway? It's more _____ than the bus.

Henry: Is it _____ _____ get to Terminal 2 _____ _____?

Claire: Yes, I _____ _____.

Mina: Good. Okay, then let's _____ _____ _____.

Mina: 너희 모두 이번 주말에 여행갈 준비 됐니?
Jinho, Claire, & Henry: 응!
Mina: 좋아! 늦지 마! 우리는 시계탑 앞에서 오전 11시에 만날 거야.
Jinho: 알았어! 우리 공항까지 어떻게 가지? 우리가 아직 결정하지 않은 것 같은데.
Henry: 진호 말이 맞아. 우리는 버스랑 지하철, 두 가지 선택이 있어.
Claire: 지하철은 어때? 그것은 버스보다 더 믿을 만하잖아.
Henry: 2터미널까지 지하철로 가는 것이 가능하니?
Claire: 응, 내가 이미 확인해 봤어.
Mina: 좋아. 그래, 그럼 지하철을 타자.

Let's Check 1

B: What are you _____, Alice?

G: It's about the _____ of the _____.

B: _____? Wasn't that an old _____ _____ to keep the half-man, half-bull _____?

G: Oh, Juwon, you know about the story.

B: Not really. I _____ the name of the monster.

G: The Minotaur. The king of Crete was _____ at it and _____ it in a _____.

B: 무엇을 읽고 있니, Alice?
G: 미궁의 기원에 관한 거야.
B: 미궁? 그건 반인반수 괴물을 가두기 위한 옛 신화 속 감옥 아니니?
G: 와, 주원아, 너 그 이야기에 대해 아는구나.
B: 그다지 잘 아는 건 아니야. 그 괴물의 이름을 잊어버렸어.
G: 미노타우루스야. 크레타의 왕이 그 괴물에 화가 나서 그것을 미궁에 가두었지.

※ 다음 우리말에 맞도록 대화를 영어로 쓰시오.

Listen & Speak 1 A

W: _____

B: _____

_____

W: _____

B: _____

_____

W: _____

W: 무엇을 도와드릴까요?
B: 안녕하세요! 제가 어제 이 신발을 샀는데요. 이것을 빨간색 신발로 교환하는 것이 가능한가요?
W: 오, 사실은 하얀색이 요즘 정말 인기 있어요.
B: 저도 알아요, 그래서 제가 어제 결정하는 데 오랜 시간을 보냈어요. 하지만 빨간색이 제게 더 잘 어울릴 것 같아요.
W: 알았어요, 문제없어요.

Listen & Speak 1 B

G: _____

W: _____

G: _____

_____

W: _____

G: _____

W: _____

G: _____

W: _____

G: 엄마, 제주도 가족 여행 동안 어디 방문할지 정하셨어요?
W: 거의. 이리 와서 내가 만든 일정표를 보렴.
G: 좋아 보여요. 흠. 엄마, 우리 두 번째 날에 거울 미로 공원에 가는 것이 가능할까요?
W: 재미있을 거 같지만, 네가 말 타러 가고 싶다고 말한 것으로 기억하는데.
G: 저도 알아요, 근데 공원이 훨씬 더 재미있다고 들었어요. 제발요....
W: 알았다. 두 번째 날 우리의 일정을 변경하자.
G: 감사합니다! 전 이번 여행에 대해 너무 신이 나요.
W: 네가 이번 여행을 고대한다니 아주 좋구나.

Listen & Speak 2 A

M: _____

G: _____

_____

M: _____

_____

G: _____

M: _____

_____

G: _____

M: _____

M: 안녕하세요, 도움이 필요하신가요?
G: 네, 부탁드려요. 이 건물에서 좋은 중국 음식점을 추천해 주실 수 있나요? 두 개 중에 결정할 수가 없네요.
M: 음… 파파첸스는 어떠세요? 그곳 음식은 훌륭하고 가격이 합리적이에요.
G: 좋을 것 같은데요! 그 음식점에 어떻게 가나요?
M: 그것은 4층에 있습니다. 당신은 저기 있는 승강기를 탈 수 있고요. 파파첸스는 승강기 옆에 있습니다.
G: 아주 좋아요! 도와주셔서 정말 감사합니다.
M: 천만에요. 저녁 맛있게 드세요.

Listen & Speak 2 B

B: _____

G: _____

B: _____

G: _____

B: _____

G: _____

B: _____

G: _____

B: _____

G: _____

B: 민주야, 너 어디야?

G: 오, Andrew, 나 가고 있어. 가고 있어.

B: 좋아. 네가 길을 잃었을까봐 걱정했어.

G: 괜찮은 것 같아. Mason이랑 지안이는?

B: 그들은 우리 집에 벌써 왔지.

G: 좋아! 오, 우체국이 보여. 여기서부터 너희 집까지 어떻게 가니?

B: 거의 다 왔네. 한 블록 더 직진해. 그럼 너는 킴스 빵집이 보일 거야.

G: 킴스 빵집? 알았어… .

B: 그럼 오른쪽으로 돌아서 100m 정도 직진해.

G: 오른쪽으로 돌아서 직진이라… . 알았어, 고마워! 곧 보자.

Real Life Communication

Mina: _____

Jinho, Claire, & Henry: _____

Mina: _____

Jinho: _____

Henry: _____

Claire: _____

Henry: _____

Claire: _____

Mina: _____

Mina: 너희 모두 이번 주말에 여행갈 준비 됐니?

Jinho, Claire, & Henry: 응!

Mina: 좋아! 늦지 마! 우리는 시계탑 앞에서 오전 11시에 만날 거야.

Jinho: 알았어! 우리 공항까지 어떻게 가지? 우리가 아직 결정하지 않은 것 같은데.

Henry: 진호 말이 맞아. 우리는 버스랑 지하철, 두 가지 선택이 있어.

Claire: 지하철은 어때? 그것은 버스보다 더 믿을 만하잖아.

Henry: 2터미널까지 지하철로 가는 것이 가능하니?

Claire: 응, 내가 이미 확인해 봤어.

Mina: 좋아. 그래, 그럼 지하철을 타자.

Let's Check 1

B: _____

G: _____

B: _____

_____

G: _____

B: _____

G: _____

B: 무엇을 읽고 있니, Alice?

G: 미궁의 기원에 관한 거야.

B: 미궁? 그건 반인반수 괴물을 가두기 위한 옛 신화 속 감옥 아니니?

G: 와, 주원아, 너 그 이야기에 대해 아는구나.

B: 그다지 잘 아는 건 아니야. 그 괴물의 이름을 잊어버렸어.

G: 미노타우루스야. 크레타의 왕이 그 괴물에 화가 나서 그것을 미궁에 가두었지.

※ 다음 우리말과 일치하도록 빈칸에 알맞은 것을 골라 쓰시오.

Enjoy the "Planned Confusion"

1 _____ the two pictures _____, you can easily _____ some _____.
  A. notice   B. comparing   C. differences   D. below

2 For _____, the picture on the left is _____ a _____ and only has an _____.
  A. entrance   B. example   C. labyrinth   D. called

3 The picture on the right is _____ a _____ and has _____ an entrance _____ an exit.
  A. both   B. and   C. called   D. maze

4 You can _____ the _____ of the _____ in Greek _____.
  A. labyrinth   B. mythology   C. origin   D. find

5 It is _____ to _____ a _____ that you cannot _____.
  A. escape   B. prison   C. be   D. said

6 But you may _____ _____ the labyrinth has only a _____ _____.
  A. single   B. notice   C. path   D. that

7 There are _____ _____ _____.
  A. dead   B. no   C. ends

8 This means you don't _____ to _____ about _____ out of it when you _____ it.
  A. enter   B. have   C. getting   D. worry

9 If you _____ the path all the _____ to the _____, you will _____ the center.
  A. end   B. follow   C. reach   D. way

10 To _____ out, you simply _____ to turn _____ and walk back out the way you _____ in.
  A. around   B. get   C. came   D. have

11 _____ you are _____ a _____, it's a _____ story.
  A. different   B. maze   C. when   D. in

12 There are many _____ to _____ and dead _____ to _____ you.
  A. frustrate   B. choices   C. ends   D. make

13 You have to _____ _____ decisions about _____ _____ to go.
  A. way   B. making   C. which   D. keep

14 _____ you are not _____, you can easily _____ your _____.
  A. way   B. careful   C. lose   D. if

15 _____ days, _____ are often _____ _____ puzzles.
  A. considered   B. these   C. left-brain   D. mazes

'계획된 혼란'을 즐겨라

1 아래 두 그림을 비교하면 몇 가지 차이를 쉽게 알아차릴 수 있습니다.

2 예를 들면, 왼쪽 그림은 미궁이라 불리고 입구만 있습니다.

3 오른쪽 그림은 미로라 불리며 입구와 출구가 둘 다 있습니다.

4 미궁의 기원은 그리스 신화에서 찾을 수 있습니다.

5 그것은 여러분이 빠져나올 수 없는 감옥으로 알려져 있습니다.

6 하지만 여러분이 알아차릴 수 있듯, 미궁은 통로가 하나입니다.

7 막다른 길이 없습니다.

8 이것은 여러분이 거기에 들어갈 때 빠져나올 것을 걱정하지 않아도 된다는 것을 의미합니다.

9 통로를 따라 끝까지 가면, 여러분은 미궁의 중앙에 도착할 것입니다.

10 빠져나오기 위해서는, 여러분은 단지 돌아서 들어간 길대로 걸어 나오면 됩니다.

11 미로 안에 있을 때에는 완전히 상황이 다릅니다.

12 결정할 많은 선택지가 있고 여러분을 좌절하게 만들 막다른 길들이 있습니다.

13 어느 길로 갈지 계속 선택을 해야만 합니다.

14 조심하지 않으면 길을 잃기 쉽습니다.

15 오늘날, 미로는 흔히 좌뇌형 퍼즐로 간주됩니다.

16 Many people _____ _____ maze parks and enjoy the "_____ _____."
A. confusion　　B. visit　　C. planned　　D. willingly

17 And some of them _____ _____ _____ their own _____.
A. solutions　　B. came　　C. with　　D. up

18 The easiest and most _____ one is to _____ a hand on one wall from the _____ _____.
A. beginning　　B. reliable　　C. place　　D. very

19 Then you just _____ _____ that _____.
A. following　　B. wall　　C. keep

20 It's _____ _____ in a _____ room.
A. walking　　B. dark　　C. like

21 _____, this simple method may not be _____ in _____ types of mazes, especially when all of the walls are not _____.
A. effective　　B. connected　　C. certain　　D. unfortunately

22 Mazes are _____ with a variety of _____ _____, like walls and rooms, _____, bricks, mirrors, and even snow.
A. hedges　　B. materials　　C. made　　D. different

23 _____ _____, they can also be _____ or _____ on paper.
A. printed　　B. fact　　C. drawn　　D. in

24 _____ is one _____ an example. This is _____ a number _____.
A. called　　B. as　　C. here　　D. maze

25 You start _____ _____ A and have to go _____ the _____ of 1 → 9 → 8 → 5 → 1 → 9 → ... .
A. order　　B. point　　C. in　　D. from

26 Why don't you _____ it a _____? You have 30 _____ to _____!
A. seconds　　B. try　　C. escape　　D. give

27 _____ and mazes _____ truly _____, but that's not the _____ of the story.
A. fun　　B. end　　C. are　　D. labyrinths

28 _____ at them closely, you may find the _____ of _____ and _____.
A. order　　B. beauty　　C. regularity　　D. looking

29 They may also show you _____ are.
A. creative　　B. beings　　C. human　　D. how

30 If _____ is a maze park on your next trip, _____ don't you _____ and _____ some time to enjoy it?
A. stop　　B. take　　C. there　　D. why

31 It will surely _____ _____ _____!
A. worth　　B. visiting　　C. be

16 많은 사람들이 미로 공원에 기꺼이 방문하여 '계획된 혼란'을 즐깁니다.

17 그리고 그들 중 몇몇은 자기들만의 해결 방법을 찾아냈습니다.

18 가장 쉽고 믿을 만한 해결 방법은 시작 지점부터 한쪽 벽에 손을 대는 것입니다.

19 그리고는 여러분은 단지 그 벽을 계속 따라가면 됩니다.

20 이것은 마치 어두운 방을 걷는 것과 같습니다.

21 불행하게도, 이 간단한 방법은 어떤 종류의 미로에서는 특히 모든 벽이 이어져 있지는 않은 경우 효과가 없을지도 모릅니다.

22 미로는 벽과 방, 울타리, 벽돌, 거울, 심지어는 눈 등 많은 다양한 재료로 제작됩니다.

23 사실, 미로는 종이에 인쇄되거나 그려질 수도 있습니다.

24 여기 그 예가 하나 있습니다. 이것은 숫자 미로라고 불립니다.

25 여러분은 A 지점에서 출발하여 1. 9. 8. 5. 1. 9 …의 순서로 이동해야 합니다.

26 한번 시도해 보시죠? 빠져나가는 데 **30**초가 주어집니다!

27 미궁과 미로는 정말 재미있지만, 그것이 전부가 아닙니다.

28 자세히 들여다보면, 여러분은 질서와 규칙성이라는 아름다움을 발견할 수 있을지도 모릅니다.

29 그것들은 또한 인간이 얼마나 창조적인가를 보여줄지도 모릅니다.

30 다음 여행에 미로 공원이 있으면, 들러서 즐겨보는 것은 어떨까요?

31 분명히 들를 가치가 있을 것입니다!

※ 다음 우리말과 일치하도록 빈칸에 알맞은 것을 골라 쓰시오.

Enjoy the "Planned Confusion"

1　_____ the two pictures _____, you can easily _____ some _____.

2　_____ _____, the picture _____ _____ _____ is _____ a _____ and only _____ an _____.

3　The picture _____ _____ _____ is _____ a maze and _____ _____ an entrance _____ an _____.

4　You can find _____ _____ the labyrinth in Greek _____.

5　It _____ _____ _____ _____ a prison _____ you _____ _____.

6　But you may _____ _____ the labyrinth has only _____ _____.

7　There are _____ _____ _____.

8　This means you _____ _____ _____ getting out of it when you _____ _____.

9　If you follow the path _____ _____ _____ _____, you _____ _____ the center.

10　_____ _____ _____, you simply _____ _____ _____ _____ and walk back out the way you _____ _____.

11　When you are _____ a _____, it's a _____ story.

12　There are many choices _____ _____ and _____ _____ _____ you.

13　You have to _____ decisions about _____ _____ _____.

14　_____ you _____ _____ _____, you can easily _____ your way.

15　These days, mazes _____ often _____ _____ puzzles.

'계획된 혼란'을 즐겨라

1　아래 두 그림을 비교하면 몇 가지 차이를 쉽게 알아차릴 수 있습니다.

2　예를 들면, 왼쪽 그림은 미궁이라 불리고 입구만 있습니다.

3　오른쪽 그림은 미로라 불리며 입구와 출구가 둘 다 있습니다.

4　미궁의 기원은 그리스 신화에서 찾을 수 있습니다.

5　그것은 여러분이 빠져나올 수 없는 감옥으로 알려져 있습니다.

6　하지만 여러분이 알아차릴 수 있듯, 미궁은 통로가 하나입니다.

7　막다른 길이 없습니다.

8　이것은 여러분이 거기에 들어갈 때 빠져나올 것을 걱정하지 않아도 된다는 것을 의미합니다.

9　통로를 따라 끝까지 가면, 여러분은 미궁의 중앙에 도착할 것입니다.

10　빠져나오기 위해서는, 여러분은 단지 돌아서 들어간 길대로 걸어 나오면 됩니다.

11　미로 안에 있을 때에는 완전히 상황이 다릅니다.

12　결정할 많은 선택지가 있고 여러분을 좌절하게 만들 막다른 길들이 있습니다.

13　어느 길로 갈지 계속 선택을 해야만 합니다.

14　조심하지 않으면 길을 잃기 쉽습니다.

15　오늘날, 미로는 흔히 좌뇌형 퍼즐로 간주됩니다.

16 Many people _____ _____ maze parks and _____ the "_____ _____."

17 And some of _____ _____ _____ _____ their own _____.

18 The easiest and _____ _____ is _____ place a hand _____ one wall from _____ _____ _____.

19 Then you just keep _____ _____ _____.

20 It's _____ _____ in a dark room.

21 _____, this simple method may not be _____ in _____ _____ of mazes, especially when all of the walls _____ _____ _____.

22 Mazes _____ _____ _____ a variety of _____ _____, _____ walls and rooms, _____, _____, mirrors, _____ even snow.

23 _____ _____, they can also _____ _____ or _____ on paper.

24 _____ _____ one as an example. This is _____ a number _____.

25 You start _____ point A and have to go _____ _____ _____ of 1 → 9 → 8 → 5 → 1 → 9 → ... .

26 _____ _____ you _____ _____ _____ _____? You have 30 seconds _____ _____!

27 Labyrinths and mazes _____ truly _____, but that's not _____ _____ of the story.

28 _____ _____ _____ _____, you may find the _____ of _____ and _____.

29 They may also show you _____ _____ _____ _____ _____.

30 If _____ _____ a maze park on your next trip, why don't you _____ and _____ _____ _____ to enjoy it?

31 It will _____ _____ _____ _____ _____!

16 많은 사람들이 미로 공원에 기꺼이 방문하여 '계획된 혼란'을 즐깁니다.

17 그리고 그들 중 몇몇은 자기들만의 해결 방법을 찾아냈습니다.

18 가장 쉽고 믿을 만한 해결 방법은 시작 지점부터 한쪽 벽에 손을 대는 것입니다.

19 그러고는 여러분은 단지 그 벽을 계속 따라가면 됩니다.

20 이것은 마치 어두운 방을 걷는 것과 같습니다.

21 불행하게도, 이 간단한 방법은 어떤 종류의 미로에서는 특히 모든 벽이 이어져 있지는 않은 경우 효과가 없을지도 모릅니다.

22 미로는 벽과 방, 울타리, 벽돌, 거울, 심지어는 눈 등 많은 다양한 재료로 제작됩니다.

23 사실, 미로는 종이에 인쇄되거나 그려질 수도 있습니다.

24 여기 그 예가 하나 있습니다. 이것은 숫자 미로라고 불립니다.

25 여러분은 A 지점에서 출발하여 1. 9. 8. 5. 1. 9 …의 순서로 이동해야 합니다.

26 한번 시도해 보시죠? 빠져나가는 데 **30**초가 주어집니다!

27 미궁과 미로는 정말 재미있지만, 그것이 전부가 아닙니다.

28 자세히 들여다보면, 여러분은 질서와 규칙성이라는 아름다움을 발견할 수 있을지도 모릅니다.

29 그것들은 또한 인간이 얼마나 창조적인가를 보여줄지도 모릅니다.

30 다음 여행에 미로 공원이 있으면, 들러서 즐겨보는 것은 어떨까요?

31 분명히 들를 가치가 있을 것입니다!

※ 다음 문장을 우리말로 쓰시오.

Enjoy the "Planned Confusion"

1 Comparing the two pictures below, you can easily notice some differences.
➡ _____

2 For example, the picture on the left is called a labyrinth and only has an entrance.
➡ _____

3 The picture on the right is called a maze and has both an entrance and an exit.
➡ _____

4 You can find the origin of the labyrinth in Greek mythology.
➡ _____

5 It is said to be a prison that you cannot escape.
➡ _____

6 But you may notice that the labyrinth has only a single path.
➡ _____

7 There are no dead ends.
➡ _____

8 This means you don't have to worry about getting out of it when you enter it.
➡ _____

9 If you follow the path all the way to the end, you will reach the center.
➡ _____

10 To get out, you simply have to turn around and walk back out the way you came in.
➡ _____

11 When you are in a maze, it's a different story.
➡ _____

12 There are many choices to make and dead ends to frustrate you.
➡ _____

13 You have to keep making decisions about which way to go.
➡ _____

14 If you are not careful, you can easily lose your way.
➡ _____

15 These days, mazes are often considered left-brain puzzles.
➡ _____

16 Many people willingly visit maze parks and enjoy the "planned confusion."
➡ _____

17 And some of them came up with their own solutions.
➡ _____

18 The easiest and most reliable one is to place a hand on one wall from the very beginning.
➡ _____

19 Then you just keep following that wall.
➡ _____

20 It's like walking in a dark room.
➡ _____

21 Unfortunately, this simple method may not be effective in certain types of mazes, especially when all of the walls are not connected.
➡ _____
_____

22 Mazes are made with a variety of different materials, like walls and rooms, hedges, bricks, mirrors, and even snow.
➡ _____

23 In fact, they can also be printed or drawn on paper.
➡ _____

24 Here is one as an example. This is called a number maze.
➡ _____

25 You start from point A and have to go in the order of $1 \rightarrow 9 \rightarrow 8 \rightarrow 5 \rightarrow 1 \rightarrow 9 \rightarrow ...$.
➡ _____

26 Why don't you give it a try? You have 30 seconds to escape!
➡ _____

27 Labyrinths and mazes are truly fun, but that's not the end of the story.
➡ _____

28 Looking at them closely, you may find the beauty of order and regularity.
➡ _____

29 They may also show you how creative human beings are.
➡ _____

30 If there is a maze park on your next trip, why don't you stop and take some time to enjoy it?
➡ _____

31 It will surely be worth visiting!
➡ _____

Step4

※ 다음 괄호 안의 단어들을 우리말에 맞도록 바르게 배열하시오.

Enjoy the "Planned Confusion"

1 (the / comparing / pictures / two / below, / can / you / notice / easily / difference. / some)
➡ _____

2 (example, / for / picture / the / the / on / left / called / is / labyrinth / a / only / and / has / entrance. / an)
➡ _____

3 (picture / the / the / on / is / right / called / maze / a / and / both / has / entrance / an / and / exit. / an)
➡ _____

4 (can / you / the / find / origin / the / of / labyrinth / in / mythology. / Greek)
➡ _____

5 (is / it / said / be / to / prison / a / you / that / escape. / cannot)
➡ _____

6 (you / but / notice / may / the / that / has / labyrinth / only / single / a / path.)
➡ _____

7 (are / there / dead / no / ends.)
➡ _____

8 (means / this / don't / you / to / have / about / worry / out / getting / of / when / it / enter / you / it.)
➡ _____

9 (you / follow / if / path / the / the / all / way / the / to / end, / will / you / the / reach / center.)
➡ _____

10 (get / to / out, / simply / you / to / have / turn / and / around / walk / out / back / way / the / came / you / in.)
➡ _____

11 (you / when / in / are / maze, / a / it's / different / a / story.)
➡ _____

12 (are / there / choices / many / make / to / and / ends / dead / to / you. / frustrate)
➡ _____

13 (have / you / keep / to / decisions / making / which / about / way / go. / to)
➡ _____

14 (you / if / not / are / careful, / can / you / lose / easily / way. / your)
➡ _____

15 (days, / these / are / mazes / considered / often / puzzles. / left-brain)
➡ _____

'계획된 혼란'을 즐겨라

1 아래 두 그림을 비교하면 몇 가지 차이를 쉽게 알아차릴 수 있습니다.

2 예를 들면, 왼쪽 그림은 미궁이라 불리고 입구만 있습니다.

3 오른쪽 그림은 미로라 불리며 입구와 출구가 둘 다 있습니다.

4 미궁의 기원은 그리스 신화에서 찾을 수 있습니다.

5 그것은 여러분이 빠져나올 수 없는 감옥으로 알려져 있습니다.

6 하지만 여러분이 알아차릴 수 있듯, 미궁은 통로가 하나입니다.

7 막다른 길이 없습니다.

8 이것은 여러분이 거기에 들어갈 때 빠져나올 것을 걱정하지 않아도 된다는 것을 의미합니다.

9 통로를 따라 끝까지 가면, 여러분은 미궁의 중앙에 도착할 것입니다.

10 빠져나오기 위해서는, 여러분은 단지 돌아서 들어간 길대로 걸어 나오면 됩니다.

11 미로 안에 있을 때에는 완전히 상황이 다릅니다.

12 결정할 많은 선택지가 있고 여러분을 좌절하게 만들 막다른 길들이 있습니다.

13 어느 길로 갈지 계속 선택을 해야만 합니다.

14 조심하지 않으면 길을 잃기 쉽습니다.

15 오늘날, 미로는 흔히 좌뇌형 퍼즐로 간주됩니다.

16 (people / many / visit / willingly / parks / maze / and / the / enjoy / confusion." / "planned)

➡ _____

17 (some / and / them / of / up / came / their / with / solutions. / own)

➡ _____

18 (easiest / the / and / reliable / most / is / one / place / to / hand / a / one / on / from / wall / very / the / beginning.)

➡ _____

➡ _____

19 (you / then / keep / just / that / following / wall.)

➡ _____

20 (like / it's / in / walking / dark / a / room.)

➡ _____

21 (this / unfortunately, / simple / may / method / be / not / in / effective / types / of / certain / mazes, / when / especially / of / all / the / walls / not / are / connected.)

➡ _____

➡ _____

22 (are / mazes / with / made / a / of / variety / materials, / different / walls / like / rooms, / and / bricks, / hedges, / and / mirrors, / snow. / even)

➡ _____

➡ _____

23 (fact, / in / can / they / be / also / printed / drawn / or / paper. / on)

➡ _____

24 (is / here / as / one / example. / an // is / this / a / called / maze. / number)

➡ _____

25 (start / you / point / from / A / have / and / go / to / the / in / order / 1 → / 8 → / 9 → / 1 → / 5 → / 9 → ....)

➡ _____

26 (don't / why / give / you / a / it / try? // have / you / seconds / 30 / escape! / to)

➡ _____

27 (mazes / and / labyrinths / truly / are / fun, / that's / but / the / not / end / of / story. / the)

➡ _____

28 (at / looking / closely, / them / may / you / the / find / beauty / order / of / regularity. / and)

➡ _____

29 (may / they / show / also / how / you / human / creative / are. / beings)

➡ _____

30 (there / if / a / is / park / maze / your / on / trip, / next / don't / why / stop / you / and / some / take / to / time / it? / enjoy)

➡ _____

➡ _____

31 (will / it / be / surely / visiting! / worth)

➡ _____

16 많은 사람들이 미로 공원에 기꺼이 방문하여 '계획된 혼란'을 즐깁니다.

17 그리고 그들 중 몇몇은 자기들만의 해결 방법을 찾아냈습니다.

18 가장 쉽고 믿을 만한 해결 방법은 시작 지점부터 한쪽 벽에 손을 대는 것입니다.

19 그러고는 여러분은 단지 그 벽을 계속 따라가면 됩니다.

20 이것은 마치 어두운 방을 걷는 것과 같습니다.

21 불행하게도, 이 간단한 방법은 어떤 종류의 미로에서는 특히 모든 벽이 이어져 있지는 않은 경우 효과가 없을지도 모릅니다.

22 미로는 벽과 방, 울타리, 벽돌, 거울, 심지어는 눈 등 많은 다양한 재료로 제작됩니다.

23 사실, 미로는 종이에 인쇄되거나 그려질 수도 있습니다.

24 여기 그 예가 하나 있습니다. 이것은 숫자 미로라고 불립니다.

25 여러분은 A 지점에서 출발하여 1. 9. 8. 5. 1. 9 …의 순서로 이동해야 합니다.

26 한번 시도해 보시죠? 빠져나가는 데 30초가 주어집니다!

27 미궁과 미로는 정말 재미있지만, 그것이 전부가 아닙니다.

28 자세히 들여다보면, 여러분은 질서와 규칙성이라는 아름다움을 발견할 수 있을지도 모릅니다.

29 그것들은 또한 인간이 얼마나 창조적인가를 보여줄지도 모릅니다.

30 다음 여행에 미로 공원이 있으면, 들러서 즐겨보는 것은 어떨까요?

31 분명히 들를 가치가 있을 것입니다!

※ 다음 우리말을 영어로 쓰시오.

Enjoy the "Planned Confusion"

1 아래 두 그림을 비교하면 몇 가지 차이를 쉽게 알아차릴 수 있습니다.

➡ _____

2 예를 들면, 왼쪽 그림은 미궁이라 불리고 입구만 있습니다.

➡ _____

3 오른쪽 그림은 미로라 불리며 입구와 출구가 둘 다 있습니다.

➡ _____

4 미궁의 기원은 그리스 신화에서 찾을 수 있습니다.

➡ _____

5 그것은 여러분이 빠져나올 수 없는 감옥으로 알려져 있습니다.

➡ _____

6 하지만 여러분이 알아차릴 수 있듯, 미궁은 통로가 하나입니다.

➡ _____

7 막다른 길이 없습니다.

➡ _____

8 이것은 여러분이 거기에 들어갈 때 빠져나올 것을 걱정하지 않아도 된다는 것을 의미합니다.

➡ _____

9 통로를 따라 끝까지 가면, 여러분은 미궁의 중앙에 도착할 것입니다.

➡ _____

10 빠져나오기 위해서는, 여러분은 단지 돌아서 들어간 길대로 걸어 나오면 됩니다.

➡ _____

11 미로 안에 있을 때에는 완전히 상황이 다릅니다.

➡ _____

12 결정할 많은 선택지가 있고 여러분을 좌절하게 만들 막다른 길들이 있습니다.

➡ _____

13 어느 길로 갈지 계속 선택을 해야만 합니다.

➡ _____

14 조심하지 않으면 길을 잃기 쉽습니다.

➡ _____

15 오늘날, 미로는 흔히 좌뇌형 퍼즐로 간주됩니다.

➡ _____

16 많은 사람들이 미로 공원에 기꺼이 방문하여 '계획된 혼란'을 즐깁니다.

➡ _____

17 그리고 그들 중 몇몇은 자기들만의 해결 방법을 찾아냈습니다.

➡ _____

18 가장 쉽고 믿을 만한 해결 방법은 시작 지점부터 한쪽 벽에 손을 대는 것입니다.

➡ _____

19 그러고는 여러분은 단지 그 벽을 계속 따라가면 됩니다.

➡ _____

20 이것은 마치 어두운 방을 걷는 것과 같습니다.

➡ _____

21 불행하게도, 이 간단한 방법은 어떤 종류의 미로에서는 특히 모든 벽이 이어져 있지는 않은 경우 효과가 없을지도 모릅니다.

➡ _____

22 미로는 벽과 방, 울타리, 벽돌, 거울, 심지어는 눈 등 많은 다양한 재료로 제작됩니다.

➡ _____

23 사실, 미로는 종이에 인쇄되거나 그려질 수도 있습니다.

➡ _____

24 여기 그 예가 하나 있습니다. 이것은 숫자 미로라고 불립니다.

➡ _____

25 여러분은 A 지점에서 출발하여 1, 9, 8, 5, 1, 9 …의 순서로 이동해야 합니다.

➡ _____

26 한번 시도해 보시죠? 빠져나가는 데 30초가 주어집니다!

➡ _____

27 미궁과 미로는 정말 재미있지만, 그것이 전부가 아닙니다.

➡ _____

28 자세히 들여다보면, 여러분은 질서와 규칙성이라는 아름다움을 발견할 수 있을지도 모릅니다.

➡ _____

29 그것들은 또한 인간이 얼마나 창조적인가를 보여줄지도 모릅니다.

➡ _____

30 다음 여행에 미로 공원이 있으면, 들러서 즐겨보는 것은 어떨까요?

➡ _____

31 분명히 들를 가치가 있을 것입니다!

➡ _____

※ 다음 우리말과 일치하도록 빈칸에 알맞은 말을 쓰시오.

Real Life Communication – C Communication Task

1. A: _____ _____ _____ you the first question. _____ do you _____ _____?
2. B: I _____ _____ there _____ _____.
3. A: Then _____ _____ does it _____ _____ _____ there?
4. B: It _____ _____ 2 hours _____ _____ there.
5. A: Is _____ _____ _____ there _____ _____?
6. A: Oh, the _____ is Gyeongju. _____?

1. A: 첫 번째 질문을 할게요. 어떻게 그 곳에 가나요?
2. B: 기차로 그곳에 갈 수 있어요.
3. A: 그러면 그곳에 가는 데 얼마나 걸리나요?
4. B: 그곳에 가는 데 약 2시간 정도 걸려요.
5. A: 그곳에 비행기로 갈 수 있나요?
6. A: 오, 정답은 경주예요. 맞죠?

After You Read

1. Today, I went to _____ _____ _____ _____ _____ _____ my friends.
2. The maze _____ _____ _____ _____ _____.
3. There were _____ _____, and I had to _____ _____ _____ about _____ _____ _____ _____.
4. My friends said _____ I should just _____ my hand on one wall _____ _____ _____ _____ and _____ _____ the same wall.
5. That solution was _____ but not _____ _____.
6. I _____ _____ very much at the park.
7. Also, I found _____ _____ _____ _____ _____ and _____ there and thought that _____ _____ are really _____.

1. 오늘 나는 친구들과 함께 근처의 미로 공원에 갔다.
2. 미로는 해결하기가 어려워 보였다.
3. 선택지가 많았고 나는 어느 길로 갈지 계속해서 결정해야만 했다.
4. 내 친구들이 내가 처음부터 벽 한쪽에 손을 얹고 계속 같은 쪽 벽을 따라가면 된다고 말했다.
5. 그 해결 방법은 간단했지만 별로 효과적이지 않았다.
6. 나는 미로 공원에서 매우 즐거웠다.
7. 또한, 나는 질서와 규칙성의 아름다움을 발견했고 인간은 정말 창조적이라고 생각했다.

Let's Write

1. I _____ _____ _____ survey about our class's preference _____ mountains _____ oceans.
2. _____ _____ the results, _____ is clear _____ our class _____ mountains _____ oceans.
3. You may wonder _____ _____ _____ _____ _____ _____.
4. _____ the _____ _____ they like mountains _____, I found key words _____ "more beautiful", "_____ _____", and "_____."

1. 나는 산과 바다 간의 우리 반의 선호도에 관한 간단한 설문 조사를 했다.
2. 결과를 보면, 우리 반이 바다보다 산을 더 선호한다는 것이 명확하다.
3. 여러분은 왜 우리 반이 산을 선호하는지 궁금할지도 모른다.
4. 그들이 산을 더 좋아하는 이유를 보자면, 나는 "더 아름다운", "더 신나는", 그리고 "더 멋진"과 같은 핵심어를 찾았다.

구석구석 지문 Test

※ 다음 우리말을 영어로 쓰시오.

Real Life Communication – C Communication Task

1. A: 첫 번째 질문을 할게요. 어떻게 그곳에 가나요?
➡ _____

2. B: 기차로 갈 수 있어요.
➡ _____

3. A: 그러면 그곳에 가는 데 얼마나 걸리나요?
➡ _____

4. B: 그곳에 가는 데 약 2시간 정도 걸려요.
➡ _____

5. A: 그곳에 비행기로 갈 수 있나요?
➡ _____

6. A: 오, 정답은 경주예요. 맞죠?
➡ _____

After You Read

1. 오늘 나는 친구들과 함께 근처의 미로 공원에 갔다.
➡ _____

2. 미로는 해결하기가 어려워 보였다.
➡ _____

3. 선택지가 많았고 나는 어느 길로 갈지 계속해서 결정해야만 했다.
➡ _____

4. 내 친구들이 내가 처음부터 벽 한쪽에 손을 얹고 계속 같은 쪽 벽을 따라가면 된다고 말했다.
➡ _____
_____

5. 그 해결 방법은 간단했지만 별로 효과적이지 않았다.
➡ _____

6. 나는 미로 공원에서 매우 즐거웠다.
➡ _____

7. 또한, 나는 질서와 규칙성의 아름다움을 발견했고 인간은 정말 창조적이라고 생각했다.
➡ _____

Let's Write

1. 나는 산과 바다 간의 우리 반의 선호도에 관한 간단한 설문 조사를 했다.
➡ _____

2. 결과를 보면, 우리 반이 바다보다 산을 더 선호한다는 것이 명확하다.
➡ _____

3. 여러분은 왜 우리 반이 산을 선호하는지 궁금할지도 모른다.
➡ _____

4. 그들이 산을 더 좋아하는 이유를 보자면, 나는 "더 아름다운", "더 신나는", 그리고 "더 멋진"과 같은 핵심어를 찾았다.
➡ _____
_____

※ 다음 영어를 우리말로 쓰시오.

01 destroy _____

02 opposite _____

03 trick _____

04 proverb _____

05 acronym _____

06 unhealthy _____

07 blame _____

08 enough _____

09 result _____

10 attract _____

11 environment _____

12 stony _____

13 harm _____

14 fascinate _____

15 wisdom _____

16 saying _____

17 complete _____

18 feather _____

19 confused _____

20 useful _____

21 flock _____

22 opportunity _____

23 grab _____

24 cause _____

25 mistake _____

26 careful _____

27 reserve _____

28 influence _____

29 unwise _____

30 rude _____

31 judge _____

32 leap _____

33 quality _____

34 regret _____

35 hand in _____

36 rely on _____

37 think over _____

38 move away _____

39 as a result _____

40 keep in touch _____

41 take A away from B _____

42 every now and then _____

43 instead of _____

※ 다음 우리말을 영어로 쓰시오.

01	깃털	
02	떼, 무리	
03	마음을 끌다	
04	실수	
05	기회	
06	비난하다	
07	결과	
08	두문자어	
09	혼란스러워 하는	
10	해를 끼치다	
11	질	
12	영향을 미치다	
13	후회하다	
14	속임수	
15	판단하다	
16	예약하다	
17	속담, 격언	
18	파괴하다	
19	건강하지 못한	
20	～을 야기하다	
21	무례한	

22	완료하다	
23	조심하는	
24	뛰어오르다	
25	반대	
26	도구	
27	현명하지 못한, 어리석은	
28	환경	
29	마음을 사로잡다	
30	붙잡다	
31	돌이 많은	
32	유용한, 쓸모 있는	
33	지혜	
34	슬프게, 애석하게도	
35	의존하다	
36	제출하다	
37	～ 대신에	
38	～을 심사숙고하다	
39	결과적으로	
40	연락을 취하다	
41	거꾸로	
42	결국, 마침내	
43	B로부터 A를 빼앗다	

※ 다음 영영풀이에 알맞은 단어를 <보기>에서 골라 쓴 후, 우리말 뜻을 쓰시오.

1 _____: to give permission: _____

2 _____: a person or thing that is contrary in character: _____

3 _____: to come into being: _____

4 _____: to feel sorrow or remorse for: _____

5 _____: to have the same opinion: _____

6 _____: cautious in one's actions: _____

7 _____: not very lively or energetic: _____

8 _____: to cause an effect on: _____

9 _____: something that happens as a consequence: _____

10 _____: to take or hold someone or something with your hand suddenly, firmly, or roughly: _____

11 _____: the greatest amount, extent, or degree of something that is possible: _____

12 _____: to damage something so badly that it no longer exists, works, etc.: _____

13 _____: to spring through the air from one point or position to another: _____

14 _____: to cause a person or animals physical injury, usually on purpose: _____

15 _____: a word formed from the first letters of the words that make up the name of something: _____

16 _____: to ask for a seat, table, room, etc. to be available for you or someone else at a future time: _____

보기

limit	careful	opposite	dull
acronym	become	harm	allow
result	agree	destroy	influence
reserve	regret	leap	grab

※ 다음 우리말과 일치하도록 빈칸에 알맞은 말을 쓰시오.

Listen and Speak 1 A

1. **B:** Minju, we need a new guitar _____ we don't have _____ _____ for one.

   G: What do you _____ _____ _____ a concert to _____ money? We can _____ our new song, _____.

   B: What a great idea! It'll be like "_____ two birds _____ _____ stone."

   G: That's _____. _____ first make a _____ for our concert.

   B: Okay.

2. **G:** Dohun, what are you doing?

   B: I'm _____ a movie about AI robots. It's really _____. _____ _____ _____ _____ _____ them?

   G: In my _____, they will _____ problems. AI robots will _____ jobs _____ _____ people.

   B: Well, I still think they are _____. There is a science festival _____ AI robots. _____ _____ _____ we go and _____ _____ more about them?

   G: Sounds good.

Listen and Speak 1 B

W: Jacob, can you _____ me?

B: What is it, Mom?

W: Well, I _____ _____ _____ from my friend, but I don't understand _____ _____ _____ _____ _____ _____.

B: Let me _____. Hmm... ASAP means "_____ _____ _____ _____" and HAND _____ "Have a nice day."

W: Oh, I see.

B: _____ _____ _____ _____ _____ these _____, Mom?

W: I think they are _____ the _____. What do you think?

B: _____ _____ _____, they are fun and _____ _____ _____.

1. B: 민주야, 우리는 새 기타가 필요하지만 충분한 돈이 없어.
   G: 너는 돈을 마련하기 위한 콘서트를 하는 것에 대해 어떻게 생각해? 우리의 신곡도 소개할 수 있어.
   B: 아주 좋은 생각이야! 그건 "한 개의 돌로 두 마리의 새를 잡는 것"과 같을 거야.
   G: 맞아. 우선 우리 콘서트를 위한 포스터를 만들자.
   B: 그래.

2. G: 도훈아, 너 뭐 하고 있니?
   B: 나는 인공지능 로봇에 관한 영화를 보고 있어. 정말 흥미로워. 너는 그것들에 대해 어떻게 생각해?
   G: 내 생각에 그것들은 문제를 일으킬 거야. 인공지능 로봇은 사람들로부터 직업을 빼앗아 갈 거야.
   B: 글쎄, 난 여전히 그것들이 유용하다고 생각해. 인공지능 로봇들을 소개하는 과학 축제가 있어. 우리가 가서 그것들에 관해 더 알아보는 게 어때?
   G: 좋은 생각이야.

W: Jacob, 나 좀 도와줄 수 있니?
B: 뭔데요, 엄마?
W: 음, 내 친구한테 문자를 하나 받았는데, 이 중 일부가 무엇을 의미하는지 이해를 못하겠어.
B: 제가 볼게요, 음… ASAP는 '가능한 한 빨리'라는 의미이고, HAND는 '좋은 하루를 보내.'라는 의미예요.
W: 아, 그렇구나.
B: 이런 두문자들에 대해 어떻게 생각하세요, 엄마?
W: 난 그것들이 언어를 파괴하고 있다고 생각해. 너는 어떻게 생각하니?
B: 제 생각엔 그것들은 사용하기 재미있고 쉬운 것 같아요.

Listen and Speak 2 A

1. **B:** Look! People are just _____ their trash _____ !

   G: Oh, no! _____ we _____ the _____, we'll be the ones who _____ it _____ _____ _____.

   B: I agree. _____ the _____ goes, "_____ _____ _____ comes around."

   G: You're right. Let's help the earth by _____ our trash with us.

2. **B:** Emma, let's _____ _____ _____.

   G: What? We've only _____ _____ 30 minutes.

   B: _____ _____ _____ _____, "All work and no play makes Jack _____ _____ _____."

   G: I _____. Then let's _____ _____ _____ _____ _____ we _____ this part.

   B: Okay.

3. **G:** Juwon, what's _____ _____ ?

   B: Mr. Han _____ _____ _____ _____ _____ _____ the art project yesterday but I _____ _____ _____ it.

   G: Well, I think you should still finish it and _____ _____ _____. Like the saying goes, "_____ _____ _____."

   B: You're _____ _____ _____ _____ _____. _____ _____ the advice.

Listen and Speak 2 B

B: Yura, what are you doing?

G: I'm _____ my pictures _____ the internet. Come and have _____ _____.

B: There are _____ _____ _____ _____ _____ show your _____ _____. Isn't it _____ ?

G: Well, my friends like my posts a lot. I think it's a good _____ _____ _____ _____ _____ _____ _____.

B: I disagree. There might be some _____ _____ _____ your pictures _____ _____ _____.

G: Come to _____ _____ it, I _____ _____ _____ _____ with my pictures. Thanks _____ your advice.

B: No problem.

1. **B:** 봐! 사람들이 자기들의 쓰레기를 놔두고 그냥 떠나고 있어!

   G: 오, 안 돼! 우리가 환경을 해치면 결국 후회하는 건 우리일 거야.

   B: 나도 동의해. 속담에 '자신이 한 대로 되돌려 받는다(자업자득).'라고 하잖아.

   G: 네 말이 맞아. 우리 쓰레기는 우리가 가져가서 지구를 돕자.

2. **B:** Emma, 우리 좀 쉬자.

   G: 뭐라고? 우리 겨우 30분 동안 공부했어.

   B: 속담에 '일만 하고 놀지 않으면 바보가 된다.'라고 하잖아.

   G: 나도 동의해. 그러면 우리 이 부분을 끝내고 쉬자.

   B: 알았어.

3. **G:** 주원아, 무슨 문제 있니?

   B: 한 선생님이 미술 과제를 어제 제출하라고 하셨는데 난 아직 끝내지 못했어.

   G: 음, 나는 네가 그래도 그것을 끝내서 제출해야 한다고 생각해. 속담에 '안하는 것보다 늦는 게 낫다.'라고 하잖아.

   B: 네 말이 맞고 나도 동의해. 조언 고마워.

B: 유라야, 너 뭐 하고 있니?

G: 내 사진들을 인터넷에 올리고 있어. 와서 봐.

B: 너의 일상생활을 보여 주는 사진이 정말 많이 있네. 그거 위험하지 않니?

G: 글쎄, 내 친구들은 내 게시물들을 많이 좋아해. 난 이것이 서로 알아가는 데 좋은 방법이라고 생각해.

B: 나는 동의하지 않아. 너의 사진들을 나쁜 수단으로 이용할 일부 사람들이 있을지도 몰라.

G: 그러고 보니 나는 내 사진들에 대해 더 신중해야겠어. 충고 고마워.

B: 천만에.

Real Life Communication

Claire: Jinho, what's the _____? You look _____.

Jinho: I _____ _____ _____ _____ Harry.

Claire: Why? What _____?

Jinho: We both _____ _____ _____ the same music room _____ _____ _____ _____.

Claire: I don't think there _____ _____ _____ _____ _____ in _____ _____.

Jinho: I agree. _____ _____ _____ _____ _____ _____ _____ _____ for the music rooms?

Claire: _____ _____ do you think it should be?

Jinho: I don't think anyone _____ _____ _____ _____ a room for _____ _____ an hour a day.

Claire: I _____. I need _____ _____ _____ _____ to practice music.

Jinho: Then how _____ _____ a music room?

Claire: That's a good idea. Then _____ _____ will have _____ _____ _____ _____.

Let's Check

1. **B:** I don't think _____ _____ _____ _____ _____ others _____ they are not there.

   G: _____ do you say _____?

   B: Well, I _____ _____ _____ _____ _____ Jimin _____ I talked about her test _____ _____ Sam.

   G: Oh, why did you _____ _____?

   B: I _____ _____ _____ _____ she would _____ _____.

   G: Well, like the saying goes, "_____ _____ _____ _____ _____."

   B: I agree. I've _____ my _____.

2. **A:** I don't _____ _____ _____ _____ today.

   B: Then _____ _____ _____ _____ _____ _____ _____ to eat?

   A: That's a good idea. What _____ we eat?

   B: _____ eat Chinese food. A new restaurant _____ down the street.

Claire: 진호야, 무슨 문제 있니? 속상해 보여.

진호: 나 Harry랑 싸웠어.

Claire: 왜? 무슨 일이 있었는데?

진호: 우리 둘 다 동시에 같은 음악실을 사용하기를 원했거든.

Claire: 난 방과 후에 연습할 수 있는 음악실이 충분히 있다고 생각하지 않아.

진호: 나도 동의해. 너는 음악실에 시간 제한을 두는 것에 대해 어떻게 생각하니?

Claire: 얼만큼 돼야 한다고 생각해?

진호: 난 누구든 하루에 1시간 이상 음악실을 사용해서는 안 된다고 생각해.

Claire: 난 동의하지 않아. 난 음악 연습을 하려면 1시간 이상이 필요해.

진호: 그렇다면 음악실을 예약하는 것은 어때?

Claire: 그거 좋은 생각이다. 그러면 각 개인은 연습할 충분한 시간을 갖게 될 거야.

1. B: 난 다른 사람들이 자리에 없을 때 그들에 대해 이야기해서는 안 된다고 생각해.

   G: 왜 그렇게 말하는 거니?

   B: 음, 나는 지민이의 시험 결과에 대해서 샘과 이야기한 것 때문에 지민이랑 싸웠어.

   G: 오, 너는 왜 그랬니?

   B: 난 지민이가 알게 될 거라고는 전혀 생각 못했어.

   G: 음, 속담에 '벽에도 귀가 있다.'라고 하잖아.

   B: 나도 동의해. 난 교훈을 얻었어.

2. A: 오늘 요리를 하고 싶지 않아.

   B: 그러면 외식하러 나가는 것은 어떻게 생각하니?

   A: 좋은 생각이야. 무엇을 먹을 거야?

   B: 중국 음식을 먹자. 길 아래쪽에 새로운 식당이 문을 열었어.

Step2

※ 다음 우리말에 맞도록 대화를 영어로 쓰시오.

Listen and Speak 1 A

1. B: _____
   G: _____
      _____
   B: _____
   G: _____
   B: _____

2. G: _____
   B: _____
      _____
   G: _____
      _____
   B: _____
      _____
   G: _____

해석

1. B: 민주야, 우리는 새 기타가 필요하지만 충분한 돈이 없어.
   G: 너는 돈을 마련하기 위한 콘서트를 하는 것에 대해 어떻게 생각해? 우리의 신곡도 소개할 수 있어.
   B: 아주 좋은 생각이야! 그건 "한 개의 돌로 두 마리의 새를 잡는 것"과 같을 거야.
   G: 맞아. 우선 우리 콘서트를 위한 포스터를 만들자.
   B: 그래.

2. G: 도훈아, 너 뭐 하고 있니?
   B: 나는 인공지능 로봇에 관한 영화를 보고 있어. 정말 흥미로워. 너는 그것들에 대해 어떻게 생각해?
   G: 내 생각에 그것들은 문제를 일으킬 거야. 인공지능 로봇은 사람들로부터 직업을 빼앗아 갈 거야.
   B: 글쎄, 난 여전히 그것들이 유용하다고 생각해. 인공지능 로봇들을 소개하는 과학 축제가 있어. 우리가 가서 그것들에 관해 더 알아보는 게 어때?
   G: 좋은 생각이야.

Listen and Speak 1 B

W: _____
B: _____
W: _____
   _____
B: _____
   _____
W: _____
B: _____
W: _____
B: _____

W: Jacob, 나 좀 도와줄 수 있니?
B: 뭔데요, 엄마?
W: 음, 내 친구한테 문자를 하나 받았는데, 이 중 일부가 무엇을 의미하는지 이해를 못하겠어.
B: 제가 볼게요, 음… ASAP는 '가능한 한 빨리'라는 의미이고, HAND는 '좋은 하루를 보내.'라는 의미예요.
W: 아, 그렇구나.
B: 이런 두문자들에 대해 어떻게 생각하세요, 엄마?
W: 난 그것들이 언어를 파괴하고 있다고 생각해. 너는 어떻게 생각하니?
B: 제 생각엔 그것들은 사용하기 재미있고 쉬운 것 같아요.

Listen and Speak 2 A

1. B: _____
   G: _____
      _____
   B: _____
   G: _____

2. B: _____
   G: _____
   B: _____
   G: _____
   B: _____

3. G: _____
   B: _____
      _____
   G: _____
      _____
   B: _____

Listen and Speak 2 B

B: _____
G: _____
B: _____
G: _____
      _____
B: _____
      _____
G: _____
      _____
B: _____

1. B: 봐! 사람들이 자기들의 쓰레기를 놔두고 그냥 떠나고 있어!
   G: 오, 안 돼! 우리가 환경을 해치면 결국 후회하는 건 우리일 거야.
   B: 나도 동의해. 속담에 '자신이 한 대로 되돌려 받는다(자업자득).'라고 하잖아.
   G: 네 말이 맞아. 우리 쓰레기는 우리가 가져가서 지구를 돕자.

2. B: Emma, 우리 좀 쉬자.
   G: 뭐라고? 우리 겨우 30분 동안 공부했어.
   B: 속담에 '일만 하고 놀지 않으면 바보가 된다.'라고 하잖아.
   G: 나도 동의해. 그러면 우리 이 부분을 끝내고 쉬자.
   B: 알았어.

3. G: 주원아, 무슨 문제 있니?
   B: 한 선생님이 미술 과제를 어제 제출하라고 하셨는데 난 아직 끝내지 못했어.
   G: 음, 나는 네가 그래도 그것을 끝내서 제출해야 한다고 생각해. 속담에 '안하는 것보다 늦는 게 낫다.'라고 하잖아.
   B: 네 말이 맞고 나도 동의해. 조언 고마워.

B: 유라야, 너 뭐 하고 있니?
G: 내 사진들을 인터넷에 올리고 있어. 와서 봐.
B: 너의 일상생활을 보여 주는 사진이 정말 많이 있네. 그거 위험하지 않니?
G: 글쎄, 내 친구들은 내 게시물들을 많이 좋아해. 난 이것이 서로 알아가는 데 좋은 방법이라고 생각해.
B: 나는 동의하지 않아. 너의 사진들을 나쁜 수단으로 이용할 일부 사람들이 있을지도 몰라.
G: 그러고 보니 나는 내 사진들에 대해 더 신중해야겠어. 충고 고마워.
B: 천만에.

Real Life Communication

Claire: _____

Jinho: _____

Claire: _____

Jinho: _____

Claire: _____

Jinho: _____

Claire: _____

Jinho: _____
_____

Claire: _____

Jinho: _____

Claire: _____

Claire: 진호야, 무슨 문제 있니? 속상해 보여.

진호: 나 Harry랑 싸웠어.

Claire: 왜? 무슨 일이 있었는데?

진호: 우리 둘 다 동시에 같은 음악실을 사용하기를 원했거든.

Claire: 난 방과 후에 연습할 수 있는 음악실이 충분히 있다고 생각하지 않아.

진호: 나도 동의해. 너는 음악실에 시간 제한을 두는 것에 대해 어떻게 생각하니?

Claire: 얼만큼 돼야 한다고 생각해?

진호: 난 누구든 하루에 1시간 이상 음악실을 사용해서는 안 된다고 생각해.

Claire: 난 동의하지 않아. 난 음악 연습을 하려면 1시간 이상이 필요해.

진호: 그렇다면 음악실을 예약하는 것은 어때?

Claire: 그거 좋은 생각이다. 그러면 각 개인은 연습할 충분한 시간을 갖게 될 거야.

Let's Check

1. B: _____

   G: _____

   B: _____
   _____

   G: _____

   B: _____

   G: _____

   B: _____

2. A: _____

   B: _____

   A: _____

   B: _____

---

1. B: 난 다른 사람들이 자리에 없을 때 그들에 대해 이야기해서는 안 된다고 생각해.

   G: 왜 그렇게 말하는 거니?

   B: 음, 나는 지민이의 시험 결과에 대해서 샘과 이야기한 것 때문에 지민이랑 싸웠어.

   G: 오, 너는 왜 그랬니?

   B: 난 지민이가 알게 될 거라고는 전혀 생각 못했어.

   G: 음, 속담에 '벽에도 귀가 있다.'라고 하잖아.

   B: 나도 동의해. 난 교훈을 얻었어.

2. A: 오늘 요리를 하고 싶지 않아.

   B: 그러면 외식하러 나가는 것은 어떻게 생각하니?

   A: 좋은 생각이야. 무엇을 먹을 거야?

   B: 중국 음식을 먹자. 길 아래쪽에 새로운 식당이 문을 열었어.

※ 다음 우리말과 일치하도록 빈칸에 알맞은 것을 골라 쓰시오.

Proverbs Upside Down

1 Every now and _____, words of _____ have _____ people and _____ their lives in a great way.

    A. influenced   B. then   C. changed   D. wisdom

2 For example, "_____ speak louder than _____," means the following: _____ you do is more important than what you _____.

    A. words   B. say   C. what   D. actions

3 So people _____ to do things _____ of just _____.

    A. saying   B. try   C. something   D. instead

4 _____, _____ people have _____.

    A. different   B. however   C. opinions   D. some

5 To them, it is _____ that _____ than _____. How?

    A. speak   B. words   C. actions   D. louder

6 They think _____ words can _____ _____ to do good _____.

    A. others   B. that   C. things   D. influence

7 It is _____ to have _____ _____.

    A. different   B. natural   C. ideas

8 Let's take a look at some _____ _____ _____.

    A. proverbs   B. down   C. other   D. upside

9 Look before you _____: Check what is in _____ of you before _____ a _____.

    A. making   B. leap   C. front   D. decision

10 I _____ _____. We should always be _____ before we _____ to do something.

    A. agree   B. decide   C. totally   D. careful

11 Then we'll _____ happy _____ the _____ of our _____.

    A. results   B. be   C. decisions   D. with

12 _____, if we don't _____ time to think things _____, we may _____ it.

    A. take   B. regret   C. however   D. over

13 Also, we'll make _____ if we do something _____ it a second _____.

    A. giving   B. mistakes   C. thought   D. without

14 _____ a _____, it will _____ us more time to _____. Posted by Suzi Kang

    A. take   B. as   C. fix   D. result

15 I don't _____. _____ don't come _____.

    A. opportunities   B. agree   C. often

16 If there is a _____, we should _____ it. _____, it will be too _____.

    A. grab   B. chance   C. late   D. or

17 Last year, I _____ _____ be the _____ of the school hockey team.

    A. asked   B. was   C. captain   D. to

속담 뒤집기

1 때때로 지혜의 말들은 사람들에게 영향을 미치고 그들의 삶을 굉장한 방향으로 바꾸었다.

2 예를 들어 '말보다 행동이 중요하다.'라는 말의 의미는 다음과 같다. 당신이 하는 것이 당신이 말하는 것보다 더 중요하다.

3 그래서 사람들은 그냥 무엇인가를 말하는 대신에 무엇인가를 하려고 노력한다.

4 그러나 몇몇 사람들은 다른 의견을 가지고 있다.

5 그들에게는 행동보다 더 중요한 것은 바로 말이다. 어떻게 그럴까?

6 그들은 말이 다른 사람들이 좋은 행동을 하는 데 영향을 미칠 수 있다고 생각한다.

7 다른 생각을 갖는 것은 자연스럽다.

8 몇 개의 다른 속담을 거꾸로 뒤집어서 살펴보자.

9 잘 생각해 보고 행동하라[돌다리도 두드려 보고 건너라]: 결정을 하기 전에 당신 앞에 있는 것이 무엇인지 확인하라.

10 나는 완전히 동의해. 우리는 무엇인가를 하기로 결정하기 전에 항상 조심해야 해.

11 그러면 우리는 우리의 결정으로 인한 결과에 행복할 거야.

12 그러나 만약 우리가 시간을 들여 어떤 일을 심사숙고하지 않는다면 우리는 후회할지도 몰라.

13 또한 우리는 다시 생각해 보지 않고 어떤 일을 한다면 실수할 거야.

14 그 결과 우리는 바로잡는 데 더 많은 시간을 들일 거야. 강수지에 의해 게시됨

15 나는 동의하지 않아. 기회는 자주 오지 않아.

16 만약 기회가 있다면 우리는 그 것을 붙잡아야 해. 그렇지 않으면 너무 늦을 거야.

17 작년에 나는 학교 하키 팀의 주장이 되기를 요청받았어.

18 _____, I _____ too much time to _____, so _____ friend became the captain.

    A. decide   B. took   C. however   D. another

19 Now, I _____ it. As the _____ goes, "_____ the iron is hot." Posted by Brian Pearson

    A. while   B. saying   C. regret   D. strike

20 Out of _____, out of _____: Something is easily _____ if it is not _____ us.

    A. mind   B. near   C. sight   D. forgotten

21 I agree _____ this _____. I had a _____ friend _____ elementary school.

    A. close   B. with   C. from   D. saying

22 _____, we _____ _____ _____ middle schools.

    A. went   B. different   C. sadly   D. to

23 At _____, we met two to three times a week. However, it was _____ _____ to _____ in _____.

    A. hard   B. first   C. touch   D. keep

24 We started to _____ _____ _____ _____ our bew friends.

    A. more   B. spend   C. with   D. time

25 I started _____ _____ and less _____ him and more and _____ about my new friends.

    A. less   B. more   C. thinking   D. about

26 Now, we _____ _____ talking or _____ each _____. Posted by Anna Brown

    A. stopped   B. other   C. have   D. seeing

27 I _____ _____ your _____.

    A. opinion   B. with   C. disagree

28 I was really _____ _____ my _____, Jenny.

    A. with   B. close   C. neighbor

29 She _____ _____ America and we _____ the _____ basketball team.

    A. liked   B. was   C. same   D. from

30 We _____ a _____ of time _____ games _____.

    A. lot   B. spent   C. together   D. watching

31 _____ her family _____ _____ three years _____.

    A. away   B. then   C. ago   D. moved

32 I _____ _____ her _____, but I still remember the times we _____.

    A. since   B. haven't   C. had   D. seen

33 I _____ her more and more _____ time _____ _____.

    A. as   B. miss   C. by   D. goes

34 It is the _____ of time _____ makes people remember _____ _____. Posted by Jaeha Park

    A. each   B. quality   C. other   D. that

35 Well, what is your _____? _____ is no _____ or _____ answer.

    A. there   B. opinion   C. wrong   D. right

36 It is you _____ should _____ _____ is _____ for you.

    A. decide   B. who   C. best   D. what

---

18 그러나 나는 결정하는 데 너무 많은 시간이 걸려서 다른 친구가 주장이 되었어.

19 지금 나는 후회해. 속담에도 있듯이 '쇠가 달았을 때 두드려야 해[쇠뿔도 단김에 빼야 해].' Brian Pearson에 의해 게시됨

20 눈에서 멀어지면, 마음에서도 멀어진다: 어떤 것이 우리 가까이에 있지 않으면 쉽게 잊힌다.

21 나는 이 말에 동의해. 나는 초등학교 때부터 친한 친구가 있었어.

22 아쉽게도 우리는 다른 중학교에 갔어.

23 처음에 우리는 일주일에 두세 번 만났어. 그러나 계속 연락을 하는 것은 어려웠어.

24 우리는 우리의 새로운 친구들과 더 많은 시간을 보내기 시작했어.

25 나는 그에 대해 점점 덜 생각하고 내 새로운 친구들에 대해 더욱 더 많이 생각하기 시작했어.

26 이제 우리는 서로 이야기하거나 만나지 않아.
Anna Brown에 의해 게시됨

27 나는 네 의견에 동의하지 않아.

28 나는 나의 이웃 Jenny와 정말 친했어.

29 그녀는 미국에서 왔고 우리는 같은 농구 팀을 좋아했어.

30 우리는 함께 경기를 보며 많은 시간을 보냈어.

31 그런데 그녀의 가족이 3년 전에 이사 갔어.

32 나는 그 이후로 그녀를 보지 못했지만 여전히 우리가 함께했던 시간들을 기억해.

33 나는 시간이 갈수록 그녀가 점점 더 그리워.

34 사람들이 서로를 기억하게 만드는 것은 바로 시간의 질이야.
박재하에 의해 게시됨

35 당신의 의견은 무엇인가? 맞고 틀린 답은 없다.

36 당신에게 최선인 것을 결정해야 하는 사람은 바로 당신이다.

※ 다음 우리말과 일치하도록 빈칸에 알맞은 말을 쓰시오.

Proverbs Upside Down

1 _____ _____ _____ _____, words of wisdom _____ _____ people and _____ their lives in a great way.

2 _____ _____, "_____ _____ _____ _____ _____," means the following: _____ _____ _____ is more important _____ _____ _____ _____.

3 So people try _____ _____ _____ _____ _____ _____ _____ just _____ _____.

4 _____, some people _____ _____ _____ _____.

5 To them, it is _____ _____ speak _____ _____ _____. How?

6 They think _____ words can _____ _____ _____ _____ good things.

7 It is natural _____ _____ _____ _____ _____.

8 Let's _____ _____ _____ at some _____ _____ _____ _____.

9 _____ _____ _____ _____ _____: Check _____ is in front of you _____ _____ a _____.

10 I _____ _____. We should always _____ _____ before we _____ _____ _____ something.

11 Then we'll be happy _____ the _____ of our _____.

12 _____, if we _____ _____ _____ things _____, we may _____ it.

13 Also, we'll _____ _____ _____ we do something _____ _____ _____ _____ _____.

14 _____ _____ _____ _____, it will take _____ _____ _____ _____ _____. Posted by Suzi Kang

15 I don't agree. _____ don't _____ _____ _____.

16 If _____ _____ _____ _____, we should _____ _____. Or, it will be _____ _____.

17 Last year, I _____ _____ _____ _____ _____ the _____ of the school hockey team.

속담 뒤집기

1 때때로 지혜의 말들은 사람들에게 영향을 미치고 그들의 삶을 굉장한 방향으로 바꾸었다.

2 예를 들어 '말보다 행동이 중요하다.'라는 말의 의미는 다음과 같다. 당신이 하는 것이 당신이 말하는 것보다 더 중요하다.

3 그래서 사람들은 그냥 무엇인가를 말하는 대신에 무엇인가를 하려고 노력한다.

4 그러나 몇몇 사람들은 다른 의견을 가지고 있다.

5 그들에게는 행동보다 더 중요한 것은 바로 말이다. 어떻게 그럴까?

6 그들은 말이 다른 사람들이 좋은 행동을 하는 데 영향을 미칠 수 있다고 생각한다.

7 다른 생각을 갖는 것은 자연스럽다.

8 몇 개의 다른 속담을 거꾸로 뒤집어서 살펴보자.

9 잘 생각해 보고 행동하라[돌다리도 두드려 보고 건너라]: 결정을 하기 전에 당신 앞에 있는 것이 무엇인지 확인하라.

10 나는 완전히 동의해. 우리는 무엇인가를 하기로 결정하기 전에 항상 조심해야 해.

11 그러면 우리는 우리의 결정으로 인한 결과에 행복할 거야.

12 그러나 만약 우리가 시간을 들여 어떤 일을 심사숙고하지 않는다면 우리는 후회할지도 몰라.

13 또한 우리는 다시 생각해 보지 않고 어떤 일을 한다면 실수할 거야.

14 그 결과 우리는 바로잡는 데 더 많은 시간을 들일 거야. 강수지에 의해 게시됨

15 나는 동의하지 않아. 기회는 자주 오지 않아.

16 만약 기회가 있다면 우리는 그것을 붙잡아야 해. 그렇지 않으면 너무 늦을 거야.

17 작년에 나는 학교 하키 팀의 주장이 되기를 요청받았어.

18 _____, I _____ _____ _____ time _____ _____, so _____ friend became the captain.

19 Now, I _____ it. As the saying goes, "_____ _____ _____ _____ _____." Posted by Brian Pearson

20 _____ _____ _____, _____ : Something is easily _____ if it is _____ _____ us.

21 I _____ _____ this _____. I had a close friend _____ elementary school.

22 Sadly, we went _____ _____ middle schools.

23 _____ _____, we met _____ _____ _____ _____. _____, it was _____ _____ _____.

24 We started to _____ _____ _____ _____ our _____ friends.

25 I started _____ _____ and _____ about him and _____ and _____ about my new friends.

26 Now, we _____ _____ _____ or _____ each other.
Posted by Anna Brown

27 I _____ _____ your _____.

28 I was really _____ _____ my _____, Jenny.

29 She was _____ America and we _____ _____ basketball team.

30 We _____ a lot of _____ _____ games together.

31 Then _____ _____ _____ _____ three years ago.

32 I haven't _____ her since, but I still _____ the times _____ _____.

33 I miss her more and more _____ _____ _____.

34 _____ _____ the quality of time _____ _____ people _____ _____ _____. Posted by Jaeha Park

35 Well, _____ is your opinion? There is _____ _____ or _____ _____.

36 It is you _____ _____ _____ _____ for you.

18 그러나 나는 결정하는 데 너무 많은 시간이 걸려서 다른 친구가 주장이 되었어.

19 지금 나는 후회해. 속담에도 있듯이 '쇠가 달았을 때 두드려야 해[쇠뿔도 단김에 빼야 해].' Brian Pearson에 의해 게시됨

20 눈에서 멀어지면, 마음에서도 멀어진다: 어떤 것이 우리 가까이에 있지 않으면 쉽게 잊힌다.

21 나는 이 말에 동의해. 나는 초등학교 때부터 친한 친구가 있었어.

22 아쉽게도 우리는 다른 중학교에 갔어.

23 처음에 우리는 일주일에 두세 번 만났어. 그러나 계속 연락을 하는 것은 어려웠어.

24 우리는 우리의 새로운 친구들과 더 많은 시간을 보내기 시작했어.

25 나는 그에 대해 점점 덜 생각하고 내 새로운 친구들에 대해 더욱 더 많이 생각하기 시작했어.

26 이제 우리는 서로 이야기하거나 만나지 않아.
Anna Brown에 의해 게시됨

27 나는 네 의견에 동의하지 않아.

28 나는 나의 이웃 Jenny와 정말 친했어.

29 그녀는 미국에서 왔고 우리는 같은 농구 팀을 좋아했어.

30 우리는 함께 경기를 보며 많은 시간을 보냈어.

31 그런데 그녀의 가족이 3년 전에 이사 갔어.

32 나는 그 이후로 그녀를 보지 못했지만 여전히 우리가 함께했던 시간들을 기억해.

33 나는 시간이 갈수록 그녀가 점점 더 그리워.

34 사람들이 서로를 기억하게 만드는 것은 바로 시간의 질이야.
박재하에 의해 게시됨

35 당신의 의견은 무엇인가? 맞고 틀린 답은 없다.

36 당신에게 최선인 것을 결정해야 하는 사람은 바로 당신이다.

※ 다음 문장을 우리말로 쓰시오.

Proverbs Upside Down

1 Every now and then, words of wisdom have influenced people and changed their lives in a great way.

➡ _____

2 For example, "Actions speak louder than words," means the following: what you do is more important than what you say.

➡ _____

3 So people try to do things instead of just saying something.

➡ _____

4 However, some people have different opinions.

➡ _____

5 To them, it is words that speak louder than actions. How?

➡ _____

6 They think that words can influence others to do good things.

➡ _____

7 It is natural to have different ideas.

➡ _____

8 Let's take a look at some other proverbs upside down.

➡ _____

9 Look before you leap: Check what is in front of you before making a decision.

➡ _____

10 I totally agree. We should always be careful before we decide to do something.

➡ _____

11 Then we'll be happy with the results of our decisions.

➡ _____

12 However, if we don't take time to think things over, we may regret it.

➡ _____

13 Also, we'll make mistakes if we do something without giving it a second thought.

➡ _____

14 As a result, it will take us more time to fix. Posted by Suzi Kang

➡ _____

15 I don't agree. Opportunities don't come often.

➡ _____

16 If there is a chance, we should grab it. Or, it will be too late.

➡ _____

17 ▶ Last year, I was asked to be the captain of the school hockey team.
➡ _____

18 ▶ However, I took too much time to decide, so another friend became the captain.
➡ _____

19 ▶ Now, I regret it. As the saying goes, "Strike while the iron is hot." Posted by Brian Pearson
➡ _____

20 ▶ Out of sight, out of mind: Something is easily forgotten if it is not near us.
➡ _____

21 ▶ I agree with this saying. I had a close friend from elementary school.
➡ _____

22 ▶ Sadly, we went to different middle schools.
➡ _____

23 ▶ At first, we met two to three times a week. However, it was hard to keep in touch.
➡ _____

24 ▶ We started to spend more time with our new friends.
➡ _____

25 ▶ I started thinking less and less about him and more and more about my new friends.
➡ _____

26 ▶ Now, we have stopped talking or seeing each other. Posted by Anna Brown
➡ _____

27 ▶ I disagree with your opinion.
➡ _____

28 ▶ I was really close with my neighbor, Jenny.
➡ _____

29 ▶ She was from America and we liked the same basketball team.
➡ _____

30 ▶ We spent a lot of time watching games together.
➡ _____

31 ▶ Then her family moved away three years ago.
➡ _____

32 ▶ I haven't seen her since, but I still remember the times we had.
➡ _____

33 ▶ I miss her more and more as time goes by.
➡ _____

34 ▶ It is the quality of time that makes people remember each other. Posted by Jaeha Park
➡ _____

35 ▶ Well, what is your opinion? There is no right or wrong answer.
➡ _____

36 ▶ It is you who should decide what is best for you.
➡ _____

※ 다음 괄호 안의 단어들을 우리말에 맞도록 바르게 배열하시오.

Proverbs Upside Down

1 (now / every / then, / and / of / words / have / wisdom / influenced / people / and / their / changed / lives / a / in / way. / great)
➡ _____
_____

2 (example, / for / "actions / louder / speak / words," / than / the / means / following: / you / what / do / more / is / than / important / you / what / say.)
➡ _____
_____

3 (people / so / to / try / things / do / of / instead / saying / just / something.)
➡ _____

4 (some / however, / have / people / opinions. / different)
➡ _____

5 (them, / to / is / it / that / words / louder / speak / actions. / than // how?)
➡ _____

6 (think / they / words / that / influence / can / to / others / do / things. / good)
➡ _____

7 (is / it / to / natural / different / have / ideas.)
➡ _____

8 (take / a / let's / look / at / some / proverbs / other / down. / upside)
➡ _____

9 (before / look / leap: / you // what / check / in / is / front / you / of / making / before / decision. / a)
➡ _____
_____

10 (totally / I / agree. // should / we / be / always / before / careful / decide / we / do / to / something.)
➡ _____
_____

11 (we'll / then / happy / be / the / with / of / results / decisions. / our)
➡ _____

12 (if / however, / don't / we / time / take / think / to / things / we / over, / regret / may / it.)
➡ _____
_____

13 (we'll / also, / mistakes / make / we / if / something / do / giving / without / it / second / a / thought.)
➡ _____
_____

14 (a / as / result, / will / it / us / take / time / more / fix. / to // by / posted / Kang / Suzi)
➡ _____

15 (don't / I / agree. // don't / opportunities / often. / come)
➡ _____

16 (there / if / a / is / chance, / should / we / it. / grab // it / or, / be / will / late. / too)
➡ _____
_____

17 (year, / last / was / I / to / asked / be / captain / the / the / of / school / team. / hockey)
➡ _____

속담 뒤집기

1 때때로 지혜의 말들은 사람들에게 영향을 미치고 그들의 삶을 굉장한 방향으로 바꾸었다.

2 예를 들어 '말보다 행동이 중요하다.'라는 말의 의미는 다음과 같다. 당신이 하는 것이 당신이 말하는 것보다 더 중요하다.

3 그래서 사람들은 그냥 무엇인가를 말하는 대신에 무엇인가를 하려고 노력한다.

4 그러나 몇몇 사람들은 다른 의견을 가지고 있다.

5 그들에게는 행동보다 더 중요한 것은 바로 말이다. 어떻게 그럴까?

6 그들은 말이 다른 사람들이 좋은 행동을 하는 데 영향을 미칠 수 있다고 생각한다.

7 다른 생각을 갖는 것은 자연스럽다.

8 몇 개의 다른 속담을 거꾸로 뒤집어서 살펴보자.

9 잘 생각해 보고 행동하라[돌다리도 두드려 보고 건너라]: 결정을 하기 전에 당신 앞에 있는 것이 무엇인지 확인하라.

10 나는 완전히 동의해. 우리는 무엇인가를 하기로 결정하기 전에 항상 조심해야 해.

11 그러면 우리는 우리의 결정으로 인한 결과에 행복할 거야.

12 그러나 만약 우리가 시간을 들여 어떤 일을 심사숙고하지 않는다면 우리는 후회할지도 몰라.

13 또한 우리는 다시 생각해 보지 않고 어떤 일을 한다면 실수할 거야.

14 그 결과 우리는 바로잡는 데 더 많은 시간을 들일 거야. 강수지에 의해 게시됨

15 나는 동의하지 않아. 기회는 자주 오지 않아.

16 만약 기회가 있다면 우리는 그것을 붙잡아야 해. 그렇지 않으면 너무 늦을 거야.

17 작년에 나는 학교 하키 팀의 주장이 되기를 요청받았어.

18 (I / however, / took / much / too / to / time / decide, / another / so / became / friend / captain. / the)

➡ _____

19 (I / now, / it. / reget // the / as / goes, / saying / "strike / the / while / is / iron / hot." / by / posted / Pearson / Brian)

➡ _____

20 (of / out / sight, / of / out / mind: // is / something / forgotten / easily / it / if / not / is / us. / near)

➡ _____

21 (agree / I / this / with / saying. // had / I / a / friend / close / from / school. / elementary)

➡ _____

22 (we / sadly, / to / went / middle / different / schools.)

➡ _____

23 (first, / at / met / we / to / two / three / a / times / week. // it / however, / hard / was / to / in / touch. / keep)

➡ _____

24 (started / we / spend / to / time / more / our / with / friends. / new)

➡ _____

25 (started / I / less / thinking / and / about / less / him / and / more / more / and / about / new / my / friends.)

➡ _____

26 (we / now, / stopped / have / talking / seeing / or / other. / each // by / posted / Brown / Anna)

➡ _____

27 (disagree / I / your / with / opinion.)

➡ _____

28 (was / I / close / really / my / with / Jenny. / neighbor,)

➡ _____

29 (was / she / America / from / and / liked / we / same / the / team. / basketball)

➡ _____

30 (spent / we / lot / a / of / watching / time / together. / games)

➡ _____

31 (her / then / moved / family / three / away / ago. / years)

➡ _____

32 (haven't / I / her / seen / since, / I / but / remember / still / times / the / had. / we)

➡ _____

33 (miss / I / more / her / and / as / more / goes / time / by.)

➡ _____

34 (is / it / quality / the / time / of / that / people / makes / each / remember / other. / by / posted / Park / Jaeha)

➡ _____

35 (what / well, / your / is / opinion? // is / there / right / no / or / answer. / wrong)

➡ _____

36 (is / it / who / you / should / what / decide / is / for / best / you.)

➡ _____

18 그러나 나는 결정하는 데 너무 많은 시간이 걸려서 다른 친구가 주장이 되었어.

19 지금 나는 후회해. 속담에도 있듯이 '쇠가 달았을 때 두드려야 해[쇠뿔도 단김에 빼야 해].' Brian Pearson에 의해 게시됨

20 눈에서 멀어지면, 마음에서도 멀어진다: 어떤 것이 우리 가까이에 있지 않으면 쉽게 잊힌다.

21 나는 이 말에 동의해. 나는 초등학교 때부터 친한 친구가 있었어.

22 아쉽게도 우리는 다른 중학교에 갔어.

23 처음에 우리는 일주일에 두세 번 만났어. 그러나 계속 연락을 하는 것은 어려웠어.

24 우리는 우리의 새로운 친구들과 더 많은 시간을 보내기 시작했어.

25 나는 그에 대해 점점 덜 생각하고 내 새로운 친구들에 대해 더욱 더 많이 생각하기 시작했어.

26 이제 우리는 서로 이야기하거나 만나지 않아.
Anna Brown에 의해 게시됨

27 나는 네 의견에 동의하지 않아.

28 나는 나의 이웃 Jenny와 정말 친했어.

29 그녀는 미국에서 왔고 우리는 같은 농구 팀을 좋아했어.

30 우리는 함께 경기를 보며 많은 시간을 보냈어.

31 그런데 그녀의 가족이 3년 전에 이사 갔어.

32 나는 그 이후로 그녀를 보지 못했지만 여전히 우리가 함께했던 시간들을 기억해.

33 나는 시간이 갈수록 그녀가 점점 더 그리워.

34 사람들이 서로를 기억하게 만드는 것은 바로 시간의 질이야.
박재하에 의해 게시됨

35 당신의 의견은 무엇인가? 맞고 틀린 답은 없다.

36 당신에게 최선인 것을 결정해야 하는 사람은 바로 당신이다.

※ 다음 우리말을 영어로 쓰시오.

Proverbs Upside Down

1 때때로 지혜의 말들은 사람들에게 영향을 미치고 그들의 삶을 굉장한 방향으로 바꾸었다.

➡ _____

_____

2 예를 들어 '말보다 행동이 중요하다.'라는 말의 의미는 다음과 같다. 당신이 하는 것이 당신이 말하는 것보다 더 중요하다.

➡ _____

_____

3 그래서 사람들은 그냥 무엇인가를 말하는 대신에 무엇인가를 하려고 노력한다.

➡ _____

4 그러나 몇몇 사람들은 다른 의견을 가지고 있다.

➡ _____

5 그들에게는 행동보다 더 중요한 것은 바로 말이다. 어떻게 그럴까?

➡ _____

6 그들은 말이 다른 사람들이 좋은 행동을 하는 데 영향을 미칠 수 있다고 생각한다.

➡ _____

7 다른 생각을 갖는 것은 자연스럽다.

➡ _____

8 몇 개의 다른 속담을 거꾸로 뒤집어서 살펴보자.

➡ _____

9 잘 생각해 보고 행동하라[돌다리도 두드려 보고 건너라]: 결정을 하기 전에 당신 앞에 있는 것이 무엇인지 확인하라.

➡ _____

10 나는 완전히 동의해. 우리는 무엇인가를 하기로 결정하기 전에 항상 조심해야 해.

➡ _____

11 그러면 우리는 우리의 결정으로 인한 결과에 행복할 거야.

➡ _____

12 그러나 만약 우리가 시간을 들여 어떤 일을 심사숙고하지 않는다면 우리는 후회할지도 몰라.

➡ _____

13 또한 우리는 다시 생각해 보지 않고 어떤 일을 한다면 실수할 거야.

➡ _____

14 그 결과 우리는 바로잡는 데 더 많은 시간을 들일 거야. 강수지에 의해 게시됨

➡ _____

15 나는 동의하지 않아. 기회는 자주 오지 않아.

➡ _____

16 만약 기회가 있다면 우리는 그것을 붙잡아야 해. 그렇지 않으면 너무 늦을 거야.

➡ _____

17 작년에 나는 학교 하키 팀의 주장이 되기를 요청받았어.
➡ _____

18 그러나 나는 결정하는 데 너무 많은 시간이 걸려서 다른 친구가 주장이 되었어.
➡ _____

19 지금 나는 후회해. 속담에도 있듯이 '쇠가 달았을 때 두드려야 해[쇠뿔도 단김에 빼야 해].' Brian Pearson에 의해 게시됨
➡ _____

20 눈에서 멀어지면, 마음에서도 멀어진다: 어떤 것이 우리 가까이에 있지 않으면 쉽게 잊힌다.
➡ _____

21 나는 이 말에 동의해. 나는 초등학교 때부터 친한 친구가 있었어.
➡ _____

22 아쉽게도 우리는 다른 중학교에 갔어.
➡ _____

23 처음에 우리는 일주일에 두세 번 만났어. 그러나 계속 연락을 하는 것은 어려웠어.
➡ _____

24 우리는 우리의 새로운 친구들과 더 많은 시간을 보내기 시작했어.
➡ _____

25 나는 그에 대해 점점 덜 생각하고 내 새로운 친구들에 대해 더욱 더 많이 생각하기 시작했어.
➡ _____

26 이제 우리는 서로 이야기하거나 만나지 않아. Anna Brown에 의해 게시됨
➡ _____

27 나는 네 의견에 동의하지 않아.
➡ _____

28 나는 나의 이웃 Jenny와 정말 친했어.
➡ _____

29 그녀는 미국에서 왔고 우리는 같은 농구 팀을 좋아했어.
➡ _____

30 우리는 함께 경기를 보며 많은 시간을 보냈어.
➡ _____

31 그런데 그녀의 가족이 3년 전에 이사 갔어.
➡ _____

32 나는 그 이후로 그녀를 보지 못했지만 여전히 우리가 함께했던 시간들을 기억해.
➡ _____

33 나는 시간이 갈수록 그녀가 점점 더 그리워.
➡ _____

34 사람들이 서로를 기억하게 만드는 것은 바로 시간의 질이야. 박재하에 의해 게시됨
➡ _____

35 당신의 의견은 무엇인가? 맞고 틀린 답은 없다.
➡ _____

36 당신에게 최선인 것을 결정해야 하는 사람은 바로 당신이다.
➡ _____

※ 다음 우리말과 일치하도록 빈칸에 알맞은 말을 쓰시오.

After You Read B Read and Correct

1. _____ _____, I _____ _____ _____ be the captain of the school soccer team.
2. _____, I _____ too much _____ _____ _____, so I _____ the captain.
3. I think you should _____ _____ _____ _____ _____.
4. I _____ _____ your idea.
5. If you do _____ _____ _____ it a second thought, you _____ _____ _____ _____.

Let's Write

1. There is a _____ that "Two _____ are _____ _____ one."
2. It means that when you _____ _____ _____ _____, it's _____ _____ _____ _____ or _____ _____ _____.
3. _____ _____ _____ _____ this saying say that first, you can _____ _____ _____ _____ _____.
4. Second, you _____ _____ _____ _____ _____ _____.
5. _____, those _____ _____ that first, you _____ _____ _____ too much information.
6. Second, you can _____ too _____ _____ _____ _____.
7. _____ _____ _____, it is my own ideas that are _____ _____ _____ _____ _____.
8. _____ _____ you?

Culture & Life

1. You can find some proverbs _____ _____ _____ _____ _____.
2. The _____ may be _____.
3. However, they show _____ _____ _____ and _____.
4. _____ read some of _____ and find _____ _____.
5. Turkey: The ground _____ _____.
6. Tanzania: _____ the night _____ _____.
7. Kenya: He _____ _____ _____ _____ _____ _____ says that the yard is _____.
8. the UK: A _____ _____ his _____.
9. Kenya: _____ _____ _____, it is the grass that _____ _____.
10. Korea: 고래 싸움에 새우 등 터진다.

1. 작년에 나는 학교 축구팀의 주장이 되기를 요청받았어.
2. 그러나 나는 결정하는 데 너무 많은 시간을 보내서 주장이 되지 못했어.
3. 나는 쇠뿔도 단김에 빼야 한다고 생각해.
4. 나는 너의 생각에 동의하지 않아.
5. 만약 네가 어떤 일을 다시 생각해 보지 않고 한다면, 너는 너의 결정을 후회할지도 몰라.

1. "두 사람의 지혜가 한 사람의 지혜보다 낫다,"라는 속담이 있다.
2. 이것은 일을 완성할 때 다른 사람들의 충고나 의견을 가지는 것이 도움이 된다는 것을 의미한다.
3. 이 속담에 동의하는 사람들은 첫 번째로 다른 사람들로부터 좋은 생각을 얻을 수 있다고 말한다.
4. 두 번째로 일을 빨리 끝낼 수 있다.
5. 하지만 동의하지 않는 사람들은 먼저 너무 많은 정보로 혼란스럽게 될 수 있다고 말한다.
6. 두 번째로, 결정하기 전에 많은 시간을 소비할 수 있다.
7. 내 생각에는 일을 완성할 때, 자신의 생각을 가지는 것이 더 도움이 된다고 생각한다.
8. 당신의 생각은 어떠한가?

1. 여러분은 여러 문화에서 비슷한 속담을 찾을 수 있다.
2. 표현은 다를지 모른다.
3. 그러나 그들은 같은 가치와 생각들을 보여 준다.
4. 몇몇 속담을 읽고, 연결 고리를 찾아 보자.
5. 터키 – 땅에 귀가 있다.
6. 탄자니아 – 심지어 밤에도 귀가 있다.
7. 케냐 – 춤을 못 추는 사람이 뜰에 돌이 많다고 말한다.
8. 영국 – 서투른 목수가 연장만 탓한다.
9. 케냐 – 코끼리들이 싸울 때 다치는 것은 풀이다.
10 한국 – 고래 싸움에 새우 등 터진다.

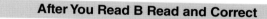
※ 다음 우리말을 영어로 쓰시오.

After You Read B Read and Correct

1. 작년에 나는 학교 축구팀의 주장이 되기를 요청받았어.
➡ _____

2. 그러나 나는 결정하는 데 너무 많은 시간을 보내서 주장이 되지 못했어.
➡ _____

3. 나는 쇠뿔도 단김에 빼야 한다고 생각해.
➡ _____

4. 나는 너의 생각에 동의하지 않아.
➡ _____

5. 만약 네가 어떤 일을 다시 생각해 보지 않고 한다면, 너는 너의 결정을 후회할지도 몰라.
➡ _____

Let's Write

1. "두 사람의 지혜가 한 사람의 지혜보다 낫다."라는 속담이 있다.
➡ _____

2. 이것은 일을 완성할 때 다른 사람들의 충고나 의견을 가지는 것이 도움이 된다는 것을 의미한다.
➡ _____

3. 이 속담에 동의하는 사람들은 첫 번째로 다른 사람들로부터 좋은 생각을 얻을 수 있다고 말한다.
➡ _____

4. 두 번째로 일을 빨리 끝낼 수 있다.
➡ _____

5. 하지만 동의하지 않는 사람들은 먼저 너무 많은 정보로 혼란스럽게 될 수 있다고 말한다.
➡ _____

6. 두 번째로, 결정하기 전에 많은 시간을 소비할 수 있다.
➡ _____

7. 내 생각에는 일을 완성할 때, 자신의 생각을 가지는 것이 더 도움이 된다고 생각한다.
➡ _____

8. 당신의 생각은 어떠한가?
➡ _____

Culture & Life

1. 여러분은 여러 문화에서 비슷한 속담을 찾을 수 있다.
➡ _____

2. 표현은 다를지 모른다.
➡ _____

3. 그러나 그들은 같은 가치와 생각들을 보여 준다.
➡ _____

4. 몇몇 속담을 읽고, 연결 고리를 찾아보자.
➡ _____

5. 터키 – 땅에 귀가 있다.
➡ _____

6. 탄자니아 – 심지어 밤에도 귀가 있다.
➡ _____

7. 케냐 – 춤을 못 추는 사람이 뜰에 돌이 많다고 말한다.
➡ _____

8. 영국 – 서투른 목수가 연장만 탓한다.
➡ _____

9. 케냐 – 코끼리들이 싸울 때 다치는 것은 풀이다.
➡ _____

※ 다음 영어를 우리말로 쓰시오.

01 flat	22 floating
02 roof	23 raised
03 hidden	24 house
04 cave	25 appear
05 huge	26 store
06 mostly	27 invader
07 colorful	28 thick
08 walkway	29 imagine
09 unwelcome	30 village
10 install	31 usually
11 tide	32 however
12 swampy	33 rise
13 wooden	34 share
14 ladder	35 upside down
15 surface	36 come over
16 straw	37 be known as
17 millionaire	38 hand down
18 invisible	39 walk around
19 opening	40 for a while
20 support	41 full of
21 everywhere	42 stop A from ~ing
	43 be made up of

Step2

※ 다음 우리말을 영어로 쓰시오.

01 보통, 대개

02 흙

03 구멍

04 높이 올린

05 습지의

06 보이다, 나타나다

07 지붕

08 침략자

09 지탱하다, 떠받치다

10 반갑지 않은

11 설치하다

12 동굴

13 저장하다, 보관하다

14 형형색색의

15 상상하다

16 평평한

17 때때로, 가끔

18 숨겨진

19 표면, 지면, 수면

20 떠다니는

21 거대한, 굉장히 큰

22 두꺼운, 살찐

23 백만장자

24 수용하다

25 눈에 보이지 않는, 투명한

26 짚, 지푸라기

27 나무로 된

28 사다리

29 주로, 일반적으로

30 통로

31 오르다, 올라가다

32 조수, 흐름

33 모든 곳에, 어디나

34 공유하다

35 ~ 위에

36 하루 종일

37 ~을 물려주다

38 들르다

39 A가 ~하지 못하게 막다

40 ~로서 알려 지다

41 돌아다니다

42 A를 당겨 올리다

43 ~로 구성되다,
   ~로 만들어지다

※ 다음 영영풀이에 알맞은 단어를 <보기>에서 골라 쓴 후, 우리말 뜻을 쓰시오.

1 _____ : impossible to see: _____

2 _____ : level, with no high hills or other raised parts: _____

3 _____ : to provide a place for somebody to live: _____

4 _____ : the dry stems of wheat and other grain plants: _____

5 _____ : a large hole in the side of a hill or under the ground: _____

6 _____ : to fix equipment or furniture into position so that it can be used:

   _____

7 _____ : a space or hole that somebody or something can pass through: _____

8 _____ : a person who has a million pounds, dollars, etc.; a very rich person:

   _____

9 _____ : very wet or covered with water land in which plants, trees, etc. are

   growing: _____

10 _____ : to put something that is not being used in a place where it can be kept

   safely: _____

11 _____ : a passage or path for walking along, often outside and raised above the

   ground: _____

12 _____ : having a large distance between the top and bottom or front and back

   surfaces: _____

13 _____ : an army or a country that enters another country by force in order to take

   control of it: _____

14 _____ : to hold somebody or something in position; to prevent somebody or

   something from falling: _____

15 _____ : a device used for climbing that has two long pieces of wood, metal, or

   rope with a series of steps or rungs between them: _____

16 _____ : the regular upward and downward movement of the level of the ocean

   that is caused by the pull of the sun and the moon on Earth: _____

보기			
walkway	cave	swampy	flat
ladder	invisible	tide	opening
thick	millionaire	store	house
support	straw	invader	install

※ 다음 우리말과 일치하도록 빈칸에 알맞은 말을 쓰시오.

Listen and Speak 1 A

G: _____ you heard from Julia? She's _____ in Turkey, right?

B: Yes, she sent me some pictures. Do you _____ to _____ them?

G: Yes, please.

B: Okay, _____ a look.

G: Oh, look at those cave houses! They look so _____, don't they? I wish I could try _____ there.

B: I like _____ balloons. They look so _____!

G: I think Turkey is a wonderful place _____ visit. I _____ to visit there _____ _____ .

B: Me _____!

Listen and Speak 1 B

B: Will _____ snow today?

G: I have no idea. _____ are you _____ _____ snow, Taeho?

B: I got a new sled for my birthday. I can't _____ to test it _____ .

G: Let me _____ the weather. Umm, there will be no snow for a while.

B: I wish I could live in Alaska. Then I _____ go sledding all day!

G: No _____! Alaska is a very _____ _____ .

B: I think it would be fun. I want to _____ a snow house and _____ there on _____ .

G: _____ in a snow house _____ fun!

Listen and Speak 1 C

A: Look at _____ houses. They look very _____ .

B: Wow, I wish I could _____ _____ here.

A: _____ house would you _____ like to _____ _____ ?

B: I wish I could live in the stone house. It looks very _____ .

Listen and Speak 2 A-1

B: This is my dream house, Alice. _____ do you think?

G: Oh, the house has wheels! Is it a _____ of car?

B: Yes, it can _____ _____ a car.

G: So _____ would you do if you _____ in that house?

B: I would _____ to many places _____ my family.

G: That sounds _____ .

G Julia한테서 소식 들었니? 그 애는 터키에서 여행 중이잖아, 맞지?
B 응, Julia가 나한테 사진 몇 장을 보내 왔어. 사진 보고 싶니?
G 응, 보고 싶어.
B 알겠어, 봐.
G 오, 저 동굴 집 좀 봐! 정말 특이하다, 그렇지 않니? 난 그곳에서 살아 봤으면 좋겠어.
B 난 저 열기구가 마음에 들어. 매우 아름다워 보여!
G 내 생각엔 터키가 방문하기에 정말 멋진 곳 같아. 언제 한 번 방문해 보고 싶다.
B 나도 그래!

B: 오늘 눈이 오는 거니?
G: 나도 모르겠어. 태호야, 왜 눈을 기다리는 거니?
B: 내 생일 선물로 새 썰매를 받았거든. 그거 빨리 시험해 보고 싶어.
G: 날씨 좀 확인해 볼게. 음, 당분간은 눈 소식이 없을 거래.
B: 알래스카에 살면 좋을 텐데. 그럼 온종일 썰매를 타러 갈 수 있을 텐데!
G: 말도 안 돼! 알래스카는 정말 추운 곳이야.
B: 내 생각엔 정말 즐거울 것 같아. 눈으로 집을 짓고 방학 때 그곳에서 지내고 싶어.
G: 눈으로 만든 집에 사는 건 재미있을 것 같아!

A: 이 집들 좀 봐. 매우 자연 그대로인 것 같아.
B: 우와, 이곳에 살아 봤으면 좋겠어.
A: 어느 집에서 가장 살아보고 싶니?
B: 돌로 만든 집에서 살아 보면 좋을 텐데. 매우 튼튼해 보여.

B: 이게 내 꿈의 집이야, Alice. 어떻게 생각하니?
G: 와, 바퀴가 달린 집이라니! 자동차의 일종이니?
B: 응, 자동차처럼 움직일 수 있어.
G: 그래서 그 집에서 살게 되면 뭘 할 거니?
B: 나는 가족들이랑 많은 곳을 여행할 거야.
G: 정말 신나게 들린다.

Listen and Speak 2 A-2

G: What would you do if you _____ a _____, Juwon?

B: I would _____ my own house.

G: What _____ of house would you _____?

B: I would build a house that is completely _____ _____ mirrors.

G: Why?

B: The _____ would make the house _____ _____. Wouldn't that be cool?

G: That _____ be cool!

Listen and Speak 2 A-3

G: Look. The house in this picture is _____ _____.

B: That's _____. Does anybody live there?

G: No, it would not be _____ to live there _____ the inside is also _____ _____.

B: Really? But I want to _____ _____ there.

G: _____ would you do if you _____ in that house?

B: I would walk upside down _____ Spider-Man. I could also see things _____.

Listen and Speak 2 B

G: Dohun, we _____ to start our project on our dream country to _____.

B: That's right. _____ _____ do you want to visit, Emma?

G: In my _____, I want to visit Spain.

B: What _____ you do if you _____ Spain?

G: I'm _____ in buildings. So I would go see La Sagrada Familia.

B: Isn't _____ the _____ Antoni Gaudi _____?

G: Yes, it is. It would be interesting to see _____ his design was _____ _____ _____.

B: Hmm.... _____ about *Gaudí and Spain* _____ the title for our project?

G: I love it!

Listen and Speak 2 C

A: _____ would you do if you could have a _____ _____?

B: I would _____ _____ a bird. Then I would be _____ _____ _____ _____ in the sky.

A: That's cool.

G: 주원아, 백만장자가 되면 뭘 할 거니?
B: 나는 나만의 집을 지을 거야.
G: 어떤 집을 짓고 싶은데?
B: 나는 거울로 완전히 덮인 집을 지을 거야.
G: 왜?
B: 그 거울들이 집을 거의 안 보이게 만들어줄 거야. 멋지지 않니?
G: 그건 멋질 거야!

G: 봐, 이 사진에 있는 집은 거꾸로 되어 있어.
B: 흥미로운데. 그 집에 누가 사는 건가?
G: 아니, 내부도 거꾸로 되어 있으니까 그곳에서 살기는 쉽지 않을 거야.
B: 정말? 하지만 나는 그곳에서 살아 보고 싶어.
G: 저 집에 살게 된다면 너는 뭘 할 거니?
B: 나는 스파이더맨처럼 거꾸로 걸어다닐 거야. 난 또한 사물을 다르게 볼 수 있을 거야.

G: 도훈아, 우리가 방문하고 싶은 꿈꾸는 나라에 대한 프로젝트를 시작해야 돼.
B: 맞아. Emma, 너는 어느 나라를 방문하고 싶니?
G: 내 경우에는 스페인에 가 보고 싶어.
B: 스페인에 가게 되면 뭘 할 건데?
G: 나는 건물들에 관심이 있어. 그래서 나는 La Sagrada Familia에 가 볼 거야.
B: 그 성당은 Antoni Gaudi가 디자인한 교회 아니니?
G: 응, 맞아. 그의 디자인이 어떻게 자연에서 영감을 얻었는지 보면 흥미로울 거야.
B: 흠… '가우디와 스페인'을 우리 프로젝트 제목으로 하는 건 어떠니?
G: 아주 좋아!

A: 마법의 힘을 갖게 된다면 너는 무엇을 할 거니?
B: 난 새로 변할 거야. 그러면 하늘을 자유롭게 날 수 있겠지.
A: 그거 멋있다.

Real Life Communication A

Jinho: I think _____ in a jungle would be really _____. Don't you think _____?

Claire: But there are _____ _____ animals in the jungle, Jinho.

Jinho: I know. But the jungle is _____ of adventure. I wish I _____ _____ there.

Claire: What _____ you do if you _____ in the jungle?

Jinho: I would _____ it. Maybe I could make some animal friends.

Claire: Then _____ would you sleep? In a _____?

Jinho: No, I would _____ _____ a tree house. _____ I would be safe from _____ _____.

Claire: That _____ _____.

Real Life Communication B

A: I wish I could _____ in a house on the water _____ my vacation.

B: What _____ you do if you _____ there?

A: I would _____ _____ _____ _____. I would also _____ _____.

B: That _____ fun.

Let's Check 1

B: _____ is my dream house. _____ do you _____, Alice?

G: Oh, it's in the _____ _____. It looks so _____. So, what _____ you do if you _____ in that house?

B: I have an _____ in _____ _____ animals. _____ I would _____ the deep sea and find some _____ sea animals.

G: _____ sounds cool!

Let's Check 2

A: What's the _____?

B: My computer is so slow. I _____ I _____ _____ a new computer.

Jinho: 내 생각엔 정글에서 사는 건 정말 신날 거야. 그렇게 생각하지 않니?
Claire: 근데 진호야, 정글에는 몇몇 위험한 동물들이 있어.
Jinho: 나도 알아. 하지만 정글은 모험으로 가득하잖아. 내가 거기서 살 수 있다면 좋을 텐데.
Claire: 정글에서 살 수 있다면 뭘 할 건데?
Jinho: 난 정글을 탐험할 거야. 아마도 동물 친구들도 좀 만들 수 있겠지.
Claire: 그러면 어디서 잠을 잘 건데? 동굴에서?
Jinho: 아니, 나무로 만든 집에서 지낼 거야. 그러면 위험한 동물들한테서 안전해지겠지.
Claire: 그건 말이 되네.

A: 방학 동안에 물 위에 있는 집에서 지내게 되면 좋을 텐데.
B: 그곳에 있다면 뭘 할 건데?
A: 난 매일 수영하러 갈 거야. 그리고 낚시도 하러 갈 거야.
B: 그거 재미있겠는데.

B: 이건 내 꿈의 집이야. Alice, 어떻게 생각하니?
G: 와, 깊은 바다에 있네. 정말 독특해 보인다. 그래서 그 집에 살게 되면 무엇을 할 거니?
B: 난 심해 동물에 관심이 있어. 그래서 심해를 탐험하고 몇몇 특이한 해양 동물을 찾을 거야.
G: 그거 정말 멋진데!

A: 무슨 일이니?
B: 내 컴퓨터가 아주 느려. 새 컴퓨터를 갖게 된다면 좋을 텐데.

※ 다음 우리말에 맞도록 대화를 영어로 쓰시오.

Listen and Speak 1 A

G: _____

B: _____

G: _____

B: _____

G: _____

　

B: _____

G: _____

B: _____

Listen and Speak 1 B

B: _____

G: _____

B: _____

G: _____

B: _____

G: _____

B: _____

G: _____

Listen and Speak 1 C

A: _____

B: _____

A: _____

B: _____

Listen and Speak 2 A-1

B: _____

G: _____

B: _____

G: _____

B: _____

G: _____

해석

G Julia한테서 소식 들었니? 그 애는 터키에서 여행 중이잖아, 맞지?
B 응, Julia가 나한테 사진 몇 장을 보내왔어. 사진 보고 싶니?
G 응, 보고 싶어.
B 알겠어, 봐.
G 오, 저 동굴 집 좀 봐. 정말 특이하다, 그렇지 않니? 난 그곳에서 살아 봤으면 좋겠어.
B 난 저 열기구가 마음에 들어. 매우 아름다워 보여!
G 내 생각엔 터키가 방문하기에 정말 멋진 곳 같아. 언제 한 번 방문해 보고 싶다.
B 나도 그래!

B: 오늘 눈이 오는 거니?
G: 나도 모르겠어. 태호야, 왜 눈을 기다리는 거니?
B: 내 생일 선물로 새 썰매를 받았거든. 그거 빨리 시험해 보고 싶어.
G: 날씨 좀 확인해 볼게. 음, 당분간은 눈 소식이 없을 거래.
B: 알래스카에 살면 좋을 텐데. 그럼 온종일 썰매를 타러 갈 수 있을 텐데.
G: 말도 안 돼! 알래스카는 정말 추운 곳이야.
B: 내 생각엔 정말 즐거울 것 같아. 눈으로 집을 짓고 방학 때 그곳에서 지내고 싶어.
G: 눈으로 만든 집에 사는 건 재미있을 것 같아!

A: 이 집들 좀 봐. 매우 자연 그대로인 것 같아.
B: 우와, 이곳에 살아 봤으면 좋겠어.
A: 어느 집에서 가장 살아보고 싶니?
B: 돌로 만든 집에서 살아 보면 좋을 텐데. 매우 튼튼해 보여.

B: 이게 내 꿈의 집이야, Alice. 어떻게 생각하니?
G: 와, 바퀴가 달린 집이라니! 자동차의 일종이니?
B: 응, 자동차처럼 움직일 수 있어.
G: 그래서 그 집에서 살게 되면 뭘 할 거니?
B: 나는 가족들이랑 많은 곳을 여행할 거야.
G: 정말 신나게 들린다!

Listen and Speak 2 A-2

G: _____

B: _____

G: _____

B: _____

G: _____

B: _____

G: _____

G: 주원아, 백만장자가 되면 뭘 할 거니?
B: 나는 나만의 집을 지을 거야.
G: 어떤 집을 짓고 싶은데?
B: 나는 거울로 완전히 덮인 집을 지을 거야.
G: 왜?
B: 그 거울들이 집을 거의 안 보이게 만들어줄 거야. 멋지지 않니?
G: 그건 멋질 거야!

Listen and Speak 2 A-3

G: _____

B: _____

G: _____

B: _____

G: _____

B: _____

G: 봐, 이 사진에 있는 집은 거꾸로 되어 있어.
B: 흥미로운데. 그 집에 누가 사는 건가?
G: 아니, 내부도 거꾸로 되어 있으니까 그곳에서 살기는 쉽지 않을 거야.
B: 정말? 하지만 나는 그곳에서 살아 보고 싶어.
G: 저 집에 살게 된다면 너는 뭘 할 거니?
B: 나는 스파이더맨처럼 거꾸로 걸어다닐 거야. 난 또한 사물을 다르게 볼 수 있을 거야.

Listen and Speak 2 B

G: _____

B: _____

G: _____

B: _____

G: _____

B: _____

G: _____

B: _____

G: _____

G: 도훈아, 우리가 방문하고 싶은 꿈꾸는 나라에 대한 프로젝트를 시작해야 돼.
B: 맞아. Emma, 너는 어느 나라를 방문하고 싶니?
G: 내 경우에는 스페인에 가 보고 싶어.
B: 스페인에 가게 되면 뭘 할 건데?
G: 나는 건물들에 관심이 있어. 그래서 나는 La Sagrada Familia에 가 볼 거야.
B: 그 성당은 Antoni Gaudi가 디자인한 교회 아니니?
G: 응, 맞아. 그의 디자인이 어떻게 자연에서 영감을 얻었는지 보면 흥미로울 거야.
B: 흠… '가우디와 스페인'을 우리 프로젝트 제목으로 하는 건 어떠니?
G: 아주 좋아!

Listen and Speak 2 C

A: _____

B: _____

A: _____

A: 마법의 힘을 갖게 된다면 너는 무엇을 할 거니?
B: 난 새로 변할 거야. 그러면 하늘을 자유롭게 날 수 있겠지.
A: 그거 멋있다.

Real Life Communication A

Jinho: _____

Claire: _____

Jinho: _____

Claire: _____

Jinho: _____

Claire: _____

Jinho: _____

Claire: _____

Real Life Communication B

A: _____

B: _____

A: _____

B: _____

Let's Check 1

B: _____

G: _____

_____

B: _____

_____

G: _____

Let's Check 2

A: _____

B: _____

Jinho: 내 생각엔 정글에서 사는 건 정말 신날 거야. 그렇게 생각하지 않니?

Claire: 근데 진호야, 정글에는 몇몇 위험한 동물들이 있어.

Jinho: 나도 알아. 하지만 정글은 모험으로 가득하잖아. 내가 거기서 살 수 있다면 좋을 텐데.

Claire: 정글에서 살 수 있다면 뭘 할 건데?

Jinho: 난 정글을 탐험할 거야. 아마도 동물 친구들도 좀 만들 수 있겠지.

Claire: 그러면 어디서 잠을 잘 건데? 동굴에서?

Jinho: 아니, 나무로 만든 집에서 지낼 거야. 그러면 위험한 동물들한테서 안전해지겠지.

Claire: 그건 말이 되네.

A: 방학 동안에 물 위에 있는 집에서 지내게 되면 좋을 텐데.

B: 그곳에 있다면 뭘 할 건데?

A: 난 매일 수영하러 갈 거야. 그리고 낚시도 하러 갈 거야.

B: 그거 재미있겠는데.

B: 이건 내 꿈의 집이야. Alice, 어떻게 생각하니?

G: 와, 깊은 바다에 있네. 정말 독특해 보인다. 그래서 그 집에 살게 되면 무엇을 할 거니?

B: 난 심해 동물에 관심이 있어. 그래서 심해를 탐험하고 몇몇 특이한 해양 동물을 찾을 거야.

G: 그거 정말 멋진데!

A: 무슨 일이니?

B: 내 컴퓨터가 아주 느려. 새 컴퓨터를 갖게 된다면 좋을 텐데.

※ 다음 우리말과 일치하도록 빈칸에 알맞은 것을 골라 쓰시오.

1 _____ people _____ _____ different _____.

A. in　　　　B. different　　　　C. houses　　　　D. live

2 _____ use _____ to _____ their houses. _____ live in houses on the water.

A. enter　　　　B. some　　　　C. ladders　　　　D. others

3 And _____ their _____ _____ many people.

A. with　　　　B. others　　　　C. houses　　　　D. share

4 _____ you live in _____ of these houses. How would that _____ your _____?

A. one　　　　B. life　　　　C. imagine　　　　D. change

Pueblos in New Mexico, USA

5 If I _____ in a *pueblo*, I _____ _____ up a ladder to _____ my house.

A. climb　　　　B. lived　　　　C. enter　　　　D. would

6 _____ a _____ _____ on _____ of the house.

A. top　　　　B. hidden　　　　C. there's　　　　D. opening

7 If _____ visitors _____, I would pull the ladder up to _____ them _____ entering.

A. stop　　　　B. unwelcome　　　　C. from　　　　D. appeared

8 The _____ walls are _____ _____ earth, _____, and water.

A. made　　　　B. thick　　　　C. straw　　　　D. of

9 They would _____ _____ _____ in summer and _____ in winter.

A. cool　　　　B. keep　　　　C. warm　　　　D. me

10 The house has a _____ _____. I would sometimes sleep _____ on the roof _____ the moon and stars.

A. under　　　　B. flat　　　　C. up　　　　D. roof

Houses on Water in Venice, Italy

11 _____ I _____ in Venice, I _____ _____ a gondola to school every morning.

A. take　　　　B. lived　　　　C. would　　　　D. if

12 Venice has 118 small islands. _____ weekends, I would travel _____ island _____ island _____ a *vaporetto*, a water bus.

A. to　　　　B. from　　　　C. by　　　　D. on

13 At high _____, the water from the Adriatic Sea often _____ and leaves the streets _____ _____ water.

A. rises　　　　B. of　　　　C. tide　　　　D. full

14 _____, I would be able to walk _____ the town _____ the _____ walkways.

A. around　　　　B. however　　　　C. raised　　　　D. through

15 Venice _____ _____ the " _____ city."

A. known　　　　B. is　　　　C. floating　　　　D. is

1 다양한 사람들이 다양한 집에서 살고 있습니다.

2 어떤 사람들은 집에 들어가기 위해 사다리를 이용합니다. 다른 사람들은 물 위에 있는 집에서 살고 있습니다.

3 그리고 또 다른 사람들은 많은 사람들과 함께 집을 공유합니다.

4 여러분이 이 집들 중 하나에 산다고 상상해 보세요. 여러분의 삶은 어떻게 바뀔까요?

푸에블로 – 미국 뉴멕시코

5 내가 만약 푸에블로에 산다면, 나는 집에 들어가기 위해 사다리를 오를 것이다.

6 집 꼭대기에는 숨겨진 구멍이 있다.

7 반갑지 않은 방문객이 나타난다면 나는 사다리를 끌어올려 그들이 들어오지 못하게 할 것이다.

8 두꺼운 벽은 흙, 지푸라기, 물로 만들어져 있다.

9 그것들은 여름에는 시원하게, 겨울에는 따뜻하게 유지시켜 준다.

10 집에는 평평한 지붕이 있다. 때때로 나는 달과 별들 아래의 지붕 위에서 잠을 잘 것이다.

물 위에 있는 집 – 이탈리아 베니스

11 내가 만약 베니스에 산다면, 나는 매일 아침 곤돌라를 타고 학교에 갈 것이다.

12 베니스는 118개의 작은 섬이 있다. 주말마다 나는 수상 버스인 바포레토를 타고 이 섬 저 섬을 여행할 것이다.

13 조수가 높을 때에는 아드리아 해의 물이 자주 범람하고 거리는 물로 가득 찬다.

14 그러나 나는 돌출되어 있는 통로로 도심 주변을 걸어다닐 수 있을 것이다.

15 베니스는 '떠다니는 도시'로 알려져 있다.

16 In Venice, _____ _____ many _____ _____ on the water.
   A. houses   B. are   C. there   D. colorful

17 You may _____ _____ and _____ they _____ the houses on the water.
   A. how   B. built   C. why   D. wonder

18 The old Venetians _____ to live there to _____ themselves _____ from _____.
   A. safe   B. decided   C. invaders   D. keep

19 But it was not _____ for them to _____ their homes on this _____ _____.
   A. swampy   B. easy   C. surface   D. build

20 _____ they _____ more than 10 million _____ in the ground.
   A. wooden   B. installed   C. so   D. poles

21 It is these _____ that _____ Venice _____ this day.
   A. poles   B. to   C. support   D. wooden

Tulou in Fujian, China

22 If I _____ in a *tulou*, a _____ _____ house in Fujian, China, I would always have friends at home to play _____.
   A. with   B. round   C. lived   D. huge

23 I would sometimes hear my _____ _____ me to _____ _____ for tea or dinner.
   A. calling   B. over   C. neighbor   D. come

24 In a *tulou*, there are usually _____ _____ _____ _____.
   A. to   B. floors   C. five   D. three

25 The first _____ _____ _____ _____ cooking and eating.
   A. used   B. floor   C. for   D. is

26 And people _____ _____ and _____ on the second _____.
   A. tools   B. store   C. floor   D. food

27 Do you _____ where I would sleep? My bedroom would be _____ the _____ or fourth _____.
   A. third   B. wonder   C. floor   D. on

28 A *tulou* is _____ a village. The people _____ in a *tulou* _____ have the _____ family name.
   A. living   B. same   C. like   D. mostly

29 Some large *tulou* can house _____ _____ 50 families. They _____ _____ and share many things.
   A. to   B. together   C. up   D. work

30 _____ _____ in one building _____ them _____.
   A. keeps   B. living   C. safe   D. together

31 Homes are _____. But they are _____ all over the world. _____ is your home _____?
   A. different   B. like   C. what   D. everywhere

16 베니스에는 물 위에 있는 색색의 건물들이 많다.

17 여러분은 어떻게, 그리고 왜 그들이 물 위에 집을 지었는지 궁금할 것이다.

18 옛 베니스 사람들은 침략자들로부터 자신들을 안전하게 지키기 위해 그곳에 살기로 결정했다.

19 하지만 그들이 이 습지 위에 집을 짓는 것은 쉽지가 않았다.

20 그래서 그들은 땅에 천만 개 이상의 나무 기둥을 설치했다.

21 이 나무 기둥들이 바로 지금까지 베니스를 지탱해 주고 있는 것이다.

토루 – 중국 푸젠

22 내가 만약 거대하고 둥그런 집인 중국 푸젠의 토루(tulou)에 산다면, 나는 항상 집에 함께 놀 친구들이 있을 것이다.

23 때때로 나의 이웃이 차를 마시거나 저녁 식사를 하러 집에 들르라고 나를 부르는 소리를 듣게 될 것이다.

24 토루는 대개 3층에서 5층으로 되어 있다.

25 1층은 요리하고 식사하는 데에 사용된다.

26 그리고 사람들은 2층에 식량과 도구를 보관한다.

27 내가 어디에서 잠을 잘지 궁금한가? 내 침실은 3층이나 4층에 있을 것이다.

28 토루는 마을과 같다. 토루에 사는 사람들은 대부분 같은 성(姓)을 가지고 있다.

29 몇몇 큰 토루는 50가구까지 수용할 수 있다. 그들은 함께 일하고 많은 것을 공유한다.

30 한 건물에 함께 사는 것은 그들을 안전하게 지켜 준다.

31 집은 어디에나 있습니다. 그러나 전 세계의 집은 모두 다릅니다. 여러분의 집은 어떤가요?

※ 다음 우리말과 일치하도록 빈칸에 알맞은 것을 골라 쓰시오.

1 _____ people _____ _____ different houses.

2 Some _____ _____ _____ _____ _____ _____ _____ _____ _____ _____.
_____ _____ _____ _____ houses _____ the water.

3 And _____ _____ their houses _____ many people.

4 _____ you _____ _____ _____ _____ _____ these houses.
How would _____ _____ your life?

Pueblos in New Mexico, USA

5 If I _____ _____ a *pueblo*, I _____ _____ up a ladder
_____ _____ _____ house.

6 There's a _____ _____ _____ _____ _____ of the house.

7 _____ unwelcome visitors _____ , I _____ _____ the
ladder _____ _____ _____ them _____ entering.

8 The thick walls _____ _____ _____ earth, straw, and
water.

9 They would _____ _____ _____ in summer and _____
in winter.

10 The house has _____ _____ _____. I would sometimes
_____ _____ _____ _____ _____ under the moon
and stars.

Houses on Water in Venice, Italy

11 If I _____ _____ Venice, I _____ _____ _____ _____
_____ to school every morning.

12 Venice _____ 118 small _____. _____ _____ , I would
travel _____ _____ _____ _____ _____ by a *vaporetto*, a
water bus.

13 At _____ _____ , the water _____ the Adriatic Sea often
_____ and _____ the streets _____ _____ _____.

14 _____, I would _____ _____ _____ _____ _____ _____
the town through the _____ _____.

15 Venice _____ _____ _____ _____ the "_____ city."

1 다양한 사람들이 다양한 집에서 살고 있습니다.

2 어떤 사람들은 집에 들어가기 위해 사다리를 이용합니다. 다른 사람들은 물 위에 있는 집에서 살고 있습니다.

3 그리고 또 다른 사람들은 많은 사람들과 함께 집을 공유합니다.

4 여러분이 이 집들 중 하나에 산다고 상상해 보세요. 여러분의 삶은 어떻게 바뀔까요?

푸에블로 - 미국 뉴멕시코

5 내가 만약 푸에블로에 산다면, 나는 집에 들어가기 위해 사다리를 오를 것이다.

6 집 꼭대기에는 숨겨진 구멍이 있다.

7 반갑지 않은 방문객이 나타난다면 나는 사다리를 끌어올려 그들이 들어오지 못하게 할 것이다.

8 두꺼운 벽은 흙, 지푸라기, 물로 만들어져 있다.

9 그것들은 여름에는 시원하게, 겨울에는 따뜻하게 유지시켜 준다.

10 집에는 평평한 지붕이 있다. 때때로 나는 달과 별들 아래의 지붕 위에서 잠을 잘 것이다.

물 위에 있는 집 - 이탈리아 베니스

11 내가 만약 베니스에 산다면, 나는 매일 아침 곤돌라를 타고 학교에 갈 것이다.

12 베니스는 118개의 작은 섬이 있다. 주말마다 나는 수상 버스인 바포레토를 타고 이 섬 저 섬을 여행할 것이다.

13 조수가 높을 때에는 아드리아 해의 물이 자주 범람하고 거리는 물로 가득 찬다.

14 그러나 나는 돌출되어 있는 통로로 도심 주변을 걸어다닐 수 있을 것이다.

15 베니스는 '떠다니는 도시'로 알려져 있다.

16 In Venice, _____ _____ many _____ _____ on the water.

17 You may _____ _____ and _____ _____ _____
_____ _____ _____ the water.

18 The old Venetians _____ _____ _____ _____ to keep
_____ _____ _____ _____ .

19 But it was not easy _____ _____ _____ _____ their
homes on this _____ _____ .

20 So they _____ more than 10 million _____ _____ in the
ground.

21 It is these _____ _____ that _____ Venice _____ this
day.

Tulou in Fujian, China

22 If I _____ in a *tulou*, a _____ _____ house in Fujian,
China, I _____ always _____ _____ at home _____
_____ _____ .

23 I would sometimes _____ my neighbor _____ _____
_____ _____ _____ for tea or dinner.

24 In a *tulou*, there _____ usually _____ _____ _____
_____ .

25 The first floor _____ _____ _____ cooking and eating.

26 And people _____ _____ and _____ _____ the
_____ _____ .

27 Do you wonder _____ _____ _____ _____ ? My
bedroom _____ _____ _____ the third or fourth floor.

28 A *tulou* is _____ a village. The people _____ _____ a
tulou mostly _____ the same _____ _____ .

29 Some large *tulou* _____ _____ _____ _____ 50
families. They _____ _____ and _____ many things.

30 _____ together in one building _____ _____ _____ .

31 Homes are everywhere. But they are _____ _____
_____ _____ . _____ is your home _____ ?

16 베니스에는 물 위에 있는 색색의 건물들이 많다.

17 여러분은 어떻게, 그리고 왜 그들이 물 위에 집을 지었는지 궁금할 것이다.

18 옛 베니스 사람들은 침략자들로부터 자신들을 안전하게 지키기 위해 그곳에 살기로 결정했다.

19 하지만 그들이 이 습지 위에 집을 짓는 것은 쉽지가 않았다.

20 그래서 그들은 땅에 천만 개 이상의 나무 기둥을 설치했다.

21 이 나무 기둥들이 바로 지금까지 베니스를 지탱해 주고 있는 것이다.

토루 – 중국 푸젠

22 내가 만약 거대하고 둥그런 집인 중국 푸젠의 토루(tulou)에 산다면, 나는 항상 집에 함께 놀 친구들이 있을 것이다.

23 때때로 나의 이웃이 차를 마시거나 저녁 식사를 하러 집에 들르라고 나를 부르는 소리를 듣게 될 것이다.

24 토루는 대개 3층에서 5층으로 되어 있다.

25 1층은 요리하고 식사하는 데에 사용된다.

26 그리고 사람들은 2층에 식량과 도구를 보관한다.

27 내가 어디에서 잠을 잘지 궁금한가? 내 침실은 3층이나 4층에 있을 것이다.

28 토루는 마을과 같다. 토루에 사는 사람들은 대부분 같은 성(姓)을 가지고 있다.

29 몇몇 큰 토루는 50가구까지 수용할 수 있다. 그들은 함께 일하고 많은 것을 공유한다.

30 한 건물에 함께 사는 것은 그들을 안전하게 지켜 준다.

31 집은 어디에나 있습니다. 그러나 전 세계의 집은 모두 다릅니다. 여러분의 집은 어떤가요?

※ 다음 문장을 우리말로 쓰시오.

1 Different people live in different houses.
➡ _____

2 Some use ladders to enter their houses. Others live in houses on the water.
➡ _____

3 And others share their houses with many people.
➡ _____

4 Imagine you live in one of these houses. How would that change your life?
➡ _____

Pueblos in New Mexico, USA

5 If I lived in a *pueblo*, I would climb up a ladder to enter my house.
➡ _____

6 There's a hidden opening on top of the house.
➡ _____

7 If unwelcome visitors appeared, I would pull the ladder up to stop them from entering.
➡ _____

8 The thick walls are made of earth, straw, and water.
➡ _____

9 They would keep me cool in summer and warm in winter.
➡ _____

10 The house has a flat roof. I would sometimes sleep up on the roof under the moon and stars.
➡ _____

Houses on Water in Venice, Italy

11 If I lived in Venice, I would take a gondola to school every morning.
➡ _____

12 Venice has 118 small islands. On weekends, I would travel from island to island by a *vaporetto*, a water bus.
➡ _____

13 At high tide, the water from the Adriatic Sea often rises and leaves the streets full of water.
➡ _____

14 However, I would be able to walk around the town through the raised walkways.
➡ _____

15 Venice is known as the "floating city."
➡ _____

16 In Venice, there are many colorful houses on the water.

➡ _____

17 You may wonder how and why they built the houses on the water.

➡ _____

18 The old Venetians decided to live there to keep themselves safe from invaders.

➡ _____

19 But it was not easy for them to build their homes on this swampy surface.

➡ _____

20 So they installed more than 10 million wooden poles in the ground.

➡ _____

21 It is these wooden poles that support Venice to this day.

➡ _____

Tulou in Fujian, China

22 If I lived in a *tulou*, a huge round house in Fujian, China, I would always have friends at home to play with.

➡ _____

23 I would sometimes hear my neighbor calling me to come over for tea or dinner.

➡ _____

24 In a *tulou*, there are usually three to five floors.

➡ _____

25 The first floor is used for cooking and eating.

➡ _____

26 And people store food and tools on the second floor.

➡ _____

27 Do you wonder where I would sleep? My bedroom would be on the third or fourth floor.

➡ _____

28 A *tulou* is like a village. The people living in a *tulou* mostly have the same family name.

➡ _____

29 Some large *tulou* can house up to 50 families. They work together and share many things.

➡ _____

30 Living together in one building keeps them safe.

➡ _____

31 Homes are everywhere. But they are different all over the world. What is your home like?

➡ _____

※ 다음 괄호 안의 단어들을 우리말에 맞도록 바르게 배열하시오.

1 (people / different / in / live / houses. / different)
➡ _____

2 (use / some / to / ladders / their / enter / houses. // live / others / houses / in / the / on / water.)
➡ _____

3 (others / and / their / share / with / houses / people. / many)
➡ _____

4 (you / imagine / live / one / in / these / of / houses. // would / how / change / that / life? / your)
➡ _____

Pueblos in New Mexico, USA
5 (I / if / in / lived / *pueblo*, / a / would / I / up / climb / ladder / a / enter / to / house. / my)
➡ _____

6 (a / there's / hidden / on / opening / top / the / of / house.)
➡ _____

7 (unwelcome / if / appeared, / visitors / would / I / the / pull / up / ladder / stop / to / from / them / entering.)
➡ _____

8 (thick / the / are / walls / of / made / earth, / and / straw, / water.)
➡ _____

9 (would / they / me / keep / in / cool / summer / and / in / warm / winter.)
➡ _____

10 (house / the / a / has / roof. / flat / would / I / sleep / sometimes / up / the / on / under / roof / moon / the / stars. / and)
➡ _____

Houses on Water in Venice, Italy
11 (I / if / in / lived / Venice, / would / I / a / take / gondola / school / to / morning. / every)
➡ _____

12 (has / Venice / small / 118 / islands. // weekends, / on / would / I / from / travel / island / to / by / island / *vaporetto*, / a / water / a / bus.)
➡ _____

13 (high / at / tide, / water / the / the / from / Sea / Adriatic / rises / often / and / the / leaves / full / streets / water. / of)
➡ _____

14 (I / however, / would / be / to / able / around / walk / town / the / the / through / walkways. / raised)
➡ _____

15 (is / Venice / as / known / the / city." / "floating)
➡ _____

1 다양한 사람들이 다양한 집에서 살고 있습니다.

2 어떤 사람들은 집에 들어가기 위해 사다리를 이용합니다. 다른 사람들은 물 위에 있는 집에서 살고 있습니다.

3 그리고 또 다른 사람들은 많은 사람들과 함께 집을 공유합니다.

4 여러분이 이 집들 중 하나에 산다고 상상해 보세요. 여러분의 삶은 어떻게 바뀔까요?

푸에블로 – 미국 뉴멕시코

5 내가 만약 푸에블로에 산다면, 나는 집에 들어가기 위해 사다리를 오를 것이다.

6 집 꼭대기에는 숨겨진 구멍이 있다.

7 반갑지 않은 방문객이 나타난다면 나는 사다리를 끌어올려 그들이 들어오지 못하게 할 것이다.

8 두꺼운 벽은 흙, 지푸라기, 물로 만들어져 있다.

9 그것들은 여름에는 시원하게, 겨울에는 따뜻하게 유지시켜 준다.

10 집에는 평평한 지붕이 있다. 때때로 나는 달과 별들 아래의 지붕 위에서 잠을 잘 것이다.

물 위에 있는 집 – 이탈리아 베니스

11 내가 만약 베니스에 산다면, 나는 매일 아침 곤돌라를 타고 학교에 갈 것이다.

12 베니스는 **118**개의 작은 섬이 있다. 주말마다 나는 수상 버스인 바포레토를 타고 이 섬 저 섬을 여행할 것이다.

13 조수가 높을 때에는 아드리아 해의 물이 자주 범람하고 거리는 물로 가득 찬다.

14 그러나 나는 돌출되어 있는 통로로 도심 주변을 걸어다닐 수 있을 것이다.

15 베니스는 '떠다니는 도시'로 알려져 있다.

16 (Venice, / in / are / there / colorful / many / houses / the / on / water.)
➡ _____

17 (may / you / wonder / and / how / why / built / they / houses / the / on / water. / the)
➡ _____

18 (old / the / Venetians / to / decided / there / live / keep / to / safe / themselves / invaders. / from)
➡ _____

19 (it / but / not / was / for / easy / to / them / build / homes / their / on / swampy / this / surface.)
➡ _____

20 (they / so / more / installed / than / million / 10 / poles / wooden / the / in / ground.)
➡ _____

21 (is / it / wooden / these / poles / support / that / to / Venice / this / day.)
➡ _____

Tulou in Fujian, China

22 (I / if / in / a / lived / *tulou*, / a / round / huge / in / house / China, / Fujian, / would / I / have / always / friends / home / at / play / to / with.)
_____

23 (would / I / hear / sometimes / neighbor / my / me / calling / to / over / come / tea / for / dinner. / or)
➡ _____

24 (a / in / *tulou*, / are / there / three / usually / five / to / floors.)
➡ _____

25 (first / the / is / floor / for / used / cooking / eating. / and)
➡ _____

26 (people / and / food / store / and / on / tools / the / floor. / second)
➡ _____

27 (you / do / where / wonder / would / I / sleep? // bedroom / my / be / would / the / on / or / third / floor. / fourth)
➡ _____

28 (*tulou* / a / like / is / village. / a // people / the / in / living / a / mostly / *tulou* / the / have / family / same / name.)
➡ _____

29 (large / some / can / *tulou* / up / house / 50 / to / families. // work / they / and / together / many / share / things.)
➡ _____

30 (together / living / one / in / keeps / building / safe. / them)
➡ _____

31 (are / everywhere. / homes // they / but / different / are / over / all / world. / the // is / what / home / your / like?)
➡ _____

16 베니스에는 물 위에 있는 색색의 건물들이 많다.

17 여러분은 어떻게, 그리고 왜 그들이 물 위에 집을 지었는지 궁금할 것이다.

18 옛 베니스 사람들은 침략자들로부터 자신들을 안전하게 지키기 위해 그곳에 살기로 결정했다.

19 하지만 그들이 이 습지 위에 집을 짓는 것은 쉽지가 않았다.

20 그래서 그들은 땅에 천만 개 이상의 나무 기둥을 설치했다.

21 이 나무 기둥들이 바로 지금까지 베니스를 지탱해 주고 있는 것이다.

토루 – 중국 푸젠

22 내가 만약 거대하고 둥그런 집인 중국 푸젠의 토루(tulou)에 산다면, 나는 항상 집에 함께 놀 친구들이 있을 것이다.

23 때때로 나의 이웃이 차를 마시거나 저녁 식사를 하러 집에 들르라고 나를 부르는 소리를 듣게 될 것이다.

24 토루는 대개 3층에서 5층으로 되어 있다.

25 1층은 요리하고 식사하는 데에 사용된다.

26 그리고 사람들은 2층에 식량과 도구를 보관한다.

27 내가 어디에서 잠을 잘지 궁금한가? 내 침실은 3층이나 4층에 있을 것이다.

28 토루는 마을과 같다. 토루에 사는 사람들은 대부분 같은 성(姓)을 가지고 있다.

29 몇몇 큰 토루는 50가구까지 수용할 수 있다. 그들은 함께 일하고 많은 것을 공유한다.

30 한 건물에 함께 사는 것은 그들을 안전하게 지켜 준다.

31 집은 어디에나 있습니다. 그러나 전 세계의 집은 모두 다릅니다. 여러분의 집은 어떤가요?

※ 다음 우리말을 영어로 쓰시오.

1 다양한 사람들이 다양한 집에서 살고 있습니다.

➡ _____

2 어떤 사람들은 집에 들어가기 위해 사다리를 이용합니다. 다른 사람들은 물 위에 있는 집에서 살고 있습니다.

➡ _____

3 그리고 또 다른 사람들은 많은 사람들과 함께 집을 공유합니다.

➡ _____

4 여러분이 이 집들 중 하나에 산다고 상상해 보세요. 여러분의 삶은 어떻게 바뀔까요?

➡ _____

Pueblos in New Mexico, USA

5 내가 만약 푸에블로에 산다면, 나는 집에 들어가기 위해 사다리를 오를 것이다.

➡ _____

6 집 꼭대기에는 숨겨진 구멍이 있다.

➡ _____

7 반갑지 않은 방문객이 나타난다면 나는 사다리를 끌어올려 그들이 들어오지 못하게 할 것이다.

➡ _____

8 두꺼운 벽은 흙, 지푸라기, 물로 만들어져 있다.

➡ _____

9 그것들은 여름에는 시원하게, 겨울에는 따뜻하게 유지시켜 준다.

➡ _____

10 집에는 평평한 지붕이 있다. 때때로 나는 달과 별들 아래의 지붕 위에서 잠을 잘 것이다.

➡ _____

Houses on Water in Venice, Italy

11 내가 만약 베니스에 산다면, 나는 매일 아침 곤돌라를 타고 학교에 갈 것이다.

➡ _____

12 베니스는 118개의 작은 섬이 있다. 주말마다 나는 수상 버스인 바포레토를 타고 이 섬 저 섬을 여행할 것이다.

➡ _____

13 조수가 높을 때에는 아드리아 해의 물이 자주 범람하고 거리는 물로 가득 찬다.

➡ _____

14 그러나 나는 돌출되어 있는 통로로 도심 주변을 걸어다닐 수 있을 것이다.

➡ _____

15 베니스는 '떠다니는 도시'로 알려져 있다.

➡ _____

16 베니스에는 물 위에 있는 색색의 건물들이 많다.

➡ _____

17 여러분은 어떻게, 그리고 왜 그들이 물 위에 집을 지었는지 궁금할 것이다.

➡ _____

18 옛 베니스 사람들은 침략자들로부터 자신들을 안전하게 지키기 위해 그곳에 살기로 결정했다.

➡ _____

19 하지만 그들이 이 습지 위에 집을 짓는 것은 쉽지가 않았다.

➡ _____

20 그래서 그들은 땅에 천만 개 이상의 나무 기둥을 설치했다.

➡ _____

21 이 나무 기둥들이 바로 지금까지 베니스를 지탱해 주고 있는 것이다.

➡ _____

Tulou in Fujian, China

22 내가 만약 거대하고 둥그런 집인 중국 푸젠의 토루(*tulou*)에 산다면, 나는 항상 집에 함께 놀 친구들이 있을 것이다.

➡ _____

_____

23 때때로 나의 이웃이 차를 마시거나 저녁 식사를 하러 집에 들르라고 나를 부르는 소리를 듣게 될 것이다.

➡ _____

24 토루는 대개 3층에서 5층으로 되어 있다.

➡ _____

25 1층은 요리하고 식사하는 데에 사용된다.

➡ _____

26 그리고 사람들은 2층에 식량과 도구를 보관한다.

➡ _____

27 내가 어디에서 잠을 잘지 궁금한가? 내 침실은 3층이나 4층에 있을 것이다.

➡ _____

28 토루는 마을과 같다. 토루에 사는 사람들은 대부분 같은 성(姓)을 가지고 있다.

➡ _____

29 몇몇 큰 토루는 50가구까지 수용할 수 있다. 그들은 함께 일하고 많은 것을 공유한다.

➡ _____

30 한 건물에 함께 사는 것은 그들을 안전하게 지켜 준다.

➡ _____

31 집은 어디에나 있습니다. 그러나 전 세계의 집은 모두 다릅니다. 여러분의 집은 어떤가요?

➡ _____

※ 다음 우리말과 일치하도록 빈칸에 알맞은 말을 쓰시오.

Let's Write

1. When you visit Korea, you _____ _____ _____ _____
_____ _____ .

2. _____ _____ _____ _____ in a *hanok*?

3. A *hanok* is _____ _____ _____ _____ .

4. If you _____ in a *hanok*, you _____ _____ on the floor
_____ _____ _____ .

5. *Hanok* houses _____ _____ _____ _____ natural
materials _____ _____ _____ _____ , stone, _____ , paper,
_____ _____ .

6. These materials _____ _____ _____ _____ _____ _____
_____ .

7. In the cold winter, the _____ _____ _____ _____
_____ _____ .

8. The doors in *hanok* _____ _____ _____ _____ _____ .

9. They _____ _____ _____ _____ _____ in summer.

1. 여러분이 한국을 방문할 때, 어디에서 머물지 궁금할 것입니다.
2. 한옥에서 머물러 보면 어떨까요?
3. 한옥은 한국의 전통 가옥입니다.
4. 만약 여러분이 한옥에서 지낸다면, 여러분은 침대가 없기 때문에 바닥에서 잠을 자게 될 것입니다.
5. 한옥 집들은 대개 나무, 돌, 지푸라기, 종이, 흙과 같은 천연 재료로 지어져 있습니다.
6. 이 재료들은 여러분의 피부를 건강하게 유지하도록 도와줍니다.
7. 추운 겨울에는 따뜻한 온돌 바닥이 여러분의 몸을 데워줍니다.
8. 한옥 문들은 얇은 종이로 덮여 있습니다.
9. 그 문들은 여름에 여러분이 시원하게 지내도록 도와줍니다.

Culture & Life

1. If you _____ _____ a street in the village of the Ndebele in
South Africa, you _____ _____ _____ _____ _____
_____ _____ and styles.

2. _____ _____ _____ a different story.

3. Some stories _____ _____ _____ _____ _____ _____ .

4. _____ express _____ _____ _____ .

5. _____ _____ _____ _____ _____ , the Ndebele _____
_____ _____ the Boers.

6. When the Boers _____ _____ _____ , the Ndebele painted
their houses _____ _____ _____ _____ .

7. So, their enemies couldn't understand _____ they were _____
_____ _____ .

8. The symbols _____ _____ _____ _____ _____ .

9. Those symbols _____ _____ _____ _____ _____ mothers
_____ daughters.

10. And they have _____ _____ _____ _____ _____ .

1. 남아프리카 은데벨레족 마을의 거리를 걸어가다 보면, 많은 독특한 모양과 양식의 집들을 보게 될 것이다.
2. 각각의 집들은 서로 다른 이야기를 한다.
3. 어떤 이야기들은 이웃 아이들에 관한 것일지 모른다.
4. 또 다른 이야기들은 개인적인 의견을 표현한다.
5. 오래전, 은데벨레족은 보어인과 전쟁을 치렀다.
6. 보어인들이 그들의 땅을 침략했을 때, 은데벨레족은 여러 색의 상징으로 집을 칠했다.
7. 그래서 적들은 그들이 비밀리에 주고받는 의사소통을 이해하지 못했다.
8. 이러한 상징들은 슬픔과 같은 감정들을 표현했다.
9. 그 상징들은 엄마들에게서 딸들에게로 전해져 왔다.
10. 그리고 그들은 자신들의 전통이 계속 살아 있도록 유지해 왔다.

※ 다음 우리말을 영어로 쓰시오.

Let's Write

1. 여러분이 한국을 방문할 때, 어디에서 머물지 궁금할 것입니다.
   ➡ _____

2. 한옥에서 머물러 보면 어떨까요?
   ➡ _____

3. 한옥은 한국의 전통 가옥입니다.
   ➡ _____

4. 만약 여러분이 한옥에서 지낸다면, 여러분은 침대가 없기 때문에 바닥에서 잠을 자게 될 것입니다.
   ➡ _____

5. 한옥 집은 대개 나무, 돌, 지푸라기, 종이, 흙과 같은 천연 재료로 지어져 있습니다.
   ➡ _____

6. 이 재료들은 여러분의 피부를 건강하게 유지하도록 도와줍니다.
   ➡ _____

7. 추운 겨울에는 따뜻한 온돌 바닥이 여러분의 몸을 데워줍니다.
   ➡ _____

8. 한옥 문들은 얇은 종이로 덮여 있습니다.
   ➡ _____

9. 그 문들은 여름에 여러분이 시원하게 지내도록 도와줍니다.
   ➡ _____

Culture & Life

1. 남아프리카 은데벨레족 마을의 거리를 걸어가다 보면, 많은 독특한 모양과 양식의 집들을 보게 될 것이다.
   ➡ _____

2. 각각의 집들은 서로 다른 이야기를 한다.
   ➡ _____

3. 어떤 이야기들은 이웃 아이들에 관한 것일지 모른다.
   ➡ _____

4. 또 다른 이야기들은 개인적인 의견을 표현한다.
   ➡ _____

5. 오래전, 은데벨레족은 보어인과 전쟁을 치렀다.
   ➡ _____

6. 보어인들이 그들의 땅을 침략했을 때, 은데벨레족은 여러 색의 상징으로 집을 칠했다.
   ➡ _____

7. 그래서 적들은 그들이 비밀리에 주고받는 의사소통을 이해하지 못했다.
   ➡ _____

8. 이러한 상징들은 슬픔과 같은 감정들을 표현했다.
   ➡ _____

9. 그 상징들은 엄마들에게서 딸들에게로 전해져 왔다.
   ➡ _____

10. 그리고 그들은 자신들의 전통이 계속 살아 있도록 유지해 왔다.
    ➡ _____

※ 다음 영어를 우리말로 쓰시오.

01 article

02 break

03 reason

04 vote

05 wave

06 adventure

07 courageous

08 repeat

09 muscle

10 equal

11 survey

12 anyway

13 represent

14 matter

15 election

16 soldier

17 chase

18 sum

19 importance

20 suddenly

21 midnight

22 facial

23 poisonous

24 struggle

25 realize

26 helpful

27 celebrate

28 solution

29 claim

30 greedy

31 result

32 match

33 lastly

34 science-fiction

35 get back

36 be related to

37 one by one

38 run for

39 pick up

40 in other words

41 be about to

42 be proud of

43 be regarded as

※ 다음 우리말을 영어로 쓰시오.

01 군인, 병사 _____

02 타자기 _____

03 설문조사하다 _____

04 세금 _____

05 일치하다 _____

06 계산, 총계 _____

07 주장하다 _____

08 투표하다 _____

09 해결책 _____

10 얼굴의 _____

11 모험 _____

12 이유 _____

13 용감한 _____

14 선거 _____

15 기념하다 _____

16 글, 기사 _____

17 게다가, 어쨌든 _____

18 같다 _____

19 자정 _____

20 나타내다 _____

21 뒤쫓다 _____

22 투쟁하다, 분투하다 _____

23 탐욕스러운, 욕심 많은 _____

24 갑자기 _____

25 도움이 되는 _____

26 근육 _____

27 중요성 _____

28 독이 있는 _____

29 결과 _____

30 짭짤한 _____

31 공상 과학의 _____

32 깨닫다 _____

33 화살 _____

34 손을 흔들다 _____

35 잠복하다 _____

36 ~을 자랑스러워하다 _____

37 올려보다 _____

38 막 ~하려고 하다 _____

39 다시 말하면 _____

40 ~와 연관되어 있다 _____

41 하나씩 _____

42 ~로 여겨지다 _____

43 더 이상 ~ 않다 _____

※ 다음 영영풀이에 알맞은 단어를 <보기>에서 골라 쓴 후, 우리말 뜻을 쓰시오.

1 _____ : to be important: _____

2 _____ : a member of an army: _____

3 _____ : 12 o'clock at night: _____

4 _____ : to understand clearly: _____

5 _____ : full of containing poison: _____

6 _____ : to say something in a loud voice: _____

7 _____ : a piece of writing appearing in a newspaper: _____

8 _____ : to express by some symbol or character: _____

9 _____ : to signal in greeting, by raising the hand and moving the fingers:
_____

10 _____ : wanting a lot more food, money, etc. than you need: _____

11 _____ : at the end; after all the other things that you have mentioned: _____

12 _____ : a long written story about characters and events that have been invented
by the writer: _____

13 _____ : the total of two or more numbers or quantities, determined by mathematical
process: _____

14 _____ : an amount of money that you have to pay to the government so that it
can pay for public services: _____

15 _____ : to say that something is true although it has not been proved and other
people may not believe it: _____

16 _____ : to take part in special enjoyable activities in order to show that a particular
occasion is important: _____

보기

lastly	wave	realize	soldier
greedy	celebrate	claim	midnight
tax	novel	matter	sum
represent	poisonous	shout	article

※ 다음 우리말과 일치하도록 빈칸에 알맞은 말을 쓰시오.

Listen & Speak 1 A

B: Minju, what is this _____ _____?

G: I did a _____ on the _____ of pets my classmates have.

B: What were the _____?

G: Eighty _____ of the students have pets. _____ five _____ _____ twenty-five students don't have pets.

B: _____ _____ _____ pets do they have?

G: Well, ten students have dogs and three students _____ _____.

B: What about _____ _____?

G: Seven students have _____.

Listen & Speak 1 B

M: Mason, how was the _____?

B: It was _____. I didn't _____.

M: _____ _____?

B: Yura won. _____ sixty percent of the students _____ _____ _____ her.

M: Well, you tried _____ _____ and that's _____ _____.

B: I _____ so. I have learned many things _____ _____ _____ _____ class _____.

M: I'm really _____ _____ you.

B: Thanks, Dad.

Listen & Speak 2 A

B: Emma, can you _____ me _____ this math problem?

G: Sure, what is it?

B: You _____ _____ move one stick _____ _____ this _____ right. _____ could four _____ five _____ six?

G: Oh, it's simple. You _____ _____ move one of the _____ in number four _____ _____ it eleven. Do you see _____ _____ _____?

B: Yes, now I see _____ you mean. Eleven _____ five _____ six. _____ clever!

G: _____ _____ _____ _____ _____ can be _____ sometimes.

B: 민주야, 이 그래프는 무엇에 관한 거야?

G: 나는 우리 반 친구들이 가지고 있는 애완동물의 종류에 대해 설문 조사했어.

B: 결과가 어땠어?

G: 학생들의 80%가 애완동물을 가지고 있었어. 25명의 학생들 중 5명만 이 애완동물이 없었어.

B: 그들은 어떤 종류의 애완동물을 가지고 있니?

G: 음. 10명은 개, 3명은 고양이를 가지고 있어.

B: 나머지는?

G: 7명은 물고기를 가지고 있어.

M: Mason, 선거는 어땠니?

B: 안 좋았어요. 저는 이기지 못했어요.

M: 어째서?

B: 유라가 이겼어요. 학생들의 60% 이상이 그녀에게 투표했어요.

M: 음, 너는 최선을 다했고, 그게 중요한 거란다.

B: 저도 그렇게 생각해요. 반장 선거에 출마한 동안 많은 것을 배웠어요.

M: 나는 네가 정말 자랑스럽구나.

B: 고마워요, 아빠.

B: Emma, 이 수학 문제 좀 도와줄래?

G: 물론이지, 뭔데?

B: 이 계산이 맞도록 너는 한 개의 막대기를 옮겨야 해. 어떻게 4빼기 5가 6이 되지?

G: 오, 이건 간단해. 너는 숫자 4를 11로 만들기 위해 막대기 하나를 옮기면 돼. 무슨 말인지 알겠니?

B: 응, 이제 네 말이 무슨 뜻인지 알겠어. 11 빼기 5는 6이지. 너 정말 똑똑하구나!

G: 틀 밖에서 생각하는 것은 때때로 도움이 될 수 있지.

Listen & Speak 2 B

B: Jian, what's _____ _____? You _____ _____.

G: My brother _____ my computer. I'm so _____.

B: _____ _____ _____ _____ that, but your _____ muscles must _____ _____.

G: _____ _____ _____ _____ _____ _____?

B: Well, it _____ a lot of _____ _____ _____ angry, but only _____ _____ to smile. Do you see _____ I mean?

G: Oh, I _____ it. I guess it's not good _____ _____ angry _____ _____ _____ _____ _____.

B: That's right. Remember, _____ always _____ _____ _____ _____!

B: 지안아, 무슨 문제 있니? 너 속상해 보여.
G: 내 남동생이 내 컴퓨터를 고장 냈어. 정말 화나.
B: 그렇다니 유감이지만, 너의 얼굴 근육은 피곤할 거야.
G: 무슨 뜻이니?
B: 음, 화난 표정을 지을 때는 많은 근육이 필요하지만, 웃을 때는 몇 개의 근육만 필요하거든. 무슨 말인지 알겠어?
G: 오, 이해했어. 오랫동안 화난 상태로 있으면 좋지 않겠구나.
B: 맞아. 기억해. 웃는 게 항상 더 낫다는 것을 말이야!

Real Life Communication

Mina: Henry, what are you _____?

Henry: I'm writing an _____ about students' _____ _____. I'_____ _____ _____ their health.

Mina: Why?

Henry: Well, I _____ 100 students and the _____ show that _____ _____ of the students liked pizza and fried chicken for snacks. _____ _____ _____ what I _____?

Mina: Oh, _____ _____ _____. Students really like fast food. _____ _____ did they like?

Henry: _____ _____ of the students _____ chocolate cake _____ their _____.

Mina: Wow, students should really _____ _____ eat _____ snacks!

미나: Henry, 너 뭐 하고 있니?
Henry: 난 학생들이 가장 좋아하는 간식에 관한 기사를 쓰고 있어. 나는 그들의 건강이 걱정 돼.
미나: 왜?
Henry: 음, 난 100명의 학생들에게 설문 조사를 했고, 학생들의 80%가 간식으로 피자나 프라이드치킨을 좋아한다는 결과가 나왔어. 무슨 뜻인지 알겠니?
미나: 아, 알겠어. 학생들은 패스트푸드를 정말 좋아하지. 그들은 또 어떤 것을 좋아했니?
Henry: 학생들의 12%가 가장 좋아하는 것으로 초콜릿 케이크를 골랐어.
미나: 와우, 학생들은 더 건강한 간식을 먹도록 정말로 노력해야겠다!

Let's Check

B: _____ _____, you don't need _____ _____ to watch a movie or go to a concert. You just need to _____ your ticket _____ your cell phone. Then _____ the ticket on your phone's _____ before you _____ _____. You _____ _____ _____ _____ _____ the _____ _____ _____ out tickets. Do you see _____ _____?

B: 요즘에, 당신은 영화를 보거나 공연장에 가기 위해 종이 티켓이 필요하지 않습니다. 당신은 단지 당신의 휴대전화에 티켓을 저장하면 됩니다. 그리고 나서 입장하기 전에 휴대전화 화면 위의 티켓을 보여줍니다. 당신은 번거롭게 티켓을 출력할 필요가 없습니다. 무슨 뜻인지 아시겠어요?

대화문 Test

※ 다음 우리말에 맞도록 대화를 영어로 쓰시오.

Listen & Speak 1 A

B: _____

G: _____

B: _____

G: _____

B: _____

G: _____

B: _____

G: _____

B: 민주야, 이 그래프는 무엇에 관한 거야?
G: 나는 우리 반 친구들이 가지고 있는 애완동물의 종류에 대해 설문 조사했어.
B: 결과가 어땠어?
G: 학생들의 80%가 애완동물을 가지고 있었어. 25명의 학생들 중 5명만이 애완동물이 없었어.
B: 그들은 어떤 종류의 애완동물을 가지고 있니?
G: 음. 10명은 개, 3명은 고양이를 가지고 있어.
B: 나머지는?
G: 7명은 물고기를 가지고 있어.

Listen & Speak 1 B

M: _____

B: _____

M: _____

B: _____

M: _____

B: _____

M: _____

B: _____

M: Mason, 선거는 어땠니?
B: 안 좋았어요. 저는 이기지 못했어요.
M: 어째서?
B: 유라가 이겼어요. 학생들의 60% 이상이 그녀에게 투표했어요.
M: 음, 너는 최선을 다했고, 그게 중요한 거란다.
B: 저도 그렇게 생각해요. 반장 선거에 출마한 동안 많은 것을 배웠어요.
M: 나는 네가 정말 자랑스럽구나.
B: 고마워요, 아빠.

Listen & Speak 2 A

B: _____

G: _____

B: _____

G: _____

B: _____

G: _____

B: Emma, 이 수학 문제 좀 도와줄래?
G: 물론이지, 뭔데?
B: 이 계산이 맞도록 너는 한 개의 막대기를 옮겨야 해. 어떻게 4빼기 5가 6이 되지?
G: 오, 이건 간단해. 너는 숫자 4를 11로 만들기 위해 막대기 하나를 옮기면 돼. 무슨 말인지 알겠니?
B: 응, 이제 네 말이 무슨 뜻인지 알겠어. 11 빼기 5는 6이지. 너 정말 똑똑하구나!
G: 틀 밖에서 생각하는 것은 때때로 도움이 될 수 있지.

Listen & Speak 2 B

B: _____

G: _____

B: _____

G: _____

B: _____

_____

G: _____

B: _____

Real Life Communication

Mina: _____

Henry: _____

_____

Mina: _____

Henry: _____

_____

Mina: _____

Henry: _____

Mina: _____

Let's Check

B: _____

_____

_____

B: 지안아, 무슨 문제 있니? 너 속상해 보여.

G: 내 남동생이 내 컴퓨터를 고장 냈어. 정말 화나.

B: 그렇다니 유감이지만, 너의 얼굴 근육은 피곤할 거야.

G: 무슨 뜻이니?

B: 음, 화난 표정을 지을 때는 많은 근육이 필요하지만, 웃을 때는 몇 개의 근육만 필요하거든. 무슨 말인지 알겠어?

G: 오, 이해했어. 오랫동안 화난 상태로 있으면 좋지 않겠구나.

B: 맞아. 기억해, 웃는 게 항상 더 낫다는 것을 말이야!

미나: Henry, 너 뭐 하고 있니?

Henry: 난 학생들이 가장 좋아하는 간식에 관한 기사를 쓰고 있어. 나는 그들의 건강이 걱정 돼.

미나: 왜?

Henry: 음, 난 100명의 학생들에게 설문 조사를 했고, 학생들의 80%가 간식으로 피자나 프라이드치킨을 좋아한다는 결과가 나왔어. 무슨 뜻인지 알겠니?

미나: 아, 알겠어. 학생들은 패스트푸드를 정말 좋아하지. 그들은 또 어떤 것을 좋아했니?

Henry: 학생들의 12%가 가장 좋아하는 것으로 초콜릿 케이크를 골랐어.

미나: 와우, 학생들은 더 건강한 간식을 먹도록 정말로 노력해야겠다!

B: 요즘에, 당신은 영화를 보거나 공연장에 가기 위해 종이 티켓이 필요하지 않습니다. 당신은 단지 당신의 휴대전화에 티켓을 저장하면 됩니다. 그리고 나서 입장하기 전에 휴대전화 화면 위의 티켓을 보여줍니다. 당신은 번거롭게 티켓을 출력할 필요가 없습니다. 무슨 뜻인지 아시겠어요?

※ 다음 우리말과 일치하도록 빈칸에 알맞은 것을 골라 쓰시오.

1 Pascal was _____ his _____ homework in his room. He was _____ _____ graphs.

    A. math   B. with   C. doing   D. struggling

2 "It's _____ hard to read and _____ graphs. Why do I need these _____ ? No one needs graphs in _____ life."

    A. anyway   B. too   C. draw   D. real

3 He _____ _____ his pen and _____ _____ his favorite book, *Robin Hood*.

    A. down   B. up   C. put   D. picked

4 He _____ to read _____ to sleep. When he was _____ to open the book, he _____ a voice.

    A. himself   B. heard   C. decided   D. about

5 He _____ _____ the book to see who was _____ .

    A. up   B. talking   C. from   D. looked

6 He _____ _____ his eyes. It was his dog, Manny, _____ _____ talking!

    A. who   B. couldn't   C. was   D. believe

7 "_____ your _____ and _____ _____ me. *Cogito ergo sum*," said Manny.

    A. repeat   B. close   C. after   D. eyes

8 "You _____ _____ ?" "_____ _____ ! *Cogito ergo sum*."

    A. talk   B. repeat   C. can   D. just

9 Pascal closed his eyes and _____ the _____ . Suddenly, he _____ men _____ .

    A. heard   B. words   C. repeated   D. shouting

10 _____ he _____ his eyes, he saw _____ _____ horses.

    A. on   B. opened   C. when   D. soldiers

11 They were _____ a man _____ _____ in his hand. The man saw Pascal and _____ .

    A. arrows   B. chasing   C. shouted   D. with

12 "It's too _____ _____ _____ to _____ there. Come on."

    A. for   B. dangerous   C. stand   D. you

1 파스칼은 그의 방에서 수학 숙제를 하고 있었습니다. 그는 그래프 문제에 고군분투하고 있었습니다.

2 "그래프를 읽고 그리는 것은 너무 어려워. 게다가 내가 왜 그래프가 필요하겠어? 아무도 실제 생활에서는 그래프가 필요하지 않아."

3 그는 그의 펜을 내려놓고, 그가 가장 좋아하는 책, '로빈 후드'를 집어 들었습니다.

4 그는 책을 읽으며 잠들기로 했습니다. 그가 책을 펴려고 할 때, 그는 목소리를 들었습니다.

5 누가 말하고 있는지 보기 위해 그는 책에서 눈을 들어 올려다 보았습니다.

6 그는 그의 눈을 믿을 수 없었습니다. 말하는 것은 바로 자신의 개, Manny였습니다!

7 "눈을 감고 내 말을 따라 말하세요. 코기토 에르고 숨." Manny가 말했습니다.

8 "너는 말할 수 있니?" "그냥 따라 하세요! 코기토 에르고 숨."

9 파스칼은 그의 눈을 감고 그 단어들을 따라 말했습니다. 갑자기 그는 남자들이 소리치는 것을 들었습니다.

10 그가 눈을 떴을 때, 그는 말을 탄 병사들을 보았습니다.

11 그들은 손에 화살을 든 남자를 뒤쫓고 있었습니다. 그 남자는 파스칼을 보고 소리쳤습니다.

12 "네가 거기 서 있는 것은 너무 위험해. 이리 와."

13 The man _____ Pascal _____ his horse and _____ into the _____ .

A. onto   B. pulled   C. woods   D. rode

14 When they _____ at a house, the man _____ and _____ his horse.

A. stopped   B. off   C. arrived   D. got

15 "Hello, _____ _____ _____ Robin Hood."

A. is   B. name   C. my

16 "Wow! _____ you the Robin Hood _____ the _____ ?"

A. from   B. are   C. book

17 "No, I'm the Robin Hood of Sherwood Forest. _____ are you and _____ are you _____ ?"

A. why   B. who   C. here

18 "My name is Pascal. I don't know why I'm here, but there _____ be a _____ . You saved me from the _____ . Thank you so much. Is there _____ I can do for you?"

A. reason   B. anything   C. soldiers   D. must

19 "Well, can you help us _____ _____ the money that the king _____ from the people? He _____ them too much.

A. took   B. get   C. taxed   D. back

20 He is too _____ to _____ with the people, so they don't have _____ money to _____ food.

A. buy   B. greedy   C. enough   D. share

21 I want to help them _____ their money _____ . However, there are many soldiers in the tower, _____ no one can get _____ ."

A. so   B. get   C. inside   D. back

22 "Hmm… I think I have a _____ . But first, can you _____ me to the tower? I need to _____ the _____ of soldiers."

A. take   B. number   C. solution   D. count

23 Robin and Pascal _____ in a tree and _____ the soldiers one _____ one.

A. by   B. hid   C. counted   D. up

24 "_____ five soldiers _____ midnight _____ six in the morning.

A. from   B. are   C. to   D. there

13 그 남자는 파스칼을 그의 말에 올려 태우고 숲으로 말을 몰았습니다.

14 그들이 한 집 앞에 이르렀을 때, 그 남자는 멈추고 말에서 내렸습니다.

15 "안녕, 내 이름은 로빈 후드야."

16 "와우! 당신이 책 속의 로빈 후드인가요?"

17 "아니, 나는 셔우드 숲의 로빈 후드야. 너는 누구이고 왜 여기에 있니?"

18 "제 이름은 파스칼이에요. 저는 제가 왜 여기 있는지 모르지만 이유가 분명 있을 거예요. 당신은 저를 병사들로부터 구해줬어요. 정말 감사드려요. 제가 당신을 위해 할 수 있는 것이 있을까요?"

19 "음, 우리가 왕이 사람들에게서 가져간 돈을 되찾는 것을 도와줄 수 있니? 그는 그들에게 세금을 너무 많이 부과했어.

20 그는 너무 탐욕스러워서 사람들과 나누지 않아. 그래서 그들은 음식을 살 충분한 돈이 없어.

21 나는 그들의 돈을 다시 찾을 수 있도록 돕고 싶어. 하지만 탑 안에 병사들이 많아서 아무도 들어갈 수 없어."

22 "흠… 제게 해결책이 있는 것 같아요. 그러나 우선 저를 탑에 데려가 주실 수 있나요? 저는 병사들의 수를 세야 해요."

23 로빈과 파스칼은 나무에 숨어서 병사들의 수를 한 명씩 세었습니다.

24 "자정부터 새벽 여섯 시까지는 다섯 명의 병사들이 있어요.

25 Next, there are _____ _____ _____ _____, and then there are eight soldiers until six in the evening.

A. until   B. three   C. noon   D. soldiers

26 _____, there are twelve soldiers _____ midnight. So, you should go inside _____ six in the morning _____ noon."

A. until   B. and   C. lastly   D. between

27 "What? I _____ _____ _____."

A. get   B. don't   C. it

28 Pascal thought for a _____. 'Hmm… A graph _____ _____ this _____ to understand.'

A. make   B. moment   C. easier   D. might

29 Pascal _____ a _____ and _____ it _____ Robin.

A. to   B. graph   C. showed   D. drew

30 "Look, _____ _____ _____ time is between six in the evening and _____.

A. dangerous   B. most   C. midnight   D. the

31 Four times more soldiers _____ at that time _____ from six in the morning until noon. Do you see _____ I _____?"

A. than   B. what   C. work   D. mean

32 "Aha! I _____ _____ now. Thank you _____ _____, Pascal!"

A. so   B. get   C. much   D. it

33 "You're welcome. Now I _____ the _____ of graphs. No one can say _____ we don't need them _____."

A. that   B. realize   C. anymore   D. importance

34 Pascal _____ _____ of the woods. When he looked _____, he saw Robin Hood _____ at him.

A. waving   B. out   C. back   D. walked

35 Pascal _____ _____ and said to _____, "It was a great _____. How do I go back? Oh, I know. I should say the words *Cogito ergo sum*!"

A. back   B. himself   C. waved   D. adventure

25 그다음, 정오까지는 세 명의 병사들이 있고, 오후 여섯 시까지는 여덟 명의 병사들이 있어요.

26 마지막으로, 자정까지는 열두 명의 병사들이 있어요. 그래서 당신은 새벽 여섯 시에서 정오 사이에 들어가야 해요."

27 "뭐라고? 나는 이해하지 못했어."

28 파스칼은 잠시 생각에 잠겼습니다. '흠…그래프가 이것을 이해하는 것을 쉽게 해 줄지도 몰라.'

29 파스칼은 그래프를 그려서 그것을 로빈에게 보여주었습니다.

30 "보세요, 가장 위험한 시간은 저녁 여섯 시에서 자정까지예요.

31 오전 여섯 시부터 정오까지보다 그 시간에 네 배나 더 많은 병사들이 일해요. 제 말이 무슨 뜻인지 아시겠어요?"

32 "아하! 이제 이해했어. 너무 고마워, 파스칼!"

33 "천만에요. 이제 저는 그래프의 중요성을 깨달았어요. 아무도 그래프가 더 이상 필요 없다고 말할 수 없을 거예요."

34 파스칼은 숲에서 걸어 나왔습니다. 그가 뒤돌아봤을 때, 그는 로빈 후드가 그에게 손을 흔들고 있는 것을 보았습니다.

35 파스칼은 손을 흔들어 답하고 혼잣말을 했습니다. "정말 멋진 모험이었어. 나는 어떻게 돌아가지? 오, 알겠어. 나는 코기토 에르고 숨이라는 말을 해야 해!"

※ 다음 우리말과 일치하도록 빈칸에 알맞은 것을 골라 쓰시오.

1 Pascal _____ _____ _____ _____ _____ in his room. He was _____ _____ graphs.

2 "It's _____ _____ _____ _____ and _____ graphs. Why do I need _____ anyway? No one _____ _____ in _____."

3 He _____ _____ his pen and _____ his favorite book, *Robin Hood*.

4 He _____ _____ _____ _____ _____ to sleep. When he _____ _____ the book, he _____ a voice.

5 He _____ _____ the book _____ _____ _____ _____ _____.

6 He couldn't believe his eyes. It was his dog, Manny, _____ _____ talking!

7 "_____ your eyes and _____ _____ me. *Cogito ergo sum*," said Manny.

8 "_____ _____ _____?" "Just _____! *Cogito ergo sum*."

9 Pascal closed his eyes and _____ _____ _____. _____, he _____ men _____.

10 _____ he opened his eyes, he saw soldiers _____.

11 They were _____ a man _____ _____ in his hand. The man saw Pascal and _____.

12 "_____ too dangerous _____ there. Come on."

13 The man _____ Pascal _____ his horse and _____ into the woods.

14 When they _____ _____ a house, the man _____ and _____ his horse.

15 "Hello, _____ _____ Robin Hood."

16 "Wow! Are you _____ _____ _____ the book?"

17 "No, I'm the Robin Hood of Sherwood Forest. _____ _____ and why _____ _____ here?"

18 "My name is Pascal. I don't know _____ _____ _____, but there _____ _____ a reason. You _____ me _____ the soldiers. Thank you so much. _____ _____ I can do _____ you?"

---

1 파스칼은 그의 방에서 수학 숙제를 하고 있었습니다. 그는 그 래프 문제에 고군분투하고 있었습니다.

2 "그래프를 읽고 그리는 것은 너무 어려워. 게다가 내가 왜 그래프가 필요하겠어? 아무도 실제 생활에서는 그래프가 필요하지 않아."

3 그는 그의 펜을 내려놓고, 그가 가장 좋아하는 책, '로빈 후드'를 집어 들었습니다.

4 그는 책을 읽으며 잠들기로 했습니다. 그가 책을 펴려고 할 때, 그는 목소리를 들었습니다.

5 누가 말하고 있는지 보기 위해 그는 책에서 눈을 들어 올려 보았습니다.

6 그는 그의 눈을 믿을 수 없었습니다. 말하는 것은 바로 자신의 개, Manny였습니다!

7 "눈을 감고 내 말을 따라 말하세요. 코기토 에르고 숨." Manny가 말했습니다.

8 "너는 말할 수 있니?" "그냥 따라 하세요! 코기토 에르고 숨."

9 파스칼은 그의 눈을 감고 그 단어들을 따라 말했습니다. 갑자기 그는 남자들이 소리치는 것을 들었습니다.

10 그가 눈을 떴을 때, 그는 말을 탄 병사들을 보았습니다.

11 그들은 손에 화살을 든 남자를 뒤쫓고 있었습니다. 그 남자는 파스칼을 보고 소리쳤습니다.

12 "네가 거기 서 있는 것은 너무 위험해. 이리 와."

13 그 남자는 파스칼을 그의 말에 올려 태우고 숲으로 말을 몰았습니다.

14 그들이 한 집 앞에 이르렀을 때, 그 남자는 멈추고 말에서 내렸습니다.

15 "안녕, 내 이름은 로빈 후드야."

16 "와우! 당신이 책 속의 로빈 후드인가요?"

17 "아니. 나는 셔우드 숲의 로빈 후드야. 너는 누구이고 왜 여기에 있니?"

18 "제 이름은 파스칼이에요. 저는 제가 왜 여기 있는지 모르지만 이유가 분명 있을 거예요. 당신은 저를 병사들로부터 구해줬어요. 정말 감사드려요. 제가 당신을 위해 할 수 있는 것이 있을까요?"

19 "Well, can you help us _____ _____ the money _____ the king _____ from the people? He _____ _____ too much.

20 He is _____ _____ _____ _____ with the people, so they don't have _____ _____ _____ _____ _____ food.

21 I want to _____ _____ _____ their money _____. _____, there are many soldiers in the tower, so _____ _____ _____ _____ _____."

22 "Hmm… I think I have a solution. But first, can you _____ _____ _____ _____ _____ _____? I need to _____ _____ _____ _____ soldiers."

23 Robin and Pascal _____ _____ in a tree and _____ the soldiers _____ _____ _____.

24 "_____ _____ five soldiers _____ midnight _____ six in the morning.

25 Next, there are _____ _____ _____ _____ _____, and then there are _____ _____ _____ six in the evening.

26 _____, _____ _____ twelve soldiers _____ midnight. So, you should _____ _____ _____ six in the morning _____ _____."

27 "What? I _____ _____ _____."

28 Pascal thought for a _____. 'Hmm… A graph _____ _____ _____ _____ _____ understand.'

29 Pascal _____ a graph and _____ _____ to Robin.

30 "Look, _____ _____ _____ _____ _____ is _____ six in the evening _____ midnight.

31 _____ _____ _____ _____ _____ work at that time _____ from six in the morning _____ noon. Do you see _____ _____ _____?"

32 "Aha! I _____ _____ now. Thank you _____ _____, Pascal!"

33 "You're welcome. Now I _____ _____ _____ _____ _____. _____ _____ can say _____ we don't need _____ anymore."

34 Pascal _____ _____ _____ the woods. When he _____ _____, he saw Robin Hood _____ at him.

35 Pascal _____ _____ and said to _____, "It was a great _____. How _____ _____ _____ _____ _____ _____? Oh, I know. I _____ _____ the words *Cogito ergo sum*!"

19 "음, 우리가 왕이 사람들에게서 가져간 돈을 되찾는 것을 도와줄 수 있니? 그는 그들에게 세금을 너무 많이 부과했어.

20 그는 너무 탐욕스러워서 사람들과 나누지 않아. 그래서 그들은 음식을 살 충분한 돈이 없어.

21 나는 그들의 돈을 다시 찾을 수 있도록 돕고 싶어. 하지만 탑 안에 병사들이 많아서 아무도 들어갈 수 없어."

22 "흠… 제게 해결책이 있는 것 같아요. 그러나 우선 저를 탑에 데려가 주실 수 있나요? 저는 병사들의 수를 세야 해요."

23 로빈과 파스칼은 나무에 숨어서 병사들의 수를 한 명씩 세었습니다.

24 "자정부터 새벽 여섯 시까지는 다섯 명의 병사들이 있어요.

25 그다음, 정오까지는 세 명의 병사들이 있고, 오후 여섯 시까지는 여덟 명의 병사들이 있어요.

26 마지막으로, 자정까지는 열두 명의 병사들이 있어요. 그래서 당신은 새벽 여섯 시에서 정오 사이에 들어가야 해요."

27 "뭐라고? 나는 이해하지 못했어."

28 파스칼은 잠시 생각에 잠겼습니다. '흠…그래프가 이것을 이해하는 것을 쉽게 해 줄지도 몰라.'

29 파스칼은 그래프를 그려서 그것을 로빈에게 보여주었습니다.

30 "보세요, 가장 위험한 시간은 저녁 여섯 시에서 자정까지예요.

31 오전 여섯 시부터 정오까지보다 그 시간에 네 배나 더 많은 병사들이 일해요. 제 말이 무슨 뜻인지 아시겠어요?"

32 "아하! 이제 이해했어. 너무 고마워, 파스칼!"

33 "천만에요. 이제 저는 그래프의 중요성을 깨달았어요. 아무도 그래프가 더 이상 필요 없다고 말할 수 없을 거예요."

34 파스칼은 숲에서 걸어 나왔습니다. 그가 뒤돌아봤을 때, 그는 로빈 후드가 그에게 손을 흔들고 있는 것을 보았습니다.

35 파스칼은 손을 흔들어 답하고 혼잣말을 했습니다. "정말 멋진 모험이었어. 나는 어떻게 돌아가지? 오, 알겠어. 나는 코기토 에르고 숨이라는 말을 해야 해!"

※ 다음 문장을 우리말로 쓰시오.

1 Pascal was doing his math homework in his room. He was struggling with graphs.
➡ _____

2 "It's too hard to read and draw graphs. Why do I need these anyway? No one needs graphs in real life."
➡ _____

3 He put down his pen and picked up his favorite book, *Robin Hood*.
➡ _____

4 He decided to read himself to sleep. When he was about to open the book, he heard a voice.
➡ _____

5 He looked up from the book to see who was talking.
➡ _____

6 He couldn't believe his eyes. It was his dog, Manny, who was talking!
➡ _____

7 "Close your eyes and repeat after me. *Cogito ergo sum*," said Manny.
➡ _____

8 "You can talk?" "Just repeat! *Cogito ergo sum*."
➡ _____

9 Pascal closed his eyes and repeated the words. Suddenly, he heard men shouting.
➡ _____

10 When he opened his eyes, he saw soldiers on horses.
➡ _____

11 They were chasing a man with arrows in his hand. The man saw Pascal and shouted.
➡ _____

12 "It's too dangerous for you to stand there. Come on."
➡ _____

13 The man pulled Pascal onto his horse and rode into the woods.
➡ _____

14 When they arrived at a house, the man stopped and got off his horse.
➡ _____

15 "Hello, my name is Robin Hood."
➡ _____

16 "Wow! Are you the Robin Hood from the book?"
➡ _____

17 "No, I'm the Robin Hood of Sherwood Forest. Who are you and why are you here?"
➡ _____

18 "My name is Pascal. I don't know why I'm here, but there must be a reason. You saved me from the soldiers. Thank you so much. Is there anything I can do for you?"
➡ _____

19 "Well, can you help us get back the money that the king took from the people? He taxed them too much.
➡ _____

20 He is too greedy to share with the people, so they don't have enough money to buy food.
➡ _____

21 I want to help them get their money back. However, there are many soldiers in the tower, so no one can get inside."
➡ _____

22 "Hmm... I think I have a solution. But first, can you take me to the tower? I need to count the number of soldiers."
➡ _____

23 Robin and Pascal hid up in a tree and counted the soldiers one by one.
➡ _____

24 "There are five soldiers from midnight to six in the morning.
➡ _____

25 Next, there are three soldiers until noon, and then there are eight soldiers until six in the evening.
➡ _____

26 Lastly, there are twelve soldiers until midnight. So, you should go inside between six in the morning and noon."
➡ _____

27 "What? I don't get it."
➡ _____

28 Pascal thought for a moment. 'Hmm... A graph might make this easier to understand.'
➡ _____

29 Pascal drew a graph and showed it to Robin.
➡ _____

30 "Look, the most dangerous time is between six in the evening and midnight.
➡ _____

31 Four times more soldiers work at that time than from six in the morning until noon. Do you see what I mean?"
➡ _____

32 "Aha! I get it now. Thank you so much, Pascal!"
➡ _____

33 "You're welcome. Now I realize the importance of graphs. No one can say that we don't need them anymore."
➡ _____

34 Pascal walked out of the woods. When he looked back, he saw Robin Hood waving at him.
➡ _____

35 Pascal waved back and said to himself, "It was a great adventure. How do I go back? Oh, I know. I should say the words *Cogito ergo sum*!"
➡ _____
_____

※ 다음 괄호 안의 단어들을 우리말에 맞도록 바르게 배열하시오.

1 (was / Pascal / his / doing / homework / math / his / in / room. // was / he / with / struggling / graphs.)
➡ _____
_____

2 (too / "it's / to / hard / and / read / graphs. / draw // do / why / need / I / anyway? / these // one / no / graphs / needs / real / in / life.")
➡ _____
_____

3 (put / he / down / pen / his / and / up / picked / favorite / his / Robin / book, / Hood.)
➡ _____

4 (decided / he / read / to / to / himself / sleep. // he / when / about / was / open / to / book, / the / heard / he / voice. / a)
➡ _____
_____

5 (looked / he / up / the / from / to / book / who / see / talking. / was)
➡ _____

6 (couldn't / he / believe / eyes. / his // was / it / dog, / his / who / Manny, / talking! / was)
➡ _____

7 (your / "close / and / eyes / after / repeat / me. // *ergo* *Cogito* *sum*," / Manny / said)
➡ _____

8 (can / "you / talk?" // repeat! / "just *ergo* *Cogito* *sum*.")
➡ _____

9 (closed / Pascal / eyes / his / and / the / repeated / words. // he / suddenly, / heard / shouting. / men)
➡ _____
_____

10 (he / when / his / opened / eyes, / saw / he / on / soldiers / horses.)
➡ _____

11 (were / they / a / chasing / man / arrows / with / his / in / hand. // man / the / Pascal / saw / shouted. / and)
➡ _____
_____

12 (too / "it's / dangerous / you / to / for / stand / there. // on." / come)
➡ _____

1 파스칼은 그의 방에서 수학 숙제를 하고 있었습니다. 그는 그래프 문제에 고군분투하고 있었습니다.

2 "그래프를 읽고 그리는 것은 너무 어려워. 게다가 내가 왜 그래프가 필요하겠어? 아무도 실제 생활에서는 그래프가 필요하지 않아."

3 그는 그의 펜을 내려놓고, 그가 가장 좋아하는 책, '로빈 후드'를 집어 들었습니다.

4 그는 책을 읽으며 잠들기로 했습니다. 그가 책을 펴려고 할 때, 그는 목소리를 들었습니다.

5 누가 말하고 있는지 보기 위해 그는 책에서 눈을 들어 올려다보았습니다.

6 그는 그의 눈을 믿을 수 없었습니다. 말하는 것은 바로 자신의 개, Manny였습니다!

7 "눈을 감고 내 말을 따라 말하세요. 코기토 에르고 숨." Manny가 말했습니다.

8 "너는 말할 수 있니?" "그냥 따라 하세요! 코기토 에르고 숨."

9 파스칼은 그의 눈을 감고 그 단어들을 따라 말했습니다. 갑자기 그는 남자들이 소리치는 것을 들었습니다.

10 그가 눈을 떴을 때, 그는 말을 탄 병사들을 보았습니다.

11 그들은 손에 화살을 든 남자를 뒤쫓고 있었습니다. 그 남자는 파스칼을 보고 소리쳤습니다.

12 "네가 거기 서 있는 것은 너무 위험해. 이리 와."

13 (man / the / Pascal / pulled / his / onto / and / horse / the / into / rode / woods.)

➡ _____

14 (they / when / arrived / a / at / house, / man / the / and / stopped / got / his / off / horse.)

➡ _____

15 ("hello, / name / my / Robin / is / Hood.")

➡ _____

16 ("wow! // you / are / Robin / the / from / Hood / book?" / the)

➡ _____

17 (I'm / "no, / the / Hood / Robin / Sherwood / of / Forest. // are / who / and / you / why / you / here?" / are)

➡ _____

18 (name / "my / Pascal. // is / don't / I / why / know / here, / I'm / there / but / be / must / reason. / a // saved / you / me / the / from / soldiers. // you / thank / much. / so // there / is / I / anything / do / can / you?" / for)

➡ _____

_____

19 (can / "well, / help / you / get / us / the / back / money / the / that / king / from / took / people? / the // taxed / he / too / them / much.)

➡ _____

_____

20 (is / he / greedy / too / share / to / the / with / people, / they / so / have / don't / money / enough / buy / to / food.)

➡ _____

_____

21 (want / I / help / to / get / them / money / their / back. // there / however, / many / are / soldiers / the / in / tower, / no / so / one / get / can / inside.")

➡ _____

_____

22 ("hmm... / think / I / have / solution. / a // first, / but / you / can / me / take / the / to / tower? // need / I / count / to / number / the / soldiers.")

➡ _____

_____

23 (Pascal / and / Robin / up / hid / a / in / tree / and / the / counted / one / soldiers / one. / by)

➡ _____

24 (are / "there / soldiers / five / midnight / from / six / to / the / in / morning.)

➡ _____

13 그 남자는 파스칼을 그의 말에 올려 태우고 숲으로 말을 몰았습니다.

14 그들이 한 집 앞에 이르렀을 때, 그 남자는 멈추고 말에서 내렸습니다.

15 "안녕, 내 이름은 로빈 후드야."

16 "와우! 당신이 책 속의 로빈 후드인가요?"

17 "아니, 나는 셔우드 숲의 로빈 후드야. 너는 누구이고 왜 여기에 있니?"

18 "제 이름은 파스칼이에요. 저는 제가 왜 여기 있는지 모르지만 이유가 분명 있을 거예요. 당신은 저를 병사들로부터 구해줬어요. 정말 감사드려요. 제가 당신을 위해 할 수 있는 것이 있을까요?"

19 "음, 우리가 왕이 사람들에게서 가져간 돈을 되찾는 것을 도와줄 수 있니? 그는 그들에게 세금을 너무 많이 부과했어.

20 그는 너무 탐욕스러워서 사람들과 나누지 않아. 그래서 그들은 음식을 살 충분한 돈이 없어.

21 나는 그들의 돈을 다시 찾을 수 있도록 돕고 싶어. 하지만 탑 안에 병사들이 많아서 아무도 들어갈 수 없어."

22 "흠… 제게 해결책이 있는 것 같아요. 그러나 우선 저를 탑에 데려가 주실 수 있나요? 저는 병사들의 수를 세야 해요."

23 로빈과 파스칼은 나무에 숨어서 병사들의 수를 한 명씩 세었습니다.

24 "자정부터 새벽 여섯 시까지는 다섯 명의 병사들이 있어요.

25 (there / next, / three / are / until / soldiers / noon, / then / and / are / there / soldiers / eight / six / until / the / evening. / in)

➡ _____

_____

26 (there / lastly, / twelve / are / until / soldiers / midnight. // you / so, / go / should / between / inside / in / six / morning / the / noon." / and)

➡ _____

_____

27 ("what? // don't / I / it." / get)

➡ _____

28 (thought / Pascal / a / for / moment. // 'hmm... // graph / a / make / might / easier / this / understand.')

➡ _____

_____

29 (drew / Pascal / graph / a / and / it / showed / Robin. / to)

➡ _____

30 (the / "look, / most / time / dangerous / between / is / in / six / evening / the / midnight. / and)

➡ _____

_____

31 (times / four / soldiers / more / at / work / time / that / from / than / in / six / morning / the / noon. / until // you / do / what / see / mean?" / I)

➡ _____

_____

32 ("aha! // I / it / get / now. // you / thank / much / Pascal!" / so)

➡ _____

33 (welcome. / "you're // I / now / the / realize / of / importance / graphs. // one / no / say / can / that / don't / we / them / need / anymore.")

➡ _____

_____

34 (walked / Pascal / of / out / woods. / the // he / when / back, / looked / saw / he / Hood / Robin / at / waving / him.)

➡ _____

35 (waved / Pascal / said / and / back / himself, / to / was / "it / great / a / adventure. // do / how / I / back? // I / oh, / know. // should / I / the / say / words / *ergo* / *Cogito* / *sum*!")

➡ _____

_____

25 그다음, 정오까지는 세 명의 병사들이 있고, 오후 여섯 시까지는 여덟 명의 병사들이 있어요.

26 마지막으로, 자정까지는 열두 명의 병사들이 있어요. 그래서 당신은 새벽 여섯 시에서 정오 사이에 들어가야 해요."

27 "뭐라고? 나는 이해하지 못했어."

28 파스칼은 잠시 생각에 잠겼습니다. '흠…그래프가 이것을 이해하는 것을 쉽게 해 줄지도 몰라.'

29 파스칼은 그래프를 그려서 그것을 로빈에게 보여주었습니다.

30 "보세요, 가장 위험한 시간은 저녁 여섯 시에서 자정까지예요.

31 오전 여섯 시부터 정오까지보다 그 시간에 네 배나 더 많은 병사들이 일해요. 제 말이 무슨 뜻인지 아시겠어요?"

32 "아하! 이제 이해했어. 너무 고마워, 파스칼!"

33 "천만에요. 이제 저는 그래프의 중요성을 깨달았어요. 아무도 그래프가 더 이상 필요 없다고 말할 수 없을 거예요."

34 파스칼은 숲에서 걸어 나왔습니다. 그가 뒤돌아봤을 때, 그는 로빈 후드가 그에게 손을 흔들고 있는 것을 보았습니다.

35 파스칼은 손을 흔들어 답하고 혼잣말을 했습니다. "정말 멋진 모험이었어. 나는 어떻게 돌아가지? 오, 알겠어. 나는 코기토 에르고 숨이라는 말을 해야 해!"

※ 다음 우리말을 영어로 쓰시오.

1 파스칼은 그의 방에서 수학 숙제를 하고 있었습니다. 그는 그래프 문제에 고군분투하고 있었습니다.

➡ _____

2 "그래프를 읽고 그리는 것은 너무 어려워. 게다가 내가 왜 그래프가 필요하겠어? 아무도 실제 생활에서는 그래프가 필요하지 않아."

➡ _____

_____

3 그는 그의 펜을 내려놓고, 그가 가장 좋아하는 책, '로빈 후드'를 집어 들었습니다.

➡ _____

4 그는 책을 읽으며 잠들기로 했습니다. 그가 책을 펴려고 할 때, 그는 목소리를 들었습니다.

➡ _____

5 누가 말하고 있는지 보기 위해 그는 책에서 눈을 들어 올려다보았습니다.

➡ _____

6 그는 그의 눈을 믿을 수 없었습니다. 말하는 것은 바로 자신의 개, Manny였습니다!

➡ _____

7 "눈을 감고 내 말을 따라 말하세요. *코기토 에르고 숨.*" Manny가 말했습니다.

➡ _____

8 "너는 말할 수 있니?" "그냥 따라 하세요! *코기토 에르고 숨.*"

➡ _____

9 파스칼은 그의 눈을 감고 그 단어들을 따라 말했습니다. 갑자기 그는 남자들이 소리치는 것을 들었습니다.

➡ _____

10 그가 눈을 떴을 때, 그는 말을 탄 병사들을 보았습니다.

➡ _____

11 그들은 손에 화살을 든 남자를 뒤쫓고 있었습니다. 그 남자는 파스칼을 보고 소리쳤습니다.

➡ _____

12 "네가 거기 서 있는 것은 너무 위험해. 이리 와."

➡ _____

13 그 남자는 파스칼을 그의 말에 올려 태우고 숲으로 말을 몰았습니다.

➡ _____

14 그들이 한 집 앞에 이르렀을 때, 그 남자는 멈추고 말에서 내렸습니다.

➡ _____

15 "안녕, 내 이름은 로빈 후드야."

➡ _____

16 "와우! 당신이 책 속의 로빈 후드인가요?"

➡ _____

17 "아니, 나는 셔우드 숲의 로빈 후드야. 너는 누구이고 왜 여기에 있니?"

➡ _____

18 "제 이름은 파스칼이에요. 저는 제가 왜 여기 있는지 모르지만 이유가 분명 있을 거예요. 당신은 저를 병사들로부터 구해줬어요. 정말 감사드려요. 제가 당신을 위해 할 수 있는 것이 있을까요?"

➡ _____

_____

19 "음, 우리가 왕이 사람들에게서 가져간 돈을 되찾는 것을 도와줄 수 있니? 그는 그들에게 세금을 너무 많이 부과했어.
➡ _____

20 그는 너무 탐욕스러워서 사람들과 나누지 않아. 그래서 그들은 음식을 살 충분한 돈이 없어.
➡ _____

21 나는 그들의 돈을 다시 찾을 수 있도록 돕고 싶어. 하지만 탑 안에 병사들이 많아서 아무도 들어갈 수 없어."
➡ _____

22 "흠… 제게 해결책이 있는 것 같아요. 그러나 우선 저를 탑에 데려가 주실 수 있나요? 저는 병사들의 수를 세야 해요."
➡ _____

23 로빈과 파스칼은 나무에 숨어서 병사들의 수를 한 명씩 세었습니다.

24 "자정부터 새벽 여섯 시까지는 다섯 명의 병사들이 있어요.
➡ _____

25 그다음, 정오까지는 세 명의 병사들이 있고, 오후 여섯 시까지는 여덟 명의 병사들이 있어요.
➡ _____

26 마지막으로, 자정까지는 열두 명의 병사들이 있어요. 그래서 당신은 새벽 여섯 시에서 정오 사이에 들어가야 해요."
➡ _____

27 "뭐라고? 나는 이해하지 못했어."
➡ _____

28 파스칼은 잠시 생각에 잠겼습니다. '흠… 그래프가 이것을 이해하는 것을 쉽게 해 줄지도 몰라.'

29 파스칼은 그래프를 그려서 그것을 로빈에게 보여주었습니다.
➡ _____

30 "보세요, 가장 위험한 시간은 저녁 여섯 시에서 자정까지예요.

31 오전 여섯 시부터 정오까지보다 그 시간에 네 배나 더 많은 병사들이 일해요. 제 말이 무슨 뜻인지 아시겠어요?"
➡ _____

32 "아하! 이제 이해했어. 너무 고마워, 파스칼!"
➡ _____

33 "천만에요. 이제 저는 그래프의 중요성을 깨달았어요. 아무도 그래프가 더 이상 필요 없다고 말할 수 없을 거예요."
➡ _____

34 파스칼은 숲에서 걸어 나왔습니다. 그가 뒤돌아봤을 때, 그는 로빈 후드가 그에게 손을 흔들고 있는 것을 보았습니다.
➡ _____

35 파스칼은 손을 흔들어 답하고 혼잣말을 했습니다. "정말 멋진 모험이었어. 나는 어떻게 돌아가지? 오, 알겠어. 나는 코기토 에르고 숨이라는 말을 해야 해!"
➡ _____
_____

※ 다음 우리말과 일치하도록 빈칸에 알맞은 말을 쓰시오.

Communication Task

1. I did a survey on the books _____ _____ _____
_____ _____.

2. _____ _____ says _____ thirteen _____ _____ twenty
students _____ _____.

3. That is _____ _____ of the _____.

4. _____ _____ _____ _____ _____ chose _____
_____.

5. _____, only _____ _____ _____ _____ _____
chose history books.

6. From this _____ _____, _____ _____ the school library
_____ _____ _____ _____ _____.

7. Do you see _____ I _____?

1. 나는 우리 학교 도서관에 필요한 책들을 조사했다.
2. 그 결과 20명 중 13명이 소설을 선택하였다.
3. 이는 전체의 65퍼센트이다.
4. 20명 중 5명은 공상 과학 책을 선택했다.
5. 그러나 20명 중 2명만이 역사책을 선택했다.
6. 이러한 조사 결과를 통해 학교 도서관은 더 많은 소설을 구해야 한다고 생각한다.
7. 무슨 뜻인지 알겠니?

Before You Read B Look and Write

1. Book Club: Your _____

2. _____: *Robin Hood*

3. Topic of the book: It's about _____ _____ _____ _____
_____ _____ people from the _____ _____.

4. My favorite character: My favorite character is Robin Hood _____
he _____ _____ _____ _____ _____ _____ _____.

5. _____ of the book: _____ bad _____ _____ too
much. _____ _____, _____ _____ _____ _____
_____ the most.

1. 책 동아리: 너의 후기들
2. 제목: 로빈 후드
3. 책의 주제: 욕심 많은 왕으로부터 사람을 구하려 고군분투하는 한 남자의 이야기이다.
4. 내가 가장 좋아하는 등장인물: 병사들보다 화살을 더 잘 쏘기 때문에 내가 가장 좋아하는 등장인물은 로빈 후드이다.
5. 책에 대한 나의 논평: 세금을 너무 많이 부과하는 것은 나쁘다. 결국, 돈이 아니라 사람이 가장 중요하다.

Let's Write

1. _____ _____ the _____ _____ on "Who is your favorite
character?"

2. Fifteen _____ _____ thirty students chose Hong Gildong.

3. _____ _____ _____, fifty percent of the students _____
_____ _____.

4. I think _____ _____ the _____ _____ _____.

5. _____, _____ _____ _____ Kongiwi and six students
chose Robin Hood.

6. _____ _____ chose Nolbu. Maybe _____ _____ the
character is _____ _____ _____ be liked _____ _____.

1. '당신이 가장 좋아하는 등장인물은 누구입니까?'라는 설문 조사 결과를 보자.
2. 30명의 학생들 중 15명이 홍길동을 선택했다.
3. 다시 말하면, 학생들 중 50퍼센트가 그 등장인물을 선택했다.
4. 내 생각에 그것은 그 등장인물이 용감하기 때문이다.
5. 그다음에 9명의 학생들이 콩쥐를 선택했고, 6명의 학생들이 로빈 후드를 선택했다.
6. 아무도 놀부를 선택하지 않았다. 아마도 그것은 그 등장인물이 다른 사람들이 좋아하기에 너무 탐욕스럽기 때문일 것이다

※ 다음 우리말을 영어로 쓰시오.

Communication Task

1. 나는 우리 학교 도서관에 필요한 책들을 조사했다.
   ➡ _____

2. 그 결과 20명 중 13명이 소설을 선택하였다.
   ➡ _____

3. 이는 전체의 65퍼센트이다.
   ➡ _____

4. 20명 중 5명은 공상 과학 책을 선택했다.
   ➡ _____

5. 그러나 20명 중 2명만이 역사책을 선택했다.
   ➡ _____

6. 이러한 조사 결과를 통해 학교 도서관은 더 많은 소설을 구해야 한다고 생각한다.
   ➡ _____

7. 무슨 뜻인지 알겠니?
   ➡ _____

Before You Read B Look and Write

1. 책 동아리: 너의 후기들
   ➡ _____

2. 제목: 로빈 후드
   ➡ _____

3. 책의 주제: 욕심 많은 왕으로부터 사람을 구하려 고군분투하는 한 남자의 이야기이다.
   ➡ _____

4. 내가 가장 좋아하는 등장인물: 병사들보다 화살을 더 잘 쏘기 때문에 내가 가장 좋아하는 등장인물은 로빈 후드이다.
   ➡ _____

5. 책에 대한 나의 논평: 세금을 너무 많이 부과하는 것은 나쁘다. 결국, 돈이 아니라 사람이 가장 중요하다.
   ➡ _____

Let's Write

1. '당신이 가장 좋아하는 등장인물은 누구입니까?'라는 설문 조사 결과를 보자.
   ➡ _____

2. 30명의 학생들 중 15명이 홍길동을 선택했다.
   ➡ _____

3. 다시 말하면, 학생들 중 50퍼센트가 그 등장인물을 선택했다.
   ➡ _____

4. 내 생각에 그것은 그 등장인물이 용감하기 때문이다.
   ➡ _____

5. 그다음에 9명의 학생들이 콩쥐를 선택했고, 6명의 학생들이 로빈 후드를 선택했다.
   ➡ _____

6. 아무도 놀부를 선택하지 않았다. 아마도 그것은 그 등장인물이 다른 사람들이 좋아하기에 너무 탐욕스럽기 때문일 것이다.
   ➡ _____

MEMO

2학기 전과정

적중 100 plus

영어 기출 문제집

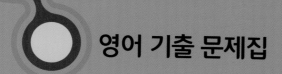

영어 기출 문제집

2학기 전과정 plus

2학기

정답 및 해설

지학 | 민찬규

중 3

적중100

영어 기출 문제집

적중100 plus

2학기

정답 및 해설

지학 | 민찬규

중 3

Lesson 5

Which Way to Go?

01 entrance   02 ②   03 ④   04 ②
05 ③
06 (1) willingly, maze, confusion   (2) connected,
     method, effective   (3) Mazes, variety, hedges

01 주어진 관계는 반의어 관계를 나타낸다. entrance: 입구, exit: 출구

02 주어진 문장에서 place는 '두다, 놓다'를 의미하며 이와 같은 의미로 쓰인 것은 ②번이다. 나머지는 모두 '장소'를 뜻한다.

03 make a choice: 선택하다, make a decision: 결정하다, make a plan: 계획을 세우다

04 '보통 들판, 정원, 마당, 도로 등의 가장자리를 따라 조밀하게 줄지어 심겨진 덤불 또는 작은 나무'를 나타내는 말은 'hedge(산울타리)'이다.

05 willingly: 기꺼이

06 willingly: 기꺼이, confusion: 혼란, connect: 연결하다, method: 방법, effective: 효과적인, a variety of: 다양한, hedge: 산울타리

01 (1) regularity   (2) worth   (3) compare   (4) exchange
     (5) decide
02 (1) This simple method may not be effective in
       certain types of mazes.
    (2) You can find the origin of the labyrinth in
       Greek mythology.
    (3) Please line up in the order of arrival.
03 (1) turn around   (2) you (s)et for   (3) a (v)ariety of
04 (1) We're really looking forward to seeing you
       again.
    (2) The first street we tried turned out to be a
       dead end.
    (3) Now is the time when we have to make a
       decision.
    (4) They go horeseback riding once a month.
    (5) I must come up with an excuse.

01 compare: 비교하다, decide: 결정하다, regularity: 규칙성, worth: ~의 가치가 있는, ~할 가치가 있는, exchange: 교환하다

02 method: 방법, effective: 효과적인, maze: 미로, origin: 기원, labyrinth: 미궁, in the order of: ~의 순서로

03 turn around: 돌다, 돌아서다, be set for: ~할 준비가 되다., a variety of: 다양한

04 (1) look forward to: ~하기를 기대하다, (2) dead end: 막다른 길, (3) make a decision: 결정하다, (4) horseback riding: 승마 (5) come up with: ~을 생각해 내다

1 Is it possible to exchange them for the red shoes?
2 ②

1 T   2 F   3 T   4 F

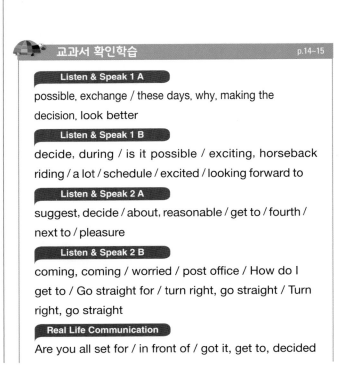

Listen & Speak 1 A

possible, exchange / these days, why, making the decision, look better

Listen & Speak 1 B

decide, during / is it possible / exciting, horseback riding / a lot / schedule / excited / looking forward to

Listen & Speak 2 A

suggest, decide / about, reasonable / get to / fourth / next to / pleasure

Listen & Speak 2 B

coming, coming / worried / post office / How do I get to / Go straight for / turn right, go straight / Turn right, go straight

Real Life Communication

Are you all set for / in front of / got it, get to, decided

/ choices / reliable / possible to, by subway / take

Let's Check 1

origin, labyrinth / Labyrinth, mythological prison / angry, put, labyrinth

---

12 나는 어제 흰색 신발을 샀다. 그것들은 너무 인기가 많았고 나는 결정하는 데 많은 시간이 걸렸다. 집에 돌아온 후, 나는 빨간색 신발이 내게 더 잘 어울릴 거라고 생각했다. 내가 신발가게에 방문해서 내 신발을 빨간색으로 교환할 수 있는지 물어보았을 때, 나는 교환할 수 있었다. 나는 내 빨간색 신발이 매우 좋다.

시험대비 기본평가 p.16

01 reasonable　　02 ①

03 ⓐ of　ⓑ to

04 Is it possible to get to Terminal 2 by subway?

02 ①번을 제외한 나머지는 모두 길을 물어보는 말이다.

03 in front of: ~앞에, get to: ~에 가다

시험대비 실력평가 p.17~18

01 prison　　02 ④　　03 ⓐ → worried

04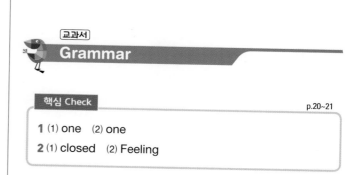
100m 50m 50m 100m

05 She should go straight for one more block.

06 ⑤

07 How do I get to the restaurant?

08 (1)

09 He wants to exchange the shoes for the red ones.

10 White is popular these days.

11 It's because he thinks that red will look better on him.

12 (A) the white shoes, making the decision
(C) the red shoes would look better on me
(D) exchange my shoes for the red ones

01 '처벌로서 범죄자를 가두거나 재판 받기 전 범죄로 고소된 사람들이 갇히는 건물'을 가리키는 말은 'prison(감옥)'이다.

02 크레타의 왕이 괴물에게 화가 나서 괴물을 감옥에 가두었다.

03 걱정스러움을 나타내는 과거분사형 형용사 worried가 적절하다.

05 민주는 우체국에서 킴스 베이커리에 가기 위해 한 블록 더 직진해야 한다.

06 ⑤번을 제외한 나머지는 모두 추천을 하는 표현이다.

09 소년은 신발을 빨간색으로 교환하기를 원한다.

10 흰색이 요즘 인기가 많다.

11 소년은 빨간색이 그에게 더 잘 어울릴 것이라고 생각하기 때문에 신발을 교환하기를 원한다.

서술형 시험대비 p.19

01 (C) → (B) → (D) → (A)

02 (A) go horseback riding　(B) Mirror Maze Park
(C) she heard that the park is a lot more fun

03 It's because their food is good and the prices are reasonable.

04 the elevator, next to, the fourth floor

01 (C) 가능성 질문 → (B) 인기 있는 색상 설명 → (D) 교환하고자 하는 이유 설명 → (A) 대답

02 지나의 가족은 곧 제주도를 방문할 계획을 세웠다. 지나와 엄마는 이에 대해 이야기했다. 모든 것이 좋아보였지만 지나는 말을 타러 가는 계획을 바꾸고 싶어했다. 대신에, 그녀는 거울 미로 공원을 방문하고 싶었다. 왜냐하면 그녀는 공원이 훨씬 더 재미있다고 들었기 때문이다. 엄마는 두 번째 날 일정을 바꾸기로 결정해서 지나는 여행에 매우 신이 났다.

04 소라는 파파첸스에 건물 안에 엘리베이터를 이용해서 갈 수 있다. 파파첸스는 4층 엘리베이터 옆에 있다.

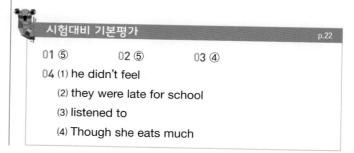

교과서
Grammar

핵심 Check p.20~21

1 (1) one　(2) one

2 (1) closed　(2) Feeling

시험대비 기본평가 p.22

01 ⑤　　02 ⑤　　03 ④

04 (1) he didn't feel

(2) they were late for school

(3) listened to

(4) Though she eats much

01 둘 중 첫 번째는 one, 나머지 하나는 the other로 쓴다.

02 분사구문을 만들 때, 주절과 주어가 같으면 주어를 생략하고 분사를 쓴다. 접속사와 주어를 모두 쓸 때는 분사구문으로 쓸 수 없으며, 완료분사구문은 주절보다 시제가 앞설 때 쓴다.

03 둘 중 나머지 하나를 가리킬 때는 the other를 써야 한다.

04 분사구문은 분사를 활용하여 부사절을 부사구로 줄인 표현이다. 대개 양보, 동시동작, 이유, 시간, 조건 등의 부사절이며, 절로 전환할 때에는 동사의 시제 등에 유의해야 한다. (4)는 내용상 양보이므로 Though 외에도 Although, Even though 등의 접속사가 가능하다.

시험대비 실력평가   p.23~25

01 ①   02 ③   03 ④   04 ④
05 ⑤   06 Tiring → Tired, or → nor
07 (1) Reading from left to right, it reads "evil"
   (2) Seeing the duck from under the water
08 ②   09 ⑤   10 ⑤   11 ④
12 ②   13 ⑤   14 ③
15 Not wanting to regret it again,
16 The girl having played with her friends without
   wearing a mask,   17 ④   18 ②

01 '마술에 흥미를 느낀 것이 그녀가 마술사가 되도록 했다.'이므로 문장에서 주어로 쓰인 '동명사'이다. 나머지는 모두 분사구문을 이끄는 분사이다.

02 ① one → it ② each는 단수 취급 are → is ④ neither는 nor와 함께 '둘 중 어느 것도 아니다'라는 뜻으로 쓴다. or → nor ⑤ 정해지지 않은 명사를 앞에서 수식하는 단어와 함께 쓸 때 one을 쓰는 것이 적절하다. it → one

03 ① Don't → Not ② Being → It being 독립분사구문 ③ Opened → Opening ⑤ Caught → Catching

04 두 학생 모두를 나타낼 때는 both, 둘 중 누구도 안 되는 경우는 no one 또는 neither one으로 쓰는 것이 적절하다.

05 'with+목적어+분사' 구문은 '목적어의 능동/수동' 여부가 중요하다. '눈을 감은 채 산책'한 것은 눈이 '감겨진 것'이므로 closed가 적절하다.

06 '하루 종일 전염병 환자들을 돌보느라 지쳐서, 그녀와 그녀의 동료의사 둘 다 시민들이 보내준 격려의 선물을 풀어볼 힘조차 없었다.'라는 내용이다. 지친 것은 수동이므로 Tired가 적절하며, neither와 nor를 함께 써서 '두 사람 모두 힘이 없었다'라는 부정의 표현을 쓰는 것이 적절하다. *infectious disease: 전염병

07 (1) '왼쪽에서 오른쪽으로 읽으면, 그것은 "evil"이라고 읽혀지

만, 반대 방향으로는 "live"가 된다.' (2) '오리를 물 아래에서 보면, 당신은 오리의 발이 결코 첨벙거리는 것을 멈추지 않는다는 것을 알게 될 것이다.' *paddle: 노를 젓다, 첨벙거리다

08 ②는 분수 5분의 1에서 1을 뜻하는 '수사'로 쓰였다. 나머지는 모두, 같은 종류의 불특정한 사람 또는 사물을 가리키는 부정대명사이다.

09 <보기>와 ①~④는 모두 '이유'를 의미하는 분사구문으로, 부사절로 전환할 때, Because 또는 Since, As 등의 접속사를 써야 한다. ⑤는 내용상 '양보'의 의미이다.

10 특정한 대상을 가리키는 경우 it 또는 that 등의 대명사를 사용한다.

11 같은 종류의 불특정한 사람 또는 사물을 가리키고 앞에 수식어가 오는 경우, 부정대명사 one 또는 ones를 사용하는데, new 앞에 a가 없으므로 ones가 적절하다. one 앞에 형용사가 있는 경우 보통 부정관사 a를 써 준다.

12 그녀의 자녀는 세 명인데, 동사는 goes로서, 단수 형태이므로, Each가 적절하다. Both 또는 Either는 세 명 이상에는 쓰지 않는 부정대명사이며, All 또는 Some은 동사가 go가 되어야 한다.

13 '비슷한 하나'이므로 it을 부정대명사 one으로 바꾼다.

14 both는 둘 모두를 가리키며 복수 취급하는 대명사이다. has → have

15 분사구문의 부정은 분사 앞에 not이나 never를 쓴다. 내용상 부사절이라면 접속사 Though 또는 Although가 적절하다.

16 종속절과 주절의 주어가 다르므로, 일단 주어를 생략하지 않는다.(독립분사구문) 그리고 종속절의 시제가 주절(현재)보다 앞서기 때문에 완료분사구문을 활용하여 문맥에 맞게 주어진 단어를 배열한다.

17 내용상 '이유'를 나타내는 분사구문이므로, 접속사는 As가 적절하다. ③의 As soon as는 보기의 Feeling 앞에 전치사 On이 있을 경우에 가능하다.

18 불특정 대상의 복수 형태로서 '다른 많은 것들'을 의미할 때는 many other ones가 적절하다.

서술형 시험대비   p.26~27

01 (1) Sarah chose the first one, then another, but neither
   (2) Could you show me a slightly bigger one?
   (3) she doesn't have enough money for one
   (4) while others are afraid of cats

02 (1) While he fixed his computer,

(2) Because he has nothing to worry about,

(3) If you look at the mazes closely,

(4) Though he was sick all day long,

03 (1) Should Mina buy the red grapes or the green ones?

(2) Frank didn't catch any fish in the lake last weekend.

(3) Each of the students has been to Bulguksa in Gyoungju.

(4) She has two pets and one is bigger than the other.

04 (1) Stuck in the maze, she calmly reviewed the map.

(2) It is really dangerous to cross the street listening to music.

05 (1) is → are (2) are → is (3) another → others

(4) one → ones (5) have → has (6) another → other

06 one is a honeybee, another is a ladybug, and the other is a spider

07 (1) Some like red roses and others love white ones.

(2) Harry sold his computer and purchased a new one.

(3) Either one of them has to do something helpful.

01 부정대명사 one, another, neither, others 등을 적절히 활용하여, 우리말에 맞게 주어진 단어들을 알맞게 배열한다.

02 문제에 쓰인 분사구문은 각각 동시동작, 이유, 조건, 양보 등의 의미로 쓰였다. (1) 컴퓨터를 고치면서, Jerry는 라디오 쇼를 들었다. (2) 걱정할 것이 아무것도 없기 때문에, 그 어린 소년은 장난감을 갖고 잘 논다. (3) 미로를 자세히 들여다보면, 당신은 질서와 규칙성의 아름다움을 발견할 것이다. (4) 하루 종일 아팠음에도 불구하고, Benny는 그 어려운 과제를 마침내 해결했다.

03 (1) 같은 종류의 불특정한 대명사로, 앞에 수식어를 받는 복수 형태는 ones (2) 부정문이나 의문문은 any (3) each of 뒤에는 복수명사가 오며 동사는 단수나 취급 (4) 둘 중에 먼저 지칭하는 불특정한 하나는 one, 나머지 하나는 the other로 쓴다.

04 (1) 미로에 갇힌 채, 그녀는 차분하게 지도를 검토했다. (2) 음악을 들으며, 길을 건너는 것은 정말 위험하다.

05 (1) Both는 항상 복수 동사를 쓴다. (2) Neither는 '둘 중 어느 것도 아니다'라는 의미로서 대명사가 되면 단수 취급한다. (3) Some ~ others (4) dolls와 병렬 구조가 되어야 하고, 앞에

부정관사 a도 없으므로(buy 뒤에 a를 쓰는 것도 좋지만, 문제의 조건은 어색한 한 단어를 찾는 것임), ones가 적절하다. (5) 대명사 either는 단수 취급한다. (6) furniture는 불가산 명사이므로 another를 쓸 수 없다. 불가산 명사와 복수명사 앞에는 other가 적절하다.

06 거미줄에 곤충 세 마리가 있다, 하나는 꿀벌, 또 다른 하나는 무당벌레, 그리고 나머지 하나는 거미이다.

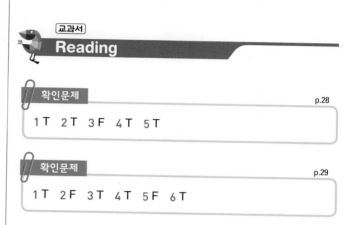

교과서
Reading

확인문제   p.28

1 T 2 T 3 F 4 T 5 T

확인문제   p.29

1 T 2 F 3 T 4 T 5 F 6 T

교과서 확인학습 A   p.30~31

01 Comparing, below, notice, differences
02 For example, on the left, called, has
03 on the right, called, has both, and
04 the origin of, mythology
05 is said to be, that
06 notice that, a single path
07 no dead ends
08 don't have to worry about, enter it
09 all the way to the end
10 To get out, have to turn around, came in
11 in, different
12 to make, dead ends
13 making, which way to go
14 If, are not careful, lose
15 are, considered left-brain
16 willingly visit, enjoy, planned confusion
17 them came up with
18 most reliable one, to, on, the very beginning
19 following that wall
20 like walking
21 Unfortunately, effective, certain types, are not connected
22 are made with, different materials, hedges, and
23 In fact, be printed, drawn

24 Here is, called

25 from, in the order

26 give it a try, to escape

27 are, fun, the end

28 Looking at them, order, regularity

29 how creative human beings are

30 there is, stop, take some time

31 be worth visiting

교과서 확인학습 B

p.32~33

1 Comparing the two pictures below, you can easily notice some differences.

2 For example, the picture on the left is called a labyrinth and only has an entrance.

3 The picture on the right is called a maze and has both an entrance and an exit.

4 You can find the origin of the labyrinth in Greek mythology.

5 It is said to be a prison that you cannot escape.

6 But you may notice that the labyrinth has only a single path.

7 There are no dead ends.

8 This means you don't have to worry about getting out of it when you enter it.

9 If you follow the path all the way to the end, you will reach the center.

10 To get out, you simply have to turn around and walk back out the way you came in.

11 When you are in a maze, it's a different story.

12 There are many choices to make and dead ends to frustrate you.

13 You have to keep making decisions about which way to go.

14 If you are not careful, you can easily lose your way.

15 These days, mazes are often considered left-brain puzzles.

16 Many people willingly visit maze parks and enjoy the "planned confusion."

17 And some of them came up with their own solutions.

18 The easiest and most reliable one is to place a hand on one wall from the very beginning.

19 Then you just keep following that wall.

20 It's like walking in a dark room.

21 Unfortunately, this simple method may not be

effective in certain types of mazes, especially when all of the walls are not connected.

22 Mazes are made with a variety of different materials, like walls and rooms, hedges, bricks, mirrors, and even snow.

23 In fact, they can also be printed or drawn on paper.

24 Here is one as an example. This is called a number maze.

25 You start from point A and have to go in the order of $1 \rightarrow 9 \rightarrow 8 \rightarrow 5 \rightarrow 1 \rightarrow 9 \rightarrow$ ... .

26 Why don't you give it a try? You have 30 seconds to escape!

27 Labyrinths and mazes are truly fun, but that's not the end of the story.

28 Looking at them closely, you may find the beauty of order and regularity.

29 They may also show you how creative human beings are.

30 If there is a maze park on your next trip, why don't you stop and take some time to enjoy it?

31 It will surely be worth visiting!

시험대비 실력평가

p.34~37

01 Comparing   02 ④   03 notice

04 ③   05 ④   06 ③   07 ⑤

08 The dead ends make us frustrated.

09 Be careful   10 ④   11 ②

12 A number maze is presented

13 30 seconds is given to solve the number puzzle.

14 ②   15 a labyrinth, an entrance, an exit

16 ⑤   17 ①   18 ③   19 ②

20 ④   21 all of the walls are connected

22 ③   23 labyrinths and mazes   24 ⑤

01 접속사가 없으므로 분사구문을 이끌기 위하여 Comparing이라고 쓰는 것이 적절하다.

02 글의 내용으로 보아, 미궁은 통로가 하나이기 때문에 빠져나오기 위해서는 미궁의 중앙에서 돌아서서 들어간 길대로 걸어 나오면 된다.

03 누군가나 무언가를 인지하게 되는 것은 '알아차리다(notice)'이다.

04 미궁은 그리스 신화에서 감옥으로 표현된다고 하였다.

05 주어진 문장은 '단지 그 벽을 계속 따라가면 된다'는 의미이므로 시작 지점부터 한쪽 벽에 손을 댄다 문장 뒤에 들어가는 것이 가장 적절하다.

06 These days는 Nowadays와 함께 '오늘날'이라는 의미로 쓰인다.

07 미로가 좌뇌형 퍼즐로 간주되며 사람들은 미로 공원에 일부러 방문하여 미로를 즐긴다고 하였다. 따라서 (B)와 같이 표현한 이유는 미로가 사람들을 혼란스럽게 하기 위하여 신중하게 계획된 것임을 알 수 있다.

08 막다른 길은 우리를 좌절하게 만든다고 하였다. 좌절을 느끼는 것이므로 과거분사로 표현하는 것이 적절하다.

09 조심하지 않으면 길을 잃기 쉽다고 하였다. 따라서 Be careful 이라고 쓰는 것이 적절하다.

10 밑줄 친 (A)는 숫자 퍼즐을 시도해 보라는 의미이므로 ④번이 가장 적절하다.

11 미로를 만들기 위해서 사용될 수 있는 것은 벽과 방, 울타리, 벽돌, 거울, 눈 등이다.

12 종이에 인쇄된 미로의 예시로 제시된 것은 숫자 미로이다.

13 숫자 퍼즐을 해결하기 위해 주어진 시간은 30초이다.

14 차이점이 어떤 것인지를 구체적으로 예를 들어 나타내고 있다. 따라서 ②번이 가장 적절하다.

15 미궁과 달리 미로는 입구뿐만 아니라 출구도 가지고 있다.

16 (B)는 '막다른 길'이라는 의미로 ⑤번이 가장 적절하다.

17 ⓐ 주절의 주어가 같으므로 분사구문의 주어가 생략되었다. 주어 You가 비교하는 주체이므로 현재분사를 쓴다. ⓑ and는 동사 is와 병렬 관계이므로 has를 쓴다. ⓒ enter는 타동사이므로 전치사 없이 목적어를 취할 수 있다.

18 미궁은 통로가 하나라고 하였다.

19 (B) 많은 사람들이 미로 공원을 기꺼이 방문함 (A) 그들 중 몇몇은 자기들만의 해결 방법을 찾아냄. 가장 쉽고 믿을 만한 방법 소개 (C) 그 방법은 마치 어두운 방을 걷는 것과 같음

20 미로에는 결정할 많은 선택지가 있고 우리를 좌절하게 만들 막다른 길들이 있다고 하였다. 어느 길로 갈지 계속 선택을 해야 하므로 조심하지 않으면 길을 잃기 쉽다고 하였다. 따라서 ④번이 가장 적절하다.

21 벽에 손을 대고 그 벽을 따라가는 것은 모든 벽이 이어져 있는 경우 효과가 있다.

22 빈칸 (A)에는 '~에서부터'라는 의미로 쓰이는 전치사 'from'이 들어간다. ① be filled with: ~로 가득 차다 ② pay attention to: ~에 관심을 기울이다 ③ graduate from: ~를 졸업하다 ④ turn down: ~을 거절하다 ⑤ be crowded with: ~으로 붐비다

23 미궁과 미로를 가리키는 인칭대명사이다.

24 글쓴이는 미로 공원이 들를 가치가 있을 것이라고 하였다.

01 Comparing the two pictures below
02 People call it a labyrinth.
03 We can find the origin of the labyrinth in Greek mythology.
04 It means that you don't have to worry about getting out of it when you enter it.
05 a prison, to escape, a single path
06 We can find the center.
07 many choices to make, dead ends to frustrate us
08 mazes are often considered left-brain puzzles
09 solution
10 The easiest and most reliable way to get out of a maze is to place a hand on one wall from the very beginning and keep following that wall.
11 reliable
12 It will surely be worth visiting!
13 A variety of different materials, like walls and rooms, hedges, bricks, mirrors, and even snow are used to make mazes.
14 The writer suggests taking some time to enjoy the maze park.

01 분사구문을 이용하여 빈칸을 완성할 수 있다. 주절의 주어와 부사절의 주어가 같으므로 부사절의 주어를 생략하고, 접속사 역시 생략한 후 동사를 현재분사로 만들면 된다.

02 사람들은 하나의 입구만 가진 것을 '미궁'이라고 부른다.

03 미궁의 기원은 그리스 신화에서 찾을 수 있다고 하였다.

04 미궁에 막다른 길이 없이 통로가 하나라는 의미는 거기에 들어갈 때 빠져나올 것을 걱정하지 않아도 된다는 것을 의미한다.

05 해석: 미궁은 그리스 신화에서 감옥인데, 그것은 탈출하는 것이 불가능하다. 그러나 사실 통로가 하나밖에 없기 때문에 그곳을 나오는 것은 쉽다.

06 통로를 따라 끝까지 가면 우리는 미궁의 중앙을 발견할 수 있다.

07 미로는 미궁과 달리 많은 선택지가 있고 우리를 좌절하게 만드는 막다른 길들이 있다고 하였다.

08 consider A B: A를 B라고 간주하다[여기다]

09 사람들이 미로를 빠져나가기 위해 찾아낸 해결 방법 중 하나를 의미하는 말이다.

10 미로를 빠져나오기 위하여 가장 쉽고 믿을 만한 해결 방법은 시작 지점부터 한쪽 벽에 손을 대고 계속 그 벽을 따라가는 것이다.

11 '믿을 가치가 있는; 의지할 가치가 있는' 것은 '믿을 만한 (reliable)'이다.

12 be worth Ving: V할 가치가 있다

13 미로는 벽과 방, 울타리, 벽돌, 거울, 심지어는 눈 등 많은 다양한 재료로 제작된다고 하였다.

14 글쓴이는 다음 여행에 미로 공원이 있으면 들러서 즐겨 볼 것을 제안하고 있다.

영역별 핵심문제

01 unreasonable **02** ⑤ **03** ⑤
04 ④
05 (1) exit (2) frustrate (3) prison (4) reliable
  (5) worth
06 (1) When I passed through the maze, I met a
  wolf.
  (2) Their food is good and the prices are
  reasonable.
07 ③ **08** ④ **09** ⓓ → excited
10 maze **11** ⑤ **12** ③ **13** ④
14 ① **15** ②, ⑤ **16** ⑤
17 (1) is (2) are (3) Each (4) likes (5) another
  (6) is (7) neither **18** ③ **19** ③
20 ④ **21** dead end **22** ② **23** ⑤
24 ④ **25** It(=The maze) looked hard to solve.
26 ③ **27** It covers about 5 kilometers.

---

01 주어진 관계는 반의어 관계를 나타낸다. reasonable: 적당한, unreasonable: 부적절한, 부당한

02 '일반적인 고대의 신화들; 특정 문화나 사회 등의 고대 신화들'을 나타내는 말은 'mythology(신화)'이다.

03 주어진 문장과 나머지는 모두 '의미하다, 뜻하다'를 의미하지만 ⑤번은 '인색한'을 뜻한다.

04 entrance: 입구

05 frustrate: 좌절시키다, prison: 감옥, worth: 가치; 가치가 있는 exit: 출구, reliable: 믿을 만한

06 maze: 미로, wolf: 늑대, resonable: 적당한

07 (A) exchange A for B: A와 B를 교환하다 (B) look better on ~: ~에게 더 좋아 보이다

08 소년이 신발에 얼마를 지불했는지는 대화를 통해 알 수 없다.

09 감정을 나타내는 과거분사 excited가 적절하다.

10 '통과할 길을 찾기가 어렵도록 설계된 공원이나 정원에 만들어진 벽이나 울타리에 의해 분리된 통로 시스템'을 가리키는 말은 'maze(미로)'이다.

12 길을 묻는 질문에 방향이나 가는 법을 설명하는 대답이 와야 한다.

13 유도부사 There가 있는 부사절을 분사구문으로 바꾸는 경우, '독립분사구문'이 된다. 독립분사구문에서 주절과 다른 주어를

앞에 쓰는 것처럼 유도부사 There를 문두에 놓고, 분사와 주어를 배치하는 것이 적절하다.

14 '비록 김여사께서 최근에 많은 사람들을 만나지만, 그녀는 전보다 더 외로움을 느낀다.'라는 양보의 부사절이다. 접속사와 주어를 생략하고, 동사 meets를 Meeting으로 바꾸면 된다.

15 ② athletes → athlete, Every는 단수 명사를 수식하고, 단수 동사를 쓴다. ⑤ one → ones, 불특정한 복수는 부정대명사 ones를 쓰는 것이 적절하다. 이 예문에서 형용사 small이 없다면, two ones로 쓰는 것보다 two만 쓰는 것이 좋다.

16 분사구문의 부정은 분사 앞에 not을 쓴다. 접속사를 쓸 경우, 접속사 뒤에 주어가 오면 분사구문은 쓸 수 없다.

17 (1) 부정대명사 either는 단수 (2) both는 복수 (3) Every와 Each 중에서 대명사로 쓸 수 있는 것은 Each이다. (4) 부정대명사 neither는 단수 (5) 접시(a plate)가 더러워서, 다른 하나를 더 달라고 하는 것이므로 another (6) 'some of+전체'는 전체에 맞춰 수를 일치시킨다. (7) 관계대명사 뒤의 동사가 is, 즉 단수이므로 neither가 적절하다. 'Julie는 두 개의 악기를 연주할 수 있는데, 그 중 어느 것도 현악기가 아니다.'라는 문장이다.
*stringed: 현악기인

18 분사구문에서의 비인칭 주어 It과 주절의 주어가 다르므로, 'It raining all day' 형태의 독립분사구문이 적절하다.

19 미궁은 통로가 하나이며 막다른 길이 없으므로 들어갈 때 빠져나올 것을 걱정하지 않아도 된다고 하였다. 따라서 빠져나오기 위해서는(To get out) 단지 돌아서 들어간 길대로 걸어 나오면 된다는 말이 가장 적절하다.

20 미로는 많은 선택지가 있고 막다른 길들이 있기 때문에 우리가 좌절할 수 있다.

21 한쪽 끝이 폐쇄된 길이나 통로는 '막다른 길(dead end)'이다.

22 밑줄 친 (B)는 choices를 수식하는 형용사로 쓰인 to부정사이다. ①, ④ 부사적 용법 중 목적(~하기 위해서) ② 형용사적 용법 ③ 명사적 용법 진주어 ⑤ 부사적 용법 중 감정의 원인

23 글쓴이는 미로 공원에서 매우 즐거웠다고 하였다. 따라서 ⑤번이 이 글의 내용과 일치한다.

24 주어진 문장의 That solution은 글쓴이의 친구가 말해준 '처음부터 벽 한쪽에 손을 얹고 계속 같은 쪽 벽을 따라가는' 방법을 가리키므로 ④번이 적절하다.

25 글쓴이에게 미로는 해결하기가 어려워 보였다.

26 세계의 유명한 미로에 관해 소개하는 글이다. 따라서 ③번이 가장 적절하다.

27 파인애플 정원 미로는 약 5킬로미터에 이를 정도로 크다.

01 (1) exchange   (2) frustrate
02 (1) He escaped from the prison this morning.
    (2) They tried to come up with effective ways to solve the problem.
    (3) Is it possible to survive on Mars?
    (4) The three-story building has about 10,000 books for kids.
03 ⓓ → making   04 ①   05 ⑤
06 How do I get to your place from here?   07 ⑤
08 Are you all set for the trip this weekend?
09 They are going to meet at 11 a.m. in front of the clock tower.
10 They will get there by subway.   11 ①
12 ①, ④
13 (1) Going to the nearby maze park with my parents,
    (2) Looking at the labyrinths closely,
    (3) Not having been invited to the wedding,
14 ⑤   15 ②   16 ③   17 ④
18 A number maze is an example of the printed maze.
19 ④   20 ④
21 They are so high that people can't see over them

01 (1) '동시에 서로에게 특별한 종류의 어떤 것을 주다'를 가리키는 말은 'exchange(교환하다)'이다. (2) '원하는 것을 하거나 이룰 수 없어서 짜증나거나 초조하게 느끼도록 만들다'를 가리키는 말은 'frustrate(방해하다, 좌절시키다)'이다.

02 prison: 감옥, escape: 탈출하다, come up with: ~을 생각해 내다, Mars: 화성, survive: 생존하다, story: 층

03 spend+시간+~ing: ~하는 데 시간을 보내다

04 대화의 내용으로 보아 상점의 판매원과 고객의 관계이다.

05 여자가 빨간색 신발이 소년에게 더 잘 어울려서 그것을 추천했다는 것은 대화의 내용과 일치하지 않는다.

09 Mina, Jiho, Claire와 Henry는 시계탑 앞에서 11시에 만날 것이다.

10 Mina, Jiho, Claire와 Henry는 터미널 2에 지하철로 갈 것이다.

11 권유하는 의문문에서는 any 대신 some을 쓸 수 있으며, cookies가 복수이므로 another, one, that 등은 부적절하다.

12 ② Writing → Written 또는 Being written ③ Worked → Working ⑤ Being looked → Looking

13 부사절을 분사구문으로 만들 때, 일반적으로 접속사를 생략한 후 주어가 같으면 주어도 생략하고, 동사를 V-ing 형태로 바꾸는

데 Being은 보통 생략한다. 주절보다 시제가 앞서면 Having been 형태가 되고, 부정문의 경우 not은 분사 앞에 쓴다.

14 each는 단수 취급이므로, were → was가 적절하다.

15 해결 방법을 찾아냈다는 의미이므로 came up with라고 쓰는 것이 자연스럽다. come down with: (병으로) 앓아눕다

16 미로 공원에 일부러 방문하는 많은 사람들을 가리키는 말이다.

17 미로는 벽과 방, 울타리, 벽돌, 거울, 심지어는 눈 등 많은 다양한 재료로 제작된다고 하였다.

18 미로는 종이에 인쇄되거나 그려질 수도 있다고 말하며 예로 든 것은 숫자 미로이다.

19 햄프턴 궁정 미로가 윌리엄 통치 시기에 만들어졌다는 것만 나와 있을 뿐 누가 만들었는지는 위 글에 나와 있지 않다.

20 미로는 만들어지는 것이므로 수동태를 쓰는 것이 적절하다.

21 so ~ that S can't V: 너무 ~해서 V할 수 없는

01 She wants to visit Mirror Maze Park on the second day.
02 It was to go horseback riding.
03 It's because she heard the Mirror Maze Park is a lot more fun.
04 (1) Comparing the two pictures below,
    (2) Not understanding Tom's method of getting out of the maze,
    (3) Following through the path to the end,
05 ⑤ Having been infected with the virus before, Anne is well aware of the fear of the disease.
06 ①
07 It's because it has only a single path without dead ends.
08 미궁: ⓑ, ⓒ, 미로: ⓐ, ⓓ
09 We may lose our way.
10 walk back out the way you came in

01 지나는 두 번째 날에 거울 미로 공원에 방문하기를 원한다.
02 원래는 두 번째 날에 말을 타러 가려고 했다.
03 지나는 거울 미로 공원이 훨씬 더 재미있다고 들었기 때문에 일정을 바꾸길 원한다.
04 주어진 어휘에 접속사들이 없으므로, 분사구문을 배열하는 문제이다. 각각 (1) 시간, (2) 이유, (3) 조건의 부사절을 분사구문으로 만든 것으로, 접속사를 생략하고 주절과 동일한 주어를 생략한 후, 동사를 분사로 만든다.

05 부사절과 주절의 주어가 같을 때, 분사구문에 주어를 쓰지 않는다. 내용상 '전에 그 바이러스에 감염된 적이 있기 때문에, Anne은 그 병의 무서움을 잘 알고 있다.'는 것이므로, Anne과 she는 동일 인물, 따라서 독립분사구문으로 쓸 필요가 없으며, Anne을 주절의 주어 자리에 쓰는 것이 적절하다.

06 ① 사자의 표정은 채소를 좋아하지 않으므로 그림과 일치한다. ② 사자 옆의 작은 토끼는 손을 올려놓지 않았다. ③ 사슴과 토끼가 당근을 집어들었다. ④ 사자는 채소를 좋아하지 않는다. ⑤ 왼쪽 끝의 토끼는 수염이 없다.

07 미궁에 들어갈 때 빠져나올 것을 걱정하지 않아도 되는 이유는 미궁은 통로가 하나이고 막다른 길이 없기 때문이다.

09 조심하지 않으면 길을 잃기 쉽다고 하였다.

10 '걸어 나오다'는 'walk back out'이며 '들어간 길대로'는 'the way you came in'이다.

창의사고력 서술형 문제
p.52

|모범답안|

01 (A) Andrew's house
　(B) she was lost
　(C) the post office
　(D) Kim's Bakery
　(E) turn right and go straight for about 100 meters

02 (1) I'd like to buy a pink one. I would also like the one with a rose on it.
　(2) I want to get a blue one. I also love the one with a parrot on it.
　(3) I'll choose a sky-blue one. I also like the one with a rainbow colored star on it.

01 민주는 Mason과 지안과 Andrew의 집에서 모이기로 했다. 민주가 늦을 때 Andrew는 그녀가 길을 잃었는지 걱정했다. 그가 그녀에게 전화했을 때, 그녀는 우체국 근처에 있었다. Andrew는 민주에게 그의 집에 어떻게 올 수 있는지 설명했다. 민주는 한 블록 정도 직진하면 킴스 빵집을 볼 수 있었다. 이후, 그녀는 오른쪽으로 돌아 약 100미터 정도 직진해야 했다.

02 그림을 잘 관찰하고, 색과 무늬의 특징을 적절히 조합하여 어법에 맞게 영작한 답이면 된다.

단원별 모의고사
p.53~57

01 suggestion　02 ①

03 (1) We got lost in the maze.
　(2) Don't be frustrated by today's failure.

(3) We're looking for someone who is reliable and hard-working.

04 (1) (c)onsidered　(2) entrance　(3) (c)losely, regularity　(4) exchange

05 (1) a variety of　(2) dead ends　(3) in the order of　(4) lose your way　(5) making decisions

06 (A) old mythological prison　(B) Minotaur　(C) the king of Crete　(D) labyrinth

07 He can borrow it this Friday.

08 ④　　　09 ⑤

10 He was worried that she was lost.

11 She is supposed to get together with Mason and Jian.

12 She should turn right and go straight for about 100 meters.

13 ④　　14 ④　　15 ⑤　　16 ②

17 (1) Some eat pizza, and others take it home.
　(2) Both are interested in catching fish.

18 ③　　19 ④　　20 ③

21 follow the path all the way to the end

22 ④　　　23 ②

24 Looking at them closely

25 We may find the beauty of order and regularity of them.

26 ⑤

01 주어진 관계는 동사와 명사의 관계를 나타낸다. suggest: 제안하다, suggestion: 제안

02 '방, 건물 또는 어떤 장소에 들어가기 위해 사용되는 문, 통로 등'을 가리키는 말은 'entrance(입구)'이다.

03 maze: 미로, frustrate: 좌절시키다, reliable: 믿을 만한

04 consider: 여기다, entrance: 입구, closely: 자세히, regularity: 규칙성, exchange: 교환하다

05 make decisions: 결정하다, a variety of: 다양한, lose one's way: 길을 잃다, dead end: 막다른 길, in the order of: ~의 순서로

06 미궁은 반인반수 괴물, 미노타우루스를 가두기 위한 옛 신화의 감옥이었다. 이것은 크레타 왕에 의해서 지어졌다. 왜냐하면 그가 그 괴물에 화가 났고 왕은 그것을 미궁에 가두기를 원했기 때문이다.

07 주원은 Alice에게 이번 주 금요일에 책을 빌릴 수 있다.

08 주어진 문장은 장소를 묻는 질문에 대한 대답으로 적절하므로 ④번이 적절하다.

09 위 대화에서 소라가 누구와 중국 음식점을 가는지는 알 수 없다.

10 Andrew는 민주가 길을 잃었을까봐 걱정했다.

11 민주는 Andrew의 집에서 Mason과 지안과 함께 모이기로 되어 있다.

12 민주는 오른쪽으로 돌아 약 100미터 정도 직진하면 Andrew의 집에 도착한다.

13 '컴퓨터 언어를 배운 것'과, '그 프로그램을 이해할 수 없었다'는 내용은 '시간'을 나타내는 when으로 표현하면 어색하다. '양보'의 접속사 though로 표현하는 것이 적절하다.

14 두 개 중 하나를 제외한 나머지 하나는 the other가 적절하다.

15 '한식당을 찾고 있는 것이라면, 한 군데를 알려 줄게.'라는 문장이므로, 불특정한 대상을 가리키는 부정대명사 one을 쓰는 것이 적절하다.

16 '급히 쓰여졌기 때문에 그 책은 오류가 많다'는 내용이므로 완료형 수동태 분사구문 'Having been written'이 적절하다.

17 (1) 부정대명사 some과 others를 활용하되, 사람들을 뜻하므로 some도 복수 취급하는 것에 유의한다. (2) 두 사람을 모두 가리키는 단어 Both와 are를 활용하도록 한다.

18 ①, ④, ⑤ '주절과 종속절의 주어'가 다르므로, 분사구문 앞에 주어를 써서 독립분사구문으로 표현하는 것이 적절하다. ① Having cut → The hero having cut ② 주절과 종속절의 주어가 같으면, 분사구문의 주어는 생략한다. Sharon going → Going, ④ Reading → Mom reading, ⑤ Being → There being

19 This가 가리키는 것은 미궁에는 막다른 길이 없이 통로가 하나라는 것이다. 이것이 의미하는 것은 미궁에 들어갈 때 빠져나올 것을 걱정하지 않아도 된다는 의미이다.

20 미로에서 조심해야 하는 이유는 길을 잃기 쉽기 때문이다.

21 통로를 따라 끝까지 가면 미궁의 중앙에 도착할 것이라고 하였다.

22 ④번은 간접의문문으로 의문사 how가 creative를 수식하고 있으므로 옳은 문장이다. 따라서 ④번의 설명은 바르지 않다.

23 미궁과 미로는 재미에 더해서 질서와 규칙성이라는 아름다움도 있다는 의미이므로 ②번이 가장 적절하다.

24 주절의 주어와 부사절의 주어가 같으므로 부사절의 주어를 생략하고 동사를 현재분사로 만들어 분사구문을 완성할 수 있다.

25 미궁과 미로를 자세히 들여다보면 질서와 규칙성이라는 아름다움을 발견할 수 있을지도 모른다고 하였다.

26 산울타리가 너무 높아서 사람들이 그 너머를 볼 수 없다고 하였다.

Lesson 6

To Each His Own

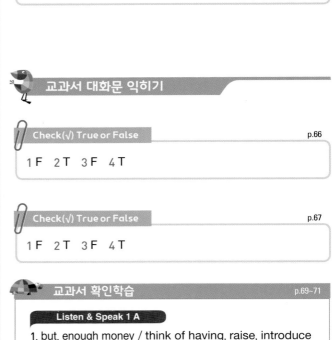

시험대비 실력평가   p.62

01 ①   02 ④   03 ④   04 ③
05 ⑤

01 ① 이외의 단어들은 un-을 붙여 반의어를 만들 수 있다. ① in-+ expensive → inexpensive 저렴한, 비싸지 않은 ② un-+ attractive → unattractive 매력적이지 못한 ③ un-+ comfortable → uncomfortable 불편한 ④ un-+ fortunate → unfortunate 불행한 ⑤ un-+ healthy → unhealthy 건강하지 못한

02 quality: 질

03 (A) raise money: 돈을 마련하다 / 그들은 수해 이재민을 돕기 위해서 돈을 모으는 중이다. (B) rely on: 의존하다 / 많은 일하는 여성들은 아이들을 돌보기 위해서 친척들에게 의존한다.

04 ① blame, blame: 비난하다 / 그 사고는 어느 운전자 책임이었나요? ② decided, decide: 결정하다 / 그는 어제 시험공부를 하기로 결정했다. ③ hand, hand in: 제출하다 / 너는 수업에 들어오기 전에 네 휴대 전화를 제출해야 한다는 것을 기억하지 않았니? ④ allow, allow: 허가하다 / 제발 제 사과를 받아주십시오. ⑤ caused, cause: ~을 야기하다 / 넌 우리에게 오늘 많은 문제들을 야기했어.

05 주어진 단어는 동의어 관계이다. allow: 허가하다 permit: 허가하다 ⓓ와 ⓔ는 비슷한 뜻을 가진 어휘이며, 나머지 보기들은 반대의 뜻을 가진 어휘이다. ⓐ rude: 무례한 polite: 예의바른 ⓑ wisdom: 지혜 foolishness: 어리석음 ⓒ rough: 거친 smooth: 매끈한 ⓓ enough: 충분히 sufficiently: 충분히 ⓔ agree: 동의하다 assent: 동의하다

서술형 시험대비   p.63

01 (1) grabbed (2) complete (3) influence (4) attracted
02 agree
03 (1) acronyms (2) judge (3) giving it a second thought
    (4) think, over, regret
04 (1) unhealthy (2) easily
05 ⓐ If you want, ⓓ drawing pictures
06 (1) It was hard to keep in touch.
    (2) Strike while the iron is hot.

01 (1) grab: 붙잡다 / 그는 그때 나의 팔을 붙잡았다. (2) complete: 완료하다 / 빌딩이 완성되는 데 2년이 걸렸다. (3) influence: 영향을 미치다 / TV 프로그램이 아이들의 행동에 영향을 미치는가? (4) attract: 마음을 끌다 / 그가 나의 마음을 끌었던 것은 그의 유머 감각이었다.

02 agree: 동의하다 / 같은 의견을 가지다

03 (1) acronyms: 두문자어 (2) judge: 판단하다 (3) give it a second thought: 다시 생각해 보다 (4) think over: ~을 심사숙고하다 regret: 후회하다

04 (1) unhealthy: 건강하지 못한 / 나는 흡연이 건강에 해롭다는 것을 알고 있다. (2) easily: 쉽게 / 나는 하루 종일 서 있기 때문에 쉽게 지친다.

05 ⓐ if 주어 동사의 현재형 ~, 주어 will 동사원형 ···: (조건) 만약 한다면, 할 것이다 / 네가 원한다면 너에게 그 모자를 사 줄게. ⓑ enough: 충분한 / 매일 운동하고 싶은데, 시간이 별로 없어. ⓒ confused: 혼란스러워 하는 / 왜곡된 속담들이 나를 혼란스럽게 만든다. ⓓ spend time V-ing: ~하는 데 시간을 보내다 / 나는 그림들을 그리면서 여가 시간을 보낸다.

06 (1) keep in touch: 연락을 취하다 (2) strike: 치다, 때리다

교과서
Conversation

핵심 Check   p.64~65

1 I think it's a great idea!
2 I agree with your opinion.

교과서 대화문 익히기

Check(√) True or False   p.66

1 F   2 T   3 F   4 T

Check(√) True or False   p.67

1 F   2 T   3 F   4 T

교과서 확인학습   p.69~71

Listen & Speak 1 A

1. but, enough money / think of having, raise, introduce / Killing, one / right, poster

2. watching, fascinating, What do you think / opinion, cause, away from / useful, ntroducing, Why don't, out

Listen & Speak 1 B

got a message, what some of it means / see, as soon as possible, means / What do you think of, acronyms / destroying / In my opinion, easy to use

Listen & Speak 2 A

1. leaving / If, harm, environment, regret, in the end / Like, What goes around / taking

2. take a break, studied for / Like the saying goes, a dull boy / agree, take a break after

3. the matter / told us to hand in, haven't finished / hand it in, Better late than never / right and I agree

Listen & Speak 2 B

posting, a look / so many pictures that, dangerous / way to get to know / people who will use / should be more careful, for

Real Life Communication

upset / had a fight with / happened / wanted to use, at the same time / are enough music rooms to practice / What do you think of setting a time limit / How long / should be allowed to use / more than an hour / about reserving / enough time to practice

Let's Check

1. we should talk about, when / Why, that / had a fight with, because, results / do that / never thought that / Walls have ears / learned

2. feel like cooking / what do you think of going out / shall / opened

---

01 ③   02 ⑤
03 You're right and I agree.

01 자신의 의견을 말할 때 'In my opinion[view] ~.', 'I think[feel/believe/think] (that) ~.', 'It seems to me ~.' 등을 이용하여 말할 수 있다.

02 새 기타가 필요하지만 돈이 없다는 남자의 말에 여자가 신곡도 소개할 수 있는 콘서트를 하는 것에 대해 상대방의 의견을 묻는 말에 좋다고 동의하고 있다. What do you think of[about] ~?: 너는 ~에 대해 어떻게 생각하니?

03 상대방의 의견에 동의할 때 'You're right.', 'I agree.' 등을 사용할 수 있다.

| 01 ④ | 02 ④, ⑤ | 03 ⑤ | 04 ③ |
| 05 ② | 06 ⑤ | 07 ① | 08 ④ |

01 'What do you think of[about] ~?'는 '너는 ~에 대해 어떻게 생각하니?'라는 뜻으로 상대방의 의견을 묻는 표현이다. 비슷한 표현으로 'How do you feel about ~?', 'What's your opinion about ~?', 'What do you say to ~?' 등이 있다.

02 ④ Jacob의 엄마는 친구한테 받은 문자 중의 일부가 무엇을 의미하는지 이해를 못하고 있었다. ⑤ Jacob은 사용하기에 재미있고 쉽다고 생각하고 있다.

03 'What do you think of[about] ~?'는 '너는 ~에 대해 어떻게 생각하니?'라는 뜻으로 상대방의 의견을 묻는 표현이다. 의견을 묻는 표현에 동의를 하는 표현인 'I agree with you.'라고 말하는 것은 어색하다.

04 환경을 해치면 결국 후회하는 건 우리일 거라고 말하는 것이 어울린다. regret: 후회하다

05 환경을 해치면 결국 후회하는 것은 자기 자신이라고 말하는 것과 어울리는 속담은 ②의 'What goes around comes around.: 자신이 한 대로 되돌려 받는다 (자업자득).'이다. ① Killing two birds with one stone.: 한 개의 돌로 두 마리의 새를 잡는다.(일석이조(一石二鳥)) ③ All work and no play makes Jack a dull boy.: 일만 하고 놀지 않으면 바보가 된다. ④ Better late than never.: 안하는 것보다 늦는 게 낫다. ⑤ Walls have ears.: 벽에도 귀가 있다.(낮말은 새가 듣고 밤말은 쥐가 듣는다.)

06 ⑤ 자신들의 쓰레기를 가져가서 지구를 돕자고 말하고 있고, 다른 사람들의 쓰레기를 가져간다고 말하지는 않았다.

07 (A) 사람들이 없을 때 그들에 대해 이야기해서는 안 된다고 생각한다고 말하는 것이 어울린다. (B) 지민이와 싸운 이유가 시험 결과에 대해 Sam과 이야기를 한 것이므로 이유의 접속사 because가 어울린다. (C) 속담에 대해 동의하며, 남자아이가 교훈을 받았다고 말하고 있다.

08 무엇을 하고 있는지 묻는 질문에 (C) 사진들을 인터넷에 올리고 있다고 대답한다. (B) 일상생활을 보여 주는 사진을 많이 올리는 것에 대해 위험하지 않느냐고 물어보는 질문에 (A) 친구들이 자신이 올린 게시물을 좋아하고, 이것이 서로를 알아가는 데 좋은 방법이라고 생각한다고 말한다. (D) 상대방은 이에 동의하지 않으면서 일부 사람들이 올린 사진들을 나쁜 수단으로 사용할 위험을 언급한다.

01 What do you think of having a concert to raise money?

02 Killing two birds with one stone.

03 (A) with   (B) at

04 limit

05 ⓑ, ⓒ, ⓕ, ⓗ

06 What do you think of having longer lunch breaks

01 'What do you think of[about] ~?'는 '너는 ~에 대해 어떻게 생각하니?'라는 뜻으로 상대방의 의견을 묻는 표현이다. raise money: 돈을 마련하다

02 돈도 마련하고 신곡도 소개하는 것이라 'Killing two birds with one stone: 한 개의 돌로 두 마리의 새를 잡는다. (일석이조(一石二鳥))'가 빈칸에 어울린다.

03 (A) have a fight with ~: ~와 싸우다 (B) at the same time: 동시에

04 limit: 제한 / 어떤 것의 가능한 최대치의 양, 범위 또는 정도

05 하루에 1시간 이상 음악실을 사용해서는 안 된다고 생각한다는 진호의 말에 Claire는 음악 연습을 하려면 1시간 이상이 필요하다고 말하고 있으므로, 진호의 생각에 동의하지 않고 있다. 상대방의 의견에 동의하는 표현으로는 'I agree.', 'Me, too.', 'Same here.', 'We're on the same page.' 등이 있으며, 의견에 동의하지 않는 표현으로는 'I don't think so.', 'I'm against the idea.', 'I don't agree.', 'I disagree.' 등이 있다.

06 'What do you think of[about] ~?'는 '너는 ~에 대해 어떻게 생각하니?'라는 뜻으로 상대방의 의견을 묻는 표현이다. of가 전치사이므로 뒤에 동사가 오려면 -ing 형태의 동명사를 써야 한다.

교과서
Grammar

핵심 Check   p.76~77

1 (1) who / that   (2) that / when

2 (1) however   (2) but

01 (1) who → that 또는 which

   (2) when → that 또는 which

   (3) therefore → however

   (4) 없음

02 However   03 ③

04 (1) It was Mijin that[who] played the cello in the school auditorium.

   (2) It was the cello that[which] Mijin played in the school auditorium.

   (3) It was in the school auditorium that[where] Mijin played the cello.

01 (1)~(2) 'It is/was ~ that ...' 강조구문에 관한 문제이다. (1) 강조된 단어가 her smile이므로 who를 that 또는 which로 고치는 것이 적절하다. (2) 강조된 단어가 my bag 이므로 when을 that 또는 which로 고치는 것이 적절하다. (3) therefore를 기준으로 앞문장과 뒷문장의 내용이 대조되고 있으므로 therefore를 however로 고치는 것이 적절하다. (4) '결과는 만족스러웠다.'는 문장과 '경기는 쉽지만은 않았다.'라는 문장을 연결하는 접속사 but이 쓰였고 '그러나'의 의미를 좀 더 강조하기 위해 however가 콤마(,) 사이에 쓰였으므로 어색한 부분이 없다.

02 빈칸을 기준으로 앞문장과 뒷문장의 내용이 대조를 이루고 있으므로 however를 쓰는 것이 적절하다. 뒤에 콤마가 있으므로 But은 쓸 수 없다.

03 'It is/was ~ that ...' 강조구문으로 강조된 어구는 last Sunday로 시간을 나타내는 부사구이므로 what을 that 또는 when으로 고치는 것이 적절하다.

04 (1) 학교 강당에서 첼로를 연주한 건 바로 Mijin이었다. 주어 Mijin(사람)을 강조하였으므로 'It was ~ that ...' 강조구문에서 that 대신 who를 쓸 수 있다. (2) 미진이가 학교 강당에서 연주한 악기는 바로 첼로였다. 목적어 첼로를 강조했으므로 'It was ~ that ...' 강조구문에서 that 대신 which를 쓸 수 있다. (3) 미진이가 첼로를 연주한 곳은 바로 학교 강당이었다. 장소를 나타내는 학교 강당을 강조했으므로 'It was ~ that ...' 강조구문에서 that 대신 where를 쓸 수 있다.

01 but → however   02 ②   03 ①

04 ④   05 ⑤   06 ①, ③

07 which   08 ②   09 ①   10 ③

01 그러나 그 노동자들은 어떠한 행동도 취하지 않기로 결정했다. 앞뒤에 콤마가 있으므로 접속사 but을 however로 고치는 것이 적절하다.

02 내가 겨울방학에 다녀온 곳은 바로 강원도였다. 'It was ~ that ...' 강조구문으로 장소를 나타내는 부사구 to Kangwon-do가 강조되고 있으므로 where가 적절하다.

03 두 여동생이 있는 건 바로 민호이다. 'It is ~ that ...' 강조구문이므로 There를 It으로 고치는 것이 적절하다.

04 그는 그녀를 좋아하지만 그녀는 그를 좋아하지 않는다. 빈칸을 기준으로 앞과 뒤의 절이 의미적으로 대조를 이루고 있다. 절과 절을 연결할 수 있는 등위접속사 but이 적절하다.

05 (A) 그 호텔은 훌륭하지만 비싸다. 빈칸을 기준으로 앞뒤가 의미상 서로 대조되고 형용사 great와 expensive를 연결해 주고 있으므로 등위접속사 but을 쓰는 것이 적절하다. (B) 나의 개는 사람은 좋아하지만 다른 개는 싫어한다. 빈칸을 중심으로 앞뒤 문장의 동사는 각각 loves와 hates가 쓰였으므로 대조된 내용이 연결됐음을 알 수 있다. 절과 절을 연결하고 있으므로 접속사 but이 올 수도 있고, 접속부사 however로 문장과 문장을 대조시킬 수도 있다. (C) 나는 네가 말하는 것을 이해한다. 그러나 나는 그것을 승인할 수는 없다. 문장 중간에 쓰였고 앞 문장과 대조되므로 however를 쓰는 것이 적절하다.

06 야생에서 사는 것은 바로 _____이다. that 바로 뒤에 동사가 나왔으므로 주어를 강조하는 구문이다. that 이하의 내용과 어울릴 수 없는 ①과 ③을 고르는 것이 적절하다.

07 강조하는 것이 목적어 the computer로 사물이므로 빈칸에는 that이나 which가 적절하다.

08 하지만 이러한 경향이 변하고 있다. 빈칸이 없어도 완전한 문장이므로 빈칸에는 '그러나'의 의미를 가지며 접속사 역할을 하는 however가 적절하다.

09 ① Mary는 Tim을 사랑한다. 그러나 그녀는 그와 결혼하고 싶진 않다. 접속부사를 기준으로 앞문장과 뒷문장의 관계가 대조되므로 hence로 두 문장을 연결하는 것이 어색하다. hence를 however로 고치는 것이 적절하다. ② 넌 나의 친구가 맞긴 하지만 네가 나를 이용한다는 느낌이 든다. ③ 괌의 해변에서 휴가를 보내는 것이 좋을 수도 있다. 다른 한편으로는 스위스 알

프스를 하이킹 하는 것도 재밌겠다. ④ Tom은 도서관에서 계속 말을 해서 결국 곤경에 빠졌다. ⑤ Jerry는 생쥐이다. 그러나 Jerry는 고양이인 Tom을 좋아한다.

10 However: 그러나, 하지만 ① Therefore: 따라서, 그러므로 ② Moreover: 게다가 ④ nonetheless: 그럼에도 불구하고 ⑤ Otherwise: 그렇지 않으면

11 그녀가 그 서점에서 산 것은 바로 그 책이었다. bought의 목적어인 the book을 강조한 'It was ~ that ...' 강조구문이다. 강조하는 대상이 사물로 that 또는 which를 쓸 수 있으므로 ④와 ⑤를 고르는 것이 적절하다.

12 ② B의 대답에서 Harry Potter를 강조하는 문장으로 'Harry Potter is my favorite book.'이므로 what을 that으로 고치는 것이 적절하다.

13 오래된 두 친구는 그토록 긴 이별 뒤에 재회하게 되어서 기뻤다. 그러나 그 만남은 두 사람 모두에게 부담이 되었다.

14 어법에 맞게 배열하면, (1) It was at the shop where Harry Potter and his friends bought magic tools. (2) However, robots don't have feelings.이다.

15 ⑤ 1925년에 링커 컬리지에서 John이 만난 것은 바로 그의 아내였다. 목적어에 해당하는 his wife가 강조된 문장이므로 where를 whom 또는 that으로 고치는 것이 적절하다. ① 어제 공항에서 그녀를 만난 사람은 바로 나였다. ② 그가 사랑하는 것은 바로 나였다. ③ 내가 매년 내 건강을 확인하는 곳은 바로 그 병원이었다. ④ 그녀가 예쁜 것은 사실이었다.

16 서툰 일꾼과 좋은 일꾼이 대조되는 문장이므로 however를 써서 문장을 나열하는 것이 적절하다.

17 ① 그녀는 어제 Tim의 집에서 주스를 만들었다. 장소 부사구가 강조된 'It is ~ that ...' 강조구문이다. ②~⑤까지는 가주어-진주어 구문이다. ② Sue가 공원에서 운동하는 것은 중요하다. ③ 네가 그 고양이 사료를 먹어 보려 시도하는 건 어리석었다. ④ 그녀가 학교에 가지 않은 것은 이상한 일이었다. ⑤ 그가 그 수업에 등록할 것은 확실하다.

18 • 우리는 우리의 결정으로 인한 결과에 행복할 거야. 그러나 만약 우리가 시간을 들여 어떤 일을 심사숙고하지 않는다면 우리는 후회할지도 몰라. • 작년에 나는 학교 하키 팀의 주장이 되기를 요청받았어. 그러나 나는 결정하는 데 너무 많은 시간이 걸려서 다른 친구가 주장이 되었어. 두 문장 모두 빈칸을 기준으로 대조된 내용이 열거되어 있으므로 접속부사 however를 고르는 것이 적절하다.

19 • 노래 가사에 가난이 반영된 것은 1980년대였다. 'It is ~ that

...' 강조구문으로 강조되고 있는 것이 in the 80's이므로 that 또는 when이 올 수 있다.

01 Harry and his friends booked a luxury hotel. When they arrived there, it was very dirty and smelled somewhere. However, they did not complain.

02 (2) It is Minjae who[또는 that] is wrong.
   (3) It is my wife who[또는 that] will decide it.

03 (1) It was Sara that[who] came into the cafe because of its name.
   (2) It was the cafe that[which] Sara came into because of its name.

04 (1) She had a lot of money. However, she lived a simple life.
   (2) It was snowing and cold. However, I didn't turn on the heater.
   (3) I don't really want to go. Besides, it's too late now.
   (4) I'm so tired. Besides, I'm hungry.

05 It was my motorcycle that[which] I parked in the garage.

06 It is natural that you should study harder than before for the final exam to come.

07 (1) was yesterday when I arrived here
   (2) is Jane who is going to go to London

08 (A) However   (B) it is   (C) that[which]

09 howeve / butr

10 (1) but   (2) However

11 (1) Besides   (2) Therefore   (3) however

01 Harry와 그의 친구들은 호화로운 호텔을 예약했다. 그들이 그곳에 도착했을 때, 그곳은 더럽고 어디선가 냄새도 났다. 그러나, 그들은 불평하지 않았다.

02 (1) 내가 공원에서 그를 만난 것은 바로 어제였다. (2) 틀린 건 바로 민재이다. 원래 문장은 'Minjae is wrong.'으로 사람 주어인 Minjae를 강조한 문장이다. 그러므로 what을 who 또는 that으로 해서 다시 쓰는 것이 적절하다. (3) 그것을 결정할 것은 바로 내 아내이다. 원래 문장은 'My wife decide it.'으로 사람 주어인 my wife를 강조한 문장이다. 그러므로 where를 who 또는 that으로 고쳐 다시 쓰는 것이 적절하다. (4) 내가 읽고 싶은 것은 바로 다른 책이다.

03 사라는 카페의 이름 때문에 그곳에 들어갔다. (1) 주어진 문장에

서 과거형 동사 came이 쓰였으므로 It was로 시작하고, 주어인 Sara를 'It was'와 that 사이에 쓰는 것이 적절하다. 강조하는 것이 사람이므로 that 대신에 who를 쓸 수 있다. (2) into의 목적어인 the cafe를 'It was'와 that 사이에 쓰는 것이 적절하다. 강조하는 것이 사물이므로 that 대신에 which를 쓸 수 있다.

04 however는 대조되는 말이 나오지만, besides는 추가하는 말이 나온다. (1) 그녀는 돈이 많았다. 하지만 그녀는 검소하게 살았다. (2) 눈이 오고 날씨가 추웠다. 그러나, 나는 히터를 켜지 않았다. (3) 정말 가고 싶은 것은 아니다. 게다가 이제 시간도 너무 늦었다. (4) 나는 몹시 피곤한데다가 배도 고프다.

05 나는 차고에 나의 오토바이를 주차했다. 과거 동사가 쓰인 문장을 강조구문으로 바꿔 쓸 때 'It was'로 시작한다. 목적어가 강조된 문장이므로 be동사와 that 사이에 my motorcycle을 쓰고 that 이하에 'I parked in the garage'로 쓰는 것이 적절하다. 사물이 강조된 문장이므로 that 대신에 which를 쓸 수 있다.

06 다가오는 기말고사를 위해 전보다 더 열심히 공부해야 하는 것은 당연한 일이다.

07 (1) '어제'라는 시간 부사를 강조하는 과거 문장이므로 It 뒤에 'was yesterday'가 오고 주어진 단어에 when이 있으므로 'when I arrived here'로 쓰는 것이 적절하다. (2) 사람 주어인 Jane을 강조하는 현재시제의 문장으로 It 뒤에 'is Jane'이 오고 괄호 안의 who를 활용하여 'who is going to go to London'으로 쓰는 것이 적절하다.

08 당신이 하는 것은 당신이 말하는 것보다 더 중요하다. 그래서 사람들은 그냥 무엇인가를 말하는 것보다 무엇인가를 하려고 노력한다. 그러나 몇몇 사람들은 다른 의견을 가지고 있다. 그들에게는 행동보다 더 중요한 것은 바로 말이다. (A)를 기준으로 앞 문장과 뒤의 문장의 내용이 대조가 되므로 접속부사 However가 오는것이 적절하다. (B)와 (C)를 포함하고 있는 원래 문장은 'Words speak louder than actions'로 주어 'words'를 강조하고 있는 문장이다. 그러므로 (B)에는 It is, (C)에는 that이나 which를 쓰는 것이 적절하다.

09 • 내가 가장 좋아하는 과목은 심리학이었지만 심리학자가 되고 싶은 생각은 없습니다. 빈칸을 중심으로 앞문장과 뒷문장이 대조를 이루고 세미콜로(;)과 함께 쓰일 수 있는 단어 however를 쓰는 것이 적절하다. (2) 그는 우둔하지는 않았지만 게을렀다. 한 문장 안에 2개의 절이 있고 빈칸을 중심으로 내용이 대조를 이루므로 등위접속사 but을 쓰는 것이 적절하다. 이러한 문장에서 접속부사 however는 보통 앞과 뒤에 콤마를 붙인다.

10 (1) 초등학교 때부터 친한 친구가 있다. 그러나 우리는 다른 고등학교를 가게 됐다. 이제 우리는 더 이상 서로를 볼 수 없다. (2) 나는 5년 전 멀리 이사 간 친한 사촌이 있다. 그러나 나는 여전히 그녀가 그립다.

11 (1) 나는 그 영화를 정말 보기 싫다. 게다가 나는 시간도 없다. (2) 너는 기껏해야 16살이다. 그러므로 운전할 수 있는 자격이 안 된다. (3) 나는 혼자가 아니다. 하지만 나는 정말 외롭다.

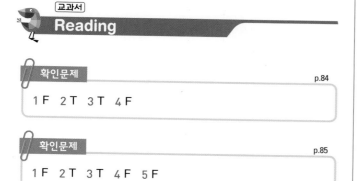

Reading

확인문제 p.84

1 F   2 T   3 T   4 F

확인문제 p.85

1 F   2 T   3 T   4 F   5 F

교과서 확인학습 A p.86~87

01 Every now and then, have influenced, changed
02 For example, Actions speak louder than words, what you do, than what you say
03 to do things instead of, saying something
04 However, have, opinions
05 words that, louder than actions
06 that, influence others to do
07 to have
08 take a look, upside down
09 Look before you leap, what, before
10 totally agree, be careful, decide to do
11 with, decisions
12 However, don't take time to think, regret
13 make mistakes if, without giving it a second thought
14 As a result, us more time to fix
15 Opportunities, come often
16 there is a chance, grab it, too late
17 was asked to be
18 However, took too much, another
19 regret, Strike while the iron is hot
20 Out of sight, out of mind, forgotten, not near
21 agree with, saying, from
22 to different

23 At first, two to three times a week, hard to keep in touch
24 spend more time, new
25 thinking less, less, more, more
26 have stopped talking, seeing
27 disagree with
28 close with, neighbor
29 from, liked the same
30 spent, time watching
31 her family moved away
32 seen, remember, we had
33 as time goes by
34 It is, that makes, remember
35 what, no right, wrong answer
36 who should decide what is best

교과서 확인학습 B p.88~89

1 Every now and then, words of wisdom have influenced people and changed their lives in a great way.
2 For example, "Actions speak louder than words," means the following: what you do is more important than what you say.
3 So people try to do things instead of just saying something.
4 However, some people have different opinions.
5 To them, it is words that speak louder than actions. How?
6 They think that words can influence others to do good things.
7 It is natural to have different ideas.
8 Let's take a look at some other proverbs upside down.
9 Look before you leap: Check what is in front of you before making a decision.
10 I totally agree. We should always be careful before we decide to do something.
11 Then we'll be happy with the results of our decisions.
12 However, if we don't take time to think things over, we may regret it.
13 Also, we'll make mistakes if we do something without giving it a second thought.
14 As a result, it will take us more time to fix. Posted by Suzi Kang
15 I don't agree. Opportunities don't come often.

16 If there is a chance, we should grab it. Or, it will be too late.

17 Last year, I was asked to be the captain of the school hockey team.

18 However, I took too much time to decide, so another friend became the captain.

19 Now, I regret it. As the saying goes, "Strike while the iron is hot." Posted by Brian Pearson

20 Out of sight, out of mind: Something is easily forgotten if it is not near us.

21 I agree with this saying. I had a close friend from elementary school.

22 Sadly, we went to different middle schools.

23 At first, we met two to three times a week. However, it was hard to keep in touch.

24 We started to spend more time with our new friends.

25 I started thinking less and less about him and more and more about my new friends.

26 Now, we have stopped talking or seeing each other. Posted by Anna Brown

27 I disagree with your opinion.

28 I was really close with my neighbor, Jenny.

29 She was from America and we liked the same basketball team.

30 We spent a lot of time watching games together.

31 Then her family moved away three years ago.

32 I haven't seen her since, but I still remember the times we had.

33 I miss her more and more as time goes by.

34 It is the quality of time that makes people remember each other. Posted by Jaeha Park

35 Well, what is your opinion? There is no right or wrong answer.

36 It is you who should decide what is best for you.

시험대비 실력평가 p.90~93

01 ⑤   02 ③   03 influence

04 ④   05 Look before you leap.   06 ①, ④

07 ⑤

08 He was asked to be the captain of the school hockey team.   09 ②   10 ③

11 He spent a lot of time with Jenny watching games.

12 She was from America.

13 proverbs

14 ⑤   15 ④   16 ⑤   17 ⑤

18 If there is a chance, we should grab it.

19 the captain of the school hockey team, too much time to decide

20 ②   21 ④   22 that, who   23 ③

24 It was because they went to different middle school.

01 밑줄 친 (A)는 '이따금, 때때로'라는 의미로 쓰인다. ⑤ 우연히

02 다른 생각을 갖는 것은 자연스럽다고 하였다.

03 누군가를 특정한 방식으로 행동하게 만드는 것은 '영향을 미치다 (influence)'이다.

04 예시로 주어진 속담은 정반대의 의미를 가지고 있으며 몇 개의 다른 속담을 거꾸로 뒤집어 살펴보자고 하였으므로 ④번이 가장 적절하다.

05 글의 내용으로 보아 '돌다리도 두드려 보고 건너라'라는 의미의 'Look before you leap.'을 쓰는 것이 가장 적절하다.

06 시간을 들여 어떤 일을 심사숙고하지 않을 경우 벌어지는 일에 대한 뒷받침 문장을 추가로 제시하고 있으므로 '또한, 게다가'라는 의미의 말이 들어가는 것이 적절하다.

07 수지는 어떤 일을 심사숙고하여 결정해야 하며 다시 생각해보지 않고 어떤 일을 한다면 실수할 것이라고 하였다. 따라서 ⑤번이 글의 내용과 일치한다. regret Ving: V했던 것을 후회하다

08 Brain은 작년에 학교 하키 팀의 주장이 되기를 요청받았다고 하였다.

09 (A)에는 강조구문을 완성하는 that이 들어간다. 모두 that이 쓰이지만 ②번에는 관계대명사 what이 쓰인다.

10 처음에는 일주일에 두세 번 만났지만 계속 연락을 하는 것이 어려워지면서 새로운 친구들과 더 많은 시간을 보냈다는 연결이 자연스럽다.

11 재하는 Jenny와 함께 경기를 보며 많은 시간을 보냈다고 하였다.

12 Jenny는 미국에서 왔다고 하였다.

13 지혜의 말은 '속담'을 의미한다.

14 사람들에게 영향을 미친 속담의 예로 (C) '말보다 행동이 중요하다'를 제시하고, (B) 그래서 사람들은 무언가를 말하는 대신에 무엇인가를 하려고 노력하지만 어떤 사람들은 다른 의견을 가지고 있으며 (A) 그들에게 행동보다 더 중요한 것은 말이라는 순서가 가장 자연스럽다.

15 말이 다른 사람들이 좋은 행동을 하는 데 영향을 미칠 수 있다고 생각하는 사람들이 있다.

16 하나의 속담을 두고 여러 의견을 갖는 일은 자연스러운 일이라

고 하였으므로 몇 개의 다른 속담을 있는 그대로 살펴보는 것이 아니라 거꾸로 뒤집어서 살펴보자고 말하는 것이 자연스럽다. as it is → upside down

17 글의 흐름상 다시 생각해 보지 않고 어떤 일을 한다면 실수할 것이라고 말하는 것이 자연스럽다.

18 Brian은 만약 기회가 있다면 우리는 그것을 붙잡아야 한다고 하였다.

19 Brian이 학교 하키 팀의 주장이 될 수 없었던 이유는 제안을 받아들일지 말지를 결정하는 데 너무 많은 시간이 걸렸기 때문이다.

20 밑줄 친 (B)는 일을 제때에 하라는 의미로 '쇠뿔도 단김에 빼라.'라는 속담에 해당한다. ① 유유상종 ② 쇠뿔도 단김에 빼라. ③ 사공이 많으면 배가 산으로 간다. ④ 백짓장도 맞들면 낫다. ⑤ 뜻이 있는 곳에 길이 있다.

21 글의 내용으로 보아 Anna의 의견에 동의하지 않는다는 내용이 들어가는 것이 적절하다.

22 강조구문을 완성하는 문제로, 강조하는 대상이 사람인 경우 that 뿐만 아니라 who를 쓸 수 있다.

23 Anna는 중학생이 되면서 초등학교 때부터 친했던 친구에 대해 점점 덜 생각하고 새로운 친구들에 대해 더욱 더 많이 생각하기 시작하였다.

24 Anna와 그녀의 친한 친구가 멀어지게 된 이유는 두 사람이 서로 다른 중학교를 갔기 때문이다.

서술형 시험대비

p.94~95

01 to do things instead of just saying something
02 However, some people have different opinions.
03 It is words of wisdom that can influence people and change their lives in a great way.
04 Words, actions, different ideas
05 It's because we will be happy with the results of our decisions if we are always careful before we decide to do something.
06 us more time to fix
07 grab a chance
08 **하키팀 주장이 되기를 요청받았을 때 결정하는 데 너무 많은 시간을 들인 것**
09 Something is easily forgotten if it is not near us.
10 It was hard to keep in touch with her close friend from elementary school.
11 We spent a lot of time watching games together.
12 He hasn't seen Jenny for three years.
13 ⑤번 → remember

---

01 말보다 행동이 중요하다는 말에 사람들은 그냥 무엇인가를 말하는 대신에 무엇인가를 하려고 노력한다는 의미이다.

02 앞선 문장과 반대되는 문장을 이어주는 문장이므로 '비슷한' 의견이 아니라 '다른' 의견 이라고 말하는 것이 적절하다.

03 사람들에게 영향을 주고 그들의 삶을 굉장한 방향으로 바꿀 수 있는 것은 지혜의 말들이다.

04 어떤 사람들은 "말보다 행동이 중요하다"고 생각하지만 다른 사람에게는 "행동보다 말이 중요하다." 속담에 대해 다른 의견과 생각을 갖는 것은 자연스럽다.

05 무언가를 하기로 결정하기 전에 항상 조심하면 우리는 우리의 결정으로 인한 결과에 행복할 것이라고 하였다.

06 무엇인가를 하기로 결정하기 전에 심사숙고하지 않으면 우리가 실수하게 되고 실수를 바로잡는 것에 더 많은 시간을 들이게 한다고 수지는 생각한다.

07 Brian은 기회가 있다면 그것을 붙잡으라고 하였다. 따라서 '기회를 붙잡는 것을 망설이지 마'라고 조언하는 것이 적절하다.

08 Brian은 하키 팀 주장이 되기를 요청받았지만 결정하는 데 너무 많은 시간을 들였고 결국 다른 친구가 주장이 되었다. 따라서 Brian은 결정에 너무 많은 시간을 들인 것을 후회하는 것이라고 볼 수 있다.

09 '눈에서 멀어지면, 마음에서도 멀어진다.'는 말은 어떤 것이 우리 가까이에 있지 않으면 쉽게 잊힌다는 의미이다. '잊혀지는' 것이므로 수동태를 쓰는 것에 유의한다.

10 Anna는 초등학교 때부터의 친한 친구와 계속 연락을 하는 것이 어려웠다고 하였다.

11 spend+시간+Ving: V하느라 시간을 보내다

12 Jenny의 가족이 3년 전에 이사를 갔고 그 후로 그녀를 보지 못했다고 하였으므로 재하는 Jenny를 3년 동안 못 봤다고 말할 수 있다.

13 재하는 눈에서 멀어지면 마음에서도 멀어진다는 말에 동의하지 않으므로 '서로를 기억하게 만든다'라고 말하는 것이 자연스럽다.

영역별 핵심문제

p.97~101

01 ②   02 ①   03 (o)pportunity
04 ④
05 (A) In   (B) away from   (C) out
06 What do you think of them?   07 ④
08 ⑤   09 result   10 ③   11 ⑤
12 I agree with the idea. → I disagree with the idea.
   또는 Students will not review the lessons. →
   Students will have less stress in learning.

13 However

14 (1) It was Jessy that[who] took first place.

   (2) It was last night that[when] my brother called me.

   (3) It was her staff that[who/whom] Jane met yesterday to discuss an important matter.

15 ⑤   16 ①

17 (A) can damage your teeth

   (B) can be good for you

   (C) however   18 ①   19 ③

20 Words can influence others to do good things.

21 ②   22 ④   23 ③   24 ⑤

25 ④

26 We should always be careful before we decide to do something.

27 ④

28 He/She thinks that getting many different ideas from others is more helpful when completing the work.

29 It is because you can get confused with too much information.

01 if+주어+동사의 현재형 ~, 주어+will 동사원형 …: (조건) 만약 ~한다면, …할 것이다 / 우리가 그가 오기 전에 음식을 먹는다면, 그는 화가 날 것이다.

02 ① 이외의 보기들은 un을 붙여서 반의어를 만든다. ① dis-+agree → disagree (~와) 의견이 다르다 ② un-+educated → uneducated 무지한 ③ un-+intelligent → unintelligent 우둔한 ④ un-+usual → unusual 특이한, 흔치 않은 ⑤ un-+wise → unwise 현명하지 못한

03 주어진 단어는 동의어 관계이다. allow: 허락하다 permit: 허락하다 chance: 가능성, 기회 opportunity: 기회

04 move away: 떠나다, 이사 가다 / 내 제일 친한 친구가 내가 10살 때 이사 갔다. take A away from B: B로부터 A를 빼앗다 / 이 청소기는 책상의 먼지를 제거할 수 있다.

05 (A) 'In my opinion, ~.'은 '내 생각에는 ~'의 의미로 의견을 말할 때 사용하는 표현이다. (B) take A away from B: B로부터 A를 빼앗다 (C) find out: 발견하다, 알아보다

06 'What do you think of[about] ~?'는 '너는 ~에 대해 어떻게 생각하니?'라는 뜻으로 상대방의 의견을 묻는 표현이다.

07 소녀는 인공지능 로봇이 문제를 일으킬 거라고 생각하는 반면에 소년은 유용하다고 생각하고 있다.

08 'I agree.'는 '나도 동의해.'의 의미이므로, 지민이의 시험 결과를 Sam과 이야기해서 싸우게 된 남자가 여자가 말한 '벽에도 귀가 있다'는 것에 동의를 하며 교훈을 얻었다고 말하는 것이 어울린다.

09 result: 결과 / 결과적으로 발생하는 것

10 (A) 다른 사람들이 자리에 없을 때 그들에 대해서 이야기해서는 안 된다고 생각하는 남자의 말에 여자가 이유를 물어보자, 남자아이가 지민이의 시험 결과에 대해 샘과 이야기해서 지민이와 싸웠다고 말하는 것이 어울린다. (B) 왜 지민이의 시험 결과를 Sam에게 말하는지 이유를 묻자, 지민이가 알게 될 거라고 전혀 생각 못했다고 대답하고 있다. (C) go: ~이라고 말하다

11 지민이의 시험 결과를 다른 사람에게 얘기한 것을 지민이가 몰랐을 것이라고 생각한 남자에게 할 수 있는 속담은 ⑤번의 'Walls have ears: 벽에도 귀가 있다.(낮말은 새가 듣고 밤말은 쥐가 듣는다.)'이다. ① Two heads are better than one.: 두 사람의 지혜가 한 사람의 지혜보다 낫다(백지장도 맞들면 낫다) ② Killing two birds with one stone.: 한 개의 돌로 두 마리의 새를 잡는다.(일석이조(一石二鳥)) ③ Better late than never.: 안하는 것보다 늦는 게 낫다 ④ What goes around comes around.: 자신이 한 대로 되돌려 받는다(자업자득)

12 학교에서 시험을 안 보는 것에 대해 생각을 묻자, 시험을 안 보는 것에 동의하며 학생들이 배운 것을 복습하지 않을 거라고 말하는 것은 어색하다. agree를 disagree로 바꾸거나, 동의를 왜 하는지에 대한 설명이 뒤에 들어가는 것이 적절하다.

13 조수가 높을 때에는 아드리아해의 물이 자주 범람하고 거리는 물로 가득 찬다. 그러나 나는 높이 올린 통로로 도심 주변을 걸어다닐 수 있을 것이다.

14 (1) 주어인 Jessy를 강조하는 문장이므로 that 다음의 she는 어색하다. (2) 시간부사 last night을 강조하는 것이므로 where를 that이나 when으로 고쳐 쓰는 것이 적절하다. (3) 주어진 문장에서 강조되는 것이 her staff로 사람이므로 which를 that이나 who 또는 whom으로 쓰는 것이 적절하다.

15 ⑤ 그가 성공할 것이란 것은 확실했다. 가주어-진주어 문장. ① 너와 내가 처음 만난 건 바로 이번 여름이다.(강조 구문) ② 아침에 나를 깨운 건 바로 그녀이다. (강조 구문) ③ 강조 구문 ④ 강조 구문

16 ① Rob은 너와 함께 있고 싶어 한다. 주어인 사람을 강조한 문장으로 that 대신 who가 쓰였다. 원래 문장은 'Rob wants to stay with you.'로 주어가 3인칭 단수이므로 동사 wants가 바르게 쓰였으므로 ①을 고르는 것이 적절하다. ② what을 that 또는 which로 고치는 것이 적절하다. ③ when을 that 또는 which로 고치는 것이 적절하다. ④ where를 who 또는 that

으로 고치는 것이 적절하다. ⑤ which를 who, whom 또는 that으로 쓰는 것이 적절하다.

17 (A)에는 '당신의 치아를 손상시킬 수 있다'는 내용이 들어가야 하므로 'can damage your teeth'로 쓰는 것이 적절하다. (B)에는 '당신에게 좋을 수 있다'가 들어가야 하므로 'can be good for you'로 쓰는 것이 적절하다. (C)에는 앞문장과 뒷문장 사이의 대조를 명확히 하기 위해 문장 말미에 콤마와 함께 쓰일 수 있는 however를 쓰는 것이 적절하다.

18 • 내 오빠는 집에 갔지만 나는 가지 않았다. • 그는 열심히 노력했지만 끝내 실패했다. 첫 번째 문장은 한 문장 내에서 절과 절을 연결할 등위접속사가 필요하고 빈칸을 중심으로 내용이 서로 대조를 이루므로 but을 고르는 것이 적절하다. 두 번째 문장은 빈칸을 중심으로 앞 문장과 뒤의 문장이 대조를 이루고 뒤에 오는 문장의 의미를 강조해 줄 만한 접속부사 however가 오는 것이 적절하다. 접속사 but은 앞에 콤마가 오기도 하지만, 뒤에는 잘 쓰지 않으며 접속부사 however는 보통 콤마와 함께 쓰인다.

19 • Susan은 어제 도서관에서 영어 공부를 했다. ③ 어제 도서관에서 Susan이 공부한 것은 바로 영어였다. what을 which나 that으로 고쳐야 하므로 ③을 고르는 것이 적절하다. ② 동사를 강조할 때는 조동사 do를 활용한다.

20 말은 다른 사람들이 좋은 행동을 하는 데 영향을 미칠 수 있다.

21 말보다 행동이 중요하다는 속담의 의미는 당신이 행동하는 것이 당신이 말하는 것보다 더 중요하다는 것이다.

22 (B)에 해당하는 사람들은 행동보다 말이 더 중요하다고 생각하는 사람들이다. 따라서 ④번이 가장 적절하다.

23 위 글의 내용은 속담을 거꾸로 뒤집어서 생각해 보자는 것이므로 글의 제목으로 ③번이 가장 적절하다.

24 앞 문장에 대한 결과를 이끄는 문장이므로 ⑤번이 가장 적절하다.

25 Brian은 학교 하키 팀의 주장이 되기를 요청받고 그것을 결정하는 데 너무 많은 시간이 걸려 다른 친구가 주장이 된 것에 대해 후회한다고 말하고 있다.

26 우리는 무엇인가를 하기로 결정하기 전에 항상 조심해야 한다.

27 주어진 문장은 '백지장도 맞들면 낫다'라는 속담에 반대하는 의견에서 두 번째에 해당하므로 ④번이 가장 적절하다.

28 글쓴이는 다른 사람들로부터 다양한 생각을 얻는 것이 일을 완수할 때 더 도움이 된다고 생각한다.

29 너무 많은 정보에 우리가 혼란을 느낄 수 있기 때문에 '백지장도 맞들면 낫다'는 말에 동의하지 않는다고 하였다.

---

01 (p)roverb　**02** ①
03 (1) proverb　(2) opportunity　(3) result　(4) captain
04 ②　　**05** ④　　**06** ④
07 ②, ④, ⑤　**08** ④　　**09** ②
10 ②, ③, ④　**11** careful　**12** ②　　**13** ③
14 (1) It is careful decisions that help you to accomplish the project.
(2) We tried to keep in touch but it was getting harder and harder to see each other.
(3) Jinho thinks setting a time limit is a good way to solve this problem. However, Chaire disagrees with his idea because she needs enough time to practice.
(4) It was Tom that saw a lion yesterday.
15 ⑤　　　　**16** ③
17 cousin → neighbor, five → three
18 The quality of time makes people remember each other.
19 ④　　　　**20** ③
21 First, you can get ideas from others. Second, you can complete the work quickly.
22 Many different ideas are more helpful when completing the work.

---

01 주어진 단어는 동의어 관계이다. leap: 뛰어오르다 jump: 뛰어오르다 saying: 속담, 격언 proverb: 속담

02 (A) keep in contact: 연락을 취하다 / 문자 메시지는 사람들이 항상 가깝게 연락을 취하는 것을 가능하게 해준다. (B) leave ~ behind: ~을 두고 가다, ~을 뒤에 남기다 / 그가 몸이 좋지 않아서 우리는 그를 두고 가야 했다.

03 (1) proverb: 속담 / '책의 표지로 책을 판단하지 말라'는 속담이다. (2) opportunity: 기회 / 인생에서 어떤 기회도 잃지 않는 것이 중요하다. (3) result: 결과 / 이것은 내가 기대하고 있던 결과가 아니었다. (4) captain: 주장 / Brian은 우리의 음악 동호회의 회장이 되었다.

04 grab: 붙잡다 / 간절히 붙잡다

05 하루에 1시간 이상 음악실을 사용해서는 안 된다는 생각을 갖고 있는 진호와 음악 연습을 하려면 1시간 이상이 필요하다고 생각하는 Claire는 다른 의견을 가지고 있으므로 Claire가 진호의 생각에 동의하지 않는다고 말하는 것이 어울린다.

06 음악실을 사용하는 시간에 대한 말이 뒤에 이어지므로 'How long(얼마나 오래)'이 들어가는 것이 적절하다.

07 'What do you think of[about] ~?'는 '너는 ~에 대해 어떻

21

게 생각하니?'라는 뜻으로 상대방의 의견을 묻는 표현이다. 비슷한 표현으로 'How do you feel about ~?', 'What's your opinion about ~?', 'What do you say to ~?' 등이 있다.

08 Harry가 아니라 Claire가 음악 연습을 하려면 1시간 이상 필요하다고 생각했다.

09 일상생활을 보여 주는 사진을 많이 올리는 여자에게 위험하지 않느냐고 질문하고, 이에 대해 친구들이 자신의 게시물을 좋아한다고 답하는 것이 적절하므로 ②에 주어진 문장이 들어가는 것이 적절하다.

10 인터넷에 올린 게시물이 일상생활을 보여 주는 사진들이 많아서 걱정을 하는 남자와 그 게시물을 친구들이 많이 좋아하고 서로 알아가는 데 좋은 방법이라 생각하는 여자는 다른 의견을 가지고 있다. 빈칸에는 동의하지 않는 표현이 들어가는 것이 적절하다. 'I agree.'는 어떤 의견에 동의하는 표현이고, 'I disagree.'는 동의하지 않는 표현이다. 동의하지 않는 다른 표현으로는 'I don't think so.', 'I'm against the idea.', 'I don't agree.' 등이 있다.

11 careful: 조심하는 / 행동에 신중한

12 이미 사람들이 나쁜 수단으로 사용한 것이 아니라, 사용할지도 모른다고 우려를 표현하고 있었다. ① 인터넷에 올린 사진들이 유라의 일상생활을 보여주고 있다. ② 몇몇 사람들이 그녀의 사진을 나쁜 수단으로 이용했다. ③ 유라는 인터넷에 사진을 올릴 때 더 신중할 것이다. ④ 유라는 그녀의 사진을 인터넷에 올리고 있는

13 ③ 내가 영어 시험을 망친 이유는 바로 내가 공부를 전혀 하지 않아서였다.(강조 구문) 나머지는 모두 가주어-진주어 구문이다. ① 네가 우리와 함께할 수 없다니 유감이다. ② 그녀가 그렇게 갑자기 떠난 것은 이상한 일이다. ④ 네 아파트가 너의 사무실만큼 소리를 흡수하지 않는 것은 너의 잘못이 아니다. ⑤ 그가 시험에 통과할 것은 확실하다.

14 (1) 'It is ~ that ...' 강조구문으로 주어 careful decisions를 강조하므로 what을 that으로 고치는 것이 적절하다. (2) 한 문장 내에서 두 개의 대조되는 내용의 절을 연결하는 것이므로 however를 but으로 고치는 것이 적절하다. however를 콤마나 세미콜론 등이 없이 단독으로 문장 중간에 쓰는 것은 어색하다. (3) Therefore를 중심으로 두 문장의 내용이 대조되고 있다. 그러므로 but 또는 however로 고치는 것이 적절하다. (4) 'It was ~ that …' 강조구문이므로 What을 It으로 고치는 것이 적절하다.

15 'keep in touch'는 '연락하다'라는 의미이다. 따라서 ⑤번이 가장 적절하다.

16 서로 이야기하거나 만나는 것을 그만두었다는 의미이므로 'talking or seeing'이라고 쓰는 것이 적절하다. stop+to V: V하기 위해 멈추다, stop+Ving: V하던 것을 멈추다

17 재하는 3년 전 이사 간 Jenny라는 가까운 동네 친구가 있었다.

18 재하는 사람들이 서로를 기억하게 만드는 것은 시간의 질이라고 하였다.

19 재하와 Jenny는 같은 농구팀을 좋아하였다. 따라서 똑같은 관심사를 가지고 있었다는 ④번이 적절하다. have something in common: (관심사나 생각을) 공통으로 가지다

20 이어지는 글의 내용으로 보아 '백지장도 맞들면 낫다'는 의미의 속담이 가장 적절하다.

21 다른 사람들에게서 조언이나 의견을 얻는 것의 두 가지 장점은 다른 사람들로부터 아이디어를 얻을 수 있는 것과 일을 빠르게 완수할 수 있는 것이다.

22 글쓴이는 일을완수 할 때 많은 다양한 생각들이 더 도움이 된다고 생각한다.

서술형 실전문제
p.106~107

01 What do you think of talking behind someone's back?

02 How do you feel about these acronyms? / What's your opinion about these acronyms? / What do you say to these acronyms?

03 (1) I agree.   (2) We're on the same page.
(3) Same here.

04 (1) last winter vacation when I dropped by
(2) to buy some gifts for my classmates. However, I didn't have enough time to choose them.

05 (1) but   (2) however

06 As

07 soccer → hockey, cold → hot, agree → disagree

08 It's because opportunities don't come often.

09 It is natural to have different ideas.

10 It means that what you do is more important than what you say.

---

01 What do you think of[about] ~?: 너는 ~에 대해 어떻게 생각하니? talk behind a person's back: 남의 험담을 하다

02 'What do you think of[about] ~?'는 '너는 ~에 대해 어떻게 생각하니?'라는 뜻으로 상대방의 의견을 묻는 표현이다. 비슷한 표현으로 'How do you feel about ~?', 'What's your

opinion about ~?', 'What do you say to ~?' 등이 있다.

03 쉬자고 말하는 남자의 말에 동의하며, 이 부분만 끝내고 쉬자고 했으므로 빈칸에는 동의하는 말이 들어가는 것이 적절하다. 'I agree.'는 어떤 의견에 동의하는 표현이고, 'Me, too.', 'Same here.', 'We're on the same page.' 등으로 바꿔 쓸 수 있다.

04 (1) 작년 겨울방학에 있던 일을 말하는 것이므로 과거 시제를 활용한 강조구문을 쓰는 것이 적절하다. (2) want는 to부정사를 목적어로 취하기 때문에 to buy를 쓰고, 앞 문장과 뒷 문장 사이의 내용이 대조되고 있으므로 접속부사 However를 써서 문장을 연결한다.

05 (1) 나는 요즘 너무 바쁘지만 그 영화를 보고 싶다. 빈칸에는 절과 절을 이어 줄 수 있는 등위접속사 but을 쓰는 것이 적절하다. (2) 나와 언니는 이번 주말에 여행을 가려고 하고 있다. 그러나 아빠가 우리의 스케줄을 듣고 허락하지 않으신다.

06 (A) As a result: 그 결과 (B) 이때의 As는 접속사로 '~하듯이'의 뜻이다.

07 Brian은 학교 하키 팀 주장이 되기를 요청받았다. 쇠뿔도 단김에 빼라는 속담은 쇠가 달았을 때 두드려야 한다는 의미이므로 cold가 아닌 hot이 옳다. 수지는 Brian의 의견에 동의하지 않는다.

08 기회는 자주 오지 않기 때문에 만약 기회가 있다면 우리는 그것을 붙잡아야 한다는 것이 Brian의 의견이다.

09 가주어 It과 진주어 to부정사를 이용하여 쓴다.

10 말보다 행동이 더 중요하다는 의미이다.

창의사고력 서술형 문제
p.108

|모범답안|

01 (1) When did Admiral Yi Sun-shin fight against Japan? It was in 1592 that[when] Admiral Yi Sun-shin fought against Japan.

(2) Who delivered a speech in 1963? It was Martin Luther King that[who] delivered a speech in 1963.

(3) What did Steve Jobs found in 1979? It was Apple Company that[which] Steve Jobs founded in 1979.

(4) Which company produced the film *Toy Story*? It was Pixar that[which] produced the first 3D computer animated feature film *Toy Story*.

02 Two heads are better than one. / get great ideas from others / complete the work quickly / get confused with too much information / spend too much time before making a decision / many different ideas / are more helpful when completing the work

---

단원별 모의고사
p.109~112

01 ③　　02 (1) over　(2) in　(3) down　(4) behind

03 ③

04 (1) harm, regret　(2) (O)pportunities　(3) Opposites
　　(4) instead

05 ②　　　　06 ②　　　　07 (a)cronyms

08 destroy

09 In my opinion, they are fun and easy to use.

10 (A) behind　(B) in　　11 ④　　　12 ③

13 ②

14 (1) The conference was held six hours ago. But it is still in progress.

(2) It was cheese pizza which Suji ate in the park last night.

15 (1) He left Busan when.

(2) It was when that he left Busan.

(3) Was it when that he left Busan?

(4) When was it that he left Busan?

16 (1) house　(2) that

17 Check what is in front of you before making a decision.

18 ④　　　　19 ③　　　　20 ④　　　　21 ②

22 ③

---

01 in a hurry: 서둘러 / 우리는 급해서 재빨리 식사를 해야만 했다. in the end: 결국, 마침내 / 결국 우리는 그것을 사지 않기로 결정했다.

02 (1) think over: ~을 심사숙고하다 / 그것을 심사숙고할 시간이 없었다. (2) keep in touch: 연락을 취하다 / 내년에 연락하자. (3) upside down: 거꾸로 / 몇 개의 다른 속담들을 거꾸로 뒤집어서 살펴보자. (4) leave ~ behind: ~을 두고 가다, 뒤에 남기다 / 쓰레기를 남기고 가는 일이 없도록 하세요.

03 blame: 비난하다 / 능숙한 일꾼은 연장을 탓하지 않는다.

04 (1) harm: 해를 끼치다 regret: 후회하다 (2) opportunity: 기회 (3) opposite: 반대(되는 사람) (4) instead of: ~ 대신에

05 ⓐ same, at the same time: 동시에 ⓑ enough, enough: 충분한 ⓒ setting, 'What do you think of[about] ~?'는 '너는 ~에 대해 어떻게 생각하니?'라는 뜻으로 상대방의 의견을 묻는 표현이다. of가 전치사이므로 뒤에 동사가 오려면 -ing 형태의 동명사를 써야 한다. set: 설정하다 ⓓ be allowed, 'allow(허락하다)+목적어+목적격보어(to V)'의 수동태 형식으로 'be allowed to 동사원형'은 '~이 허락되다'로 해석할 수 있다. ⓔ more, more than: ~보다 많이, ~ 이상

06 친구에게서 받은 문자 내용 중 일부가 무엇을 의미하는지 이해를 못하고 있다고 말하는 것이 어울리므로 ②에 들어가는 것이 적절하다.

07 acronym: 두문자어

08 destroy: 파괴하다 / 어떤 것을 매우 심하게 훼손하여 더 이상 존재하거나 작동하지 않다

09 'In my opinion, ~.'은 '제 생각엔 ~.'의 뜻으로 의견을 말할 때 사용하는 표현이다. to use는 형용사 easy를 수식하여 '사용하기 재미있고 쉬운'으로 해석한다.

10 (A) leave ~ behind: ~을 두고 가다, 뒤에 남기다 (B) in the end: 결국, 마침내

11 쓰레기를 놔두고 떠나가는 사람들을 보면서 환경을 해치면 결국 후회하는 것은 우리라고 말하고 있다. 그러므로 빈칸에는 우리 쓰레기는 우리가 가져가서 지구를 돕자는 말이 나오는 것이 적절하다.

12 ③ 물리 시험에서 떨어진 게 너였니? Were를 Was로 바꾸는 것이 적절하다. ① 네가 어제 잠깐 들린 곳이 음악 가게지? ② 우리가 우리의 여행을 계획한 게 작년이지? ④ 학교에서 영향력 있는 사람으로 뽑힌 게 너랑 나지? ⑤ 네가 가족을 만난 곳이 놀이공원이었지?

13 • 내가 의자에 앉아 연주를 한 건 바로 기타였다. • 내 할머니 무릎 위에 앉아 있던 것은 고양이였다. • 우리는 지난 일요일에 좋은 시간을 보냈다. 그러나, 언니는 합류하지 못했다.

14 (1) 회의가 개최된 것은 과거 시제이므로 was held를 쓰고, 아직 진행 중이므로 현재시제와 주어진 단어를 활용하여 is in progress로 쓰는 것이 적절하다. (2) 과거 시제로 치즈피자를 강조하는 것이므로 It was와 which 사이에 cheese pizza를 넣어 강조한다.

15 그가 부산을 떠난 게 언제였니? 의문문의 의문사를 강조할 때는 'It is/was ~ that ...'을 활용하여 평서문의 형태로 바꾸고 다시 의문문의 형태로 전환하면 쉽다.

16 우리말에 맞게 배열하면, (1) It was to your house that she sent her letter. (2) It is the quality of time that makes people remember each other.이다.

17 돌다리도 두드려 보고 건너라는 것은 결정을 하기 전에 당신 앞에 있는 것이 무엇인지 확인하라는 의미이다.

18 이어지는 Brian의 의견으로 보아 기회가 있다면 무시하는 것이 아니라 붙잡아야 한다고 말하는 것이 자연스럽다. ignore → grab

19 수지는 결정을 하기 전에 심사숙고 하지 않으면 실수를 저질러 그것을 바로잡는 데 더 많은 시간을 들일 것이라고 하였으므로 '서두르면 일을 그르친다.'는 표현이 가장 적절하다. ① 금상첨화이다. ② 웃음은 만병통치약이다. ③ 서두르면 일을 그르친다. ④ 소귀에 경 읽기. ⑤ 필요할 때 친구가 진짜 친구다.

20 '또' 다른 친구라는 의미로 another가 적절하다.

21 재하는 헤어진 Jenny를 시간이 갈수록 더 그리워하게 된다고 하였으므로 '눈에서 멀어지면 마음에서도 멀어진다.'는 속담과 달리 더욱더 그립다고 말하는 것이 적절하다. ① 짚신도 짝이 있다. ② 눈에서 멀어지면 마음에서도 멀어진다. ③ 시작이 반이다. ④ 불행은 한꺼번에 닥친다. ⑤ 하늘은 스스로 돕는 자를 돕는다.

22 함께 많은 시간을 보내다가 Jenny의 가족이 3년 전에 이사를 갔고, 그 이후로 그녀를 보지 못했다는 연결이 자연스럽다.

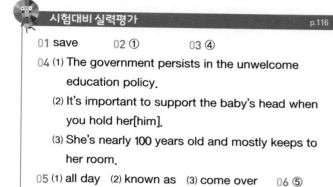

Homes Everywhere

시험대비 실력평가
p.116

01 save   02 ①   03 ④

04 (1) The government persists in the unwelcome education policy.

   (2) It's important to support the baby's head when you hold her[him].

   (3) She's nearly 100 years old and mostly keeps to her room.

05 (1) all day   (2) known as   (3) come over   06 ⑤

01 hidden(숨겨진)과 concealed(숨겨진)은 동의어 관계에 있는 단어들이다. 따라서 store(저장하다, 보관하다)와 동의어 관계에 있는 단어로는 save(모으다, 저축하다)가 있다.

02 '언덕이나 다른 높이 올라 있는 곳이 없는, 평평한'이라는 영영풀이가 가리키는 단어는 ① flat(평평한)이다.

03 ④ take는 '~을 타다'라는 뜻이 아닌 '가져가다'라는 뜻으로 사용되었다.

04 (1) unwelcome 반갑지 않은 (2) support 지탱하다, 떠받치다 (3) mostly 주로, 일반적으로

05 (1) all day 하루 종일 (2) be known as ~로서 알려지다 (3) come over 들르다

06 hand down ~을 물려주다 / upside down 거꾸로 된, 뒤집힌 / stop A from ~ing A가 ~하지 못하게 막다 / prevent A from ~ing A가 ~하지 못하게 막다

서술형 시험대비
p.117

01 install

02 disappear

03 (1) walk around   (2) pull up   (3) make sense

04 handed down

05 (1) I cannot imagine why they want to leave.

   (2) New towns were designed to house Seoul's over-population.

   (3) The children playing in the garden appear happy today.

06 (1) Many people usually go to work by bike in Berlin.

   (2) I often like to be on my own.

   (3) What I mostly do during the weekend is reading.

01 '장비나 가구를 사용할 수 있도록 제자리에 고정시키다'라는 뜻을 가진 단어는 install(설치하다)이다.

02 enter(~에 들어가다)와 exit(나가다, 퇴거하다)는 반의어 관계에 있는 단어들이다. 따라서 appear(보이다, 나타나다)와 반의어 관계에 있는 단어는 disappear(사라지다)이다.

03 (1) walk around 돌아다니다 (2) pull up A A를 당겨 올리다 (3) make sense 이치에 맞다

04 hand down ~을 물려주다

05 (1) imagine 상상하다, 짐작하다 (2) house 수용하다 (3) appear 보이다, 나타나다

06 (1) usually 보통, 대개 (2) often 종종 (3) mostly 주로, 일반적으로

Conversation
교과서

핵심 Check
p.118~119

1 ⑤

2 (A) could have   (B) would turn

01 I wish 뒤에는 could를 이용해 현재 사실과 반대되는 내용, 혹은 가능성이 없는 일을 가정한다. 따라서 ⑤ I wish I could have가 정답이다.

02 현재 사실과 반대되는 사실에 대해 가정하는 문장이므로 가정법 과거를 쓴다. 또한 'What would you do ~?'라고 물어봤기 때문에 대답할 때는 'I would ~'라고 답한다.

교과서 대화문 익히기

Check(√) True or False
p.120

1 T   2 F   3 T   4 T

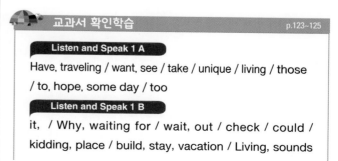

교과서 확인학습
p.123~125

Listen and Speak 1 A

Have, traveling / want, see / take / unique / living / those / to, hope, some day / too

Listen and Speak 1 B

it, / Why, waiting for / wait, out / check / could / kidding, place / build, stay, vacation / Living, sounds these, natural / try / Which, most, live in / strong

What / kind / like / what, lived / travel / cool

became / build / kind / build / covered / mirrors, invisible / would

upside / interesting / easy, upside down / What / like, differently

need, visit / Which / case / would, visited / interested / that, designed / how, inspired / How

What / turn into, able to fly

living, exciting / some / full, could live / would, lived / explore / where, cave / Then, dangerous animals / makes

stay, during / would, were / every day, fishing / sounds

This, What / unique, lived / interest, deep sea, explore, unique / That

matter, have

---

01 I wish I could try living there.　　　02 ④

03 I wish I could

04 B wants to live in the stone house most.

01 I wish 뒤에는 could를 이용해 현재 사실과 반대되는 내용, 혹은 가능성이 없는 일을 가정한다. try ~ing 시험삼아 ~해 보다

02 ④ 'G가 언제 터키를 방문할 계획인지'는 위 대화에서 언급되지 않았다.

03 I wish I could ~.'는 '내가 ~할 수 있으면 좋겠다.'라는 뜻으로, 바람이나 소원을 나타내는 표현이다. I wish 뒤에는 사실과 반대되거나 가능성이 거의 없는 일이 온다.

04 A의 질문에 B가 돌로 만든 집에서 살고 싶다고 대화 후반에 언급했다.

---

01 ⓔinterested → interesting

02 What would you do if you visited Spain?

03 inspire

04 (A) lived　(B) would travel

05 ④　　　　06 ①　　　　07 ④　　　　08 ③

09 Then I would be safe from dangerous animals.

10 ②

11 What would you do if you could have a magical power?

01 interest는 '흥미롭게 하다'라는 뜻을 가진 동사로, 어떤 사물이나 사실이 흥미로울 때는 interesting(흥미롭게 하는)이라고 쓴다. interested는 사람이 어떤 사물에 대해 '흥미롭다고 느끼는'이라는 뜻이다. 따라서 ⓔinterested를 interesting이라고 고쳐야 한다.

02 'What would you do if ~?'는 '만약 ~라면 너는 무엇을 하겠니?'라는 뜻으로 상상하여 말하는 표현이다. 이때, 현재 사실에 반대되는 내용을 가정하는 것이므로 if절에는 가정법 과거형을 쓴다.

03 '어떤 사람에게 책이나 영화, 물건을 위한 아이디어를 주다'라는 뜻을 가진 단어는 'inspire'(영감을 주다)이다.

04 현재 사실에 반대되는 상황을 가정할 때에는 가정법 과거형을 사용한다.

05 ④ '어디서 대화를 하고 있는지'는 대화에서 언급되지 않았다.

06 위의 대화에서 B와 G는 ①'꿈에 그리던 집에 대한 상상'에 대해서 이야기하고 있다.

07 '난 거기를 탐험하고 싶어.'라는 문장이 들어갈 곳은, 대화의 문맥상 '정글에 간다면 뭘 할 거니?'라고 물어본 직후인 ④에 들어가야 적절하다.

08 ③ '모든 정글들이 신나는 모험으로 가득 차 있다.'는 말은 위 대화에서 언급되지 않았다.

09 safe from ~로부터 안전한 / dangerous 위험한

10 ② 가정법으로 물었으므로 가정법으로 대답해야 한다.

11 '만약 ~라면 너는 뭘 할 거니?'라는 뜻으로 상상하여 말할 때 'What would you do if ~?'를 쓸 수 있으며, 비슷한 표현으로 'Suppose ~', 'What if ~?' 등이 있다.

---

01 I would build my own house

02 He would cover his dream house completely with mirrors.

03 I wish I could have a new computer.

04 What would you do if you were there?

05 She[He] would go swimming and go fishing.

06 They are talking about the house that[which] is upside down.

07 B would walk upside down and see things differently.

01 상대방이 'What would you do if ~?'라고 물어 볼 때 대답은 'I would ~'라고 한다.

02 B는 자신이 꿈꾸는 집을 거울로 완전히 덮을 것이라고 말했다.

03 바람이나 소원을 나타내는 표현으로 '내가 ~했으면 좋겠다'라는 뜻을 가진 'I wish I could ~'를 쓸 수 있다.

04 '만약 ~라면 너는 무엇을 할 거니?'라는 뜻으로 상상하여 말하는 표현은 'What would you do if ~?'를 쓴다.

05 위 대화의 후반에 언급되었듯이, 수영하러 가고 낚시를 할 것이라고 말했다.

06 위 대화에서 G와 B는 사진 속에서 본 거꾸로 된 집에 대해 이야기하고 있다.

07 위에 언급되었듯이, 거꾸로 걷고 사물을 다르게 볼 것이라고 말했다.

교과서

Grammar

핵심 Check
p.130~131

1 (1) were a robot, I would listen to her
  (2) would buy an apartment in Seoul if I had some money

2 (1) walking (2) closed

시험대비 기본평가
p.132

01 (1) live → lived (2) can → could (3) calls → called
   (4) will → would

02 ③   03 ④   04 ⑤

01 문제에서 각 문장이 가정법 문장이라고 했고, 모든 문장들의 구조는 '가정법 과거' 형태로 볼 수 있으므로, 조건절의 동사를 과거로, 주절의 조동사도 과거형으로 고치는 것이 적절하다.

02 모두 5형식으로서, 목적보어를 갖는 문장들이다. call은 목적어와 목적보어 사이에 전치사 of를 필요로 하지 않는다.

03 주절에 조동사의 과거형이 나왔으므로, 가정법 문장이다. 가정법 과거에서 동사의 과거형 또는 조동사의 과거형을 사용하는 것이 적절하다.

04 'keep+목적어(A)+형용사/분사'는 5형식으로 'A가 어떤 상태가 되도록 유지하다'는 의미이고, 'keep+목적어(A)+from+V-ing'는 'A가 ~하지 못하도록 막다'라는 뜻이다. 모든 빈칸을 충족시키는 것은 kept이다.

시험대비 실력평가
p.133~135

01 ④   02 ③, ④
03 to keep themselves safe from invaders
04 Living together in one building keeps them safe.
05 it rained, we could not go to the swimming pool
06 would always havefriends to play with
07 ③   08 ②   09 ⑤
10 have → had, will → would   11 ⑤
12 ②   13 ②   14 ③   15 ⑤

01 가정법 과거 형태의 문장들이다. If절에는 동사의 과거형을, 주절에는 조동사의 과거형을 쓰는 것이 적절하다.

02 5형식 동사 made에 관련된 문제이다. '눈속에서 썰매를 타러 가는 것은 Tom과 Sophie를 흥분하게 만들었다.'는 문장의 made와 같은 용법으로 쓰인 것은 ③과 ④이다. ③ '그 경연 쇼에서의 보컬 코치들과 감독은 그 어린 소녀를 세계적으로 유명한 가수로 만들었다.' ④ '그 당시에 해결이 불가능해 보였던 문제들이 광장에 모인 사람들을 더욱 강하게 만들었다.'

03 5형식 동사 keep 관련 문제이다. *keep oneself safe from ~: ~로부터 자신을 안전하게 지키다

04 '동명사 주어' Living과 5형식 동사 keeps에 유의하여 적절하게 배열한다.

05 가정법 과거 시제의 문장이다. If절에 과거동사 rained가 오고, 주절에 조동사의 과거형 could를 쓰는 것에 유의하여 알맞게 배열한다.

06 If절에 과거동사 lived가 있는 가정법 과거 시제의 문장이다. 주절에 조동사의 과거형 would와 빈도부사 always의 순서에 유의하고, friends를 뒤에서 수식하는 to부정사에 with가 함께 있는 것에 유의하여 주어진 단어들을 배열한다.

07 가정법 과거로서 '반대' 개념의 직설법 현재 시제와 적절하게 전환된 문장은 ③번뿐이다.

08 'keep+목적어+목적보어(형용사)'가 적절히 사용된 것을 고른다.

09 'keep/make+목적어+목적보어(형용사)'가 적절히 사용된 것을 고른다. ① keep → keeps ② warmly → warm ③ actively →active ④ make → makes

10 '만약 당신이 사막에서 살고, 함께 살 사람이 없다면, 무엇을 할 것인가?'라는 문장이다. 가정법 과거 문장이라고 했으므로, if절의 동사를 과거형인 lived, had로, 주절의 will도 과거형 would로 고친다.

11 나머지는 5형식 문장으로 쓰였는데, ⑤만 4형식으로 쓰였다. '시골의 그 할머니가 그들에게 전통 한식을 만들어줬다.'라는 뜻이다.

12 ①은 'keep+목적어+목적보어(형용사)'로 5형식 문장이다. 그러나 ②는 'keep+목적어+from+V-ing'로서 '그가 제안한 방법이 당신의 가방이 도둑맞지 않도록 할 것이다.'라는 뜻을 가진 3형식 문장이고, 나머지는 모두 5형식 문장들이기 때문에 정답은 ②이다.

13 가정법 과거 문장이라고 했으므로, if절의 동사가 과거형이고, 주절에 조동사의 과거형이 있는 문장을 찾는다. ① has → had ③ will → would ④ had seen → saw, can → could ⑤ know → knew

14 조건에 맞게 if절의 동사가 과거형이고, 주절에 조동사의 과거형이 있는 문장을 찾는다. ① is → were ② won't → wouldn't ④ have got → get ⑤ know → knew

15 ⑤는 '공손한 질문'을 위한 조동사 Could이다. 나머지 다른 문장들과, <보기>에 주어진 could는 가정법의 주절에 사용된 can의 과거시제형이다.

서술형 시험대비
p.136~137

01 (1) won't → wouldn't (2) has → had
   (3) will → would (4) will → would
   (5) would be → would have been
   (6) will → would (7) can → could
02 (1) Those wooden poles support Venice
   (2) walls would keep people cool in summer and warm
   (3) made a huge round building their house
   (4) water bus makes it easier to travel from island
03 (1) If it were not for
   (2) If there were no
   (3) Were it not for
   (4) As there are many wooden poles in the ground
04 lived in a house with a soccer field, he could invite

05 (1) made them bored
   (2) saw the koalas eating leaves
   (3) heard their names called by
   (4) made it difficult for them to build
06 I lived in a stone house, the typhoon couldn't shake it
07 Living in the house made of earth keeps us cool
08 (1) If there were food left, the homeless man would not work today.
   (2) If he were[was] strong enough, he would not exercise at the gym every day.

01 문제에서 각 문장이 가정법이라고 했으므로, 내용상 가정법 과거시제 문장은 'if절' 또는 'I wish' 뒤의 동사를 과거형으로, be동사는 were또는 was로 고치고, 주절의 조동사는 과거형으로 바꾼다. (5) yesterday로 보아 과거시제이므로 '가정법 과거완료'로 표현한다. 가정법 과거완료의 주절에는 '조동사+have+p.p.'를 쓴다.

02 (2), (3), (4) 5형식 동사 'keep/make+목적어+목적보어(형용사)'를 사용하여, 주어진 단어들을 적절히 배열한다. (4)의 경우, '여행하는 것'을 목적어 'to부정사'로 하여, 5형식을 만들려면 '가목적어 it'을 취하고 '진목적어 to travel'은 뒤로 보내는 것에 유의한다.

03 '땅 속의 많은 나무기둥들이 없다면, 베니스는 매우 다를 텐데.'라는 가정법 문장이다. 직설법으로는, '땅 속의 많은 나무기둥들이 있어서, 베니스는 많이 다르지 않다.'가 된다. 가정법 표현, 'Without = If it were not for = Were it not for'임에 유의하여, 주어진 조건대로 빈칸을 채운다.

04 'Matthew가 축구장이 있는 집에 살고 있지 않기 때문에, 방과 후에 친구들을 초대해서 축구를 할 수 없다.'라는 직설법 문장을 가정법으로 바꾸면 'Matthew가 축구장이 있는 집에 산다면, 방과 후에 친구들을 초대해서 축구를 할 수 있을 텐데.'가 된다. If절에 과거동사, 주절에 조동사 can의 과거형 could에 유의하여 영작한다.

05 5형식 문장에서 목적어 뒤의 목적보어는 '형용사, to부정사, 현재분사, 과거분사' 등이 올 수 있고, 목적어가 to부정사인 경우, 가목적어를 취해야 한다. (1), (3)은 과거분사가, (2)는 현재분사가 목적보어 (4)는 가목적어-진목적어 구조이다.

06 가정법 과거시제를 활용해서 동사를 lived로, 조동사는 could not을 써야 하는데, 글자 수 제한이 있으므로 couldn't로 활용하는 것에 유의하여 영작한다.

07 동명사가 주어이므로 live는 Living, 동사 keep은 keeps 형태를 쓴다. 흙으로 만든 집은 the house made of earth로 하는 것에 유의하여, 알맞게 영작한다.

08 가정법 과거는 직설법 현재 반대, 가정법 과거완료는 직설법 과거의 반대를 나타낸다. (3)은 가정법 과거완료이다.

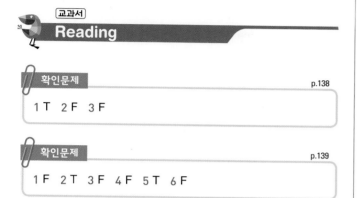

Reading 〔교과서〕

확인문제 p.138

1 T 2 F 3 F

확인문제 p.139

1 F 2 T 3 F 4 F 5 T 6 F

교과서 확인학습 A p.140~141

01 live in
02 use ladders to enter their houses. live in, on
03 others share, with
04 Imagine, live in, that change
05 lived in, would climb, to enter my
06 hidden opening
07 If, appeared, would pull, up to stop, from
08 are made of
09 keep me cool, warm
10 a flat roof, sleep up on the roof
11 lived in, would take a gondola
12 has, islands, On weekend, from island to island
13 from, rises, leaves, full of water
14 However, be able to walk around
15 is known as, floating
16 there are, colorful houses
17 how, why they built the houses on
18 decided to live there, themselves safe from
19 for them to build, swampy
20 installed, wooden poles
21 wooden poles, support, to
22 lived, would, have friends, to play with
23 hear, calling me to come over
24 are, three to five floors
25 is used for
26 store food, tools on
27 where I would sleep, would be on
28 like, living in, have
29 can house up to, work together, share
30 Living, keeps them safe
31 different all over the world, What, like

교과서 확인학습 B p.142~143

1 Different people live in different houses.
2 Some use ladders to enter their houses. Others live in houses on the water.
3 And others share their houses with many people.
4 Imagine you live in one of these houses. How would that change your life?
5 If I lived in a *pueblo*, I would climb up a ladder to enter my house.
6 There's a hidden opening on top of the house.
7 If unwelcome visitors appeared, I would pull the ladder up to stop them from entering.
8 The thick walls are made of earth, straw, and water.
9 They would keep me cool in summer and warm in winter.
10 The house has a flat roof. I would sometimes sleep up on the roof under the moon and stars.
11 If I lived in Venice, I would take a gondola to school every morning.
12 Venice has 118 small islands. On weekends, I would travel from island to island by a *vaporetto*, a water bus.
13 At high tide, the water from the Adriatic Sea often rises and leaves the streets full of water.
14 However, I would be able to walk around the town through the raised walkways.
15 Venice is known as the "floating city."
16 In Venice, there are many colorful houses on the water.
17 You may wonder how and why they built the houses on the water.
18 The old Venetians decided to live there to keep themselves safe from invaders.
19 But it was not easy for them to build their homes on this swampy surface.
20 So they installed more than 10 million wooden poles in the ground.
21 It is these wooden poles that support Venice to this day.

22 If I lived in a *tulou*, a huge round house in Fujian, China, I would always have friends at home to play with.

23 I would sometimes hear my neighbor calling me to come over for tea or dinner.

24 In a *tulou*, there are usually three to five floors.

25 The first floor is used for cooking and eating.

26 And people store food and tools on the second floor.

27 Do you wonder where I would sleep? My bedroom would be on the third or fourth floor.

28 A *tulou* is like a village. The people living in a *tulou* mostly have the same family name.

29 Some large *tulou* can house up to 50 families. They work together and share many things.

30 Living together in one building keeps them safe.

31 Homes are everywhere. But they are different all over the world. What is your home like?

 시험대비 실력평가   p.144~147

01 ②   02 ④   03 ⑤

04 The writer would sometimes sleep up on the roof under the moon and stars.

05 ②   06 swampy

07 There are many colorful houses on the water.

08 ⑤   09 ③

10 It is a huge round house in Fujian, China.

11 ⑤

12 He or she would sleep on the third or fourth floor.

13 ③   14 ④

15 There is a hidden opening on top of a *pueblo*.

16 ④   17 (B)─(D)─(A)─(C)

18 A *vaporetto* is a water bus.

19 steel → wood   20 ⑤   21 ②

22 calling(또는 call)   23 ⑤   24 ④

25 Some large *tulous* can house up to 50 families.

01 이어지는 글의 내용은 다양한 사람들이 다양한 집에서 살고 있다는 내용이므로 ②번이 가장 적절하다.

02 주어진 문장의 They가 가리키는 것은 The thick walls이다. 따라서 ④번에 들어가는 것이 가장 적절하다.

03 달갑지 않은 방문객이 나타나면 사다리를 끌어올려 그들이 들어오지 못하게 할 것이라고 하였다. 따라서 ⑤번이 글의 내용과 일치한다.

04 글쓴이는 때때로 나는 달과 별들 아래의 지붕 위에서 잠을 잘 것이라고 하였다.

05 아드리아 해의 물이 자주 범람하고 거리는 물로 가득 차지만 돌출되어 있는 통로로 도심 주변을 걸어다닐 수 있을 것이라는 연결이 자연스럽다. 따라서 ②번이 적절하다.

06 '항상 아주 습한'은 '습지의(swampy)'이다.

07 물 위에 색색의 건물들이 많다고 하였다.

08 지금까지 베니스를 지탱해 주고 있는 것은 천만 개 이상의 나무 기둥이라고 하였다.

09 토루에 사는 사람들은 대부분 같은 성을 가지고 있고 함께 일하고 많은 것을 공유한다고 하였으므로 '마을'과 같다는 말이 가장 적절하다.

10 토루는 중국 푸젠에 있는 거대하고 둥그런 집이라고 하였다.

11 토루는 50가구까지 수용할 수 있으며 이곳에 사는 사람들은 함께 일하고 많은 것을 공유한다고 하였다.

12 침실은 3층이나 4층에 있을 것이라고 하였다.

13 반갑지 않은 방문객이 나타나면 사다리를 끌어올려 그들이 들어오지 못하게 할 것이라고 말하는 것이 자연스러우므로 unwelcome이라고 쓰는 것이 적절하다.

14 위에 언급한 집들 중 하나에 산다고 상상해 보면 삶이 어떻게 바뀔 것인지를 묻고 있으므로 ④번이 가장 적절하다.

15 푸에블로 집 꼭대기에는 숨겨진 구멍이 있다고 하였다.

16 푸에블로에는 평평한 지붕이 있고 달과 별들 아래의 지붕 위에서 잠을 잘 것이라고 하였으므로 ④번이 답이다.

17 (B) 베니스는 '떠다니는 도시'로 알려짐 - (D) 집을 물 위에 지은 이유 설명 - (A) 습지 위에 집을 짓는 것이 쉽지 않음 - (C) 나무 기둥 설치로 베니스 지탱

18 바포레토는 수상버스라고 하였다.

19 나무로 만들어진 기둥(wooden poles)이라고 하였다.

20 조수가 높을 때에는 아드리아 해의 물이 자주 범람하여 거리가 물로 가득 찬다고 하였다.

21 밑줄 친 ⓐ는 주어와 목적어가 같을 때 목적어로 재귀대명사를 쓰는 재귀적 용법에 해당한다. seat는 타동사로 명령문에 생략된 주어 you와 목적어가 같으므로 목적어로 재귀대명사를 쓴 경우이다. 나머지는 모두 강조 용법의 재귀대명사이다.

22 지각동사의 목적어와 목적격 보어의 관계가 능동인 경우 목적격 보어로 동사원형이나 현재분사를 쓸 수 있다. 따라서 calling 혹은 call이라고 쓰는 것이 적절하다.

23 침실이 어디에 있는지 궁금한지 묻는 질문에 대한 답이 ⑤번 다음 문장에 이어지고 있으므로 ⑤번이 적절하다.

24 토루는 3층에서 5층으로 되어 있다고 하였으므로 ④번이 옳다. 토루가 중국의 전통 가옥이라는 말은 나와 있지 않다.

25 몇몇 큰 토루는 50가구까지 수용할 수 있다고 하였다.

01 Some people have to use ladders to enter their houses.

02 If unwelcome visitors appeared, the writer would pull the ladder up to stop them from entering.

03 The walls are made of earth, straw, and water.

04 It is possible to sleep on the roof of the house because it has a flat roof.

05 ladder

06 lived

07 He[She] would travel from island to island by *vaporetto*, a water bus.

08 Venice is known as the "floating city."

09 from themselves → from invaders

10 Do you wonder where I would sleep?

11 **어디에나 있는 집**

12 the same family name, share many things, cooking and eating, store food and tools, sleeping

01 어떤 사람들은 집에 들어가기 위해 사다리를 이용한다고 하였다.

02 반갑지 않은 방문객이 나타난다면 글쓴이는 사다리를 끌어올려 그들이 들어오지 못하게 할 것이다.

03 두꺼운 벽은 흙, 지푸라기, 물로 만들어져 있다.

04 푸에블로는 평평한 지붕을 가진 집이기 때문에 지붕 위에서 잠을 잘 수 있다.

05 어딘가에 오르기 위해 사용되는 장치로, 두 개의 긴 나무, 금속 혹은 밧줄 사이에 일련의 계단을 가진 것은 '사다리(ladder)'이다.

06 현재 사실과 반대되는 가정을 할 때 쓰는 가정법 과거이므로 If절에는 과거동사로 쓴다.

07 글쓴이는 수상버스 바포레토를 타고 이 섬 저 섬을 여행할 것이라고 하였다.

08 베니스는 '떠다니는 도시'로 알려져 있다.

09 옛 베니스 사람들은 침략자들로부터 자신들을 안전하게 지키기 위해 도시 베니스를 건설하였다.

10 '내가 어디에서 잠을 잘지'는 동사 wonder의 목적어 역할을 하는 간접의문문으로 쓰는 것에 유의한다. 간접의문문의 어순은 '의문사+주어+동사'이다.

11 앞 문장 homes를 가리키는 말이다. 복수명사를 지칭하므로 they라고 쓴다.

12 토루에 사는 사람들은 대부분 같은 성을 가지고 있다. 그들은 함께 일하고 많은 것을 공유한다. 1층은 요리하고 식사하는 데에 사용되고 2층에 식량과 도구를 보관한다. 3층은 잠을 자기 위해 사용된다.한 재료로 제작된다고 하였다.

01 (1) unwelcome   (2) invisible   02 ②

03 ③

04 What you are saying doesn't make sense.

05 ②   06 ①   07 (B) – (C) – (A)

08 ⑤   09 But the jungle is full of adventure.

10 ②   11 the jungle   12 ②

13 (1) I lived in a house with a swimming pool, I would enjoy

    (2) I don't live in a house with a swimming pool, I won't enjoy

14 (1) had not installed these wooden poles in the ground, they couldn't have lived

    (2) they installed these wooden poles in the ground, they could live

15 ④   16 ③   17 ①   18 ②

19 ③

20 A *pueblo* has a hidden opening on top of the house.

21 ④   22 ②   23 ⑤

24 The raised walkways would make it possible for the writer to walk around the town at high tide.

25 Because there are no beds.

26 The warm *ondol* floors heat your body in the cold winter.

27 ④

01 <보기>의 단어들의 관계는 반의어 관계이다.

02 ②에서 travel은 '여행, 이동'이라는 명사적 의미로 사용되었다.

03 주어진 문장의 take는 '~을 타다'라는 뜻으로 사용되었다. ③은 '여기서 시청까지 가는 버스를 탈 수 있나요?'라는 뜻으로 주어진 문장과 같은 뜻으로 사용되었다.

04 make sense 이치에 맞다

05 'I wish I could ~'는 '내가 ~하면 좋겠다'라는 뜻으로, 바람이나 소원을 나타내는 표현이다.

06 '만약 ~라면 너는 무엇을 할 거니?'라는 뜻으로 상상하여 말하는 표현은 ①'What would you do if ~?'이다.

07 B가 자신이 꿈꾸는 집에 대해 어떻게 생각하느냐고 Alice에게 물었고 이에 그녀는 (B) 특이하다고 생각한다고 말하면서 그 집에서 살면 무엇을 할 것이냐고 되묻는다. 그 대답으로 (C)에서 심해를 탐험하고 특이한 해양 동물을 찾을 것이라고 대답하는 순서로 가는 것이 적절하다. 그리고 마지막으로 이에 대한 Alice의 대답(A)이 오는 것이 문맥상 가장 자연스럽다.

08 ⑤ 'B가 꿈꾸는 집 주변에서 무엇을 찾을 수 있는지'에 대한 대답은 '몇몇 신기한 해양 동물들'(some unique sea animals)

이라고 (C)에 나와 있다.

09 be full of ~로 가득 차 있다

10 (B)는 '만약 ~라면 너는 무엇을 할 거니?'라는 뜻으로 상상하여 말하는 표현으로, 'Suppose ~', 'What if ~?' 등으로 대체할 수 있다.

11 대명사 it은 일반적으로 앞 문장에서 언급한 명사를 가리킨다. 대화의 문맥으로 미루어 보아, 앞 문장에서 물어본 it은 정글(the jungle)을 가리킨다.

12 '한 건물에 함께 사는 것은 우리를 침입자들이나 도둑들로부터 안전하게 지켜준다.'라는 문장이다. ② '우리는 한 건물에서 함께 살고 있는데, 그것은 우리를 침입자들이나 도둑들로부터 안전하게 만들어준다.'와 가장 가까운 뜻이 된다. ① '우리가 한 건물에서 함께 살았을 때, 우리는 안전했다.' ③ '우리가 한 건물에 함께 산다면, 안전할 텐데.'(가정법, 직설법의 반대 의미) ④ '침입자들로부터 안전하게 느끼기 위해서 함께 살고 있다.' ⑤ '침입자들의 위협 때문에 함께 살고 있다.' 등은, 비슷하지만 모두 의미상 거리가 있는 문장들이다.

13 가정법 과거에는 동사의 과거형을 쓰기 때문에 lived와 would를 사용한다. 직설법에는 don't live와 주절에 won't를 쓰는 것에 유의한다.

14 주어진 우리말의 내용상 '가정법 과거완료' 문장이다. If절에 'had p.p.' 형태, 주절에는 '조동사 과거형+have p.p.' 형태를 쓰기 때문에, If절에는 had not installed를, 주절에는 주어진 can't를 couldn't have p.p.로 쓴다. 나무 기둥들이 복수이므로 this는 these로 고쳐서 쓰는 것에 유의한다. 직설법으로 바꿀 때는 not이 없는 과거 시제 installed와 조동사 과거형 could를 사용하면 된다.

15 ④ that morning으로 보아 내용상 가정법 과거완료 문장이다. If절에 'had+p.p.', 주절에는 '조동사 과거+have+p.p.' 형태가 와야 한다. 'didn't fail'을 'hadn't failed'로 고치는 것이 적절하다.

16 'keep+목적어+목적보어' 형태의 5형식 문장에서 목적어와 목적보어의 동작의 관계에 따라 '능동은 현재분사, 수동은 과거분사'를 쓴다. '수업이 끝날 때까지 손을 들고 있도록 했다'는 내용이므로 raised를 raising으로 쓰는 것이 적절하다.

17 '~가 없다면'이라는 가정법 표현은 'If there were no ~'로 나타내며, without 또는 'If it were not for ~'로 대체할 수 있고, 'Were it not for ~'도 표현 가능하다. ① couldn't have lived → couldn't live ⑤ are → were가 적절하다.

18 '~로 들어가다'는 타동사 'enter'이다. 'enter into'는 '~을 시작하

다, (사업에) 착수하다'라는 의미로 쓰인다.

19 위 글은 다양한 사람들이 다양한 집에서 살고 있다는 내용으로 뉴멕시코의 푸에블로가 예시로 제시되어 있다. 따라서 ③번 '세계의 다양한 집들'이 가장 적절하다.

20 푸에블로는 꼭대기에 숨겨진 구멍을 가지고 있다.

21 빈칸 (A)에는 전치사 as가 들어간다. ① be in the mood for: ~할 기분이 나다 ② be ashamed of: ~을 부끄러워하다 ③ be related to: ~와 관련이 있다 ④ be regarded as: ~라고 여겨지다 ⑤ be absent from: ~에 결석하다

22 어떻게, 그리고 왜 베니스인들이 물 위에 집을 지었는지를 설명하는 말 앞에 들어가는 것이 자연스럽다. 따라서 ②번이 적절하다.

23 지금까지 베니스를 지탱해 주고 있는 천만 개 이상의 기둥은 나무로 만들어졌다.

24 조수가 높을 때에는 돌출되어 있는 통로로 도심 주변을 걸어 다닐 수 있을 것이라고 하였다.

25 한옥에서 지낸다면 침대가 없기 때문에 바닥에서 잠을 자게 될 것이라고 하였다.

26 추운 겨울에는 따뜻한 온돌 바닥이 몸을 데워준다고 하였다.

27 한옥 집은 대개 나무, 돌, 지푸라기, 종이, 흙과 같은 천연 재료로 지어져 있다고 하였다.

단원별 예상문제
p.156~159

01 ②
02 (1) take a look
(2) on weekends
(3) for a while
03 ②
04 He would build a snow house and stay there on vacation.
05 ③　　　　**06** ⑤
07 (A) some pictures　(B) those cave houses
(C) Turkey
08 ④　　**09** ⑤　　**10** ②　　**11** ①
12 ④　　**13** ⑤
14 If unwelcome visitors appeared, I would pull up the ladder to stop them from entering
15 ④　　**16** ③　　**17** ②　　**18** ⑤
19 It usually has three to five floors.　　**20** ④
21 It was because the Ndebele painted their houses with many colorful symbols when the Boers invaded their land.
22 The symbols expressed feelings such as sadness.
23 ③

01 '어떤 사람에게 살 곳을 제공하다'는 뜻을 가진 단어는 ② house(수용하다)이다.

02 (1) take a look 보다 (2) on weekends 주말마다 (3) for a while 당분간, 잠시 동안

03 위 대화에서 B는 생일 선물로 새 썰매를 받았다고 했으므로 ② '그것을 어서 시험 삼아 타보고 싶다.'라는 말이 들어가야 문맥상 가장 적절하다.

04 대화 후반에 B가 눈으로 만든 집을 짓고 거기서 휴가를 보내고 싶다고 언급했다.

05 G가 날씨를 확인하고 '당분간은 눈이 오지 않을 것'(there will be no snow for a while.)이라고 말했다.

06 주어진 문장에서 대명사 They가 가리키는 것이 무엇인지 파악하는 것이 중요하다. '그것들은 매우 아름다워 보여!'라고 했으므로 복수의 어떤 것을 의미한다. 따라서 대화의 문맥상 they는 those balloons를 가리킨다.

07 (A) 대명사 them이 가리키는 것은 앞 문장에서 언급된 Julia가 보낸 사진을 의미한다. (B) 대명사 They가 가리키는 것은 바로 앞 문장에서 G가 언급한 those cave houses를 가리킨다. (C) there는 대화 속에서 이야기하고 있는 터키(Turkey)를 의미한다.

08 ① can → could ② will → would ③ wins → won ⑤ 가정법 과거완료. would feel → would have felt

09 모든 빈칸에 들어갈 수 있는 단어는 made이다. 모든 문장은 5형식이지만, ⑤는 3형식 동사로 사용되었다. *cozy: 안락한, 아늑한

10 'I wish 가정법' 구문을 쓴다. be 동사의 과거형 were 또는 was와 조동사의 과거형을 알맞게 활용한 문장을 찾는다.

11 가정법 과거완료에 맞게 If절에 'had p.p.'를 쓰되, 이 예문의 경우 비인칭 주어 it을 활용하는 것에 유의한다. 또한, 주절에는 '조동사 과거형+have+p.p.' 형태가 와야 한다. *overflow: (물이) 흘러넘치다.

12 ④를 해석해 보면, '경찰관들이 그 어린 소녀를 폭력배들로부터 안전하게 지켜줬다.'라는 문장이다. 동사 keep은 목적어 뒤에 '형용사'를 '목적보어'로 받아서 목적어의 상태를 설명해 준다. 그러므로 '부사' safely를 '형용사' safe로 고치는 것이 적절하다.

13 5형식 문장들이다. 목적보어는 목적어와의 관계에 맞게 현재분사 또는 과거분사로 쓸 수 있다. ⑤를 해석해 보면, '이 박물관의 소장품들은 방문객들에게 고대 한국 예술에 관해 흥미를 느끼도록 만든다.'라는 문장이다. 방문객들이 '흥미를 느끼는 것'이므로 'interested'가 옳다.

14 가정법이므로 if절에 appear 동사의 과거형과, 주절에 조동사 will의 과거형을 사용하되, 'stop A from V-ing' 구문에 유의한다.

15 각 밑줄 친 make는 ⓐ, ⓕ: 4형식 ⓑ, ⓒ, ⓓ, ⓖ: 5형식 ⓔ: 3형식 등으로 쓰였다.

16 위 글은 대부분 같은 성을 가지고 있는 사람들이 모여 사는 마을과 같은 집인 토루에 관하여 설명하는 글이다. 따라서 '토루: 푸젠의 공동체 집'이 가장 적절하다.

17 '함께 놀 친구'라는 의미이므로 'to play with'라고 쓰는 것이 적절하다.

18 이웃이 차를 마시거나 저녁 식사를 하러 집에 들르라고 부르는 소리를 듣게 될 것이라고 하였으므로 ⑤번이 글의 내용과 일치한다.

19 토루는 대개 3층에서 5층으로 되어 있다고 하였다.

20 주절의 시제 및 내용으로 미루어 보아 가정법 과거 문장임을 알 수 있다.

21 보어인들이 은데벨레족의 땅을 침략했을 때, 은데벨레족은 여러 색의 상징으로 집을 칠하였고 그래서 적들은 그들이 비밀리에 서로 의사소통하고 있었던 것을 이해할 수 없었다.

22 상징들은 슬픔과 같은 감정들을 표현했다.

23 남아프리카 은데벨레족 마을의 집은 독특한 모양과 양식의 집들이라고 하였다. ordinary: 평범한

서술형 실전문제
p.160~161

01 It has wheels and can move like a car.

02 He would travel to many places with his family.

03 (1) building keeps the people safe and
   (2) poles to make them support Venice

04 ④, ④ If the officer knew the driver, he wouldn't give her a ticket. 또는 If the officer knows the driver, he won't give her a ticket.

05 Andrew knew the title of the song, he could sing it at the school festival

06 wish my sisters were as nice as Abigail

07 Others live in houses on the water.

08 Imagine you live in one of these houses.

09 The writer would hear her or his neighbor calling her or him to come over for tea or dinner.

10 The people living in a *tulou* mostly have the same family name.

01 위 대화 초반에 나와 있듯이, 바퀴가 달려 있고 자동차처럼 움직일 수 있다고 한다.

p.162

02 위 대화 후반부에 가족들과 함께 많은 곳을 여행할 것이라고 언급했다.

03 5형식 동사 keep과 make의 쓰임새에 관한 문제이다. 특히 (2)의 make는 목적보어 자리에 원형부정사를 쓰는 사역동사로 사용되었음에 유의한다. (1) 한 건물에 함께 사는 것은 사람들은 안전하고 편안하게 지켜준다. (2) 옛 베니스인들은 베니스를 지탱하도록 하기 위해, 천만 개 이상의 나무 기둥을 설치했다.

05 직설법 문장을 해석해 보면, 'Andrew가 그 노래 제목을 모르고, 학교 축제에서 그 곡을 부를 수 없다.'이므로, 가정법 과거시제 'Andrew가 그 노래 제목을 안다면, 학교 축제에서 그 곡을 부를 수 있을 텐데.'라고 하는 것이 적절하다.

06 직설법에서 '누나들이 Abigail처럼 착하면 좋은데, 그렇지 않아 유감이다'라고 했으므로, 'I wish 가정법'을 활용하여, '누나들이 Abigail처럼 착하면 좋을 텐데'로 표현한다.

07 the others는 나머지 전체를 지칭할 때 쓰인다. 물 위에 있는 집에서 사는 다른 사람들을 의미하는 것이므로 others라고 쓰는 것이 적절하다.

08 Imagine의 목적어를 이끄는 명사절 접속사 that이 생략된 문장이다. '~에 살다'는 'live in'으로 표현한다.

09 글쓴이는 이웃이 차를 마시거나 저녁 식사를 하러 집에 들르라고 자신을 부르는 소리를 듣게 될 것이라고 하였다.

10 토루에 사는 사람들은 대부분 같은 성을 가지고 있다고 하였다.

창의사고력 서술형 문제   p.162

|모범답안|

01 (1) I would say hello to the fish every morning
   (2) I could swim with sharks
   (3) I would race with many sea horses
02 would do, would build, covered with, invisible

01 어법에 맞게 적절하게 영작한다. 가정법 과거의 주절이므로 조동사의 과거형이 반드시 들어가도록 한다.

02 최근에 나는 친구와 대화를 하고 있었다. 그녀는 나에게 내가 백만장자가 되면 무엇을 할 것인지 물어 보았다. 나는 거울로 완전히 덮인 나 자신의 집을 지을 것이라고 말했다. 나는 항상 거울이 그 집을 거의 안 보일 수 있게 만들 것이라고 생각해 왔고 그것이 멋지다고 생각한다.

단원별 모의고사   p.165~169

01 ⑤   02 ①   03 be used for
04 I wish I could live in Alaska!

05 ⓒ test out it → test it out
06 ④
07 (A) would   (B) lived
08 ④
09 So I would go see La Sagrada Familia.
10 to see how his design was inspired by nature
11 ①
12 What would you do if
13 ④   14 ①   15 ④   16 ③
17 ②   18 ④   19 ③   20 ③
21 If I could enter a house only by using ladders, it would be fun.
22 ④   23 ⑤
24 At high tide, the water from the Adriatic Sea often rises and leaves the streets full of water.
25 ⑤
26 Because they wanted to keep themselves safe from invaders.
27 ④   28 ⓐ to   ⓑ for
29 Living together in one building keeps them safe.

01 '지구 위에 있는 태양과 달의 인력에 의해 발생하는 바다 수면 높이의 정기적인 상하 움직임'이라는 영영 풀이가 가리키는 단어는 ⑤tide(조수, 흐름)이다.

02 주어진 단어들의 관계는 형용사와 그 부사형의 관계이다. 따라서 high의 부사형은 형용사형과 같은 ①high이다.

03 be used for~ ~로 사용되다

04 현재 사실과 반대되는 내용, 혹은 가능성이 없는 일을 가정할 때, I wish 뒤에는 과거형 동사를 이용한다.

05 동사와 부사로 이루어진 이어동사에서 인칭대명사가 목적어일 때는 두 단어 사이에 쓴다. 따라서 ⓒ 인칭대명사 it은 test와 out 사이에 들어가야 한다.

06 위 대화에서는 거꾸로 된 집에서 살아보는 것을 상상하는 내용이 담겨 있다. ④ '난 혼자서 살기를 원해 왔어.'라는 문장은 대화의 흐름과 관계 없다.

07 'What would you do if ~?'는 '만약 ~한다면 너는 무엇을 할 거니?'라는 뜻으로 상상하여 말하는 표현이다. 이때 현재 사실에 반대되는 내용을 가정할 때는 가정법 과거형을 쓴다.

08 'I wish I could ~.'는 '내가 ~한다면 좋겠다'라는 뜻으로, 바람이나 소원을 나타내는 표현이다.

09 B가 G에게 'What would you do if ~?'라고 물었으므로, G는 'I would~' 라고 답하는 것이 옳다.

10 (B)가 가주어 It이 쓰인 문장으로, 그 It은 뒤에 오는 to부정사 구문을 대신하는 가주어이다.

11 '~으로'의 뜻을 가진 전치사 as가 적절하다.

12 '만약 ~한다면 너는 무엇을 할 거니?'라는 뜻으로 상상하여 말할 때 'What would you do if ~?'를 쓸 수 있다.

13 ④를 제외한 나머지는 모두 '목적보어'를 받는 5형식 동사 make로 쓰였다. ④는 '간접목적어와 직접목적어'를 받는 4형식 구조의 make이다. '요리 교실의 학생들이 당신에게 맛있는 빵을 만들어 줄 것이다.'

14 ①을 제외한 모든 문장은 가정법 과거 시제이다. ①의 if는 의문사가 없는 간접의문문의 명사절을 이끄는 접속사로 사용되었다.

15 ④를 제외한 나머지는 모두 '목적보어'를 받는 5형식 동사 make로 쓰였다. ④는 '간접목적어와 직접목적어'를 받는 4형식 구조의 make이다. '대학교 연구실의 내 삼촌이 나에게 환상적인 공룡 피규어를 만들어 주었다.'

16 <보기>의 would는 가정법의 주절에서 쓰이는 조동사로서, "Dennis는 친구 Sean이 그녀를 안내해 주라고 부탁하면, Canada에서 온 그 여성을 만날 것이다."라는 문장이다. 같은 가정법의 조동사 would는 ③이다. "그녀가 자신의 기술을 향상시키면, 그 회사의 대표이사가 그 사람을 고용할 것이다." 나머지는 각각 ① 과거의 습관적 행위 ② would like to = want to ④ (상대에게) 공손한 질문 ⑤ will의 과거형 등이다.

17 <보기>의 keep은 '목적보어'를 받는 5형식 동사로 쓰였다. ②도 같은 용법이다. 나머지는 3형식의 타동사로 사용되었고, 각각 ① 간직하다 ③ (월세 등을) 감당하다, 유지하다 ④ (약속 등을) 지키다 ⑤ 'keep A from V-ing: A가 V하지 못하게 금지하다.' 등의 뜻이다.

18 주어진 문장은 'Choo가 상태가 좋으면, 다른 선수들보다 두 배의 홈런을 성공시킬 텐데'라는 가정법 과거 문장이다. 직설법으로는 반대의 현재시제이므로, As가 이끄는 종속절과 주절에 모두 현재시제가 있는 ④가 정답이다.

19 곤돌라가 없다면, 베네치아 사람들은 그들이 원하는 만큼 자유롭게 돌아다닐 수 없을 텐데.'라는 문장이다. '~가 없다면'은 If it were not for = Were it not for = Without = But for 등으로 표현하며, ③ 'Had it not been for'는 'If it had not been for'에서 if를 생략하고 도치된 표현으로 가정법 과거완료시제에 사용한다.

20 ⓒ keep의 목적보어 자리 동사 형태는 능동일 때 현재분사를 쓴다. 'walk → walking' ⓓ 목적보어 자리에는 부사가 아니라 형용사가 와야 한다. 'safely → safe' ⓔ keep의 목적보어 자리이다. 'to stand → standing' ⓗ 동사 allow가 5형식에 쓰일 때 목적보어 자리에는 to부정사가 온다. 'be → to be'

21 가정법 과거이다. If절에 could, 주절에 would, only by using ladders 표현에 유의하여 알맞게 영작한다.

22 옛 베니스인들이 물 위에 집을 지었고 그 이유에 대한 내용이 이어지고 있으므로 ④ '떠 있는 도시'가 가장 적절하다.

23 주어진 문장은 습지 위에 집을 짓는 것이 불가능했지만 그것을 가능하게 만든 방법에 관한 것이며, ⑤번 이후의 문장은 지금까지 베니스를 지탱해 주고 있는 것이 바로 이 나무 기둥들이라고 강조하고 있으므로 ⑤번이 가장 적절하다.

24 조수가 높을 때 아드리아해의 물이 자주 범람하여 거리가 물로 가득 찬다고 하였다.

25 베니스에는 118개의 작은 섬들이 있다. over: ~를 넘는, ~ 이상의

26 옛 베니스인들은 침략자들로부터 자신들을 안전하게 지키기 위해 베니스에서 살기로 결정한 것이었다.

27 밑줄 친 (B)는 It ~ that 강조 구문이다. ④번은 It ~ that 가주어와 진주어이다.

28 ⓐ three to five floors: 3층에서 5층 ⓑ be used for: ~하는 데 사용되다

29 한 건물에 함께 사는 것이 토루에 사는 사람들을 안전하게 지켜준다고 하였다.

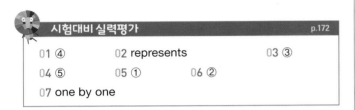

Behind the Numbers

시험대비 실력평가　　　　　　　　　　p.172

01 ④	02 represents	03 ③
04 ⑤	05 ①	06 ②
07 one by one		

01 • 플라스틱 섬에 관한 기사를 읽어봤니? • 샴푸통과 같은 플라스틱 물품은 재활용할 수 있지만, 깨끗해야 한다. '기사, 물품, 물건'의 의미를 가지는 단어는 'article'이 적절하다.

02 각 주제는 조선 시대의 역사와 문화를 나타냅니다. <영영풀이> '어떤 상징이나 특징으로 표현하다'의 의미로 3인칭 단수 주어 다음에 'represents'가 적절하다.

03 (A) '난 학생들이 가장 좋아하는 간식에 대한 기사를 쓰고 있어. 나는 그들의 건강이 걱정 돼.'라는 의미로 'be worried about'이 '~에 관해 걱정하다'의 의미로 적절하다. 'be related to'는 '~와 연관되어 있다'의 의미이다. (B) '나는 내년에 대통령 선거에 출마할 것이다.'라는 뜻으로 '~에 입후보하다'라는 'run for'가 적절하다.

04 ⑤는 '용감한-겁이 많은'의 뜻을 가진 반의어 관계이고, 나머지는 유의어 관계이다. ①은 '주장하다', ②는 '일치하다, 같다', ③은 '애쓰다, 분투하다', ④는 '소설'이란 뜻이다.

05 '정부가 공공 서비스에 대한 지불을 하도록 정부에 내야 하는 돈'의 의미로 'tax(세금)'가 적절하다.

06 '작가에 의해 지어진 등장인물과 사건에 대한 긴 이야기'의 의미로 'novel(소설)'이 적절하다.

07 one by one: 하나씩

서술형 시험대비　　　　　　　　　　p.173

01 (1) facial　(2) celebrated　(3) election
　　(4) adventures
02 solution
03 (1) repeated　(2) struggle　(3) greedy
　　(4) matter, matters
04 (1) celebrate, 기념하다　(2) wav, 손을 흔들다
　　(3) sum, 총계　(4) greedy, 탐욕스러운

01 (1) 침팬지는 얼굴의 표정과 소리를 통해서 감정을 표현할 수 있습니다. / 명사 'expression'을 수식하는 형용사 'facial'이 적

절하다. (2) 사실, Valentine's Day는 세계의 대부분의 지역에서 기념한다. / Valentine's Day가 기념되는 수동 의미로 수동태 'be celebrated'가 적절하다. (3) 학교에서 반장 선거가 있었어. / 관사 'an' 뒤에는 명사가 오기 때문에 동사 'elect'를 명사 'election'으로 바꾸어 준다. (4) 이러한 스포츠는 사람들에게 빠른 속도의 스릴 또는 모험을 느낄 수 있는 기회를 줍니다.

02 • 정부는 도움을 필요로 하는 사람들에게 돈을 주는 가장 좋은 해결책이다. • 그들은 그 용액에 향을 내기 위해 여러 허브와 꽃을 첨가했습니다. • 우리는 갈등에 대한 더 나은 해결책을 찾아야 한다. / 'solution'은 '해결책', '용액', '방안' 등의 의미를 가지고 있다.

03 (1) repeat: 반복하다 (2) struggle: 고군분투하다 (3) greedy: 탐욕스러운 (4) matter: 중요하다

04 (1) 특정한 행사가 중요하다는 것을 보여주기 위해 특별하고 즐거운 활동에 참여하다 (2) 손을 들고 손가락을 움직여 인사로 신호하다 (3) 수학적 과정에 의해 결정되는 둘 또는 그 이상의 숫자 혹은 수량의 전체 (4) 필요한 것보다 더 많은 돈이나 음식 등을 원하는

교과서
Conversation

핵심 Check　　　　　　　　　　p.174~175

1 out of
2 Yes, I get it.

교과서 대화문 익히기

Check(√) True or False　　　　　　　　p.176

1 T　2 F　3 T　4 T

교과서 확인학습　　　　　　　　p.178~179

Listen & Speak 1 A
graph / survey, kinds / results / percent, out of / What kind of / the rest / fish

Listen & Speak 1 B
election / bad, win / How come / Over / your best, what matters / guess, running for, president / proud of

Listen & Speak 2 A

help, with / have to, to make, sum, How, minus, equal /
need to, sticks, to make, what I mean / what, minus,
How / Thinking outside the box, helpful

Listen & Speak 2 B

the matter, look upset / broke / I'm sorry to hear,
facial, be tired / What do you mean / takes, muscles
to look, a few, what / get, to stay, for a long time /
it's, to smile

Real Life Communication

article, favorite snacks / (I')m worried about /
surveyed, results, eighty percent, Do you see / I get it,
What else / Twelve percent, chose, favorite / try to,
healthier

Let's Check

These days, paper tickets, store, in, show, screen,
go in, don't need to go through, trouble, printing,
what I mean

시험대비 기본평가   p.180

01 Do you see what I mean?   02 ④
03 ②

01 Do you see what I mean?은 '내 말이 무슨 뜻인지 알겠
어?'라는 뜻으로 상대방에게 어떤 상황에 대해 그것을 이해했
는지 묻는 표현이다.

02 대화의 내용상 상대방에게 어떤 상황에 대해 그것을 이해했는
지 묻는 표현이 오는 것이 적절하다. ④번은 '막대를 옮겼니?'
의 뜻이다.

03 대화의 흐름상 '왜 선거에서 이기지 못했니?'의 의미가 오는
것이 적절하다.

시험대비 실력평가   p.181~182

01 ③   02 ⑤   03 ④   04 ③
05 ②   06 ④   07 ②
08 How could four minus five equal six?   09 ④

01 뒤에서 Henry가 한 말로 보아 건강에 대해 염려한다는 내용이
적절하다.

02 Henry가 조사한 내용을 통해 대부분의 학생들이 fast food를 좋
아하는 것을 알 수 있다.

---

03 '내 말이 무슨 뜻인지 알겠어?'라는 물음에, B가 '그것을 전에 본
적이 있어.'라고 말하는 것은 어색하다.

04 B의 세 번째 말에서 '화난 표정을 지을 때는 많은 근육이 필요하
다'고 말하므로 얼굴 근육을 많이 사용한다는 것을 알 수 있다.
그러므로 'relaxed(이완된)'를 'tired(피곤한)'로 바꾸는 것이
적절하다.

05 80%의 학생들이 애완동물을 가지고 있지 않다는 것은 도표와
다르다.

06 (C) 방과 후 수업으로 테니스 수업을 더 해야 한다는 말에 →
(D) 그렇게 말하는 이유를 묻고 → (A) 이유에 대해 상술을 하
고 이해했냐고 묻자 → (B) 알았다고 대답하는 것이 자연스럽
다.

07 빈칸에는 '숫자 4를 11로 만들기 위해 막대기 하나를 옮겨야 한다'
라는 내용이 들어가는 것이 적절하다.

08 '의문사+조동사+주어+동사 ~?' 어순을 사용하고, 'minus'는 전
치사로 '~을 뺀'의 의미로 주어인 'four'를 수식하는 역할을 한다.
'equal'이 동사로 '~와 같다'라는 의미이다.

09 '당신은 번거롭게 티켓을 출력할 필요가 없습니다.'라는 의미가 적
절하므로 'need to'를 'don't need to'로 바꾸어야 한다.

서술형 시험대비   p.183

01 Eighty students liked them.
02 Do you see what I mean?
03 out of, romance movies, thirty percent of, Two out
of, ten percent
04 move one of the sticks in number four to make it
eleven

01 질문: '얼마나 많은 학생들이 간식으로 피자와 프라이드치킨을
좋아했는가?' / 100명 중에 80%가 피자와 프라이드치킨을 좋
아한다고 했으므로 80명의 학생들이 그것을 좋아한다는 것을
알 수 있다.

02 "Do you see what I mean?"은 '내 말이 무슨 뜻인지 알겠
어?' 라는 뜻으로 상대방에게 어떤 상황에 대해 그것을 이해했는
지 묻는 표현이다.

03 원 도표를 보면, 20명 중 6명이 로맨스 영화를 좋아하는데, 그
것은 전체의 30%에 해당된다. 그리고 20명 중 2명이 공포영화
를 좋아하는데 그것은 전체의 10%에 해당된다는 것을 알 수 있
다.

04 '너는 숫자 4를 11로 만들기 위해 막대기 하나를 옮기면 돼.'라
는 의미가 적절하다.

Grammar

핵심 Check p.184~185

1 (1) too, to (2) enough (3) for (4) enough
2 (1) is (2) comes
3 Nobody

시험대비 기본평가 p.186

01 (1) 없음 → 없음 (2) believe → believes
　 (3) studying → study (4) it → 제거
02 seems 또는 seemed　　　03 ⑤
04 (1) I slept so late that I couldn't get up early.
　 (2) He was so wise that he could accept the offer.
　 (3) The box was so heavy that I couldn't lift it.
　 (4) The problem was too difficult for me to solve.
　 (5) She was lucky enough to be chosen for the team.

01 (1) 'None of 복수 명사' 뒤에 단수 동사나 복수 동사가 오므로 어법상 적절하다. (2) Not everyone 뒤에는 단수 동사가 오므로 believe를 believes로 고치는 것이 적절하다. (3) 'too 형/부 to 동사원형' 구문이므로 studying을 study로 고치는 것이 적절하다. (4) 'too 형/부 to 동사원형' 구문에서 주어와 to부정사의 목적어가 일치하는 경우, 목적어를 삭제한다.
02 'None of+불가산명사' 뒤에는 단수 동사가 오므로 현재형일 경우 seems가 오고, 과거형일 때는 seemed가 오는 것이 적절하다.
03 too 형/부 to동사원형 구문에서 주어와 to부정사의 목적어가 일치하는 경우, 목적어를 삭제한다.
04 (1), (3), (4) too 형/부 to 동사원형 구문은 so 형/부 that 주어 can't 동사원형으로 바꿔 쓸 수 있다. (2)와 (5) 형/부 enough to 동사원형 구문은 so 형/부 that 주어 can 동사원형으로 바꿔 쓸 수 있다.

시험대비 실력평가 p.187~189

01 so → too　02 ②　　03 ②　　04 ①
05 ④　　06 ④, ⑤　07 ⑤　　08 ⑤
09 ④　　10 so, that, them　　11 ①
12 ④　　13 ⑤　　14 ②　　15 ①
16 ③　　17 ①
18 (1) none (2) Not (3) for 19 ③, ⑤　20 ⑤

01 나는 그 차가 너무 뜨거워서 마실 수 없다. 'too 형용사 to 동사원형' 구문으로 so를 too로 고치는 것이 적절하다.
02 그에게 그 자동차는 너무 비싸서 살 수 없다. 'too 형/부 to 동사원형' 구문으로 to부정사의 의미상의 주어는 'for+목적격'이므로 빈칸에 for가 적절하다.
03 다행히도, 화재가 났을 때 집에는 아무도 없었다. 'no one+단수 동사'이므로 were를 was로 고쳐야 한다. 그러므로 ②를 고르는 것이 적절하다.
04 '모든 이가 그것을 볼 수는 없다'는 '부분 부정'이므로 everyone을 수식할 어휘로 빈칸에 not을 넣는 것이 적절하다. 'not+전체를 나타내는 말'은 부분 부정'의 의미이다.
05 첫 번째 문장은 '무슨 일이 없다'는 의미가 들어가야 하므로 nothing이 적절하다. 두 번째 문장은 '모든 사람들이 ~하지 않습니다.'라는 부분 부정이 들어가야 하므로 not everyone이 적절하다. 세 번째 문장은 no one이 주어이므로 단수 동사가 적절하다.
06 승객 중 심하게 다친 사람은 아무도 없었다. 'None of 복수명사' 뒤에는 단수 동사나 복수 동사가 온다.
07 '그 책은 ____가 읽기엔 어렵다.'의 의미로 'too 형/부 to 동사원형' 구문이다. to부정사의 의미사의 주어는 'for+목적격'이므로 주격으로 쓰인 ⑤는 부적절하다.
08 그 농담은 너무 무례해서 차마 옮길 수가 없다. 'too 형/부 to동사원형' 구문으로 주어와 to부정사의 목적어가 일치하는 경우 목적어를 삭제한다.
09 • 그 무리들 중 누구도 서로 알지 못했다. ④ 그 무리에 있는 어느 누구도 서로를 알지 못했다. ① 그 무리에 있는 모두는 서로를 알았다. ② 그 무리들에 있는 모두가 서로를 아는 것은 아니었다. ③ 그 무리들에서 몇몇은 서로를 알고 있었고, 다른 이들은 서로를 몰랐다. ⑤ 그 무리들에서 몇몇은 서로를 알고 있었고, 다른 몇몇은 서로를 모르고 있었으며 또 다른 몇몇은 새로운 멤버들이었다.
10 so~that ... 구문으로 바꿔 쓰는 문제이다.
11 '모든 사람들이 ~하지는 않다.'이므로 '부분 부정'이다. 그러므로 ①을 고르는 것이 적절하다. ② 네 환상을 깨고 싶진 않지만 모든 사람이 너만큼 정직하지는 않다.(= 당신만큼 정직한 사람은 없다. 전체 부정) ③ 네 환상을 깨고 싶지는 않지만 모든 이가 너만큼 정직하지는 않다. ④ 네 환상을 깨고 싶지만 모든 사람이 너만큼 정직하지는 않다. ⑤ 네 환상을 깨고 싶지만 모든 사람이 너만큼 정직하지는 않다.
12 그녀는 너무 수줍음이 많아서 누구에게 도와 달라고 하지를 못

38 정답 및 해설

했다. 'too 형용사/부사 to 동사원형' 구문이므로 asking을 ask로 고치는 것이 적절하다.

13 밖에서 식사를 해도 될 정도로 날이 따뜻해요. 'It's 형/부 enough to동사원형' 구문은 'It's so 형/부 that 주어 can 동사원형'으로 바꿔 쓸 수 있다. ① 너무 따뜻해서 밖에서 식사할 수 없다. ② 따뜻하지만 밖에서 식사할 수 없다. ③ 밖에서 식사할 만큼 따뜻하지 않다. ④ 밖에서 식사할 만큼 시원하다.

14 • 평서문은 The cable is long enough to reach the socket.이므로 의문문으로 전환될 때 첫 번째 빈칸에는 Is, 두 번째 빈칸에는 enough to를 넣는 것이 적절하다.

15 ① 아무도 다치지 않았다는 것을 알고 우리는 놀랐다. no one 은 단수로 받으므로 were를 was로 고치는 것이 적절하다. ② 상심해서 죽은 사람은 없다. ③ 아무도 그녀의 판단에 이의를 제기한 적이 없다. ④ 주인공에 아직 아무도 선정이 되지 않았다. ⑤ 아무도 오지 않을 거라는 것이 곧 분명해졌다.

16 모두가 이 새로운 유행이 아시아 영화계를 위해 바람직하다고 생각하는 것은 아니다. 주어 'Not everyone' 뒤에 단수 동사가 적절하다.

17 • 반드시 아무도 이것에 대해서 알지 못하도록 해라. 주어 'no one' 뒤에 이어지는 동사는 단수이며 의미상 finds out이 오는 것이 적절하다.

18 어법에 맞게 배열하면, (1) It is none of your business. (2) Not everyone thinks alike. (3) The snow was too deep for him to walk.

19 ③ 이제 그들이 그것을 연기하기에는 너무 늦다. 'too 형용사 to 동사원형' 구문으로 of를 for로 고치는 것이 적절하다. ⑤ 세일 가격이 너무 좋아서 놓칠 수가 없었다. 'too 형/부 to 동사원형' 구문으로 주어와 to부정사의 목적어가 일치하는 경우 목적어를 삭제한다. ① 좀 조용히 해 달라는 것이 너무 많은 요구인가요? 'too 부사 to 동사원형' 구문의 의문문 형태이다. ② 제가 주문을 취소하기에 너무 늦었나요? 'too 형용사 to 동사원형' 구문의 의문문 형태이다. ④ 그날 밤은 항해를 하기엔 폭풍우가 너무 심했다.

20 죽음은 삶보다 보편적이다. 모든 사람은 죽기 마련이지만 모든 이가 사는 것은 아니다. 전제가 죽음은 삶보다 보편적이라고 했으므로 (A)는 '죽다' 동사와 어울리는 보편적인 사실이 들어가야 하므로 everyone이 적절하다. (B)는 '살다' 동사와 어울리면서 앞 문장에서 'than life'와 논리적으로 알맞은 not everyone이 들어가는 것이 적절하다.

01 No one was supposed to know about it.
02 he can't ask me → I can't ask him
03 (1) (f)or   (2) (N)o
04 (1) The machine is so dangerous that people can't handle it.
    (2) The shop is too crowded to look around.
05 (1) No one could have predicted the final outcome.
    (2) Not everyone could have predicted the final outcome.
    (3) She has been well enough to go out lately.
    (4) Is she well enough to travel?
06 (1) He's strong enough to lift a car.
    (2) The food wasn't enough to satisfy his hunger.
    (3) She is so tall that she can reach the top of the bookcase.
07 (1) Nobody parked their car in the garage.
    (2) Some parked their car in the garage, but others didn't.
08 The door is too stiff to open.
09 (1) no one   (2) no one
10 read
11 (1) No one was to be
    (2) enough sugar to make
    (3) enough time for us to
    (4) so tired that he couldn't climb up

01 'No one+단수 동사'이므로 were를 was로 고치는 것이 적절하다.

02 난 이제 너무 겁이 나서 그에게 물어 볼 수가 없어요. 'too 형/부 to 동사원형'은 'so 형/부 that 주어 can't 동사원형'으로 바꿔 쓸 수 있다. (A)에서 내가 그에게 물어보는 것이 겁이 난 것이므로 (B)에서 that절 이하의 주어와 목적어를 I 와 him으로 바꿔주는 것이 적절하다.

03 (1) to부정사의 의미상의 주어는 'for+목적격'이므로 빈칸에 for를 쓰는 것이 적절하다. (2) 빈칸 앞에 주어진 철자와 문맥상 내용을 보면 '아무도 모른다'는 내용이 들어가야 하므로 no를 쓰는 것이 적절하다.

04 'so 형/부 that 주어 can't 동사원형'은 'too 형/부 to 동사원형' 과 같다. 'too 형/부 to 동사원형' 구문에서 to부정사의 의미상의 주어가 일반 사람들을 지칭할 경우 생략이 가능하다.

05 (1)은 우리말에 맞게 보기에서 could have predicted와 outcome을 이용하여 전체 부정의 문장(No one ~)을 쓰는 것이 적절하다. (2) '모두가 ~한 것은 아니다.' 부분 부정 (3) '최근에 그녀의 컨디션이 좋아진 것'으로 'she has been well'을

쓰고, '~하기에 충분하다.'는 'be well enough to'로 쓰는 것이 적절하다. (4)의 평서문은 She is well enough to travel. 이므로 이를 의문문으로 전환하여 쓰고, '~할 정도로 충분하다.' 표현은 'be well enough to'로 쓴다.

06 (1) '충분히 ~할 정도'의 표현은 형/부 enough to동사원형으로 할 수 있으므로 strong enough to lift, (3) so~that ... 구문

07 (1) 아무도 차고에 그들의 차를 주차하지 않았다. 'No one 대신 Nobody를 써도 같은 뜻이다. (2) 모두가 차고에 그들의 차를 주차한 것은 아니었다. 'Not everyone'은 '부분 부정'의 문장으로 주어진 단어를 활용하여 'Some parked ~, but others didn't.'로 다시 쓰는 것이 적절하다.

08 보기의 우리말을 영작할 때 어순은 the door / is / too / stiff / to / open. 이다. 주어진 단어에서 it은 open의 목적어로 쓸 수 없다. 'too ~ to ...' 구문에서 주어와 to부정사의 목적어가 일치하는 경우, 목적어를 생략한다.

09 (1) '~는 없다'라는 전체 부정은 'no one'으로 나타낸다. (2) '아무도 ~ 않다'를 'no one'으로 나타낸다.

10 'too+형용사+to 동사원형' 구문으로 빈칸에 '읽다'의 동사원형 형태가 와야 하므로 read를 쓰는 것이 적절하다.

11 (1) 우리말에 '한 사람도'라고 되어 있고 주어진 단어에 no가 있으므로 no one을 주어로 하고, to be가 있으므로 수동태로 영작한다. (2) '만들기에 충분한 설탕'은 'enough sugar to make'로 쓴다. (3) to go의 의미상의 주어로 'for us'를 쓰고'충분한 시간'은 enough time으로 쓴다. (4) so ~ that 주어 can't …: 너무 ~해서 …할 수 없다.

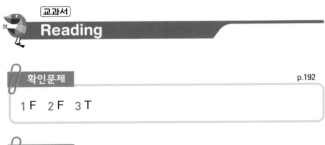
Reading

확인문제	p.192

1 F   2 F   3 T

확인문제	p.193

1 T   2 T

교과서 확인학습 A	p.194~195

01 was doing his math homework, struggling with
02 too hard to read, draw, these, needs graphs

03 put down, picked up
04 decided to read himself, was about to open
05 looked up from, to see who was talking
06 who was
07 Close, repeat after
08 You can talk, repeat
09 repeated the words, heard, shouting
10 When, on horses
11 chasing, with arrows, shouted
12 It's, for you to stand
13 pulled, rode
14 arrived at, stopped, got off
15 my name is
16 the Robin Hood from
17 Who are you, are you
18 why I'm here, must be, saved, from, Is there anything, for
19 get back, that, took, taxed them
20 too greedy to share, enough money to buy
21 help them get, back, However, no one can get
22 take me to the tower, count the number of
23 hid up, counted, one by one
24 There are, from, to
25 three soldiers until noon, eight soldiers until
26 Lastly, until, go inside between, and noon
27 don't get it
28 might make this easier to
29 drew, showed it
30 the most dangerous time
31 Four times more soldiers, than, what I mean
32 get it, so much
33 realize the importance of graphs, that, them
34 walked out of, looked back, waving
35 waved back, himself, adventure, do I go back, should say

교과서 확인학습 B	p.196~197

01 Pascal was doing his math homework in his room. He was struggling with graphs.
02 "It's too hard to read and draw graphs. Why do I need these anyway? No one needs graphs in real life."
03 He put down his pen and picked up his favorite book, *Robin Hood*.
04 He decided to read himself to sleep. When he

was about to open the book, he heard a voice.

05 He looked up from the book to see who was talking.

06 He couldn't believe his eyes. It was his dog, Manny, who was talking!

07 "Close your eyes and repeat after me. *Cogito ergo sum*," said Manny.

08 "You can talk?" "Just repeat! *Cogito ergo sum*."

09 Pascal closed his eyes and repeated the words. Suddenly, he heard men shouting.

10 When he opened his eyes, he saw soldiers on horses.

11 They were chasing a man with arrows in his hand. The man saw Pascal and shouted.

12 "It's too dangerous for you to stand there. Come on."

13 The man pulled Pascal onto his horse and rode into the woods.

14 When they arrived at a house, the man stopped and got off his horse.

15 "Hello, my name is Robin Hood."

16 "Wow! Are you the Robin Hood from the book?"

17 "No, I'm the Robin Hood of Sherwood Forest. Who are you and why are you here?"

18 "My name is Pascal. I don't know why I'm here, but there must be a reason. You saved me from the soldiers. Thank you so much. Is there anything I can do for you?"

19 "Well, can you help us get back the money that the king took from the people? He taxed them too much.

20 He is too greedy to share with the people, so they don't have enough money to buy food.

21 I want to help them get their money back. However, there are many soldiers in the tower, so no one can get inside."

22 "Hmm... I think I have a solution. But first, can you take me to the tower? I need to count the number of soldiers."

23 Robin and Pascal hid up in a tree and counted the soldiers one by one.

24 "There are five soldiers from midnight to six in the morning.

25 Next, there are three soldiers until noon, and then there are eight soldiers until six in the evening.

26 Lastly, there are twelve soldiers until midnight. So, you should go inside between six in the morning and noon."

27 "What? I don't get it."

28 Pascal thought for a moment. 'Hmm... A graph might make this easier to understand.'

29 Pascal drew a graph and showed it to Robin.

30 "Look, the most dangerous time is between six in the evening and midnight.

31 Four times more soldiers work at that time than from six in the morning until noon. Do you see what I mean?"

32 "Aha! I get it now. Thank you so much, Pascal!"

33 "You're welcome. Now I realize the importance of graphs. No one can say that we don't need them anymore."

34 Pascal walked out of the woods. When he looked back, he saw Robin Hood waving at him.

35 Pascal waved back and said to himself, "It was a great adventure. How do I go back? Oh, I know. I should say the words *Cogito ergo sum*!"

시험대비 실력평가
p.198~201

01 ③ 02 repeat 03 ④ 04 ⑤
05 ④
06 Pascal wants Robin to take him to the tower.
07 ⑤ 08 ⑤
09 Robin Hood stopped and got off his horse when they arrived at a house.
10 ④ 11 ③
12 He saw Robin Hood waving at him.
13 Pascal was doing his math homework in his room.
14 ④ 15 ④ 16 ⑤ 17 ⑤
18 ⑤
19 He wants to help people get their money back.
20 ④ **21 파스칼이 로빈에게 설명해 준 것**
22 He realized the importance of graphs. 23 ⑤

---

01 주어진 문장은 파스칼이 책을 펴려고 할 때 목소리를 들었다는 것이므로, 누가 이야기를 하는지 보기 위해 책에서 눈을 들어 보았다는 내용 앞에 위치하는 것이 자연스럽다.

02 무언가를 다시 또는 한 번 이상 말하거나 쓰다는 '반복하다, 한 번 더 말하다'이다.

03 Manny는 파스칼에게 자신을 따라 말하라고 하였다.

04 이어지는 파스칼의 말로 보아 로빈 후드는 그에게 누구이며 왜 여기에 있는지를 물어본 것임을 알 수 있다.

05 사람들의 돈을 다시 찾을 수 있도록 돕고 싶지만 탑 안에 병사들

이 많아서 아무도 들어갈 수 없다는 연결이 자연스럽다. 따라서 However가 적절하다.

06 파스칼은 로빈이 자신을 탑에 데려가 주기를 원한다.

07 모두 파스칼을 가리키지만 ⑤번은 로빈 후드를 가리키고 있다.

08 말을 탄 병사들이 화살을 들고 있는 로빈 후드를 뒤쫓고 있는 상황에서 로빈 후드는 파스칼을 말에 올려 태우고 숲으로 말을 몰았다. 따라서 ⑤번이 가장 적절하다.

09 그들이 한 집에 이르렀을 때, 로빈 후드는 멈추고 말에서 내렸다.

10 오전 여섯 시부터 정오까지보다 저녁 여섯시와 자정 사이에 네 배나 더 많은 병사들이 일하므로 가장 위험한 시간이다. 따라서 the most dangerous라고 쓰는 것이 적절하다.

11 파스칼은 그래프의 중요성을 깨달으며 아무도 그래프가 더 이상 필요 없다고 말할 수 없을 것이라고 하였다.

12 파스칼이 뒤돌아봤을 때 그는 로빈 후드가 그에게 손을 흔들고 있는 것을 보았다.

13 파스칼은 그의 방에서 수학 숙제를 하고 있었다.

14 파스칼은 아무도 실제 생활에서는 그래프를 필요로 하지 않는다고 하였으므로 ④번이 가장 적절하다.

15 파스칼은 그래프 문제에 고군분투하고 있었고, Manny는 파스칼의 개다. Manny는 파스칼에게 눈을 감고 자신의 말을 따라 말하라고 하였고 파스칼은 Manny의 말대로 했다.

16 왕이 사람들에게 세금을 너무 많이 부과하고 사람들이 음식을 살 충분한 돈이 없다고 하였으므로 왕은 '탐욕스러운' 사람임을 알 수 있다.

17 로빈은 파스칼이 그곳에 서 있는 것이 너무 위험하다며 파스칼을 그의 말에 올려 태웠다.

18 밑줄 친 ⓐ는 강한 추측을 나타내어 '~임에 틀림없다'라는 의미로 쓰이고 있다. ① 꼭 필요한 것 ②, ③, ④ ~해야만 한다 ⑤ ~임에 틀림없다

19 로빈은 사람들의 돈을 다시 찾을 수 있도록 돕고 싶다고 하였다.

20 자정부터 새벽 여섯 시까지는 다섯 명의 병사들이 있고 정오까지는 세 명의 병사들이 있다. 그 외의 시간에는 그보다 더 많은 병사들이 있으므로 새벽 여섯시에서 정오 사이에 들어가야 한다고 말하는 것이 적절하다.

21 로빈이 언제 들어가는 것이 좋은지 파스칼이 설명했지만 그가 알아듣지 못하자 그래프가 자신의 설명을 이해하는 걸 쉽게 해줄지도 모른다고 말한 것이다.

22 파스칼은 그래프의 중요성을 깨달았다고 하였다.

23 파스칼은 손을 흔드는 로빈에게 손을 흔들어 답하고는 정말 멋진 모험이라고 생각하였다.

01 He had hard time with graphs.
02 He picked up his favorite book, *Robin Hood*.
03 It was because his dog, Manny, could talk.
04 When he was about to open the book, he heard a voice.
05 He saw soldiers on horses.
06 He had arrows in his hand.
07 It was because the king taxed the people too much.
08 the woods, get the money back
09 It was because there were many soldiers in the tower.
10 They counted the soldiers one by one.
11 There are eight soldiers from midnight to noon.
12 He used a graph.
13 He saw Robin Hood waving at him.

01 'struggle with'는 '~에 고군분투하다'는 의미로 'have hard time with'와 같은 의미로 쓰인다.

02 파스칼은 그의 펜을 내려놓고, 그가 가장 좋아하는 책, '로빈 후드'를 집어 들었다.

03 눈을 들어 올려 보았을 때 파스칼이 놀란 이유는 그의 개가 말을 할 수 있어서였다.

04 파스칼이 책을 펴려고 할 때, 그는 목소리를 들었다.

05 눈을 떴을 때 파스칼은 말을 탄 병사들을 보았다.

06 로빈은 손에 화살을 들고 있었다.

07 왕이 사람들에게 세금을 너무 많이 부과해서 음식을 살 충분한 돈이 없다고 하였다.

08 파스칼을 태우고 숲으로 말을 타고 간 로빈은 파스칼에게 상황을 설명하고 사람들에게 돈을 돌려줄 수 있도록 자신을 도와달라고 하였다.

09 아무도 탑 안으로 들어갈 수 없다고 말한 이유는 탑 안에 병사들이 많아서이다.

10 로빈과 파스칼은 나무에 숨어서 병사들의 수를 한 명씩 세었다.

11 자정부터 새벽 여섯 시까지는 다섯 명의 병사들이 있고 정오까지는 세 명의 병사들이 있으므로 자정부터 정오까지는 총 여덟 명의 병사들이 있다.

12 로빈을 이해시키기 위해서 파스칼은 그래프를 사용하였다.

13 파스칼이 뒤돌아봤을 때 그는 로빈 후드가 자기에게 손을 흔들고 있는 것을 보았다.

01 novel	02 ④	03 ②	04 ⑤
05 get off	06 ④	07 ③	08 ①

09 In other words, most students liked pizza more than any other snack.

10 ③	11 ③

12 (1) I'm too scared to go on my own.

   (2) I'm too busy to take a rest.

   (3) He is so honest that he can't tell a lie.

   (4) None of the passengers and crew were injured.

13 (1) They were so brave that they could face the strong enemy.

   (2) He is so clever that he can solve the riddle.

14 ②	15 ④

16 This chance is too good to miss.   17 ③

18 ②	19 ④	20 ⑤	21 ⑤
22 ②			

23 Robin asked Pascal if he could help him get back people's money.

24 ③   25 the sound   26 ④

01 유의어 관계이다. 나타내다 : 소설

02 (A) 노벨상은 세계에서 가장 인정받는 상으로 여겨지고 있다. (B) 나도 네게 똑같은 걸 막 물어보려던 참이었어. be about to: 막 ~하려고 하다

03 신체의 특정 부분을 움직일 수 있도록 도와주는 신체 조직: 근육 (muscle)

04 활에서 쏘는 한 쪽 끝에 날카로운 뾰족한 끝을 가진 얇은 막대: 화살(arrow)

05 get off: 내리다

06 ④번의 'salty'는 형용사로 '맛이 짠, 짭짤한'의 의미이다. '소금'은 'salt'다.

07 대화는 반장 선거에 출마한 내용으로 'run for'가 적절하다.

08 6 더하기 2를 11로 만들기 위해서 숫자 6의 왼쪽 아래에 있는 막대를 옮겨서 9로 만들면 된다.

10 주어진 문장은 내 말이 무슨 뜻인지 알겠어?'라는 뜻으로 'I get it.(이해했어.)'라는 문장 앞에 위치하는 것이 자연스럽다.

11 ③번에 대한 답은 대화에서 언급되어 있지 않다.

12 (1), (2) '너무 ~해서 …할 수 없다'로 'too 형/부 to동사원형' 구문을 활용한다. 괄호 안의 단어를 활용하여 (1) 'too scared to go on my own.', (2) 'too busy to take a rest.'로 쓴다, (3) 괄호 안의 단어를 활용하여 'so honest that he can't tell a lie.'로 쓴다. (4) 전체 부정 문장으로 주어가 복수이므로 '아무도 ~하

지 않았다.'는 none of를 활용하고 were injured로 쓴다.

13 '형/부 enough to동사원형'은 'so 형/부 that 주어 can 동사원형'으로 바꿔 쓸 수 있다. (1) 그들은 강한 적을 대적할 만큼 충분히 용감했다. (2) 그는 아주 영리해서 그 수수께끼를 풀 수 있다.

14 ② 바다에서 아무도 수영하지 않는다. 'No one+단수 동사'를 써야 하므로 어법상 적절하다. ① 아무도 교복을 입고 있지 않는다. are를 is로 고쳐야 한다. ③ 아무도 그 소식에 기뻐하는 사람이 없었다. were를 was로 고치는 것이 적절하다. ④ 아무도 가방을 가지고 다니지 않습니다. carry를 carries로 고치는 것이 적절하다. ⑤ 그가 틀릴 때 그를 고쳐주는 이가 아무도 없다. correct를 corrects로 고치는 것이 적절하다.

15 ④ The toy was too expensive for me to buy.가 적절하다.

16 'too 형/부 to 동사원형' 구문에서 주어와 to부정사의 목적어가 일치하는 경우, 목적어를 삭제한다. 그러므로 miss의 목적어로 쓰여 있는 it을 삭제하는 것이 적절하다.

17 그 개는 너무 커서 박스 안에 들어갈 수 없다. 'too 형/부 to 동사원형'은 'so 형/부 that 주어 can't 동사원형'과 같으므로 can을 can't로 고쳐야 한다.

18 빈칸 (A)에는 전치사 with가 들어간다. ① refer to: ~을 참고하다, 보다 ② be concerned with: ~와 관련이 있다 ③ in terms of: ~라는 점에서 ④ result from: ~이 원인이다 ⑤ bring about: ~을 야기하다, 초래하다

19 목소리를 듣고 누가 말하는지 보기 위해 책에서 눈을 들어 올렸다고 말하는 것이 가장 자연스럽다.

20 파스칼은 눈을 감은 채로 Manny의 말을 따라하였다.

21 병사들의 수를 셀 필요가 있다고 말하는 것이 자연스럽다. a number of: 많은, the number of: ~의 수

22 밑줄 친 (A)는 money를 수식하는 형용사로 쓰인 to부정사이다. ① 진주어 ② 형용사적 용법 ③ 부사적 용법 중 목적 ④ 명사적 용법 중 목적격 보어 ⑤ 부사적 용법 중 감정의 원인

23 로빈은 파스칼에게 사람들의 돈을 되찾을 수 있도록 도와줄 수 있는지 물었다.

24 위 글은 세계 여러 문화에서 숫자가 가지는 의미에 관한 것이다. 따라서 ③번이 가장 적절하다.

25 숫자 4라는 단어의 소리는 중국 단어에서 죽음이라는 단어의 소리와 비슷하다는 의미이다.

26 성 안토니오는 잃어버린 물건들이나 사람들을 위해 기도했다고 하였다.

01 midnight 02 ④ 03 ③ 04 ⑤

05 ④

06 How come you didn't win?

07 run for 08 ⑤

09 Do you get what I mean?

10 (A) it takes a lot of muscles to look angry

   (B) it's not good to stay angry for a long time

11 (1) Forty percent of the students like red.

   (2) Twenty percent of the students like blue.

12 Not everyone

13 (1) No one was at home.

   (2) No one has told me about the new rules.

   (3) Not everyone is able to join these active groups.

   (4) Not everyone seems to be happy.

14 (1) He was too young to understand it.

   (2) Alex was too shy to talk to her.

   (3) The manual was too complicated for him to understand.

15 ⓐ waving ⓑ waved 16 ②

17 Twelve soldiers work from six in the evening to midnight.

18 ⑤ 19 ④ 20 ②

21 There were four characters.

22 ⑤

01 반의어 관계이다. 탐욕스러운–관대한 : 정오–자정

02 신문에 나오는 글: 기사(article)

03 그림에서 숫자 4를 11로 만들어야 하므로 'five'를 'four'로 바꾸어야 한다.

04 대화의 소년은 Emma가 말한 내용을 이해했다고 말한다.

05 'percent of'는 'of' 뒤에 오는 명사의 수에 동사를 일치시킨다. '단수명사+단수동사 / 복수명사+복수동사'를 사용한다. 'doesn't'를 'don't'로 고쳐야 한다.

06 'How come?'은 놀람을 표현하는 말로 '왜(Why?)'의 의미를 가진다. 'How come' 뒤에는 '주어+동사'가 올 수 있다. 'How come you didn't win?'의 줄임말이다.

07 '선거에서 후보자로 경쟁하다'의 의미로 'run for(출마하다)'가 적절하다.

08 이 조사에서 학생들이 얼마나 많은 종류의 간식을 먹을 수 있는지는 언급되어 있지 않다.

09 'Do you see what I mean?'과 같은 표현으로 'Do you get what I mean?', 'Do you understand?' 등을 사용할 수 있다.

10 (A) '~하는 데 …을 필요로 하다'라는 구문은 'it takes+목적어

+to V'를 이용한다. (B) 가주어(it) ~ 진주어(to V) 구문을 이용한다.

11 질문: 도표에서 무엇을 알 수 있는가?

12 '모두가 ~하는 것은 아니다.'라는 의미를 지니는 '부분 부정'이므로 not everyone이 적절하다. 'no one'은 '전체 부정'이다.

13 nobody = no one, not+everyone: 부분 부정 (1) 집에는 아무도 없었다. nobody는 no one으로 바꿔 쓸 수 있고 두 단어 모두 단수 취급을 하므로 was를 쓰는 것이 적절하다. (2) 아무도 내게 새로운 규칙에 대해 말해주지 않았다. (3) 모든 사람이 이 활동적인 모임에 참여할 수 있는 것은 아니다. (4) 모든 사람들이 행복한 것 같지는 않아 보인다.

14 (1) 그는 너무 어려서 그것을 이해할 수 없었다. (2) Alex는 너무 부끄러워서 그녀에게 말을 걸 수 없었다. (3) 그 매뉴얼은 너무 복잡해서 그가 이해할 수 없었다.

15 지각동사의 목적어와 목적격 보어의 관계가 능동인 경우, 목적격 보어로 현재분사나 동사원형을 모두 쓸 수 있다. 단, 이 경우에는 진행을 강조하는 현재분사 waving다.

16 밑줄 친 (A)는 이해가 안 된다는 말이다. 따라서 ②번이 적절하다.

17 오후 여섯시부터 자정까지 일하는 병사들은 열 두 명이라고 하였다.

18 파스칼이 그래프를 그려서 로빈에게 보여줬을 때, 로빈은 즉시 이해하였다.

19 두 사람이 병사들의 수를 센 이유는 안으로 들어가기에 가장 좋은 시간을 찾기 위해서임을 알 수 있다.

20 다른 어구를 사용하여 앞 문장과 똑같은 내용을 말하고 있으므로 '다시 말해서(In other words)'가 가장 적절하다.

21 학생들은 홍길동, 콩쥐, 로빈 후드, 놀부 중 하나의 캐릭터를 선택할 수 있었다.

22 ⑤ 놀부는 너무 탐욕스러워서 선택되지 않았다고 하였다. ④ 서른 명의 학생 중 아홉 명이 콩쥐를 선택하였으므로, 삼십 퍼센트의 학생이 콩쥐를 선택한 셈이다.

01 (A) I'm worried about their health.

   (B) Do you see what I mean?

02 (1) big enough to fit me

   (2) enough food to go

   (3) enough money to buy me a drink

03 (1) about (2) pets (3) five out of (4) ten students

(5) fish

04 (1) Despite Covid-19, not everyone wears a mask.

   (2) During this rainy season, no one was walking on the streets due to heavy rain.

   (3) [1] The pandemic is so severe that you[we] can't travel to Berlin.

     [2] The pandemic is too severe for me to travel to Berlin.

05 he saw Robin Hood waving at him

06 It was between six in the evening and midnight.

07 Four times more soldiers worked at that time than from six in the morning until noon.

08 Pascal drew a graph to make it easier for Robin to understand.

09 the character is so greedy that it can't be liked by others.

10 Twenty percent of students chose Robin Hood.

01 (A) '~에 관해 걱정하다'라는 의미로 'be worried about'을 사용한다. (B) 동사 'see'의 목적어 자리에 사용된 문장으로 'mean'의 목적어가 빠져 있는 불완전한 문장이므로 'that'을 관계대명사 'what'으로 바꾸는 것이 적절하다.

02 (1) 빈칸에는 '나에게 맞을 만큼 충분히 큰'이 들어가야 하므로 '형/부 enough to동사원형' 구문을 활용하여 'big enough to fit me'로 쓰는 것이 적절하다. (2) 빈칸에는 '골고루 돌아갈 만큼 충분한 음식'이 들어가야 하므로 'enough 명사 to동사원형' 구문을 활용하여 'enough food to go'로 쓰는 것이 적절하다. (3) 빈칸에는 '나에게 음료수를 살 만큼 충분한 돈'이 들어가야 하므로 'enough money to buy me a drink'로 쓰는 것이 적절하다.

03 (1) '이 그래프는 무엇에 관한 거야?'라는 의미로 'What ~ about?'이 적절하고, (2)는 '애완동물'에 관한 조사라는 것을 알 수 있다. (3) '25명의 학생들 중 5명'의 의미로 'out of+전체'가 적절하다. (4) 개를 가지고 있는 학생은 10명이다. (5) 7명의 학생은 물고기를 가지고 있다.

05 글의 내용이 과거시제로 전개되고 있으므로 see를 과거 시제로 표현한다. 지각동사의 목적어와 목적격 보어의 관계가 능동인 경우 목적격 보어로 동사원형이나 현재분사를 쓰지만 여기서는 waving이 더 적절하다.

06 파스칼에 따르면 저녁 여섯 시에서 자정까지가 가장 위험한 시간이다.

07 오전 여섯 시부터 정오까지보다 네 배나 더 많은 병사들이 저녁 여섯 시에서 자정까지 일한다고 하였다.

08 파스칼은 로빈이 이해하기 더 쉽게 만들기 위해서 그래프를 그린 것이다.

09 too ~ to V = so ~ that 주어 can't V: 너무 ~해서 V할 수 없는

10 서른 명의 학생 중 여섯 명이 로빈 후드를 선택하였으므로 20퍼센트의 학생이 로빈 후드를 선택했다고 말할 수 있다.

창의사고력 서술형 문제   p.216

|모범답안|

01 thirteen out of, percent of the total, Five out of twenty students, science-fiction books, two out of twenty students, history books

02 (1) 65%   (2) 25%   (3) 10%

03 Fifteen, Hong Gildong, fifty, courageous, nine, Kongiwi, six, Robin Hood, Nolbu, too greedy to be

01 나는 우리 학교 도서관에 필요한 책들을 조사했다. 그 결과 20명 중 13명이 소설을 선택하였다. 이는 전체의 65퍼센트이다. 20명 중 5명은 공상 과학책을 선택했다. 그러나 20명 중 2명만이 역사책을 선택했다.

02 (1) 65% of students in my class read 'novels'. 또는 Most students in my class read 'novels'. (2) 25% of students in my class read 'science-fiction books'. (3) 10% of students in my class read 'history books'. (4) No one in my class reads 'fiction'. 또는 Nobody in my class reads 'fiction'.

단원별 모의고사   p.217~221

01 ⑤   02 lastly   03 ③   04 ④

05 ④

06 Thinking outside the box can be helpful sometimes.

07 it takes only a few muscles to smile

08 facial muscles, smile, angry

09 ④

10 (1) You are too big to ride this bike.

   (2) John's son is too smart to hang out with his friends.

   (3) This coffee is too bitter to drink.

   (4) This apple pie is so delicious that I can't stop buying it.

   (5) This rope is too thick to cut with scissors.

11 ②, ④   12 ①, ②

13 (1) No one really stands out among new recruits.
   (2) Therefore, nobody is able to help the gorillas.
   (3) 없음
   (4) Would you be kind enough to close the window?

14 ②

15 (1) thinks   (2) too   (3) can't   (4) it

16 (C)–(B)–(A)   **17** ⑤   **18** ⑤

19 It is too dangerous for you to stand there.

20 ②

21 They were chasing a man with arrows in his hand.

22 ④   **23** ①, ③   **24** ④

25 It was because he needed to count the number of soldiers.

---

01 ⑤번은 'rich(부유한)'에 관한 설명이다. 'greedy(탐욕스러운)'의 영어 설명은 'wanting more money, power, food, etc. than you really need(당신이 정말로 필요로 하는 것보다 더 많은 돈, 힘, 음식 등을 원하는)'이다.

02 반의어 관계이다. 행운의 - 불행의 : 첫째로 – 마지막으로

03 '무슨 문제 있니? 너 무척 속상해 보여.'라는 A의 말에 B가 '안됐구나.'라고 대답하는 것은 어색하다.

04 '앞서 제시한 설명보다 더 간단한 설명을 소개하는 데 사용되는'의 의미로 'in other words(다시 말해)'가 적절하다.

05 ④번의 'Do you see what I mean?'은 '내 말이 무슨 뜻인지 알겠어?'라는 의미는 맞지만, 'What do you mean?'은 상대방의 말이 이해되지 않을 때 '무슨 말이야?'라고 되묻는 표현이다.

06 '틀 밖에서 생각하다'라는 표현은 'think outside the box'이다.

07 웃을 때는 몇 개의 근육만 필요하다는 의미이다.

08 화난 표정을 지을 때는 많은 근육이 필요하지만, 웃을 때는 많은 근육을 필요로 하지 않아. 그러니 오랫동안 화난 상태로 있지 마.

09 (d) 'don't need to'는 '~할 필요가 없다'라는 의미이다.

10 (1), (2), (3), (5)는 'too 형/부 to 동사원형' 구문이다. 'too 형/부 to 동사원형' 구문에서 주어와 to 부정사의 목적어가 일치하는 경우 목적어를 생략해야 하는 것에 주의해야 한다. (5)는 'so 형/부 that 주어 can't 동사원형' 구문이다.

11 • 너무 추워서 우리는 밖에서 를 할 수 없다. 'too 형/부 to 동사원형' 구문이므로 빈칸에 going과 swimming을 넣는 것은 적절치 않다.

12 ① 그는 너무 일이 많아서 쉴 틈이 없었다. '너무 ~해서 …하지 못하다.'는 'so 형/부 that 주어 can't 동사원형' 형태이다, could

를 couldn't로 고쳐야 한다. ② 그 컨테이너는 그가 들기에 너무 무거웠다. 'too 형/부 to동사원형' 구문에서 주어와 to부정사의 목적어가 일치하는 경우, 목적어를 생략하므로 lift의 목적어 it을 지워야 한다.

13 (1)과 (2)는 전체 부정 문장으로 No one과 nobody 뒤에는 단수동사를 쓰므로 각각 stand를 stands로, are를 is로 고치는 것이 적절하다. (3) '모든 사람이 ~하는 것은 아니다.'라는 '부분 부정'의 표현은 'not everyone'을 쓰고 이어서 '조동사+동사원형'이 쓰였으므로 어색한 곳이 없다. (4) '형/부 enough to 동사원형' 구문으로 to부정사로 쓰는 것이 적절하다.

14 ② 모든 학생이 애완동물을 기르는 것은 아니다. 그래프에서 보면 no pets에 학생 수가 없으므로 학생들은 모두 애완동물을 기른다고 추측할 수 있다. ① 대부분의 학생들은 개를 키운다. ③ 어느 누구도 고양이를 기르지 않는다. ④ 학급 친구들 중 대략 40퍼센트는 물고기를 키운다. ⑤ 모두가 애완동물을 기른다.

15 우리말에 맞게 배열하면, (1) Not everyone thinks like that. (2) She said the situation was just too stressful for her to deal. (3) I am so full that I can't eat more. (4) The stone was so heavy that he couldn't move it.

16 파스칼은 그래프 문제에 고군분투하다가 (C) 그래프를 읽고 그리는 것이 너무 어렵다며 (B) 펜을 내려놓고 그가 가장 좋아하는 책을 막 펴려고 할 때 어떤 목소리를 들었고 (A) 누가 말하고 있는지 보기 위해 책에서 눈을 들어 올려다보았다.

17 파스칼이 얼마나 오랫동안 숙제를 했는지는 위 글을 읽고 답할 수 없다.

18 be about to V: 막 V하려고 하다

19 '너무 ~해서 …할 수 없는'은 'too ~ to V'로 표현할 수 있다.

20 get off: ~에서 내리다

21 병사들은 손에 화살을 든 남자를 쫓고 있었다.

22 ④번 'greedy'는 '탐욕스러운'이라는 의미이지만, 풀이는 '관대한(generous)'에 해당한다.

23 탐욕스러운 왕이 사람들에게서 가져간 돈을 되찾고자 하므로 Robin의 성품은 정의롭고 용감하다고 말할 수 있다.

24 병사들이 숲에서 로빈을 발견할 때까지 계속해서 추격했다는 말은 위 글에 나와 있지 않다.

25 파스칼이 로빈에게 탑에 데려가 달라고 한 이유는 병사들의 수를 셀 필요가 있어서였다.

교과서 파헤치기

Lesson 5

1 exit, 출구   2 worth, ～할 가치가 있는
3 connect, 연결하다, 이어지다   4 origin, 기원
5 choice, 선택   6 entrance, 입구
7 difference, 차이   8 exchange, 교환하다
9 labyrinth, 미궁   10 mythology, 신화
11 escape, 탈출하다   12 prison, 감옥
13 confusion, 혼란   14 frustrate, 방해하다, 좌절하다
15 hedge, 산울타리   16 maze, 미로

단어 TEST Step 1   p.02

01 결정, 결심   02 차이   03 특히
04 편리한   05 막다른 길
06 방해하다, 좌절시키다   07 산울타리
08 미, 아름다움   09 기원   10 해결책
11 혼란, 혼동   12 비교하다   13 불행하게도
14 미로   15 미궁   16 실제로
17 기꺼이   18 연결하다, 이어지다
19 ～할 가치가 있는   20 괴물   21 자세히
22 여기다   23 제안하다   24 교환하다
25 감옥   26 (가격이) 적당한   27 효과적인
28 신화   29 탈출하다   30 규칙성
31 입구   32 믿을 만한   33 선택
34 출구   35 ～에서 나오다, 도망치다
36 ～을 기대하다   37 시도하다, 한번 해보다
38 결정하다   39 돌다, 돌아서다   40 길을 잃다
41 다양한   42 ～을 생각해 내다   43 선택하다

단어 TEST Step 2   p.03

01 confusion   02 beauty   03 reliable
04 decide   05 suggest   06 closely
07 monster   08 escape   09 floor
10 careful   11 frustrate   12 exit
13 mythology   14 choice   15 convenient
16 hedge   17 consider   18 labyrinth
19 maze   20 difference   21 entrance
22 notice   23 exit   24 prison
25 connect   26 order   27 reasonable
28 decision   29 regularity   30 unfortunately
31 solution   32 willingly   33 compare
34 effective   35 a variety of   36 get out of
37 make a choice   38 turn around
39 look forward to   40 give it a try
41 come up with   42 make a decision
43 lose one's way

Listen & Speak 1 A

bought, possible, exchange / popular these days /
why, making the decision, look better on / problem

Listen & Speak 1 B

decide, to visit during / plan I made / is it possible, on
/ exciting, horseback riding / a lot / Let's change,
schedule / excited / looking forward to

Listen & Speak 2 A

beed, help / suggest, decide between / about,
reasonable / get to / fourth floor, over there, next to /
for, help / pleasure

Listen & Speak 2 B

coming, coming / worried, lost / What about / post
office, How do I get to / Go straight for / turn right,
go straight / Turn right, go straight

Real Life Communication

Are you all set for / be late, in front of / got it, get to,
decided / choices, subway / reliable / possible to, by
subway / already checked / take the subway

Let's Check 1

reading / origin, labyrinth / Labyrinth, mythological
prison / monster / forgot / angry, put, labyrinth

Listen & Speak 1 A

W: How may I help you?
B: Hi! I bought these shoes yesterday. Is it possible
   to exchange them for the red shoes?
W: Oh, actually white is really popular these days.
B: I know, and that's why I spent a long time making
   the decision yesterday. But I think that red will
   look better on me.
W: Okay, no problem.

G: Mom, did you decide where to visit during our family trip to Jeju?

W: Almost. Come here and see the plan I made.

G: It looks good. Hmm… Mom, is it possible to visit Mirror Maze Park on our second day?

W: It sounds exciting, but I remember you said you wanted to go horseback riding.

G: I know, but I heard the park is a lot more fun. Please ….

W: All right. Let's change our schedule for the second day.

G: Thank you! I'm very excited about the trip.

W: It's great to hear that you're looking forward to the trip.

M: Hi, do you need any help?

G: Yes, please. Could you suggest a good Chinese restaurant in this building? I can't decide between the two.

M: Hmm…. What about Pappa Chen's? Their food is good and the prices are reasonable.

G: Sounds great! How do I get to the restaurant?

M: It's on the fourth floor. You can use the elevator over there. Pappa Chen's is next to the elevator.

G: Great! Thank you very much for your help.

M: My pleasure. Enjoy your dinner.

B: Hey, Minju, where are you?

G: Oh, Andrew, I'm coming. I'm coming.

B: Good. I was worried that you were lost.

G: I think I'm okay. What about Mason and Jian?

B: They are already here at my house.

G: Good! Oh, I see the post office. How do I get to your place from here?

B: You are almost here. Go straight for one more block. Then you will see Kim's Bakery.

G: Kim's Bakery? Okay ….

B: Then turn right and go straight for about 100 meters.

G: Turn right and go straight …. Okay, thanks! I'll see you soon.

Mina: Are you all set for the trip this weekend?

Jinho, Claire, & Henry: Yes!

Mina: Good! Don't be late! We're meeting at 11 a.m. in front of the clock tower.

Jinho: You got it! How do we get to the airport? I don't

think we've decided yet.

Henry: Jinho is right. We have two choices, bus or subway.

Claire: What about the subway? It's more reliable than the bus.

Henry: Is it possible to get to Terminal 2 by subway?

Claire: Yes, I already checked.

Mina: Good. Okay, then let's take the subway.

B: What are you reading, Alice?

G: It's about the origin of the labyrinth.

B: Labyrinth? Wasn't that an old mythological prison to keep the half-man, half-bull monster?

G: Oh, Juwon, you know about the story.

B: Not really. I forgot the name of the monster.

G: The Minotaur. The king of Crete was angry at it and put it in a labyrinth.

p.09~10

01 Comparing, below, notice, differences

02 example, called, labyrinth, entrance

03 called, maze, both, and

04 find, origin, labyrinth, mythology

05 said, be, prison, escape

06 notice that, single path

07 no dead ends

08 have, worry, getting, enter

09 follow, way, end, reach

10 get, have, around, came

11 When, in, maze, different

12 choices, make, ends, frustrate

13 keep making, which way

14 If, careful, lose, way

15 These, mazes, considered left-brain

16 willingly visit, planned confusion

17 came up with, solutions

18 reliable, place, very beginning

19 keep following, wall

20 like walking, dark

21 Unfortunately, effective, certain, connected

22 made, different materials, hedges

23 In fact, printed, drawn

24 Here, as, called, maze

25 from point, in, order

26 give, try, seconds, escape

27 Labyrinths, are, fun, end

28 Looking, beauty, order, regularity
29 how creative human beings
30 there, why, stop, take
31 be worth visiting

본문 TEST Step 2   p.11~12

01 Comparing, below, notice, differences
02 For example, on the left, called, labyrinth, has, entrance
03 on the right, called, has both, and, exit
04 the origin of, mythology
05 is said to be, that, cannot escape
06 notice that, a single path
07 no dead ends
08 don't have to worry about, enter it
09 all the way to the end, will reach
10 To get out, have to turn around, came in
11 in, maze, different
12 to make, dead ends to frustrate
13 keep making, which way to go
14 If, are not careful, lose
15 are, considered left-brain
16 willingly visit, enjoy, planned confusion
17 them came up with, solutions
18 most reliable one, to, on, the very beginning
19 following that wall
20 like walking
21 Unfortunately, effective, certain types, are not connected
22 are made with, different materials, like, hedges, bricks, and
23 In fact, be printed, drawn
24 Here is, called, maze
25 from, in the order
26 Why don't, give it a try, to escape
27 are, fun, the end
28 Looking at them closely, beauty, order, regularity
29 how creative human beings are
30 there is, stop, take some time
31 surely be worth visiting

본문 TEST Step 3   p.13~14

1 아래 두 그림을 비교하면 몇 가지 차이를 쉽게 알아차릴 수 있습니다.
2 예를 들면, 왼쪽 그림은 미궁이라 불리고 입구만 있습니다.

---

3 오른쪽 그림은 미로라 불리며 입구와 출구가 둘 다 있습니다.
4 미궁의 기원은 그리스 신화에서 찾을 수 있습니다.
5 그것은 여러분이 빠져나올 수 없는 감옥으로 알려져 있습니다.
6 하지만 여러분이 알아차릴 수 있듯, 미궁은 통로가 하나입니다.
7 막다른 길이 없습니다.
8 이것은 여러분이 거기에 들어갈 때 빠져나올 것을 걱정하지 않아도 된다는 것을 의미합니다.
9 통로를 따라 끝까지 가면, 여러분은 미궁의 중앙에 도착할 것입니다.
10 빠져나오기 위해서는, 여러분은 단지 돌아서 들어간 길대로 걸어 나오면 됩니다.
11 미로 안에 있을 때에는 완전히 상황이 다릅니다.
12 결정할 많은 선택지가 있고 여러분을 좌절하게 만들 막다른 길들이 있습니다.
13 어느 길로 갈지 계속 선택을 해야만 합니다.
14 조심하지 않으면 길을 잃기 쉽습니다.
15 오늘날, 미로는 흔히 좌뇌형 퍼즐로 간주됩니다.
16 많은 사람들이 미로 공원에 기꺼이 방문하여 '계획된 혼란'을 즐깁니다.
17 그리고 그들 중 몇몇은 자기들만의 해결 방법을 찾아냈습니다.
18 가장 쉽고 믿을 만한 해결 방법은 시작 지점부터 한쪽 벽에 손을 대는 것입니다.
19 그러고는 여러분은 단지 그 벽을 계속 따라가면 됩니다.
20 이것은 마치 어두운 방을 걷는 것과 같습니다.
21 불행하게도, 이 간단한 방법은 어떤 종류의 미로에서는 특히 모든 벽이 이어져 있지는 않은 경우 효과가 없을지도 모릅니다.
22 미로는 벽과 방, 울타리, 벽돌, 거울, 심지어는 눈 등 많은 다양한 재료로 제작됩니다.
23 사실, 미로는 종이에 인쇄되거나 그려질 수도 있습니다.
24 여기 그 예가 하나 있습니다. 이것은 숫자 미로라고 불립니다.
25 여러분은 A 지점에서 출발하여 1, 9, 8, 5, 1, 9 …의 순서로 이동해야 합니다.
26 한번 시도해 보시죠? 빠져나가는 데 30초가 주어집니다!
27 미궁과 미로는 정말 재미있지만, 그것이 전부가 아닙니다.
28 자세히 들여다보면, 여러분은 질서와 규칙성이라는 아름다움을 발견할 수 있을지도 모릅니다.
29 그것들은 또한 인간이 얼마나 창조적인가를 보여줄지도 모릅니다.
30 다음 여행에 미로 공원이 있으면, 들러서 즐겨보는 것은 어떨까요?
31 분명히 들를 가치가 있을 것입니다!

본문 TEST Step 4-Step 5   p.15~18

1 Comparing the two pictures below, you can easily notice some differences.
2 For example, the picture on the left is called a labyrinth and only has an entrance.

3 The picture on the right is called a maze and has both an entrance and an exit.

4 You can find the origin of the labyrinth in Greek mythology.

5 It is said to be a prison that you cannot escape.

6 But you may notice that the labyrinth has only a single path.

7 There are no dead ends.

8 This means you don't have to worry about getting out of it when you enter it.

9 If you follow the path all the way to the end, you will reach the center.

10 To get out, you simply have to turn around and walk back out the way you came in.

11 When you are in a maze, it's a different story.

12 There are many choices to make and dead ends to frustrate you.

13 You have to keep making decisions about which way to go.

14 If you are not careful, you can easily lose your way.

15 These days, mazes are often considered left–brain puzzles.

16 Many people willingly visit maze parks and enjoy the "planned confusion."

17 And some of them came up with their own solutions.

18 The easiest and most reliable one is to place a hand on one wall from the very beginning.

19 Then you just keep following that wall.

20 It's like walking in a dark room.

21 Unfortunately, this simple method may not be effective in certain types of mazes, especially when all of the walls are not connected.

22 Mazes are made with a variety of different materials, like walls and rooms, hedges, bricks, mirrors, and even snow.

23 In fact, they can also be printed or drawn on paper.

24 Here is one as an example. This is called a number maze.

25 You start from point A and have to go in the order of $1 \rightarrow 9 \rightarrow 8 \rightarrow 5 \rightarrow 1 \rightarrow 9 \rightarrow ... $.

26 Why don't you give it a try? You have 30 seconds to escape!

27 Labyrinths and mazes are truly fun, but that's not the end of the story.

28 Looking at them closely, you may find the beauty

of order and regularity.

29 They may also show you how creative human beings are.

30 If there is a maze park on your next trip, why don't you stop and take some time to enjoy it?

31 It will surely be worth visiting!

Real Life Communication – C Communication Task

1. Let me ask, How, get there

2. can go, by train

3. how long, take to get

4. takes about, to get

5. it possible to get, by airplane

6. answer, Right

After You Read

1. the nearby maze park with

2. looked hard to solve

3. many choices, keep making decisions, which way to go

4. that, place, from the beginning, keep following

5. simple, very effective

6. enjoyed myself

7. the beauty of order, regularity, human beings, creative

Let's Write

1. took a short, between, and

2. Looking at, it, that, prefers, to

3. why our class prefers mountains

4. Regarding, resons why, more, like, more exciting, lovelier

Real Life Communication – C Communication Task

1. A: Let me ask you the first question. How do you get there?

2. B: I can go there by train.

3. A: Then how long does it take to get there?

4. B: It takes about 2 hours to get there.

5. A: Is it possible to get there by airplane?

6. A: Oh, the answer is Gyeongju. Right?

After You Read

1. Today, I went to the nearby maze park with my friends.

2. The maze looked hard to solve.

3. There were many choices, and I had to keep making decisions about which way to go.

4. My friends said that I should just place my hand on one wall from the beginning and keep following the same wall.

5. That solution was simple but not very effective.

6. I enjoyed myself very much at the park.

7. Also, I found the beauty of order and regularity there and thought that human beings are really creative.

Let's Write

1. I took a short survey about our class's preference between mountains and oceans.

2. Looking at the results, it is clear that our class prefers mountains to oceans.

3. You may wonder why our class prefers mountains.

4. Regarding the resons why they like mountains more, I found key words like "more beautiful", "more exciting", and "lovelier."

단어 TEST Step 1   p.21

01 파괴하다	02 반대	03 속임수
04 속담	05 두문자어	06 건강하지 못한
07 비난하다	08 충분히	09 결과
10 마음을 끌다	11 환경	12 돌이 많은
13 해를 끼치다	14 마음을 사로잡다	15 지혜
16 속담, 격언	17 완료하다	18 깃털
19 혼란스러워 하는	20 유용한, 쓸모 있는	21 떼, 무리
22 기회	23 붙잡다	24 ~을 야기하다
25 실수	26 조심하는	27 예약하다
28 영향을 미치다	29 현명하지 못한, 어리석은	
30 무례한	31 판단하다	32 뛰어오르다
33 질	34 후회하다	35 제출하다
36 의존하다	37 ~을 심사숙고하다	
38 떠나다, 이사가다	39 결과적으로	40 연락을 취하다
41 B로부터 A를 빼앗다		42 때때로, 가끔
43 ~ 대신에		

단어 TEST Step 2   p.22

01 feather	02 flock	03 attract
04 mistake	05 opportunity	06 blame
07 result	08 acronym	09 confused
10 harm	11 quality	12 influence
13 regret	14 trick	15 judge
16 reserve	17 saying(= proverb)	
18 destroy	19 unhealthy	20 cause
21 rude	22 complete	23 careful
24 leap	25 opposite	26 tool
27 unwise	28 environment	29 fascinate
30 grab	31 stony	32 useful
33 wisdom	34 sadly	35 rely on
36 hand in	37 instead of	38 think over
39 as a result	40 keep in touch	41 upside down
42 in the end	43 take A away from B	

단어 TEST Step 3   p.23

1 allow, 허가하다 2 opposite, 반대 3 become, ~이 되다

4 regret, 후회하다 5 agree, 동의하다 6 careful, 조심하는

7 dull, 둔한, 따분한 8 influence, 영향을 미치다

9 result, 결과 10 grab, 붙잡다 11 limit, 제한

12 destroy, 파괴하다 13 leap, 뛰어오르다

14 harm, 해를 끼치다, 손상시키다   15 acronym, 두문자어
16 reserve, 예약하다

Listen & Speak 1 A

1. but, enough money / think of having, raise, introduce, too / Killing, with one / right, Let's, poster

2. watching, fascinating, What do you think of / opinion, cause, take, away from / useful, introducing, Why don't, find out

Listen & Speak 1 B

help / got a message, what some of it means / see, as soon as possible, means / What do you think of, acronyms / destroying, language / In my opinion, easy to use

Listen & Speak 2 A

1. leaving, behind / If, harm, environment, regret, in the end / Like, saying, What goes around / taking

2. take a break / studied for / Like the saying goes, a dull boy / agree, take a break after, finish

3. the matter / told us to hand in, haven't finished / hand it in, Better late than never / right and I agree, Thanks for

Listen & Speak 2 B

posting, on, a look / so many pictures that, everyday life, dangerous / way to get to know one another / people who will use, in a bad way / think of, should be more careful, for

Real Life Communication

matter, upset / had a fight with / happened / wanted to use, at the same time / are enough music rooms to practice, after school / What do you think of setting a time limit / How long / should be allowed to use, more than / disagree, more than an hour / about reserving / each person, enough time to practice

Let's Check

1. we should talk about, when / Why, that / had a fight with, because, results with / do that / never thought that, find out / Walls have ears / learned, lesson

2. feel like cooking / what do you think of going out / shall / Let's, opened

Listen & Speak 1 A

1. B: Minju, we need a new guitar but we don't have enough money for one.

   G: What do you think of having a concert to raise money? We can introduce our new song, too.

   B: What a great idea! It'll be like "Killing two birds with one stone."

   G: That's right. Let's first make a poster for our concert.

   B: Okay.

2. G: Dohun, what are you doing?

   B: I'm watching a movie about AI robots. It's really fascinating. What do you think of them?

   G: In my opinion, they will cause problems. AI robots will take jobs away from people.

   B: Well, I still think they are useful. There is a science festival introducing AI robots. Why don't we go and find out more about them?

   G: Sounds good.

Listen & Speak 1 B

W: Jacob, can you help me?

B: What is it, Mom?

W: Well, I got a message from my friend, but I don't understand what some of it means.

B: Let me see. Hmm... ASAP means "as soon as possible" and HAND means "Have a nice day."

W: Oh, I see.

B: What do you think of these acronyms, Mom?

W: I think they are destroying the language. What do you think?

B: In my opinion, they are fun and easy to use.

Listen & Speak 2 A

1. B: Look! People are just leaving their trash behind!

   G: Oh, no! If we harm the environment, we'll be the ones who regret it in the end.

   B: I agree. Like the saying goes, "What goes around comes around."

   G: You're right. Let's help the earth by taking our trash with us.

2. B: Emma, let's take a break.

   G: What? We've only studied for 30 minutes.

   B: Like the saying goes, "All work and no play makes Jack a dull boy."

   G: I agree. Then let's take a break after we finish this part.

   B: Okay.

3. G: Juwon, what's the matter?

B: Mr. Han told us to hand in the art project yesterday but I still haven't finished it.

G: Well, I think you should still finish it and hand it in. Like the saying goes, "Better late than never."

B: You're right and I agree. Thanks for the advice.

B: Yura, what are you doing?

G: I'm posting my pictures on the internet. Come and have a look.

B: There are so many pictures that show your everyday life. Isn't it dangerous?

G: Well, my friends like my posts a lot. I think it's a good way to get to know one another.

B: I disagree. There might be some people who will use your pictures in a bad way.

G: Come to think of it, I should be more careful with my pictures. Thanks for your advice.

B: No problem.

Real Life Communication

Claire: Jinho, what's the matter? You look upset.

Jinho: I had a fight with Harry.

Claire: Why? What happened?

Jinho: We both wanted to use the same music room at the same time.

Claire: I don't think there are enough music rooms to practice in after school.

Jinho: I agree. What do you think of setting a time limit for the music rooms?

Claire: How long do you think it should be?

Jinho: I don't think anyone should be allowed to use a room for more than an hour a day.

Claire: I disagree. I need more than an hour to practice music.

Jinho: Then how about reserving a music room?

Claire: That's a good idea. Then each person will have enough time to practice.

Let's Check

1. B: I don't think we should talk about others when they are not there.

G: Why do you say that?

B: Well, I had a fight with Jimin because I talked about her test results with Sam.

G: Oh, why did you do that?

B: I never thought that she would find out.

G: Well, like the saying goes, "Walls have ears."

B: I agree. I've learned my lesson.

2. A: I don't feel like cooking today.

B: Then what do you think of going out to eat?

A: That's a good idea. What shall we eat?

B: Let's eat Chinese food. A new restaurant opened down the street.

본문 TEST Step 1   p.30~31

01 then, wisdonm, influenced, changed

02 Actions, words, what, say

03 try, instead of, saying something

04 However, some, different opinions

05 words, speak louder, actions

06 that, influence others, things

07 natural, different ideas

08 other proverbs upside down

09 leap, front, making, decision

10 totally agree, careful, decide

11 be, with, results, decisions

12 However, take, over, regret

13 mistakes, without giving, thought

14 As, result, take, fix

15 agree, Opportunities, often

16 chance, grab, Or, late

17 was asked to, captain

18 However, took, decide, another

19 regret, saying, Strike while

20 sight, mind, forgotten, near

21 with, saying, close, from

22 Sadly, went to different

23 first, hard, keep, touch

24 spend more time with

25 thinking less, about, more

26 have stopped, seeing, other

27 disagree with, opinion

28 close with, neighbor

29 was from, liked, same

30 spent, lot, watching, together

31 Then, moved away, ago

32 haven't seen, since, had

33 miss, as, goes by

34 quality, that, each other

35 opinion, There, right, wrong

36 who, decide what, best

53

01 Every now and then, have influenced, changed
02 For example, Actions speak louder than words, what you do, than what you say
03 to do things instead of, saying something
04 However, have different opinions
05 words that, louder than actions
06 that, influence others to do
07 to have different ideas
08 take a look, other proverbs upside down
09 Look before you leap, what, before making, decision
10 totally agree, be careful, decide to do
11 with, results, decisions
12 However, don't take time to think, over, regret
13 make mistakes if, without giving it a second thought
14 As a result, us more time to fix
15 Opportunities, come often
16 there is a chance, grab it, too late
17 was asked to be, captain
18 However, took too much, to decide, another
19 regret, Strike while the iron is hot
20 Out of sight, out of mind, forgotten, not near
21 agree with, saying, from
22 to different
23 At first, two to three times a week, However, hard to keep in touch
24 spend more time with, new
25 thinking less, less, more, more
26 have stopped talking, seeing
27 disagree with, opinion
28 close with, neighbor
29 from, liked the same
30 spent, time watching
31 her family moved away
32 seen, remember, we had
33 as time goes by
34 It is, that makes, remember each other
35 what, no right, wrong answer
36 who should decide what is best

1 때때로 지혜의 말들은 사람들에게 영향을 미치고 그들의 삶을 굉장한 방향으로 바꾸었다.
2 예를 들어 '말보다 행동이 중요하다.'라는 말의 의미는 다음과 같다. 당신이 하는 것이 당신이 말하는 것보다 더 중요하다.
3 그래서 사람들은 그냥 무엇인가를 말하는 대신에 무엇인가를 하려고 노력한다.
4 그러나 몇몇 사람들은 다른 의견을 가지고 있다.
5 그들에게는 행동보다 더 중요한 것은 바로 말이다. 어떻게 그럴까?
6 그들은 말이 다른 사람들이 좋은 행동을 하는 데 영향을 미칠 수 있다고 생각한다.
7 다른 생각을 갖는 것은 자연스럽다.
8 몇 개의 다른 속담을 거꾸로 뒤집어서 살펴보자.
9 잘 생각해 보고 행동하라[돌다리도 두드려 보고 건너라]: 결정을 하기 전에 당신 앞에 있는 것이 무엇인지 확인하라.
10 나는 완전히 동의해. 우리는 무엇인가를 하기로 결정하기 전에 항상 조심해야 해.
11 그러면 우리는 우리의 결정으로 인한 결과에 행복할 거야.
12 그러나 만약 우리가 시간을 들여 어떤 일을 심사숙고하지 않는다면 우리는 후회할지도 몰라.
13 또한 우리는 다시 생각해 보지 않고 어떤 일을 한다면 실수할 거야.
14 그 결과 우리는 바로잡는 데 더 많은 시간을 들일 거야. 강수지에 의해 게시됨
15 나는 동의하지 않아. 기회는 자주 오지 않아.
16 만약 기회가 있다면 우리는 그것을 붙잡아야 해. 그렇지 않으면 너무 늦을 거야.
17 작년에 나는 학교 하키 팀의 주장이 되기를 요청받았어.
18 그러나 나는 결정하는 데 너무 많은 시간이 걸려서 다른 친구가 주장이 되었어.
19 지금 나는 후회해. 속담에도 있듯이 '쇠가 달았을 때 두드려야 해[쇠뿔도 단김에 빼야 해].' Brian Pearson에 의해 게시됨
20 눈에서 멀어지면, 마음에서도 멀어진다: 어떤 것이 우리 가까이에 있지 않으면 쉽게 잊힌다.
21 나는 이 말에 동의해. 나는 초등학교 때부터 친한 친구가 있었어.
22 아쉽게도 우리는 다른 중학교에 갔어.
23 처음에 우리는 일주일에 두세 번 만났어. 그러나 계속 연락을 하는 것은 어려웠어.
24 우리는 우리의 새로운 친구들과 더 많은 시간을 보내기 시작했어.
25 나는 그에 대해 점점 덜 생각하고 내 새로운 친구들에 대해 더욱 더 많이 생각하기 시작했어.
26 이제 우리는 서로 이야기하거나 만나지 않아.
27 나는 네 의견에 동의하지 않아.
28 나는 나의 이웃 Jenny와 정말 친했어.
29 그녀는 미국에서 왔고 우리는 같은 농구 팀을 좋아했어.
30 우리는 함께 경기를 보며 많은 시간을 보냈어.
31 그런데 그녀의 가족이 3년 전에 이사 갔어.
32 나는 그 이후로 그녀를 보지 못했지만 여전히 우리가 함께했던 시간들을 기억해.

33 나는 시간이 갈수록 그녀가 점점 더 그리워.

34 사람들이 서로를 기억하게 만드는 것은 바로 시간의 질이야.

35 당신의 의견은 무엇인가? 맞고 틀린 답은 없다.

36 당신에게 최선인 것을 결정해야 하는 사람은 바로 당신이다.

본문 TEST Step 4~Step 5 p.36~39

1 Every now and then, words of wisdom have influenced people and changed their lives in a great way.

2 For example, "Actions speak louder than words," means the following: what you do is more important than what you say.

3 So people try to do things instead of just saying something.

4 However, some people have different opinions.

5 To them, it is words that speak louder than actions. How?

6 They think that words can influence others to do good things.

7 It is natural to have different ideas.

8 Let's take a look at some other proverbs upside down.

9 Look before you leap: Check what is in front of you before making a decision.

10 I totally agree. We should always be careful before we decide to do something.

11 Then we'll be happy with the results of our decisions.

12 However, if we don't take time to think things over, we may regret it.

13 Also, we'll make mistakes if we do something without giving it a second thought.

14 As a result, it will take us more time to fix. Posted by Suzi Kang

15 I don't agree. Opportunities don't come often.

16 If there is a chance, we should grab it. Or, it will be too late.

17 Last year, I was asked to be the captain of the school hockey team.

18 However, I took too much time to decide, so another friend became the captain.

19 Now, I regret it. As the saying goes, "Strike while the iron is hot." Posted by Brian Pearson

20 Out of sight, out of mind: Something is easily forgotten if it is not near us.

21 I agree with this saying. I had a close friend from elementary school.

22 Sadly, we went to different middle schools.

23 At first, we met two to three times a week. However, it was hard to keep in touch.

24 We started to spend more time with our new friends.

25 I started thinking less and less about him and more and more about my new friends.

26 Now, we have stopped talking or seeing each other. Posted by Anna Brown

27 I disagree with your opinion.

28 I was really close with my neighbor, Jenny.

29 She was from America and we liked the same basketball team.

30 We spent a lot of time watching games together.

31 Then her family moved away three years ago.

32 I haven't seen her since, but I still remember the times we had.

33 I miss her more and more as time goes by.

34 It is the quality of time that makes people remember each other. Posted by Jaeha Park

35 Well, what is your opinion? There is no right or wrong answer.

36 It is you who should decide what is best for you.

구석구석지문 TEST Step 1 p.40

After You Read B Read and Correct

1. Last year, was asked to

2. However, took, time to decide, didn't become

3. strike while the iron is hot

4. disagree with

5. something without giving, may regret your decision

Let's Write

1. saying, heads, better than

2. complete the work, helpful to have the advice, opinion of others

3. People who agree with, get great ideas from others

4. can complete the work quickly

5. However, who disagree say, can get confused with

6. spend, much time before making a decision

7. In my opinion, more helpful when completing the work

8. How about

Culture & Life

1. with similar meanings in different culutres

2. expressions, different

3. the same values, thoughts

4. Let's, the proverbs, some connections

5. has ears

6. Even, has ears

7. who is unable to dance, stony

8. bad workman blames, tools

9. When elephants fight, gets hurts

9. Kenya: When elephants fight, it is the grass that gets hurts.

After You Read B Read and Correct

1. Last year, I was asked to be the captain of the school soccer team.

2. However, I took too much time to decide, so I didn't become the captain.

3. I think you should strike while the iron is hot.

4. I disagree with your idea.

5. If you do something without giving it a second thought, you may regret your decision.

Let's Write

1. There is a saying that "Two heads are better than one."

2. It means that when you complete the work, it's helpful to have the advice or opinion of others.

3. People who agree with this saying say that first, you can get great ideas from others.

4. Second, you can complete the work quickly.

5. However, those who disagree say that first, you can get confused with too much information.

6. Second, you can spend too much time before making a decision.

7. In my opinion, it is my own ideas that are more helpful when completing the work.

8. How about you?

Culture & Life

1. You can find some proverbs with similar meanings in different culutres.

2. The expressions may be different.

3. However, they show the same values and thoughts.

4. Let's read some of the proverbs and find some connections.

5. Turkey: The ground has ears.

6. Tanzania: Even the night has ears.

7. Kenya: He who is unable to dance says that the yard is stony.

8. the UK: A bad workman blames his tools.

단어 TEST Step 1   p.42

01 평평한	02 지붕	03 숨겨진
04 동굴	05 거대한, 굉장히 큰	06 주로, 일반적으로
07 형형색색의	08 통로	09 반갑지 않은
10 설치하다	11 조수, 흐름	12 습지의
13 나무로 된	14 사다리	15 표면, 지면, 수면
16 짚, 지푸라기	17 백만장자	
18 눈에 보이지 않는, 투명한		19 구멍
20 지탱하다, 떠받치다		21 모든 곳에, 어디나
22 떠다니는	23 높이 올린	24 수용하다
25 보이다, 나타나다	26 저장하다, 보관하다	
27 침략자	28 두꺼운, 살찐	29 상상하다
30 마을, 촌락	31 보통, 대개	32 그러나, 하지만
33 오르다, 올라가다	34 공유하다	35 거꾸로 된, 뒤집힌
36 들르다	37 ~로서 알려지다	38 ~을 물려주다
39 돌아다니다	40 당분간, 잠시 동안	41 ~로 가득 찬
42 A가 ~ 하지 못하게 막다		
43 ~로 구성되다, ~로 만들어지다		

단어 TEST Step 2   p.43

01 usually	02 earth	03 opening
04 raised	05 swampy	06 appear
07 roof	08 invader	09 support
10 unwelcome	11 install	12 cave
13 store	14 colorful	15 imagine
16 flat	17 sometimes	18 hidden
19 surface	20 floating	21 huge
22 thick	23 millionaire	24 house
25 invisible	26 straw	27 wooden
28 ladder	29 mostly	30 walkway
31 rise	32 tide	33 everywhere
34 share	35 on top of	36 all day
37 hand down	38 come over	39 stop A from ~ing
40 be known as	41 walk around	42 pull A up
43 be made up of		

단어 TEST Step 3   p.44

1 invisible, 눈에 보이지 않는, 투명한   2 flat, 평평한

3 house, 수용하다   4 straw, 짚   5 cave, 동굴

6 install, 설치하다   7 opening, 구멍

8 millionaire, 백만장자   9 swampy, 습지의

10 store, 저장하다, 보관하다   11 walkway, 통로

12 thick, 두꺼운   13 invader, 침략자

14 support, 지탱하다, 떠받치다   15 ladder, 사다리

16 tide, 조수

대화문 TEST Step 1   p.45~47

Listen and Speak 1 A

Have, traveling / want, see / take / unique, living / those, beautiful / to, hope, some day / too

Listen and Speak 1 B

it, / Why, waiting for / wait, out / check / could / kidding, cold place / build, stay, vacation / Living, sounds

Listen and Speak 1 C

these, natural / try living / Which, most, live in / strong

Listen and Speak 2 A-1

What / kind / move like / what, lived / travel, with / cool

Listen and Speak 2 A-2

became, millionaire / build / kind, build / covered with / mirrors, almost invisible / would

Listen and Speak 2 A-3

upside down / interesting / easy, because, upside down / try living / What, lived / like, differently

Listen and Speak 2 B

need, visit / Which country / case / would, visited / interested / that, church, designed / how, inspired by nature / How, as

Listen and Speak 2 C

What, magical power / turn into, able to fly freely

Real Life Communication A

living, exciting, so / some dangerous / full, could live / would, lived / explore / where, cave / stay in, Then, dangerous animals / makes sense

Real Life Communication B

stay, during / would, were / go swimming every day, go fishing / sounds

Let's Check 1

This, What, think / deep sea, unique, would, lived / interest, deep sea, So, explore, unique / That

Let's Check 2

matter, wish, could have

p.48~50

Listen and Speak 1 A

G: Have you heard from Julia? She's traveling in Turkey, right?

B: Yes, she sent me some pictures. Do you want to see them?

G: Yes, please.

B: Okay, take a look.

G: Oh, look at those cave houses! They look so unique, don't they? I wish I could try living there.

B: I like those balloons. They look so beautiful!

G: I think Turkey is a wonderful place to visit. I hope to visit there some day.

B: Me too!

Listen and Speak 1 B

B: Will it snow today?

G: I have no idea. Why are you waiting for snow, Taeho?

B: I got a new sled for my birthday. I can't wait to test it out.

G: Let me check the weather. Umm, there will be no snow for a while.

B: I wish I could live in Alaska. Then I could go sledding all day!

G: No kidding! Alaska is a very cold place.

B: I think it would be fun. I want to build a snow house and stay there on vacation.

G: Living in a snow house sounds fun!

Listen and Speak 1 C

A: Look at these houses. They look very natural.

B: Wow, I wish I could try living here.

A: Which house would you most like to live in?

B: I wish I could live in the stone house. It looks very strong.

Listen and Speak 2 A-1

B: This is my dream house, Alice. What do you think?

G: Oh, the house has wheels! Is it a kind of car?

B: Yes, it can move like a car.

G: So what would you do if you lived in that house?

B: I would travel to many places with my family.

G: That sounds cool.

Listen and Speak 2 A-2

G: What would you do if you became a millionaire, Juwon?

B: I would build my own house.

G: What kind of house would you build?

B: I would build a house that is completely covered with mirrors.

G: Why?

B: The mirrors would make the house almost invisible. Wouldn't that be cool?

G: That would be cool!

Listen and Speak 2 A-3

G: Look. The house in this picture is upside down.

B: That's interesting. Does anybody live there?

G: No, it would not be easy to live there because the inside is also upside down.

B: Really? But I want to try living there.

G: What would you do if you lived in that house?

B: I would walk upside down like Spider-Man. I could also see things differently.

Listen and Speak 2 B

G: Dohun, we need to start our project on our dream country to visit.

B: That's right. Which country do you want to visit, Emma?

G: In my case, I want to visit Spain.

B: What would you do if you visited Spain?

G: I'm interested in buildings. So I would go see La Sagrada Familia.

B: Isn't that the church Antoni Gaudi designed?

G: Yes, it is. It would be interesting to see how his design was inspired by nature.

B: Hmm... . How about Gaudí and Spain as the title for our project?

G: I love it!

Listen and Speak 2 C

A: What would you do if you could have a magical power?

B: I would turn into a bird. Then I would be able to fly freely in the sky.

A: That's cool.

Real Life Communication A

Jinho: I think living in a jungle would be really exciting. Don't you think so?

Claire: But there are some dangerous animals in the jungle, Jinho.

Jinho: I know. But the jungle is full of adventure. I wish I could live there.

Claire: What would you do if you lived in the jungle?

Jinho: I would explore it. Maybe I could make some animal friends.

Claire: Then where would you sleep? In a cave?

Jinho: No, I would stay in a tree house. Then I would be safe from dangerous animals.

Claire: That makes sense.

A: I wish I could stay in a house on the water during my vacation.

B: What would you do if you were there?

A: I would go swimming every day. I would also go fishing.

B: That sounds fun.

Let's Check 1

B: This is my dream house. What do you think, Alice?

G: Oh, it's in the deep sea. It looks so unique. So, what would you do if you lived in that house?

B: I have an interest in deep sea animals. So I would explore the deep sea and find some unique sea animals.

G: That sounds cool!

Let's Check 2

A: What's the matter?

B: My computer is so slow. I wish I could have a new computer.

본문 TEST Step 1   p.51~52

01 Different, live in, houses

02 Some, ladders, enter, Others

03 others share, houses with

04 Imagine, one, change, life

05 lived, would climb, enter

06 There's, hidden opening, top

07 unwelcome, appeared, stop, from

08 thick, made of, straw

09 keep me cool, warm

10 flat roof, up, under

11 If, lived, would take

12 On, from, to, by

13 tide, rises, full of

14 However, around, through, raised

15 is known as, floating

16 there are, colorful houses

17 wonder how, why, built

18 decided, keep, safe, invaders

19 easy, build, swampy surface

20 So, installed, wooden poles

21 wooden poles, support, to

22 lived, huge round, with

23 neighbor calling, come over

---

24 three to five floors

25 floor is used for

26 store food, tools, floor

27 would, on, third, floor

28 like, living, mostly, same

29 up to, work together

30 Living together, keeps, safe

31 everywhere, different, What, like

본문 TEST Step 2   p.53~54

01 Different, live in

02 use ladders to enter their houses. Others live in, on

03 others share, with

04 Imagine, live in one of, that change

05 lived in, would climb, to enter my

06 hidden opening on top

07 If, appeared, would pull, up to stop, from

08 are made of

09 keep me cool, warm

10 a flat roof, sleep up on the roof

11 lived in, would take a gondola

12 has, islands, On weekend, from island to island

13 high tide, from, rises, leaves, full of water

14 However, be able to walk around, raised walkways

15 is known as, floating

16 there are, colorful houses

17 wonder how, why they built the houses on

18 decided to live there, themselves safe from invaders

19 for them to build, swampy surface

20 installed, wooden poles

21 wooden poles, support, to

22 lived, huge round, would, have friends, to play with

23 hear, calling me to come over

24 are, three to five floors

25 is used for

26 store food, tools on, second floor

27 where I would sleep, would be on

28 like, living in, have, family name

29 can house up to, work together, share

30 Living, keeps them safe

31 different all over the world, What, like

1 다양한 사람들이 다양한 집에서 살고 있습니다.

2 어떤 사람들은 집에 들어가기 위해 사다리를 이용합니다. 다른 사람들은 물 위에 있는 집에서 살고 있습니다.

3 그리고 또 다른 사람들은 많은 사람들과 함께 집을 공유합니다.

4 여러분이 이 집들 중 하나에 산다고 상상해 보세요. 여러분의 삶은 어떻게 바뀔까요?

5 내가 만약 푸에블로로 산다면, 나는 집에 들어가기 위해 사다리를 오를 것이다.

6 집 꼭대기에는 숨겨진 구멍이 있다.

7 반갑지 않은 방문객이 나타난다면 나는 사다리를 끌어올려 그들이 들어오지 못하게 할 것이다.

8 두꺼운 벽은 흙, 지푸라기, 물로 만들어져 있다.

9 그것들은 여름에는 시원하게, 겨울에는 따뜻하게 유지시켜 준다.

10 집에는 평평한 지붕이 있다. 때때로 나는 달과 별들 아래의 지붕 위에서 잠을 잘 것이다.

11 내가 만약 베니스에 산다면, 나는 매일 아침 곤돌라를 타고 학교에 갈 것이다.

12 베니스는 118개의 작은 섬이 있다. 주말마다 나는 수상 버스인 바포레토를 타고 이 섬 저 섬을 여행할 것이다.

13 조수가 높을 때에는 아드리아 해의 물이 자주 범람하고 거리는 물로 가득 찬다.

14 그러나 나는 돌출되어 있는 통로로 도심 주변을 걸어다닐 수 있을 것이다.

15 베니스는 '떠다니는 도시'로 알려져 있다.

16 베니스에는 물 위에 있는 색색의 건물들이 많다.

17 여러분은 어떻게, 그리고 왜 그들이 물 위에 집을 지었는지 궁금할 것이다.

18 옛 베니스 사람들은 침략자들로부터 자신들을 안전하게 지키기 위해 그곳에 살기로 결정했다.

19 하지만 그들이 이 습지 위에 집을 짓는 것은 쉽지가 않았다.

20 그래서 그들은 땅에 천만 개 이상의 나무 기둥을 설치했다.

21 이 나무 기둥들이 바로 지금까지 베니스를 지탱해 주고 있는 것이다.

22 내가 만약 거대하고 둥그런 집인 중국 푸젠의 토루(tulou)에 산다면, 나는 항상 집에 함께 놀 친구들이 있을 것이다.

23 때때로 나의 이웃이 차를 마시거나 저녁 식사를 하러 집에 들르라고 나를 부르는 소리를 듣게 될 것이다.

24 토루는 대개 3층에서 5층으로 되어 있다.

25 1층은 요리하고 식사하는 데에 사용된다.

26 그리고 사람들은 2층에 식량과 도구를 보관한다.

27 내가 어디에서 잠을 잘지 궁금한가? 내 침실은 3층이나 4층에 있을 것이다.

28 토루는 마을과 같다. 토루에 사는 사람들은 대부분 같은 성(姓)을 가지고 있다.

29 몇몇 큰 토루는 50가구까지 수용할 수 있다. 그들은 함께 일하고 많은 것을 공유한다.

30 한 건물에 함께 사는 것은 그들을 안전하게 지켜 준다.

31 집은 어디에나 있습니다. 그러나 전 세계의 집은 모두 다릅니다. 여러분의 집은 어떤가요?

1 Different people live in different houses.

2 Some use ladders to enter their houses. Others live in houses on the water.

3 And others share their houses with many people.

4 Imagine you live in one of these houses. How would that change your life?

5 If I lived in a *pueblo*, I would climb up a ladder to enter my house.

6 There's a hidden opening on top of the house.

7 If unwelcome visitors appeared, I would pull the ladder up to stop them from entering.

8 The thick walls are made of earth, straw, and water.

9 They would keep me cool in summer and warm in winter.

10 The house has a flat roof. I would sometimes sleep up on the roof under the moon and stars.

11 If I lived in Venice, I would take a gondola to school every morning.

12 Venice has 118 small islands. On weekends, I would travel from island to island by a *vaporetto*, a water bus.

13 At high tide, the water from the Adriatic Sea often rises and leaves the streets full of water.

14 However, I would be able to walk around the town through the raised walkways.

15 Venice is known as the "floating city."

16 In Venice, there are many colorful houses on the water.

17 You may wonder how and why they built the houses on the water.

18 The old Venetians decided to live there to keep themselves safe from invaders.

19 But it was not easy for them to build their homes on this swampy surface.

20 So they installed more than 10 million wooden poles in the ground.

21 It is these wooden poles that support Venice to this day.

22 If I lived in a *tulou*, a huge round house in Fujian, China, I would always have friends at home to

23 I would sometimes hear my neighbor calling me to come over for tea or dinner.

24 In a *tulou*, there are usually three to five floors.

25 The first floor is used for cooking and eating.

26 And people store food and tools on the second floor.

27 Do you wonder where I would sleep? My bedroom would be on the third or fourth floor.

28 A *tulou* is like a village. The people living in a *tulou* mostly have the same family name.

29 Some large *tulou* can house up to 50 families. They work together and share many things.

30 Living together in one building keeps them safe.

31 Homes are everywhere. But they are different all over the world. What is your home like?

Let's Write

1. might wonder where you can stay

2. Why don't you stay

3. a traditional Korean house

4. stayed, would sleep, because there are no beds

5. are mostly built with, such as wood, straw, and earth

6. help you keep your skin healthy

7. warm *ondol* floors heat your body

8. are covered with thin paper

9. help keep you cool

Culture & Life

1. walked down, would see houses with many unique patterns

2. Each house tells

3. might be about neighbors' babies

4. Others, personal opinions

5. A long time ago, were at war with

6. invaded their land, with many colorful symbols

7. what, secretly communicating to each other

8. expressed feelings such as sadness

9. were handed down from, to

10. kept their traditions alive

Let's Write

1. When you visit Korea, you might wonder where you can stay.

2. Why don't you stay in a *hanok*?

3. A *hanok* is a traditional Korean house.

4. If you stayed in a *hanok*, you would sleep on the floor because there are no beds.

5. *Hanok* houses are mostly built with natural materials such as wood, stone, straw, paper, and earth.

6. These materials help you keep your skin healthy.

7. In the cold winter, the warm *ondol* floors heat your body.

8. The doors in *hanok* are covered with thin paper.

9. They help keep you cool in summer.

Culture & Life

1. If you walked down a street in the village of the Ndebele in South Africa, you would see houses with many unique patterns and styles.

2. Each house tells a different story.

3. Some stories might be about neighbors' babies.

4. Others express personal opinions.

5. A long time ago, the Ndebele were at war with the Boers.

6. When the Boers invaded their land, the Ndebele painted their houses with many colorful symbols.

7. So, their enemies couldn't understand what they were secretly communicating to each other.

8. The symbols expressed feelings such as sadness.

9. Those symbols were handed down from mothers to daughters.

10. And they have kept their traditions alive.

단어 TEST Step 1 — p.63

01 글, 기사	02 고장 내다	03 이유
04 투표하다	05 손을 흔들다	06 모험
07 용감한	08 반복하다, 따라 말하다	
09 근육	10 같다	11 설문조사하다
12 게다가, 어쨌든	13 나타내다	14 중요하다
15 선거	16 군인, 병사	17 뒤쫓다
18 계산, 총계	19 중요성	20 갑자기
21 자정	22 얼굴의	23 독이 있는
24 투쟁하다, 분투하다		25 깨닫다
26 도움이 되는	27 기념하다	28 해결책
29 주장하다	30 탐욕스러운, 욕심 많은	
31 결과	32 일치하다	33 마지막으로
34 공상 과학의	35 되찾다	36 ~와 연관되어 있다
37 하나씩	38 출마하다	39 집어들다
40 다시 말하면	41 막 ~하려고 하다	42 ~을 자랑스러워하다
43 ~로 여겨지다		

단어 TEST Step 2 — p.64

01 soldier	02 typewriter	03 survey
04 tax	05 match	06 sum
07 claim	08 vote	09 solution
10 facial	11 adventure	12 reason
13 courageous	14 election	15 celebrate
16 article	17 anyway	18 equal
19 midnight	20 represent	21 chase
22 struggle	23 greedy	24 suddenly
25 helpful	26 muscle	27 importance
28 poisonous	29 result	30 salty
31 science-fiction	32 realize	33 arrow
34 wave	35 hide up	36 be proud of
37 look up	38 be about to	39 in other words
40 be related to	41 one by one	42 be regarded as
43 not ~ anymore		

단어 TEST Step 3 — p.65

1 matter, 중요하다 2 soldier, 군인, 병사

3 midnight, 자정 4 realize, 깨닫다

5 poisonous, 독이 있는 6 shout, 외치다, 소리치다

7 article, 글, 기사 8 represent, 나타내다

9 wave, 손을 흔들다 10 greedy, 탐욕스러운, 욕심 많은

11 lastly, 마지막으로 12 novel, 소설

13 sum, 총계, 계산 14 tax, 세금 15 claim, 주장하다

16 celebrate, 기념하다

대화문 TEST Step 1 — p.66~67

Listen & Speak 1 A

graph about / survey, kinds / results / percent, Only, out of / What kind of / have cats / the rest / fish

Listen & Speak 1 B

election / bad, win / How come / Over, voted for / your best, what matters / guess, while running for, president / proud of

Listen & Speak 2 A

help, with / have to, to make, sum, How, minus, equal / need to, sticks, sticks, to make, what I mean / what, minus, equals, How / Thinking outside the box, helpful

Listen & Speak 2 B

the matter, look upset / broke, angry / I'm sorry to hear, facial, be tired / What do you mean / takes, muscles to look, a few, what / get, to stay, for a long time / it's, better to smile

Real Life Communication

doing, article, favorite snacks / (I')m worried about / surveyed, results, eighty percent / Do you see, mean / I get it, What else / Twelve percent, chose, as favorite / try to, healthier

Let's Check

These days, paper tickets, store, in, show, screen, go in, don't need to go through, trouble of printing, what I mean

대화문 TEST Step 2 — p.68~69

Listen & Speak 1 A

B: Minju, what is this graph about?

G: I did a survey on the kinds of pets my classmates have.

B: What were the results?

G: Eighty percent of the students have pets. Only five out of twenty-five students don't have pets.

B: What kind of pets do they have?

G: Well, ten students have dogs and three students have cats.

B: What about the rest?

G: Seven students have fish.

M: Mason, how was the election?

B: It was bad. I didn't win.

M: How come?

B: Yura won. Over sixty percent of the students voted for her.

M: Well, you tried your best and that's what matters.

B: I guess so. I have learned many things while running for class president.

M: I'm really proud of you.

B: Thanks, Dad.

B: Emma, can you help me with this math problem?

G: Sure, what is it?

B: You have to move one stick to make this sum right. How could four minus five equal six?

G: Oh, it's simple. You need to move one of the sticks in number four to make it eleven. Do you see what I mean?

B: Yes, now I see what you mean. Eleven minus five equals six. How clever!

G: Thinking outside the box can be helpful sometimes.

B: Jian, what's the matter? You look upset.

G: My brother broke my computer. I'm so angry.

B: I'm sorry to hear that, but your facial muscles must be tired.

G: What do you mean?

B: Well, it takes a lot of muscles to look angry, but only a few to smile. Do you see what I mean?

G: Oh, I get it. I guess it's not good to stay angry for a long time.

B: That's right. Remember, it's always better to smile!

Mina: Henry, what are you doing?

Henry: I'm writing an article about students' favorite snacks. I'm worried about their health.

Mina: Why?

Henry: Well, I surveyed 100 students and the results show that eighty percent of the students liked pizza and fried chicken for snacks. Do you see what I mean?

Mina: Oh, I get it. Students really like fast food. What else did they like?

Henry: Twelve percent of the students chose chocolate cake as their favorite.

Mina: Wow, students should really try to eat healthier snacks!

B: These days, you don't need paper tickets to watch a movie or go to a concert. You just need to store your ticket in your cell phone. Then show the ticket on your phone's screen before you go in. You don't need to go through the trouble of printing out tickets. Do you see what I mean?

본문 TEST Step 1   p.70~72

01 doing, math, struggling with

02 too, draw, anyway, real

03 put down, picked up

04 decided, himself, about, heard

05 looked up from, talking

06 couldn't believe, who was

07 Close, eyes, repeat after

08 can talk, Just repeat

09 repeated, words, heard, shouting

10 When, opened, soldiers on

11 chasing, with arrows, shouted

12 dangerous for you, stand

13 pulled, onto, rode, woods

14 arrived, stopped, got off

15 my name is

16 Are, from, book

17 Who, why, here

18 must, reason, soldiers, anything

19 get back, took, taxed

20 greedy, share, enough, buy

21 get, back, so, inside

22 solution, take, count, number

23 hid up, counted, by

24 There are, from, to

25 three soldiers until noon

26 Lastly, until, between, and

27 don't get it

28 moment, might make, easier

29 drew, graph, showed, to

30 the most dangerous, midnight

31 work, than, what, mean

32 get it, so much

33 realize, importance, that, anymore

34 walked out, back, waving

35 waved back, himself, adventure

01 was doing his math homework, struggling with
02 too hard to read, draw, these, needs graphs, real life
03 put down, picked up
04 decided to read himself, was about to open, heard
05 looked up from, to see who was talking
06 who was
07 Close, repeat after
08 You can talk, repeat
09 repeated the words, Suddenly, heard, shouting
10 When, on horses
11 chasing, with arrows, shouted
12 It's, for you to stand
13 pulled, onto, rode
14 arrived at, stopped, got off
15 my name is
16 the Robin Hood from
17 Who are you, are you
18 why I'm here, must be, saved, from, Is there anything, for
19 get back, that, took, taxed them
20 too greedy to share, enough money to buy
21 help them get, back, However, no one can get inside
22 take me to the tower, count the number of
23 hid up, counted, one by one
24 There are, from, to
25 three soldiers until noon, eight soldiers until
26 Lastly, there are, until, go inside between, and noon
27 don't get it
28 moment, might make this easier to
29 drew, showed it
30 the most dangerous time, between, and
31 Four times more soldiers, than, until, what I mean
32 get it, so much
33 realize the importance of graphs, No one, that, them
34 walked out of, looked back, waving
35 waved back, himself, adventure, do I go back, should say

1 파스칼은 그의 방에서 수학 숙제를 하고 있었습니다. 그는 그래프 문제에 고군분투하고 있었습니다.
2 "그래프를 읽고 그리는 것은 너무 어려워. 게다가 내가 왜 그래프가 필요하겠어? 아무도 실제 생활에서는 그래프가 필요하지 않아."
3 그는 그의 펜을 내려놓고, 그가 가장 좋아하는 책, '로빈 후드'를 집어 들었습니다.
4 그는 책을 읽으며 잠들기로 했습니다. 그가 책을 펴려고 할 때, 그는 목소리를 들었습니다.
5 누가 말하고 있는지 보기 위해 그는 책에서 눈을 들어 올려다보았습니다.
6 그는 그의 눈을 믿을 수 없었습니다. 말하는 것은 바로 자신의 개, Manny였습니다!
7 "눈을 감고 내 말을 따라 말하세요. 코기토 에르고 숨." Manny가 말했습니다.
8 "너는 말할 수 있어?" "그냥 따라 하세요! 코기토 에르고 숨."
9 파스칼은 그의 눈을 감고 그 단어들을 따라 말했습니다. 갑자기 그는 남자들이 소리치는 것을 들었습니다.
10 그가 눈을 떴을 때, 그는 말을 탄 병사들을 보았습니다.
11 그들은 손에 화살을 든 남자를 뒤쫓고 있었습니다. 그 남자는 파스칼을 보고 소리쳤습니다.
12 "네가 거기 서 있는 것은 너무 위험해. 이리 와."
13 그 남자는 파스칼을 그의 말에 올려 태우고 숲으로 말을 몰았습니다.
14 그들이 한 집 앞에 이르렀을 때, 그 남자는 멈추고 말에서 내렸습니다.
15 "안녕, 내 이름은 로빈 후드야."
16 "와우! 당신이 책 속의 로빈 후드인가요?"
17 "아니, 나는 셔우드 숲의 로빈 후드야. 너는 누구이고 왜 여기에 있니?"
18 "제 이름은 파스칼이에요. 저는 제가 왜 여기 있는지 모르지만 이유가 분명 있을 거예요. 당신은 저를 병사들로부터 구해줬어요. 정말 감사드려요. 제가 당신을 위해 할 수 있는 것이 있을까요?"
19 "음, 우리가 왕이 사람들에게서 가져간 돈을 되찾는 것을 도와줄 수 있니? 그는 그들에게 세금을 너무 많이 부과했어.
20 그는 너무 탐욕스러워서 사람들과 나누지 않아, 그래서 그들은 음식을 살 충분한 돈이 없어.
21 나는 그들의 돈을 다시 찾을 수 있도록 돕고 싶어. 하지만 탑 안에 병사들이 많아서 아무도 들어갈 수 없어."
22 "흠… 제게 해결책이 있는 것 같아요. 그러나 우선 저를 탑에 데려가 주실 수 있나요? 저는 병사들의 수를 세야 해요."
23 로빈과 파스칼은 나무에 숨어서 병사들의 수를 한 명씩 세었습니다.
24 "자정부터 새벽 여섯 시까지는 다섯 명의 병사들이 있어요.
25 그다음, 정오까지는 세 명의 병사들이 있고, 오후 여섯 시까지는 여덟 명의 병사들이 있어요.

26 마지막으로, 자정까지는 열두 명의 병사들이 있어요. 그래서 당신은 새벽 여섯 시에서 정오 사이에 들어가야 해요."

27 "뭐라고? 나는 이해하지 못했어."

28 파스칼은 잠시 생각에 잠겼습니다. '흠…그래프가 이것을 이해하는 것을 쉽게 해 줄지도 몰라.'

29 파스칼은 그래프를 그려서 그것을 로빈에게 보여주었습니다.

30 "보세요, 가장 위험한 시간은 저녁 여섯 시에서 자정까지예요.

31 오전 여섯 시부터 정오까지보다 그 시간에 네 배나 더 많은 병사들이 일해요. 제 말이 무슨 뜻인지 아시겠어요?"

32 "아하! 이제 이해했어. 너무 고마워, 파스칼!"

33 "천만에요. 이제 저는 그래프의 중요성을 깨달았어요. 아무도 그래프가 더 이상 필요 없다고 말할 수 없을 거예요."

34 파스칼은 숲에서 걸어 나왔습니다. 그가 뒤돌아봤을 때, 그는 로빈 후드가 그에게 손을 흔들고 있는 것을 보았습니다.

35 파스칼은 손을 흔들어 답하고 혼잣말을 했습니다. "정말 멋진 모험이었어. 나는 어떻게 돌아가지? 오, 알겠어. 나는 코기토 에르고 숨이라는 말을 해야 해!"

본문 TEST Step 4~Step 5
p.77~81

01 Pascal was doing his math homework in his room. He was struggling with graphs.

02 "It's too hard to read and draw graphs. Why do I need these anyway? No one needs graphs in real life."

03 He put down his pen and picked up his favorite book, *Robin Hood*.

04 He decided to read himself to sleep. When he was about to open the book, he heard a voice.

05 He looked up from the book to see who was talking.

06 He couldn't believe his eyes. It was his dog, Manny, who was talking!

07 "Close your eyes and repeat after me. *Cogito ergo sum*," said Manny.

08 "You can talk?" "Just repeat! *Cogito ergo sum*."

09 Pascal closed his eyes and repeated the words. Suddenly, he heard men shouting.

10 When he opened his eyes, he saw soldiers on horses.

11 They were chasing a man with arrows in his hand. The man saw Pascal and shouted.

12 "It's too dangerous for you to stand there. Come on."

13 The man pulled Pascal onto his horse and rode into the woods.

14 When they arrived at a house, the man stopped and got off his horse.

15 "Hello, my name is Robin Hood."

16 "Wow! Are you the Robin Hood from the book?"

17 "No, I'm the Robin Hood of Sherwood Forest. Who are you and why are you here?"

18 "My name is Pascal. I don't know why I'm here, but there must be a reason. You saved me from the soldiers. Thank you so much. Is there anything I can do for you?"

19 "Well, can you help us get back the money that the king took from the people? He taxed them too much.

20 He is too greedy to share with the people, so they don't have enough money to buy food.

21 I want to help them get their money back. However, there are many soldiers in the tower, so no one can get inside."

22 "Hmm… I think I have a solution. But first, can you take me to the tower? I need to count the number of soldiers."

23 Robin and Pascal hid up in a tree and counted the soldiers one by one.

24 "There are five soldiers from midnight to six in the morning.

25 Next, there are three soldiers until noon, and then there are eight soldiers until six in the evening.

26 Lastly, there are twelve soldiers until midnight. So, you should go inside between six in the morning and noon."

27 "What? I don't get it."

28 Pascal thought for a moment. 'Hmm… A graph might make this easier to understand.'

29 Pascal drew a graph and showed it to Robin.

30 "Look, the most dangerous time is between six in the evening and midnight.

31 Four times more soldiers work at that time than from six in the morning until noon. Do you see what I mean?"

32 "Aha! I get it now. Thank you so much, Pascal!"

33 "You're welcome. Now I realize the importance of graphs. No one can say that we don't need them anymore."

34 Pascal walked out of the woods. When he looked back, he saw Robin Hood waving at him.

35 Pascal waved back and said to himself, "It was a great adventure. How do I go back? Oh, I know. I should say the words *Cogito ergo sum*!"

Communication Task

1. we want for our school library
2. The result, that, out of, chose novels
3. sixty-five percent, total
4. Five out of twenty students, science-fiction books
5. However, two out of twenty students
6. survey result, I think, should get more novels
7. what, mean

Before You Read B Look and Write

1. Reviews
2. Title
3. a man who struggles to help, greedy king
4. because, shoots arrows better than soldiers
5. My opinion, It's, to tax, After all, not money but people matter

Let's Write

1. Look at, survey result
2. out of
3. In other words, chose the character
4. it's because, character is courageous
5. Next, nine students chose
6. No one, it's because, too greedy to, by others

Communication Task

1. I did a survey on the books we want for our school library.
2. The result says that thirteen out of twenty students chose novels.
3. That is sixty-five percent of the total.
4. Five out of twenty students chose science-fiction books.
5. However, only two out of twenty students chose history books.
6. From this survey result, I think the school library should get more novels.
7. Do you see what I mean?

Before You Read B Look and Write

1. Book Club: Your Reviews
2. Title: *Robin Hood*
3. Topic of the book: It's about a man who struggles to help people from the greedy king.
4. My favorite character: My favorite character is Robin Hood because he shoots arrows better than soldiers.

5. My opinion of the book: It's bad to tax too much. After all, not money but people matter the most.

Let's Write

1. Look at the survey result on "Who is your favorite character?"
2. Fifteen out of thirty students chose Hong Gildong.
3. In other words, fifty percent of the students chose the character.
4. I think it's because the character is courageous.
5. Next, nine students chose Kongiwi and six students chose Robin Hood.
6. No one chose Nolbu. Maybe it's because the character is too greedy to be liked by others.

MEMO

적중 100 + 특별부록

Plan B

우리학교 최신기출

지학 · 민찬규 교과서를 배우는

학교 시험문제 분석 · 모음 · 해설집

전국단위 학교 시험문제 수집 및 분석
출제 빈도가 높은 문제 위주로 선별
문제 풀이에 필요한 상세한 해설

중3-2
영어

지학 · 민찬규

◎ 선택형 문항의 답안은 컴퓨터용 수정 싸인펜을 사용하여 OMR 답안지에 바르게 표기하시오.
◎ 서술형 문제는 답을 답안지에 반드시 검정 볼펜으로 쓰시오.
◎ 총 30문항 100점 만점입니다. 문항별 배점은 각 문항에 표시되어 있습니다.

[서울 영등포구 ○○중]

01 다음 영영 풀이에 해당하는 단어로 적절한 것은? (3점)

to believe or say that a person is responsible for something bad or that he/she caused it

① lend
② blame
③ influence
④ exchange
⑤ frustrate

[울산 ○○중]

02 다음 영영 풀이에 해당하는 단어가 들어갈 문장으로 알맞은 것은? (3점)

a way out of a public building

① We sell good quality food at _____ prices.
② Puzzles with _____ are easy to find answers.
③ To avoid _____, let's use our real names here.
④ When there is a fire, you should find an _____.
⑤ Most people want to talk about their problems with _____ friends or family.

[부산 ○○중]

03 다음 괄호 안에서 적절한 것을 골라 답안지에 쓰시오. (3점)

[Arrive / Arriving] in her home, she saw her parents dancing.

→ _____

[경북 ○○중]

04 다음 〈보기〉 문장을 분사구문을 써서 바꿔 쓸 때 5번째로 오는 것은? (3점)

보기
Since I felt disappointed, I didn't do anything.

① anything
② do
③ feeling
④ disappointed
⑤ I

[서울 영등포구 ○○중]

05 다음 중 밑줄 친 one의 쓰임이 어색한 것은? (3점)

① One must try to obey law.
② I prefer the yellow ones.
③ We need to buy a new guitar, but we don't have enough money for one.
④ After making a pie for my mom's birthday, I asked my dad to put one in a box.
⑤ Pick the ones that are round and red first.

06 다음 중 어법상 <u>어색한</u> 것은? (3점)

① If you open this box, you will be surprised.
→ Opening this box, you will be surprised.

② As I walked along the road, I felt peaceful.
→ Walking along the road, I felt peaceful.

③ When he finished the work, he heard his doorbell ring.
→ Finishing the work, he heard his doorbell ring.

④ As I don't know him, I didn't say anything.
→ Knowing not him, I didn't say anything.

⑤ If you turn to the right, you can find me.
→ Turning to the right, you can find me.

07 다음 〈보기〉 중에서 어법상 옳은 문장을 있는 대로 고른 것은? (4점)

> **보기**
> (A) Confusing, I asked him a question.
> (B) Being tired, Jenny stayed at home all day.
> (C) He feeling sleepy, he went back to bed.
> (D) Having no classes, Jack played with his friends all day.
> (E) Knowing not what to do, we waited for the teacher.

① (A), (B)
② (B), (D)
③ (A), (C), (D)
④ (B), (D), (E)
⑤ (A), (B), (D), (E)

08 다음 빈칸에 들어갈 말이 나머지 넷과 <u>다른</u> 것은? (3점)

① Where is your car? - _____ is right there.

② I lost my wallet. So I need to buy _____.

③ My laptop is broken. _____ is under repair.

④ I bought a jacket. _____ was the newest jacket in the store.

⑤ My brother likes his new cell phone but I don't like _____.

09 다음 대화의 빈칸에 들어갈 말로 적절한 것은? (3점)

> A: I'd like to go to Busan.
> B: What is it popular for?
> A: Haeundae beach is a famous place to visit.
> B: I see. _____
> A: I can go there either by train or bus.

① What is it known for?
② What can you do there?
③ How can you get there?
④ How was taking the airplane?
⑤ How long does it take to get there?

Mina: Are you all set for the trip this weekend?

Jinho, Claire, & Henry: Yes!

Mina: Good! Don't be late! We're meeting at 11 a.m. in front of the clock tower.

Jinho: You got it! How do we get to the airport? I don't think we've decided yet.

Henry: Jinho is right. We have two choices, bus or subway.

Claire: What about the subway? It's more reliable than the bus.

Henry: (가)지하철로 2터미널에 가는 것이 가능하니?

Claire: Yes, I already checked.

Mina: Good. Okay, then let's take the subway.

10 According to the conversation, which is NOT true? (3점)

① They are all ready to go to the trip.

② There is only one way to go to the airport.

③ Claire suggests the subway is better than the bus.

④ They promised to meet in front of the clock tower.

⑤ They are going to take a subway to the airport.

11 위 대화의 밑줄 친 우리말 (가)와 일치하도록 괄호 안의 주어진 단어를 포함하여 문장을 완성하시오. (단, 의문문으로 작성할 것) (4점)

지하철로 2터미널에 가는 것이 가능하니?
(it, possible, Terminal 2, to)

→ _____ ?

→ _____

12 다음 중 짝지어진 대화가 <u>어색한</u> 것은? (3점)

① A: Oh, I didn't bring my eraser.

B: Do you want me to lend you one?

② A: I think I left my pen here.

B: Okay, let's see if one is still here.

③ A: The shoes look great on you! How do they fit?

B: Well, do you have bigger ones?

④ A: My bike is too old.

B: I think you need to buy a new one.

⑤ A: I forget my room number. Could you check it for me?

B: Sure. Just a moment, please.

[13~14] 다음 대화를 읽고 물음에 답하시오.

S: Mom, did you decide where to visit during our family trip to Jeju?

M: Almost. Come here and see the plan I made.

S: It looks good. Hmm... Mom, is it possible to visit Mirror Maze Park on our second day?

M: It sounds exciting, but I remember you said you wanted to go horseback riding.

S: I know, but I heard the park is a lot more fun. Please.

M: All right. Let's change our schedule for the second day.

S: Thank you! I'm very excited about the trip.

M: It's great to hear that (A)_____.

*S: Son, M: Mom

13 위 대화의 빈칸 (A)에 적절하지 <u>않은</u> 표현은? (3점)

① you're interested in the park

② you're happy with the schedule

③ you can't wait for the trip to Jeju

④ you're looking forward to the trip

⑤ you decided to stop changing your mind

14 위 대화의 내용과 일치하지 <u>않는</u> 것은? (3점)

① They are going to have a family trip to Jeju.

② The son wants to go horseback riding instead of visiting Mirror Maze Park.

③ Mom is not sticking to the original plan.

④ Mom is willing to change their schedule for his son.

⑤ The son is very pleased with their new schedule on the second day.

[15~17] 다음 대화를 읽고 물음에 답하시오.

휘빈: Hey, Hyeona, where are you?
현아: Oh, Hwibin, I'm coming. I'm coming.
휘빈: Good. (가)I was worried that you were losing.
현아: I think I'm okay. What about Minjun and Sanghyeon?
휘빈: They are already here at my house.
현아: Good, oh, I see the post office. (나)[get to / do / I / how / your place](내가 어떻게 너의 집에 가지) from here?
휘빈: You are almost here. Go straight for one more block. Then you will see Doil's Bakery.
현아: Doil's Bakery? Okay.
휘빈: Then turn right and go straight for about 100 meters.
현아: Turn right and go straight. Okay, thanks! I'll see you soon.

15 위 대화의 밑줄 친 (가)를 어법에 맞게 고쳐 쓰시오. (4점)

(가) I was worried that you were losing.

→ _____

16 위 대화의 밑줄 친 (나)를 우리말에 맞게 배열하시오. (4점)

(나) [get to / do / I / how / your place]
내가 어떻게 너의 집에 가지

→ _____

17 위 대화에 대한 내용으로 알 수 <u>없는</u> 것은? (3점)

① 현아는 휘빈이 집에 가고 있다.

② 휘빈이는 현아가 길을 잃었다고 걱정했었다.

③ 민준이랑 상현이는 휘빈의 집에 온 적이 있다.

④ 현아는 휘빈이의 집에 거의 근접해 있다.

⑤ 휘빈이는 현아에게 오른쪽으로 돌아서 약 100m 가량 직진하라고 말했다.

ⓐCompared the two pictures below, you can easily notice some differences. For example, the picture on the left is called a labyrinth and only has an entrance. The picture on the right ⓑis called a maze and has both an entrance and an exit.

You can find the origin of the labyrinth in Greek mythology. It is said to be a prison ⓒthat you cannot escape. But you may notice that the labyrinth has only a single path. There are no dead ends. (가)This means you don't have to worry about getting out of it when you enter it. (나)If you follow the path all the way to the end, you will reach the center. To get out, you simply have to turn around and walk back out the way you came in.

When you are in a maze, it's a different story. There are many choices to make and dead ends ⓓto frustrate you. You have to keep ⓔmaking decisions about which way to go. If you are not careful, you can easily lose your way.

[경북 ○○중]

18 위 글의 밑줄 친 부분 중, 문법적으로 어색한 것은? (3점)

① ⓐ　　　② ⓑ　　　③ ⓒ

④ ⓓ　　　⑤ ⓔ

[부산 ○○중]

19 위 글의 밑줄 친 (가)This가 의미하는 것을 〈조건〉을 준수하여 적으시오. (4점)

> 조건
> • 주어진 단어로 시작하는 완전한 문장으로 쓰시오.
> • 지문에 있는 단어만을 활용해서 쓰시오.

→ The labyrinth _____.

[경남 ○○중]

20 위 글의 밑줄 친 (나)를 분사구문으로 바꾸시오. (4점)

> (나) If you follow the path all the way to the end

→ _____

[경북 ○○중]

21 위 글에 대한 내용으로 알맞은 것은? (3점)

① labyrinth와 maze는 같은 구조를 가지고 있다.

② labyrinth의 기원은 로마 신화에서 찾을 수 있다.

③ maze에서 빠져나오기 위해서는 돌아서지 말고 곧장 앞으로 직진해야 한다.

④ maze는 labyrinth보다 다소 선택지가 적다.

⑤ maze는 조심하지 않으면 길을 잃기 쉽다.

[부산 ○○중]

22 위 글의 제목으로 가장 적절한 것은? (4점)

① How to Get Out of Labyrinths

② The Origin of Labyrinths and Mazes

③ Why Mazes Have Both Entrance and Exit

④ The Differences between Labyrinths and Mazes

⑤ Interesting Greek Mythology: Labyrinths and Mazes

Labyrinths and mazes are truly fun, but that's not the end of the story. (A)As you look at them closely, you may find the beauty of order and regularity. They may also show you how creative human beings are.

If there is a maze park on your next trip, why don't you stop and take some time to enjoy it? Surely, (B)그것은 방문할 가치가 있을 것이다!

[충북 ○○중]

23 위 글의 밑줄 친 (A)를 분사구문을 사용하여 문장을 다시 쓰시오. (4점)

> As you look at them closely, you may find the beauty of order and regularity.

→ _____

[충북 ○○중]

24 위 글의 밑줄 친 (B)의 우리말과 일치하도록 주어진 단어를 배열하여 영작할 때, 네 번째 빈칸에 오는 단어는? (3점)

그것은 방문할 가치가 있을 것이다!
(be / visiting / will / worth / it)
→ _____ _____ _____ _____ _____!

① worth
② visiting
③ will
④ it
⑤ be

When you are in a maze, it's a different story. There are many choices to make and dead ends to (가)[frustrate / please] you. You have to keep (나)[to make / making] decisions about which way to go. If you are not careful, you can easily (다)[find / lose] your way.

These days, mazes are often considered left-brain puzzles. (A) Many people willingly visit maze parks and enjoy the "planned confusion." And some of them come up with their own solutions. The easiest and most reliable (라)one is to place a hand on one wall from the very beginning. Then you just keep following that wall. (B) It's like walking in a dark room. Unfortunately, this simple method may not be effective in certain types of mazes, especially when all of the walls are not connected.

(C) In fact, they can also be printed or drawn on paper. Here is one as an example. This is called a number maze. You start from point A and have to go in the order of $1 \rightarrow 9 \rightarrow 8 \rightarrow 5 \rightarrow 1 \rightarrow 9 \rightarrow \cdots$. Why don't you give it a try? You have 30 seconds to escape!

Labyrinths and mazes are truly fun, but that's not the end of the story. (D) Looking at them closely, you may find the beauty of order and regularity. ⓐ그것들은 또한 인간이 얼마나 창조적인가를 보여 줄지도 모른다.

If there is a maze park on your next trip, why don't you stop and take some time to enjoy it? It will surely be worth visiting! (E)

[충북 ○○중]

25 위 글의 (가)~(다)에 들어갈 말이 바르게 짝지어진 것은? (4점)

	(가)	(나)	(다)
①	frustrate	to make	lose
②	please	making	find
③	frustrate	making	lose
④	please	to make	find
⑤	frustrate	making	find

26 위 글의 흐름상 주어진 문장이 들어가야 할 곳으로 가장 적절한 것은? (3점)

> Mazes are made with a variety of different materials, like walls and rooms, hedges, bricks, mirrors, and even snow.

① (A) ② (B) ③ (C) ④ (D) ⑤ (E)

27 위 글의 ⓐ를 영작한 것으로 가장 적절한 것은? (3점)

① They may also show you how creative human beings are.
② They may also show you what creative human beings.
③ They can also show you what creative human beings are.
④ They may also show how creative human beings are you.
⑤ They can also show how creative human beings are you.

28 위 글의 밑줄 친 (라)one이 가리키는 것으로 가장 적절한 것은? (3점)

① left-brain puzzle   ② maze park
③ solution   ④ wall
⑤ dark room

[29~30] 다음 글을 읽고 물음에 답하시오.

USA — Pineapple Garden Maze
If you visit Oahu, Hawaii, the Pineapple Garden Maze is a must-see. It is the world's longest maze, and it attracts visitors from around the world. The maze has 11,400 native plants and covers about 5 kilometers.

England — Hampton Court Maze
The oldest hedge maze in Britain is the Hampton Court Maze. It was built in 1689. Hundred of thousands of people visit this maze that was created during the time of William of Orange.

Italy — Labirinto di Villa Pasani
It was created in 1720 and is known as the most difficult one to solve. Part of the problem is the height of the hedges. They are so high that people can't see over them. You get a perfect view only once you've got to the center and climbed the stairs to the top of the tower.

29 위 글의 내용과 일치하는 것은? (4점)

① 파인애플 정원 미로는 런던에 있다.
② 파인애플 정원 미로는 세계에서 가장 복잡한 미로이다.
③ 미국의 햄프턴 궁정 미로는 1689년에 만들어졌다.
④ 이탈리아의 빌라파사니 미로의 산울타리는 너무 높아서 사람들은 그 너머를 볼 수가 없다.
⑤ 이탈리아의 빌라파사니 미로의 입구에 있는 탑의 입구에 있는 계단을 올라가야만 완전한 시야를 확보하게 된다.

30 위 글의 제목으로 적절한 것은? (3점)

① Number Maze
② Mazes Around the World
③ How to Get Out of a Maze
④ The Origin of the Famous Mazes
⑤ Finding Your Own Path in Your Life

3학년 영어 2학기 중간고사(5과) 2회

문항수 : 선택형(19문항) 서술형(11문항)

20 . . .

[경북 ○○중]

01 다음 어휘의 영영 풀이로 어색한 것은? (3점)

① certain: not knowing what to do or believe, or not able to decide about something

② exit: the door through which you might leave a building

③ confusion: a situation in which people do not understand what is happening or what they should do

④ leap: to jump from a surface

⑤ origin: the beginning or cause of something

[충북 ○○중]

02 다음 빈칸에 들어갈 단어를 〈보기〉에서 고를 때 완성할 수 없는 문장은? (단, 중복 사용 불가) (3점)

보기
confusion / influence / leap / exit / material

① Parents usually _____ their children greatly.

② Clothes are made with a variety of _____s.

③ When there is a fire, you should find a(n) _____.

④ It is important not to miss any _____ in your life.

⑤ Some jumping frogs can _____ more than ten times their length.

[서울 강동구 ○○중]

03 다음 밑줄 친 부분 중 어법상 어색한 것은? (2점)

① I lost my pencil case. I must buy it.

② He bought a camera, and it was nice.

③ John has a blue car, but I have a red one.

④ Do you have a notebook? ‑ Yes, I have one.

⑤ My uncle bought me a watch. I like it very much.

[부산 ○○중]

04 다음 〈조건〉을 준수하여 우리말에 맞게 영어로 쓰시오. (3점)

지도를 자세히 보면, 너는 우리 학교를 찾을 수 있다.

→ _____.

(the map / our school / look at / closely)

조건
• 분사구문을 이용하시오.
• 주어진 단어를 모두 활용하고, 필요한 단어를 추가로 적으시오.
• 필요시 단어의 형태를 바꾸시오.

→ _____

05 다음 〈조건〉을 준수하여 알맞은 문장으로 바꿔 쓰시오. (3점)

> **조건**
> • 분사구문을 이용하시오.
> • 의미 변화 없이, 완전한 하나의 문장으로 작성
>   하시오.

> When the dog saw the stranger, it began to
> bark.

→ _____

06 다음 중 어법상 올바른 문장을 <u>모두</u> 고른 것은? (3점)

> ⓐ Fix the air conditioner or buy a new it.
> ⓑ Turning off the computer, she went to
>   bed.
> ⓒ If you want this watch, I'll give it to you.
> ⓓ My brother is considered the toy train
>   valuable.
> ⓔ My mom likes green apples better than
>   red ones.
> ⓕ Wearing sunscreen will keep you safely
>   from sunburn.

① ⓐ, ⓒ, ⓓ
② ⓐ, ⓔ, ⓕ
③ ⓑ, ⓒ, ⓓ
④ ⓑ, ⓒ, ⓔ
⑤ ⓒ, ⓓ, ⓕ

07 다음 각 문장을 다음과 같이 바꾸어 썼을 때 의미가 <u>달라지는</u>
것은? (3점)

① Seeing the stranger, the dog began to bark.
  → When the dog saw the stranger, it began to
    bark.
② Humming a song only he knew, Charlie
  walked down the street.
  → As Charlie hummed a song only he knew,
    he walked down the street.
③ Reading books may be a hard task, but it is
  always good for your soul.
  → Because reading books may be a hard
    task, it is always good for your soul.
④ Walking straight for two blocks, you will
  reach the library.
  → If you walk straight for two blocks, you
    will reach the library.
⑤ Locking the door tight, he turned around and
  walked away.
  → After he locked the door tight, he turned
    around and walked away.

08 다음 대화를 읽고 (A), (B)에 들어갈 말을 주어진 단어를 포함
하여 우리말 표현에 맞게 영작하시오. (4점)

> A: (A)도서관에 어떻게 가나요?
> B: (B)교차로에서 오른쪽으로 돌아.
>   After that, go straight for 100 meters.

(A) (to the library)

→ _____

(B) (at the crossroad)

→ _____

[9~11] 다음 대화를 읽고 물음에 답하시오.

B: What are you reading, Alice?

(A) Not really. I forgot the name of the monster.

(B) Labyrinth? Wasn't that an old mythological prison to keep the half-man, half-bull monster?

(C) It's about the origin of the labyrinth.

(D) Oh, Juwon, you know about the story.

G: The Minotaur. The king of Crete was angry at it and put it in a labyrinth.

B: Interesting! Alice, (가)책을 빌리는 게 가능할까 after you're finished with it?

G: Sure, no problem. I will lend it to you this Friday.

*B: Juwon, G: Alice

[경남 ○○중]

09 자연스러운 대화가 되도록 (A)~(D)를 바르게 배열한 것은?
(3점)

① (A) - (C) - (B) - (D)

② (A) - (D) - (C) - (B)

③ (B) - (A) - (D) - (C)

④ (C) - (B) - (D) - (A)

⑤ (C) - (B) - (A) - (D)

[경남 ○○중]

10 위 대화의 밑줄 친 (가)의 표현을 영어 두 단어를 추가하여 쓰시오.
(3점)

(가)책을 빌리는 게 가능할까?
→ Is it _____ to _____ the book

→ _____ , _____

[서울 강동구 ○○중]

11 위 대화를 올바르게 이해한 사람들은?
(3점)

- Paik: Juwon is expecting to get the book this Friday.
- Kim: The monster was put in an old mythological prison.
- Yeon: Alice and Juwon already know the monster's name.
- Choi: The boy fully knows the story they are talking about.
- Lee: What Alice is reading is about the origin of the labyrinth.

① Paik, Yeon

② Kim, Choi

③ Paik, Kim, Lee

④ Kim, Yeon, Lee

⑤ Yeon, Choi, Lee

[12~13] 다음 대화를 읽고 물음에 답하시오.

Andrew: Hey, Suji, where are you?

Suji: Oh, Andrew, I'm coming. I'm coming.

Andrew: Good. I was worried that you were lost.

Suji: I think I'm okay. What about Mason and Jian?

Andrew: They are already here at my house.

Suji: Good! Oh, I see the post office. (A)_____ _____.

Andrew: You are almost here. (B)_____. Then you will see Kim's Bakery.

Suji: Kim's Bakery? Okay ....

Andrew: Then (C)_____ and (D)_____.

Suji: Okay, thanks! I'll see you soon.

12 위 대화의 빈칸 (A)에 들어갈 수 <u>없는</u> 것은?　　(3점)

① Tell me where your house is from here.

② How can I get to your house from here?

③ How long does it take to go to your house from here?

④ Can you tell me the way to your house from here?

⑤ Could you tell me how to get to your house from here?

[14~16] 다음 대화를 읽고 물음에 답하시오.

> G: Mom, did you decide where to visit during our family trip to Jeju?
>
> W: (가)_____. Come here and see the plan I made.
>
> G: It looks good. Hmm... Mom, (A)_____ Mirror Maze Park on our second day?
>
> W: It sounds exciting, but I remember you said you wanted to go horseback riding.
>
> G: I know, but I heard the park is a lot more fun. Please...
>
> W: (나)_____. Let's change our schedule for the second day.
>
> G: Thank you! I'm very excited about the trip.
>
> W: It's great to hear that you're looking forward to the trip.
>
> *G: Girl, W: Woman

14 위 대화의 빈칸 (가)와 (나)에 적절한 표현을 보기에서 찾아 쓰시오.　　(4점)

> **보기**
>
> • Not at all.　　　• Almost.
> • All right.　　　• I'm sorry.

(가): _____

(나): _____

13 위 대화의 빈칸 (B)~(D)에 들어갈 문장을 다음 그림을 보고 주어진 단어를 활용하여 영어로 완성하시오.　　(6점)

(B)_____

　　(one more block)

(C)_____

　　(right)

(D)_____

　　(for about 100 meters)

15 위 대화의 빈칸 (A) 부분에 들어갈 내용으로 적절하지 않은 것은?　　(3점)

① can we go to

② how about visiting

③ why don't we go to

④ is it possible to visit

⑤ why do you want to visit

16 위 대화의 내용과 일치하는 것은? (정답 2개)   (3점)

① 엄마는 여행 중 방문할 곳을 거의 완성했다.
② 딸은 여행 첫날에 거울 미로공원에 가고 싶어 한다.
③ 딸은 승마를 하고 싶어 했었다.
④ 엄마는 딸의 여행 계획 변경에 반대했다.
⑤ 엄마는 거울 미로공원에 관심이 없다.

17 다음 대화의 빈칸 (가)와 (나)에 적절한 표현을 〈보기〉에서 찾아 쓰시오.   (4점)

B: Minju, we need a new guitar but we don't have enough money for one.
G: What do you think of having a concert to raise money? We can introduce our new song, too.
B: (가)_____ It'll be like (나)"_____."
G: That's right. Let's first make a poster for our concert.

*B: Boy, G: Girl

┌─ 보기 ─
• What a great idea!
• What a stupid idea!
• Better late than never.
• Killing two birds with one stone.
└─

(가)_____

(나)_____

18 다음 대화가 자연스러운 대화가 되도록 빈칸 (A)에 들어갈 내용을 순서대로 배열한 것은?   (3점)

A: Hi, do you need any help?

(A)

B: Great! Thank you very much for your help.
A: My pleasure. Enjoy your dinner.

ⓐ Hmm... What about Papa Chen's? Their food is good and the prices are reasonable.
ⓑ Yes, please. Could you suggest a good Chinese restaurant in this building? I can't decide between the two.
ⓒ It's on the fourth floor. You can use the elevator over there. Papa Chen's is next to the elevator.
ⓓ Sounds great! How do I get to the restaurant?

① ⓐ - ⓑ - ⓓ - ⓒ
② ⓐ - ⓓ - ⓒ - ⓑ
③ ⓑ - ⓒ - ⓐ - ⓓ
④ ⓑ - ⓐ - ⓓ - ⓒ
⑤ ⓒ - ⓓ - ⓑ - ⓐ

When you are in a maze, it's a different story. There are many choices to make and dead ends to frustrate you. You have to keep making decisions about which way to go. If you are not careful, you can easily lose your way.

These days, mazes are often considered left-brain puzzles. (A) Many people willingly visit maze parks and enjoy the "(가)_____." (B) And some of them come up with their own solutions. (C) ⓐ_____ you just keep following that wall. (D) It's like walking in a dark room. (E) ⓑ_____, this simple method may not be effective in certain types of mazes, especially when all of the walls are not connected.

19 위 글에서 다음 주어진 문장이 들어갈 위치로 가장 알맞은 곳은? (3점)

> The easiest and most reliable one is to place a hand on one wall from the very beginning.

① (A)   ② (B)   ③ (C)

④ (D)   ⑤ (E)

20 위 글의 빈칸 ⓐ, ⓑ에 들어갈 말이 맞게 짝지어진 것은? (3점)

	ⓐ	ⓑ
①	Then	Luckily
②	Then	Unfortunately
③	In addition	Unfortunately
④	In addition	Luckily
⑤	As a result	Luckily

21 위 글의 흐름상 빈칸 (가)에 들어갈 말로 적절한 것은? (3점)

① planned order

② effective solution

③ creative decision

④ natural beauty

⑤ planned confusion

22 위 글의 내용과 일치하지 <u>않는</u> 것은? (3점)

① When you are in a maze, you should choose carefully which way to go.

② Recently people think of mazes as left-brain puzzles.

③ Many people visit maze parks to enjoy solving the planned confusion.

④ The easiest solution to escape mazes is to place a hand on one wall and keep following it.

⑤ It is effective to use the easiest and most reliable way in all types of mazes.

23 위 글을 읽고, 주어진 질문의 답을 찾아 영어로 쓰시오. (반드시 주어, 동사가 있는 문장으로 쓰시오.)   (4점)

> Q: What do you have to keep doing when you are in a maze?
> A: _____

→ _____

24 위 글의 (A)~(C)를 순서에 맞게 배열한 것으로 가장 적절한 것은?   (3점)

① (A) - (C) - (B)
② (B) - (A) - (C)
③ (B) - (C) - (A)
④ (C) - (A) - (B)
⑤ (C) - (B) - (A)

25 위 글의 밑줄 친 (가)order와 같은 의미로 쓰인 것은?   (3점)

① Is it too late to cancel my <u>order</u>?
② Your <u>order</u> will arrive within 5 days.
③ The captain had to give the <u>order</u> to abandon ship.
④ I'd like to place an <u>order</u> for five copies of this book.
⑤ Make sure that you put the books back in the right <u>order</u>.

[24~26] 다음 글을 읽고 물음에 답하시오.

(A) In fact, they can also be printed or drawn on paper.
(B) Mazes are made with a variety of different materials, like walls and rooms, hedges, bricks, mirrors, and even snow.
(C) Here is one as an example. This is called a number maze.
You start from point A and have to go in the order of 1 → 9 → 8 → 5 → 1 → 9 → ⋯. Why don't you give it a try? You have 30 seconds to escape!

Labyrinths and mazes are truly fun, but that's not the end of the story. Looking at them closely, you may find the beauty of (가)<u>order</u> and regularity. (나)<u>그것들은 또한 인간이 얼마나 창조적인가를 너에게 보여줄지도 모른다.</u>

If there is a maze park on your next trip, why don't you stop and take some time to enjoy it? (다)<u>그것은 틀림없이 방문할 가치가 있을 것이다!</u>

26 위 글의 밑줄 친 (나), (다)의 우리말 의미에 맞게 주어진 단어를 활용하여 문장을 완성하시오.   (5점)

> (나) They may also show you _____
> _____.
> (creative / human beings)
>
> (다) _____
> (will / worth / surely)

(나) _____
(다) _____

(A)<u>Comparing the two pictures below</u>, you can easily notice some differences. For example, the picture on the left is called a labyrinth and only has an entrance. The picture on the right is called a maze and has both an entrance and an exit.

You can find the origin of the labyrinth in Greek mythology. ⓐ<u>It</u> is said to be a prison that you cannot escape. But you may notice that the labyrinth has only a single path. There are no dead ends. ⓑ<u>This</u> means you don't have to worry about getting out of it when you enter it. (B)<u>Following</u> the path all the way to the end, you will reach the center. To get out, you simply have to turn around and walk back out the way you came in.

[울산 ○○중]

28 위 글의 밑줄 친 (A), (B)를 의미에 알맞게 '접속사+주어+동사'의 형태를 사용하여 쓰시오.　(4점)

(A) _____

(B) _____

[울산 ○○중]

29 위 글의 밑줄 친 ⓐ, ⓑ가 가리키는 것을 영어로 쓰시오.　(4점)

ⓐ It: _____

ⓑ This: _____

[울산 ○○중]

27 위 글의 제목으로 가장 알맞은 것은?　(3점)

① The Reason Why People Made a Labyrinth and a Maze

② The Origin of a Labyrinth and a Maze

③ How To Get Out of a Labyrinth and a Maze

④ The Most Effective Way of Escaping a Maze

⑤ The Differences Between a Labyrinth and a Maze

[충북 ○○중]

30 위 글의 내용과 일치하지 <u>않는</u> 것은?　(3점)

① The labyrinth only has an entrance.

② The maze has an entrance and an exit.

③ The labyrinth has only a single path, without dead ends.

④ You can escape the labyrinth easily because it has only one path.

⑤ If you enter the labyrinth, you cannot reach the center.

◎ 선택형 문항의 답안은 컴퓨터용 수정 싸인펜을 사용하여 OMR 답안지에 바르게 표기하시오.
◎ 서술형 문제는 답을 답안지에 반드시 검정 볼펜으로 쓰시오.
◎ 총 30문항 100점 만점입니다. 문항별 배점은 각 문항에 표시되어 있습니다.

[서울 강동구 ○○중]

01 다음 중 빈칸에 공통으로 들어갈 단어의 의미에 해당되는 것은? (3점)

> • Let's _____ in touch.
> • _____ the chance.

① 놓치다, 가지고 있다
② 반복하다, 유지하다
③ 반복하다, 그리워하다
④ 유지하다, 그리워하다
⑤ 유지하다, 가지고 있다

[울산 ○○중]

02 다음 단어와 영영 풀이의 연결이 어색한 것은? (3점)

① leap: to jump high or a long way
② disagree: to have the same opinion about something
③ harm: to cause a person or animals physical injury, usually on purpose
④ influence: to make somebody/something behave in a particular way
⑤ regret: to feel sorry about something you have done or about something that you haven't done

[서울 강동구 ○○중]

03 다음 주어진 문장의 한 부분을 강조한 문장으로 알맞지 않은 것은? (3점)

> Sean met Jane at the station.

① Sean did meet Jane at the station.
② It was met that Sean at the station.
③ It was Sean who met Jane at the station.
④ It was Jane who Sean met at the station.
⑤ It was at the station that Sean met Jane.

[경북 ○○중]

04 다음 중 문법적 성질이 다른 하나는? (3점)

① It was my computer that Mike broke.
② It was yesterday that Ann saw Jiho.
③ It is at the museum that we have met.
④ It is true that Yumin will get a perfect score in the exam.
⑤ It was I who was hanging out with Dongmi.

[서울 강동구 ○○중]

05 다음 중 however의 쓰임이 바르지 않은 것은? (3점)

① I was tired. However, I couldn't sleep.
② He was upset. He didn't show his feelings, however.
③ It was snowing and cold. I turned on the heater, however.
④ The boy went inside the maze. However, he couldn't find the exit.
⑤ You shouldn't judge a book by its cover. However, clothes make the man.

06 다음 문장의 밑줄 친 부분을 강조하고자 할 때, It으로 시작하는 문장을 완성하시오. (5점)

> (A) I ride a bike <u>at the park</u>.
> (B) <u>Tom</u> broke the window.

(A) It_____.

(B) It_____.

08 다음 (A)~(D)를 자연스러운 대화가 되도록 바르게 배열한 것은? (3점)

> (A) I agree. Then let's take a break after we finish this part.
> (B) Like the saying goes, "All work and no play makes Jack a dull boy."
> (C) Emma, let's take a break.
> (D) What? We've only studied for 30 minutes.

① (A) - (B) - (C) - (D)

② (A) - (C) - (D) - (B)

③ (C) - (A) - (D) - (B)

④ (C) - (D) - (B) - (A)

⑤ (C) - (D) - (A) - (B)

07 다음 대화의 문맥상 (A), (B)에 들어가야 할 어구로 가장 적절한 것은? (3점)

> 채현: Yubin, what are you doing?
> 유빈: I'm watching a movie about AI robots. It's really (A)_____. What do you think of them?
> 채현: In my opinion, they will cause problems. AI robots will (B)_____ jobs from people.

	(A)	(B)
①	fascinating	get in
②	fascinating	take away
③	fascinated	take up
④	fascinated	take away
⑤	fascinating	take up

09 다음 대화의 빈칸에 들어갈 말로 알맞은 것은? (3점)

> A:_____ eating fast food every day?
> B: I think it's unhealthy.

① How come

② What makes you

③ Do you agree that

④ How is your opinion

⑤ What do you think of

10 다음 대화의 빈칸에 알맞은 속담은? (3점)

> B: I don't think we should talk about others when they are not there.
> G: Why do you say that?
> B: Well, I had a fight with Jimin because I talked about her test results with Sam.
> G: Oh, why did you do that?
> B: I never thought that she would find out.
> G: Well, like the saying goes, "_____"
> B: I agree. I've learned my lesson.

① Walls have ears.

② Better late than never.

③ Birds of a feather flock together.

④ A bad workman blames his tools.

⑤ What goes around comes around.

11 다음 대화의 빈칸에 들어갈 문장으로 가장 알맞은 것은? (3점)

> B: Look! People are just leaving their trash behind!
> G: Oh, no! If we harm the environment, we'll be the ones who regret it in the end.
> B: I agree. Like the saying goes, "_____"
> G: You're right. Let's help the Earth by taking our trash with us.

① You are what you eat.

② What goes around comes around.

③ All work and no play makes Jack a dull boy.

④ Two heads are better than one.

⑤ Killing two birds with one stone.

12 다음 대화를 읽고, ⓐ~ⓔ의 우리말을 영작한 것 중 그 표현이 옳지 않은 것은? (4점)

> G: Dohun, what are you doing?
> B: ⓐ나는 AI 로봇에 관한 영화를 보고 있어. It's really fascinating. ⓑ너는 그것들에 대해 어떻게 생각해?
> G: ⓒ내 의견으로는 그것들은 문제를 야기할 거야. AI robots will take jobs away from people.
> B: Well, ⓓ나는 여전히 그것들이 유용하다고 생각해. There is a science festival introducing AI robots. ⓔ가서 그것들에 대해 더 많이 알아보는 것은 어때?
> G: Sounds good.

① ⓐ: I'm watching a movie about AI robots.

② ⓑ: What do you think of them?

③ ⓒ: In my opinion, they will cause problems.

④ ⓓ: I still think they are useless.

⑤ ⓔ: Why don't we go and find out more about them?

13 다음 대화의 밑줄 친 단어의 뜻풀이가 바르지 <u>않은</u> 것은? (4점)

---

(1)

B: Look! People are just ⓐ<u>leaving</u> their trash <u>behind</u>!

G: Oh, no! If we ⓑ<u>harm</u> the environment, we'll be the ones who regret it ⓒ<u>in the end</u>.

(2)

B: Minju, we need a new guitar but we don't have enough money for one.

G: What do you think of having a concert to ⓓ<u>raise</u> money? We can introduce our new song, too.

(3)

G: Juwon, what's the matter?

B: Mr. Han told us to ⓔ<u>hand in</u> the art project yesterday but I still haven't finished it.

---

① ⓐ leave ~ behind : ~를 두고 가다

② ⓑ harm : 손상시키다

③ ⓒ in the end : 결국

④ ⓓ raise : 올리다

⑤ ⓔ hand in : ~를 제출하다

[14~16] 다음 대화를 읽고 물음에 답하시오.

W: Jacob, can you help me?

B: What is it, Mom?

W: Well, I got a message from my friend, but I don't understand what some letters of it mean.

B: Let me see. Hmm... ASAP means "as soon as possible" and HAND means "Have a nice day."

W: Oh, I see.

B: (가)엄마, 이러한 '두문자어'들에 대해서 어떻게 생각하세요?

W: I think they are destroying the language. What do you think?

B: In my opinion, they are fun and easy to use.

14 다음 주어진 질문에 대한 답을 위 대화에서 찾아 쓰시오. (3점)

Q: What does HAND mean?
A: _____

→ _____

15 위 대화의 밑줄 친 (가)의 표현을 영어 3단어를 추가하여 완성하시오. (4점)

(가) What do _____ _____ of these _____, Mom?

→ _____

16 위 대화의 내용으로 바르지 <u>않은</u> 것은?　　(3점)

① Jacob thinks that people can use acronyms easily.

② ASAP and HAND are the examples of acronyms.

③ Mom wants Jacob to help her to understand a message from her friend.

④ Jacob doesn't agree that acronyms destroy the language.

⑤ Mom doesn't understand any parts of the message she got from her friend.

17 다음 중 대화가 자연스러운 것은?　　(3점)

① A: Students should have pocket money.

　 B: I agree. They will rely on their parents too much.

② A: Students should have a part-time job.

　 B: I agree. They will have more time to study.

③ A: What do you think of having longer lunch breaks?

　 B: I disagree. Students will have more time to eat.

④ A: What do you think of having no tests at school?

　 B: I agree. Students will not review the lessons.

⑤ A: What do you think of posting pictures online?

　 B: I disagree. Some people may use your pictures in a bad way.

18 다음 대화를 구성할 때, 흐름상 가장 자연스럽게 순서대로 나열한 것은?　　(4점)

> B: Yura, what are you doing?
>
> G: I'm posting my pictures on the internet. Come and have a look.
>
> B: _____
>
> G: _____
>
> B: _____
>
> G: _____
>
> B: No problem.

> ⓐ Come to think of it, I should be more careful with my pictures. Thanks for your advice.
>
> ⓑ I disagree. There might be some people who will use your pictures in a bad way.
>
> ⓒ Well, my friends like my posts a lot. I think it's a good way to get to know one another.
>
> ⓓ There are so many pictures that show your everyday life. Isn't it dangerous?

① ⓑ-ⓒ-ⓐ-ⓓ

② ⓑ-ⓓ-ⓒ-ⓐ

③ ⓒ-ⓑ-ⓐ-ⓓ

④ ⓓ-ⓑ-ⓒ-ⓐ

⑤ ⓓ-ⓒ-ⓑ-ⓐ

Look before you leap: Check what is in front of you before making a decision.

I totally agree. (A) We should always be careful before we decide to do something. (B) Then we'll be happy with the results of our decisions. (C) However, if we don't take time to think things over, we may regret it. (D) Also, we'll make mistakes if we do something without giving it a second thought. (E)

Posted by Suzi Kang

I don't agree. Opportunities don't come often. If there is a chance, we should grab it. Or, it will be too late. Last year, I was asked to be the captain of the school hockey team. However, I took too much time to decide, so another friend became the captain. Now, I regret it. As the saying goes, "(가)_____."

Posted by Brian Pearson

19 위 글에서 다음 문장이 들어갈 위치로 가장 알맞은 것은? (3점)

As a result, it will take us more time to fix.

① (A)   ② (B)   ③ (C)
④ (D)   ⑤ (E)

20 위 글의 빈칸 (가)에 들어갈 속담으로 알맞은 것은? (3점)

① Practice makes perfect.
② Strike while the iron is hot.
③ Don't judge a book by its cover.
④ A bad workman blames his tools.
⑤ An apple a day keeps the doctor away.

21 다음 중 위 글에 나온 표현의 의미가 바르지 <u>않은</u> 것은? (3점)

① before you leap: 뛰기 전에
② think things over: 심사숙고하다
③ regret it: 그것을 후회하다
④ give it a second thought: 다른 생각을 하다
⑤ take us more time: 더 시간이 걸리다

22 위 글을 읽고, 주어진 어구를 활용하여 〈보기〉에서 설명하고 있는 속담을 쓰시오. (4점)

> **보기**
> 1) Meaning: To solve two problems with one single action.
> 2) Example: When I jog, I listen to English rap music.

→ _____

(kill / one stone)

23 위 글의 내용으로 바른 것은? (3점)

① Brian became the captain of the hockey team.
② Suzi Kang disagrees that you should look before you leap.
③ Brian didn't give it a second thought when he was asked to be a captain.
④ Suzi Kang thinks that if you do something in a hurry, you'll make mistakes.
⑤ Brian thinks that if there is a chance, you should grab it with thinking it over.

Every now and then, words of wisdom have influenced people and changed their lives in a great way. For example, "Actions speak louder than words," means the following: (A)what you do is more important than what you say. So people try to do things instead of just saying something. (B)_____, some people have different opinions. To them, it is ⓐ_____ that speak louder than ⓑ_____. How? They think that ⓒ_____ can influence others to do good things. It is natural to have different ideas. Let's take a look at some other proverbs upside down.

25 위 글의 흐름상 빈칸 ⓐ~ⓒ에 알맞은 것은?   (4점)

	ⓐ	ⓑ	ⓒ
①	words	actions	words
②	words	actions	actions
③	words	words	actions
④	actions	words	actions
⑤	actions	words	words

26 위 글의 빈칸 (B)에 들어갈 가장 알맞은 표현은?   (3점)

① Also
② Then
③ However
④ As a result
⑤ Unfortunately

27 위 글 다음에 이어질 내용으로 알맞은 것은?   (3점)

① 말의 중요성
② 속담과 인간 행동의 관계
③ 말보다 행동이 중요한 이유
④ 다양한 의견을 가질 수 있는 속담 제시
⑤ 세계 여러 나라의 속담과 한국 속담의 비교

24 위 글의 밑줄 친 (A)를 우리말로 해석하시오.   (3점)

(A) what you do is more important than what you say.

→ _____

[28~30] 다음 글을 읽고, 물음에 답하시오.

Out of sight, out of mind: Something is easily forgotten if it is not near us.

I agree with this saying. I had a close friend from elementary school. Sadly, we went to different middle schools. At first, we met two to three times a week. However, it was hard to keep in touch. ⓐWe started to spend more time with our new friends. I started thinking less and less about him and more and more about my new friends. ⓑNow, we have stopped talking or seeing each other.

Posted by Anna Brown

I disagree with your opinion. I was really close with my neighbor, Jenny. She was from America and we liked the same basketball team. ⓒWe spent a lot of time watching games together. Then her family moved away three years ago. ⓓI haven't seen her since, but I still remember the times we had. I miss her more and more as time goes by. ⓔIt is the quality of time that make people remember each other.

Posted by Jaeha Park

Well, what is your opinion? There is no right or wrong answer. (A)You should decide what is best for you.

29 위 글에서 Anna Brown이 말하고자 하는 것과 일치하는 것은?
(4점)

① If you want true friends, be a good listener.
② Friends are the most important part of your life.
③ Childhood friendship is the best of all friendships.
④ If you can't see someone, it's easy to forget them.
⑤ If a friend moves away, you have to write a letter regularly.

30 위 글의 밑줄 친 (A)를 주어진 우리말에 맞게 강조하는 문장으로 쓰시오.
(4점)

(A) You should decide what is best for you.
해석: 당신에게 최고인 것을 결정해야 하는 사람은 바로 당신이다.

조건
• 강조 구문 (It is[was] ~ that …)을 사용할 것.

→ _____

28 위 글의 ⓐ~ⓔ 중에서 어법상 옳지 <u>않은</u> 것은?
(3점)

① ⓐ   ② ⓑ   ③ ⓒ
④ ⓓ   ⑤ ⓔ

◎ 선택형 문항의 답안은 컴퓨터용 수정 싸인펜을 사용
하여 OMR 답안지에 바르게 표기하시오.
◎ 서술형 문제는 답을 답안지에 반드시 검정 볼펜으
로 쓰시오.
◎ 총 30문항 100점 만점입니다. 문항별 배점은 각
문항에 표시되어 있습니다.

[경북 ○○중]

01 다음 (A), (B) 두 문장의 빈칸에 공통으로 들어갈 단어로 가장
알맞은 것은? (3점)

(A) The media has a powerful _____
on a public opinion.
(B) A number of social factors _____
our life.

① opportunity
② influence
③ leap
④ captain
⑤ regret

[서울 영등포구 ○○중]

02 다음 중 단어의 영영 풀이가 올바른 것은? (3점)

① strike: to hit someone or something softly
② straw: the wet roots of wheat and other grain
plants
③ explain: to make something unclear or
uneasy to understand
④ labyrinth: a simple series of paths, which it is
difficult to find your way through
⑤ reliable: able to be trusted to do what is
needed

[서울 영등포구 ○○중]

03 다음 중 단어의 뜻풀이가 올바른 것을 <u>모두</u> 골라 묶은 것은?
(3점)

(A) independent - being able to stay or do
something alone
(B) frightening - extremely good
(C) cause - to look at how two things are
different
(D) raise - to collect money
(E) regret - to feel sad or sorry about
something

① (A), (B), (D)
② (A), (C), (D)
③ (A), (D), (E)
④ (B), (C), (E)
⑤ (C), (D), (E)

[서울 영등포구 ○○중]

04 다음 각 문장의 밑줄 친 부분을 강조한 문장을 만든 것 중 어법
상 <u>잘못된</u> 것은? (3점)

① I met Jenny <u>in the park</u>.
→ It was in the park that I met Jenny.
② He bought <u>a movie ticket</u> for me.
→ It was a movie ticket that he bought for
me.
③ Frogs come out of the water <u>when it rains</u>.
→ It is when it rains that frogs come out of
the water.
④ <u>Greg</u> introduced me to this game.
→ It was Greg who introduced me to this
game.
⑤ I <u>threw away</u> the trash yesterday.
→ It was threw away that I trash yesterday.

05 다음 중 문장이 올바른 것은? (3점)

① It was my uncle who lives in Mexico.

② It was at the station that Sean met Jane.

③ It was March that we met each other.

④ It was Chris who he took my dog for a walk.

⑤ It was went hiking that Lisa with Jinsu last Friday.

07 다음 대화의 빈칸에 어울리는 속담으로 알맞은 것은? (3점)

> A: What do you think of talking behind someone's back?
> B: I think it's rude. Remember, _____.

① Walls have ears.

② You are what you eat.

③ Two heads are better than one.

④ Killing two birds with one stone.

⑤ What goes around comes around.

06 다음 중 대화가 가장 자연스러운 것은? (3점)

① A: What is the book about?

  B: It was interesting.

② A: Don't be late! We're meeting at 11 a.m. in front of the clock tower.

  B: You got it!

③ A: Which did you like better, the movie or the book?

  B: It was fun to compare the movie with the original book.

④ A: It sounds exciting, but I remember you said you wanted to go horseback riding.

  B: Did you decide where to visit during our trip to Jeju?

⑤ A: Is it possible to exchange these white shoes for the red ones?

  B: But I think that red will look better on me.

08 다음 대화의 밑줄 친 부분이 공통으로 가리키는 것은? (3점)

> G: Dohun, what are you doing?
> B: I'm watching a movie about AI robots. It's really fascinating. What do you think of <u>them</u>?
> G: In my opinion, <u>they</u> will cause problems. AI robots will take jobs away from people.
> B: Well, I still think <u>they</u> are useful. There is a science festival introducing AI robots. Why don't we go and find out more about <u>them</u>?
> G: Sounds good.

① people

② AI robots

③ problems

④ science festivals

⑤ movies about AI robots

[9~10] 다음 대화를 읽고 물음에 답하시오.

경빈: Doil, what are you doing?

도일: I'm ⓐposting my pictures on the Internet. Come and have a look.

경빈: There are so ⓑmany pictures that show your everyday life. Isn't it dangerous?

도일: Well, my friends like my posts a lot. I think it's a good way to get to know ⓒone another.

경빈: I ⓓagree. I think you should be more careful with it. (가)_____

도일: Come to think of ⓔit, I should be more careful with my pictures. Thanks for your advice.

경빈: No problem.

[경북 ○○중]

09 위 대화의 ⓐ~ⓔ 중 문맥이나 어법상 <u>어색한</u> 것은? (3점)

① ⓐ 　　② ⓑ 　　③ ⓒ

④ ⓓ 　　⑤ ⓔ

[서울 강동구 ○○중]

10 위 대화의 흐름상 빈칸 (가)에 들어갈 내용으로 가장 알맞은 것은? (3점)

① 사진을 악용하는 사람이 있을 수도 있어.

② 서로를 알아 가는 데 좋은 방법이야.

③ 조심하면 금방 친해질 수 있어.

④ 사진을 보고 사람들이 좋아해.

⑤ 인터넷은 위험하지 않아.

[11~12] 다음 대화를 읽고 물음에 답하시오.

Claire: Jinho, what's the matter? You look upset.

Jinho: I had a fight with Harry.

Claire: Why? What happened?

Jinho: We both wanted to use the same music room at the same time.

Claire: I don't think ⓐthere are enough music rooms to practice in after school.

Jinho: I agree. What do you think of setting a time limit for the music rooms?

Claire: ⓑHow long do you think it should be?

Jinho: I don't think anyone ⓒshould allow to use a room for more than an hour a day.

Claire: I disagree. I need more than an hour ⓓto practice music.

Jinho: Then how about ⓔreserving a music room?

Claire: That's a good idea. Then each person will have enough time to practice.

[충북 ○○중]

11 위 대화의 밑줄 친 ⓐ~ⓔ 중 어법상 <u>어색한</u> 것은? (3점)

① ⓐ 　　② ⓑ 　　③ ⓒ

④ ⓓ 　　⑤ ⓔ

[서울 영등포구 ○○중]

12 위 대화의 내용과 관련하여 대답할 수 <u>없는</u> 질문은? (3점)

① Why is Jinho upset?

② Why did Jinho fight with Harry?

③ How long does Jinho think the time limit for using the music rooms should be?

④ Does Claire agree with the idea of setting a time limit for the music rooms?

⑤ What does Claire think they should use to reserve the music rooms?

A: Jacob, can you help me?

B: What is it, Mom?

A: Well, I got a message from my friend, but I don't understand what some letters of it mean.

B: Let me see. Hmm... *ASAP* means "as soon as (A)_____", and *HAND* means "Have A Nice Day."

A: Oh, I see.

B: What do you think of these (B)_____, Mom?

A: I think they're destroying the language. What do you think?

B: In my (C)_____, they are fun and easy to use.

* A: Jacob's mom, B: Jacob

13 위 대화의 각 빈칸에 들어갈 말을 바르게 짝지은 것은? (4점)

	(A)	(B)	(C)
①	possible	antonyms	option
②	possible	acronyms	option
③	polite	antonyms	opinion
④	polite	acronyms	opinion
⑤	possible	acronyms	opinion

14 위 대화를 통해 알 수 있는 것은? (3점)

① ASAP과 HAND는 acronyms의 예에 해당된다.

② Jacob과 그의 엄마는 acronyms에 대한 의견이 일치한다.

③ Jacob은 친구로부터 acronyms가 있는 메시지를 받았다.

④ Jacob은 acronyms의 사용으로 인한 언어의 파괴를 걱정한다.

⑤ Jacob의 엄마는 acronyms에 대해 알고 있어 Jacob에게 설명을 한다.

15 다음 글의 빈칸에 들어갈 문장으로 가장 알맞은 것은? (정답 2개) (4점)

I disagree with your opinion. I was really close with my neighbor, Jenny. She was from America and we liked the same basketball team. We spent a lot of time watching games together. Then her family moved away three years ago. I haven't seen her since, but I still remember the times we had. I miss her more and more as time goes by. It is the quality of time that makes people remember each other.

Posted by Jaeha Park

Well, what is your opinion? There is no right or wrong answer. _____

① You should decide what is best for you.

② You should decide what is not best for you.

③ What is best for you is not for you to decide.

④ It is you that should decide what is best for you.

⑤ It is not what is best for you that you should decide.

16 아래 속담의 내용이 바르게 짝지어진 것은? (4점)

> *Two heads are better than one.*
> ⓐ You can get great ideas from others.
> ⓑ You can spend too much time before making a decision.
> ⓒ You can complete the work quickly.
> ⓓ You can get confused with too much information.
> ⓔ It is my own ideas that are more helpful when completing the work.

① ⓑ, ⓒ, ⓔ   ⓐ, ⓓ
② ⓐ, ⓑ   ⓒ, ⓓ, ⓔ
③ ⓑ, ⓓ, ⓔ   ⓐ, ⓒ
④ ⓐ, ⓒ, ⓓ   ⓑ, ⓔ
⑤ ⓐ, ⓒ   ⓑ, ⓓ, ⓔ

[17~20] 다음 글을 읽고 물음에 답하시오.

> Every now and then, words of wisdom have influenced people and changed their lives in a great way. (A) For example, "(ㄱ)_____," means the following: what you do is more important than what you say. (B) So people try to do things instead of just saying something. (C) To them, it is words (가)_____ speak louder than actions. (D) How? They think that words can influence others to do good things. (E) It is natural (나)_____ have different ideas. Let's take a look at some other proverbs upside down.

17 위 글의 흐름으로 보아, 주어진 문장이 들어가기에 가장 적절한 곳은? (3점)

> However, some people have different opinions.

① (A)   ② (B)   ③ (C)   ④ (D)   ⑤ (E)

18 위 글의 빈칸 (ㄱ)에 들어갈 알맞은 표현은? (3점)

① Look before you leap
② Out of sight, out of mind
③ Don't judge a book by its cover
④ Actions speak louder than words
⑤ An apple a day keeps the doctor away

19 위 글의 빈칸 (가), (나)에 각각 알맞은 표현으로 짝지어진 것은? (3점)

	(가)	(나)
①	that	that
②	that	to
③	to	that
④	to	to
⑤	that	which

20 위 글의 제목으로 알맞은 것은? (3점)

① Proverbs Upside Down
② Meaning of Proverbs
③ Which Way to Go?
④ Go to the World Chain Game
⑤ Happy Meaning

Look before you leap: Check what is in front of you before making a decision.

I totally agree. We should always be careful before we decide to do something. Then we'll be happy with the results of our decisions. (A)_____, if we don't take time to think things over, we may regret it. Also, we'll make mistakes if we do something without giving it a second thought. (B)_____, it will take us more time to fix.

Posted by Suzi Kang

I don't agree. (가)기회들은 자주 오지 않는다. (나)_____ Or, it will be too late. Last year, I was asked to be the captain of the school hockey team. However, I took too much time to decide, so another friend became the captain. Now, I regret it. As the saying goes, "(다)_____."

Posted by Brian Pearson

[충북 ○○중]

22 위 글의 빈칸 (A), (B)에 알맞은 말이 바르게 짝지어진 것은?

(3점)

	(A)	(B)
①	Therefore	In addition
②	However	For example
③	Therefore	However
④	However	As a result
⑤	For example	Therefore

[충북 ○○중]

23 위 글을 읽고 빈칸 (나)에 들어갈 말을 주어진 단어를 포함하여 우리말 표현에 맞게 영작하시오. (4점)

(나) 만약 기회가 있다면 우리는 그것을 잡아야 한다.

(a chance / if / grab / should)

→ _____

→ _____

[서울 강동구 ○○중]

24 다음 중 위 글의 Suzi와 같은 생각을 가진 두 사람은? (정답 2개) (3점)

① Yura: 쇠뿔도 단김에 빼라.

② Jacob: 돌다리도 두들겨 보고 건너라.

③ Claire: Slow and steady wins the race.

④ Jinho: A bad workman blames his tools.

⑤ Min: Check what is in front of you before making a decision.

[경남 ○○중]

21 위 글의 밑줄 친 (가)의 표현을 영어 두 단어를 추가하여 완성하시오. (4점)

(가) 기회들은 자주 오지 않는다.
→ _____ don't come _____.

→ _____, _____

25 다음 중 위 글의 내용과 일치하는 것은? (3점)

① "Look before you leap."과 "Strike while the iron is hot."은 비슷한 의미의 속담이다.

② Suzi는 "Look before you leap."이라는 속담에 동의하지 않는다.

③ Suzi는 실수는 나중에 만회할 수 있으므로 기회가 왔을 때 잡아야 한다고 생각한다.

④ Brian은 학교 하키 팀의 주장이 되어달라는 요청을 받았다.

⑤ Brian은 신중했기 때문에 학교 하키 팀의 주장이 될 수 있었다.

Out of sight, out of mind: Something is easily forgotten if it is not near us.

I agree with this saying. I had a ⓐclosely friend from elementary school. Sadly, we went to different middle schools. At first, we met two to three times a week. However, it was hard to keep in touch. We started to spend more time with our new friends. I started ⓑthinking less and less about him and more and more about my new friends. Now, we have stopped (가)[to talk / talking] each other.

Posted by Anna Brown

I disagree with your opinion. I was really ⓒclose with my neighbor, Jenny. She was from America and we liked the same basketball team. We spent a lot of time (나)[watching / watch] games together. Then her family moved away three years ago. I (다)[haven't seen / wasn't seen] her since, but I still remember the times we had. I miss her more and more as time goes by. It is the quality of time ⓓwhen makes people remember each other.

Posted by Jaeha Park

Well, what is your opinion? There is no right or wrong answer. It is you who should decide ⓔthat is best for you.

26 위 글의 빈칸 (다)에 들어갈 속담을 〈보기〉의 표현을 반드시 포함하여 영작하시오. (4점)

> **보기**
>
> iron / strike / while

→ _____

27 위 글의 밑줄 친 ⓐ~ⓔ 중 문법적으로 <u>어색한</u> 것의 개수는?

(4점)

① one

② two

③ three

④ four

⑤ five

29 위 글에 대한 내용으로 <u>어색한</u> 것은? (3점)

① Anna Brown의 친한 친구는 다른 중학교에 갔다.

② Anna Brown은 보이지 않으면 마음도 멀어진다 생각한다.

③ Jaeha는 3년 전에 이사를 갔다.

④ Jenny는 미국에서 왔다.

⑤ Jaeha는 서로를 기억하게 만드는 것은 바로 시간의 질이라 생각한다.

28 위 글의 괄호 (가)~(다)에 알맞은 말이 바르게 짝지어진 것은?

(3점)

(가)	(나)	(다)
① to talk	watching	haven't seen
② to talk	watch	haven't seen
③ talking	watching	haven't seen
④ talking	watch	wasn't seen
⑤ talking	watching	wasn't seen

30 다음 글에서 틀린 곳을 세 군데 찾아 바르게 고치시오. (6점)

There is a saying, "Strike while the iron is cold." This means that when opportunities come, you should grab them. If you give it a second thought before making a decision, you might lose the chance. However, you could regret your decision if you don't take enough time to think. In my opinion, it is careful decisions what help you not to make mistakes. Therefore, it is always better to look before you leap.

(a) _____ → _____

(b) _____ → _____

(c) _____ → _____

반		점수
이름		

문항수 : 선택형(22문항) 서술형(8문항)   20 . . .

◎ 선택형 문항의 답안은 컴퓨터용 수정 싸인펜을 사용하여 OMR 답안지에 바르게 표기하시오.
◎ 서술형 문제는 답을 답안지에 반드시 검정 볼펜으로 쓰시오.
◎ 총 30문항 100점 만점입니다. 문항별 배점은 각 문항에 표시되어 있습니다.

[경북 ○○중]

01 다음 〈보기〉의 영영 풀이에 해당하는 단어로 알맞은 것은?

(3점)

보기
to cause someone to admire or respect you

① depress
② impress
③ suspect
④ expect
⑤ express

[부산 ○○중]

02 다음 단어의 영영 풀이로 알맞지 <u>않은</u> 것은?   (4점)

① flat : with no high hills or other raised parts
② house : to provide a place for somebody to live
③ swampy : very wet or covered with water land in which plants, trees are growing
④ store : to put something that is not being used in a place where it can be kept safely
⑤ support : to fix equipment or furniture into position so that it can be used

[부산 ○○중]

03 다음 빈칸에 들어갈 알맞은 영어 문장을 보기의 단어를 사용하여 완성하시오.   (4점)

보기
a lot

We don't have much snow this year.
→ _____(9단어)
만약 눈이 많이 온다면, 우리는 썰매를 타러 갈텐데.

→ _____

[경북 ○○중]

04 다음 〈보기〉를 영작한 것으로 가장 적절한 것은?   (3점)

보기
만약 비가 오지 않는다면 우리는 시험을 칠 수 있을 거야.

① If the weather weren't rainy, we could have a test.
② If the weather were rainy, we should have a test.
③ If the weather is rainy, we could have a test.
④ If the weather isn't rainy, we should have a test.
⑤ If the weather were rainy, we have a test.

05 다음 중 어법상 옳은 것은? (3점)

① These gloves keep my hand warmly.

② The tests in school make students worriedly.

③ The news makes him surprising.

④ He kept her waiting for a long time.

⑤ The new machine made our job doing easily.

06 다음 중 어울리는 표현끼리 올바르게 연결하지 <u>않은</u> 문장은? (3점)

> Ⓐ If I had a sister,
> Ⓑ If I lived in a house with a garden,
> Ⓒ If I lived in a jungle,
> Ⓓ If I had a car,
> Ⓔ If I were a bird,

> ㉠ I would plant many flowers in the garden.
> ㉡ I would fly in the sky.
> ㉢ I would play tennis with her every week.
> ㉣ I would go on a picnic more often.
> ㉤ I would go to Mars first.

① Ⓐ - ㉢

② Ⓑ - ㉠

③ Ⓒ - ㉤

④ Ⓓ - ㉣

⑤ Ⓔ - ㉡

07 다음 주어진 상황과 그에 대한 소망을 나타낸 것 중 <u>어색한</u> 것을 2개 고르시오. (4점)

① 상황: As I don't have his number, I can't call him.

　소망: If I had his number, I could call him.

② 상황: She doesn't live there, so she can't see the sea every day.

　소망: If she lived there, she could see the sea every day.

③ 상황: As it was raining, I could not go out to play soccer.

　소망: If it were not raining, I couldn't go out to play soccer.

④ 상황: I don't live in a jungle, so I could not build a tree house.

　소망: If I lived in a jungle, I could build a tree house.

⑤ 상황: As I lived in a house with a garden, I planted many flowers in the garden.

　소망: If I lived in a house with a garden, I would plant many flowers in the garden.

08 다음 주어진 문장이 들어갈 알맞은 위치는? (3점)

> So, what would you do if you lived in that house?
>
> B: This is my dream house, Alice. What do you think?
> G: Oh, it's in the deep sea! (A) It looks so unique. (B)
> B: I have an interest in deep sea animals. (C) So I would explore the deep sea and find some unique sea animals. (D)
> G: That sounds cool! (E)

① (A)　　　② (B)　　　③ (C)
④ (D)　　　⑤ (E)

09 위 대화의 흐름상 밑줄 친 (가)it이 의미하는 바로 가장 적절한 것은? (3점)

① visiting Spain
② starting the project
③ going to see La Sagrada Familia
④ setting Gaudi and Spain as the title for the project
⑤ seeing how Antoni Gaudi's design was inspired by nature

10 위 대화의 밑줄 친 (A)를 어법에 맞게 고쳐 쓰시오. (3점)

> (A) Antoni Gaudi has designed

→ _____

[9~11] 다음 대화를 읽고 물음에 답하시오.

> G: Dohun, we need to start our project on our dream country to visit.
> B: That's right. Which country do you want to visit, Emma?
> G: In my case, I want to visit Spain.
> B: What would you do if you visited Spain?
> G: I'm interested in buildings. So I would go see *La Sagrada Familia*.
> B: Isn't that the church (A)Antoni Gaudi has designed?
> G: Yes, it is. It would be interesting to see (B)[by / how / inspired / was / his design / nature](그의 디자인이 어떻게 자연으로부터 영감을 받았는지).
> B: Hmm... How about Gaudi and Spain as the title for our project?
> G: I love (가)it!

11 위 대화의 밑줄 친 (B)를 우리말에 맞게 배열하시오. (4점)

> (B) [by / how / inspired / was / his design / nature]
> 그의 디자인이 어떻게 자연으로부터 영감을 받았는지

→ _____

12 다음 대화의 빈칸 (가)와 (나)에 적합한 표현을 보기에서 찾아 쓰시오. (4점)

> G: What would you do if you became a millionaire, Juwon?
> B: I would build my own house.
> G: What kind of house would you build?
> B: I would build a house that is completely covered with mirrors.
> G: (가)_____
> B: The mirrors would make the house almost invisible. Wouldn't that be cool?
> G: (나)_____
>
> *B: Boy, G: Girl

보기
- Why?
- Who?
- That would be cool.
- That's too bad.

(가): _____

(나): _____

[13~14] 다음 대화를 읽고 물음에 답하시오.

> 채현: Have you heard from Julia? She's traveling in Turkey, right?
> 유민: Yes, she sent me some pictures. Do you want to see them?
> 채현: Yes, please.
> 유민: Okay, take a look.
> 채현: Oh, look at those cave houses! They look so unique, don't they? I wish I could try living there.
> 유민: I like those balloons. They look so beautiful!
> 채현: I think Turkey is a wonderful place to visit. I hope to visit there some day.
> 유민: Me too!

13 According to the conversation, what are the speakers mainly talking about? (3점)

① plans to visit Turkey
② how to lift balloons
③ who settled in cave houses
④ items required during a long trip
⑤ photos sent from a friend traveling abroad

14 위 대화에 대한 내용으로 어색한 것은? (3점)

① 유민이는 채현이로부터 터키 여행에 대한 사진을 받았다.
② 유민이는 채현이와 함께 터키 여행 사진을 봤다.
③ 채현이는 동굴 집들을 보고 매우 독특하다고 생각한다.
④ 채현이는 터키가 방문하기에 훌륭한 장소라고 생각한다.
⑤ 유민이 또한 터키를 방문하고 싶어 한다.

15 다음 대화의 내용과 일치하는 것은? (4점)

> Jinho: I think living in a jungle would be really exciting. Don't you think so?
>
> Claire: But there are some dangerous animals in the jungle, Jinho.
>
> Jinho: I know. But the jungle is full of adventure. I wish I could live there.
>
> Claire: What would you do if you lived in the jungle?
>
> Jinho: I would explore it. Maybe I could make some animal friends.
>
> Claire: Then where would you sleep? In a cave?
>
> Jinho: No, I would stay in a tree house. Then I would be safe from dangerous animals.
>
> Claire: That makes sense.

① Jinho is positive about the life in the jungle.

② Claire believes animals in the jungle are safe.

③ Jinho is afraid of adventurous situations.

④ Jinho hopes to find a cave to live in.

⑤ Claire thinks staying in a tree house is not safe.

[16~19] 다음 글을 읽고 물음에 답하시오.

> (A)_____. Some use ladders to enter their houses. Others live in houses on the water. And others share their houses with many people. Imagine you live in one of these houses. How would that change your life?
>
> Pueblos in New Mexico, USA
>
> If I lived in a pueblo, I would climb up a ladder to enter my house. There's a hidden opening on top of the house. (가)만약 반갑지 않은 방문객이 나타난다면, 나는 사다리를 끌어 올려 그들이 들어오지 못하게 할 것이다. The thick walls are made of earth, straw, and water. They would keep me cool in summer and warm in winter. (나)The houses has a flat roof. I would sometimes sleep up on the roof under the moon and stars.

16 위 글의 내용과 일치하지 <u>않는</u> 것을 고르시오. (3점)

① 푸에블로에는 평평한 지붕이 있다.

② 다양한 사람들이 다양한 집에서 살고 있다.

③ 많은 사람들과 함께 집을 공유하며 사는 사람들도 있다.

④ 푸에블로의 두꺼운 벽은 흙과 물로만 만들어져 있다.

⑤ 푸에블로의 벽은 겨울을 따뜻하게 보낼 수 있게 만들어져 있다.

17 위 글의 빈칸 (A)에 들어갈 말로 가장 적절한 것은? (3점)

① There are so beautiful places to visit.

② Different people live in different houses.

③ The environment can influence people's thinking.

④ People live together to avoid dangerous situations.

⑤ It is important for people to choose a good place.

18 위 글의 (가)의 내용에 맞게 다음 빈칸에 들어갈 말이 바르게 짝지어진 것을 고르시오. (4점)

> If (ⓐ_____) visitors appeared. I would (ⓑ_____) the ladder up to (ⓒ_____) them (ⓓ_____) entering.

	ⓐ	ⓑ	ⓒ	ⓓ
①	unwelcome	pull	stop	with
②	unwelcome	pull	stop	from
③	welcome	pull	stopping	with
④	welcome	push	stopping	from
⑤	unwelcome	push	stop	with

19 위 글의 밑줄 친 (나)를 우리말로 쓰시오. (3점)

> (나) The houses has a flat roof.

→ _____

[20~25] 다음 글을 읽고 물음에 답하시오.

> If I lived in Venice, I would take a gondola to school every morning. Venice has 118 small islands. On weekends, I would travel from island to island (A)[by / at] a *vaporetto*, a water bus. At (B)[low / high] tide, the water from the Adriatic Sea often rises and leaves the streets (C)[full / fill] of water. However, I would be able to walk around the town through the raised walkways.
>
> Venice is known as the "(가)_____." ⓐIn Venice, there are many colorful houses on the water. ⓑYou may wonder how and why they built the houses on the water. (나)옛 베니스 사람들은 침략자들로부터 자신들을 안전하게 지키기 위해 그곳에 살기로 결정했다. But it was not easy for them to build their homes on this swampy surface. ⓒSo they installed more than 10 million wooden poles in the ground. ⓓMany visitors are inspired by the woods in the city. ⓔIt is these wooden poles that support Venice to this day.

20 위 글의 제목으로 가장 적절한 것은? (3점)

① The Great Venetians

② Wooden Poles for Venice

③ Many Colorful Houses in Venice

④ The Floating City: How and Why?

⑤ How to Keep People Safe from Invaders

21 위 글에 빈칸 (가)에 들어갈 내용으로 가장 적절한 것은? (3점)

① flying city

② living city

③ floating city

④ exciting city

⑤ changing city

22 위 글의 밑줄 친 (나)의 우리말에 맞게 〈조건〉을 준수하여 주어진 단어를 배열하여 쓰시오. (4점)

themselves / safe / to / from / keep / invaders

┌ 조건 ┐
• 주어진 단어를 모두 사용할 것.

→ The old Venetians decided to live there _____.

→ _____

23 위 글의 내용에 근거하여 대답할 수 <u>없는</u> 질문은? (3점)

① 글쓴이가 베니스에 산다면 학교에 갈 때 타고 갈 이동 수단은?

② 베니스의 섬 개수는?

③ 베니스의 수상 버스 이름은?

④ 거리가 물에 잠겼을 때 걸을 수 있는 가교 통로의 이름은?

⑤ 베니스의 알려진 또 다른 이름(별명)은?

24 위 글의 밑줄 친 ⓐ~ⓔ 중 글의 흐름상 <u>어색한</u> 것은? (3점)

① ⓐ   ② ⓑ   ③ ⓒ

④ ⓓ   ⑤ ⓔ

25 위 글의 (A)~(C)에 들어갈 말로 가장 적절한 것은? (3점)

	(A)	(B)	(C)
①	by	low	full
②	by	high	full
③	by	high	fill
④	at	high	full
⑤	at	low	fill

[26~30] 다음 글을 읽고 물음에 답하시오.

Tulou in Fujian, China

(가)_____. I would sometimes hear my neighbor calling me to come over for tea or dinner. In a tulou, there are usually three to five floors.

(A) A tulou is like a village. (나)<u>The people live in a tulou mostly has the same family name.</u> Some large tulou can house up to 50 families. They work together and share many things. Living together in one building keeps them safe.

(B) Homes are everywhere. But they are different all over the world. What is your home like?

(C) The first floor is used for cooking and eating. And people store food and tools on the second floor. (다)<u>[sleep / would / wonder / I / do / where / you / ?]</u> My bedroom would be on the third or fourth floor.

26 주어진 글 다음에 이어질 글의 순서로 가장 적절한 것은? (3점)

① (A) - (B) - (C)

② (B) - (A) - (C)

③ (B) - (C) - (A)

④ (C) - (A) - (B)

⑤ (C) - (B) - (A)

29 위 글의 밑줄 친 (다)의 배열이 바르게 된 것은? (3점)

① Do you wonder where I would sleep?

② Do you wonder where would I sleep?

③ Do I sleep where you would wonder?

④ Where I do wonder you would sleep?

⑤ Where you sleep do I would wonder?

27 위 글의 빈칸 (가)를 주어진 조건에 맞게 쓰시오. (4점)

> 조건
>
> • 해석: 내가 만약 tulou에 산다면, 나는 항상 집에 함께 놀 친구들이 있을 것이다.
> • 가정법과거 구문을 사용할 것.
> • 빈칸 하나에 단어 하나씩 사용할 것.

→ If I _____ in a tulou, I _____ always have friends at home _____ play with.

30 위 글의 Tulou에서의 삶의 모습으로 적절한 것은? (정답 2개) (3점)

① 항상 집에 함께 놀 친구들이 있다.

② Tulou는 일반적으로 3~5개의 거실이 있다.

③ 제일 아래층은 보통 음식이나 도구들을 보관하는 곳이다.

④ Tulou의 주민들은 대부분 같은 성씨이다.

⑤ Tulou의 주민들은 독립적인 생활을 한다.

28 위 글의 밑줄 친 (나)에서 틀린 두 부분을 고쳐 쓰시오. (4점)

> (나) The people live in a tulou mostly has the same family name.

(1) _____ → _____

(2) _____ → _____

◎ 선택형 문항의 답안은 컴퓨터용 수정 싸인펜을 사용하여 OMR 답안지에 바르게 표기하시오.
◎ 서술형 문제는 답을 답안지에 반드시 검정 볼펜으로 쓰시오.
◎ 총 30문항 100점 만점입니다. 문항별 배점은 각 문항에 표시되어 있습니다.

[부산 ○○중]

01 다음 문장의 빈칸에 들어가지 <u>않는</u> 단어는? (3점)

> • She made a hole in the soft _____ and planted an apple tree.
> • People are using a moving _____.
> • The _____ turns four times a day.
> • Thank you for saving me from the _____.

① walkway
② invader
③ install
④ tide
⑤ earth

[경북 ○○중]

02 다음 중 영영 풀이가 <u>어색한</u> 것은? (3점)

① flat: with no curved, high, or hollow parts
② walkaway: a passage or path, especially one that is covered or raised above the ground
③ invasion: an occasion when a country enjoys peace
④ swampy: soft and very wet
⑤ floor: the part of a room on which you stand

[부산 ○○중]

03 다음 주어진 단어를 이용하여 우리말을 영어로 옮기시오. (4점)

> 그는 그 문을 계속 닫아 두었다. (keep)
> → _____(5단어)

→ _____

[부산 ○○중]

04 다음 질문에 대한 답을 'If'를 포함한 가정법 문장을 사용하여 영어로 쓰시오. (4점)

> Q: 네가 새라면 무엇을 할래?
> A: _____

→ _____

[부산 ○○중]

05 다음 중 어법상 틀린 문장은? (3점)

① If I were a bird, I could fly in the sky.
② If I had a little brother, I would take good care of him.
③ If James were here, he will help us.
④ If I visited Iceland, I would see the amazing northern lights.
⑤ If I traveled to space, I would go to Mars first.

06 다음 중 어법상 올바른 문장을 <u>2개</u> 고르시오.   (3점)

① She always makes me happily.

② Brian kept me waited for hours.

③ You must keep your teeth clean.

④ Tests in school make me worried.

⑤ Those winter shoes keep me warmly.

08 〈보기〉의 단어를 사용하여 다음 주어진 문장과 의미가 같은 문장을 쓰시오.   (4점)

> 보기
>
> Because

> If I had enough money, I could buy a better computer.
> → _____(12단어)

→ _____

07 다음 문장이 내포한 의미로 가장 적절한 것은?   (3점)

> As I don't have a camera, I don't take pictures.

① If I have a camera, I won't take pictures.

② If I had a camera, I would take pictures.

③ If I had a camera, I would not take pictures.

④ If I didn't have a camera, I would take pictures.

⑤ If I didn't have a camera, I would not take pictures.

09 다음 두 사람의 대화 ⓐ~ⓓ를 순서에 맞게 나열한 것은? (4점)

> ⓐ I would explore the deep sea and find some unique sea animals.
>
> ⓑ Oh, it's in the deep sea. It looks so unique. So, what would you do if you lived in that house?
>
> ⓒ This is my dream house. What do you think, Alice?
>
> ⓓ That sounds cool!

① ⓑ - ⓐ - ⓒ - ⓓ

② ⓑ - ⓒ - ⓐ - ⓓ

③ ⓒ - ⓐ - ⓓ - ⓑ

④ ⓒ - ⓑ - ⓐ - ⓓ

⑤ ⓓ - ⓐ - ⓑ - ⓒ

[10~11] 다음 대화를 읽고 물음에 답하시오.

A: Will it snow today?
B: I have no idea. Why are you waiting for snow, Taeho?
A: I got a new sled for my birthday. I can't wait to test it out.
B: Let me check the weather. Umm, there will be no snow for a while.
A: (A)_____. Then I could go sledding all day!
B: No kidding! Alaska is a very cold place.
A: I think it would be fun. I want to build a snow house and stay there on vacation.
B: Living in a snow house sounds fun!

[경기 ○○중]

10 위 대화를 통해 알 수 없는 내용은? (3점)

① Why is Taeho waiting for snow?
② What did Taeho get for his birthday?
③ Why does Taeho want to live in Alaska?
④ What does Taeho want to build in Alaska?
⑤ When will Taeho move to Alaska?

[부산 ○○중]

11 위 대화의 빈칸 (A)에 들어갈 말로 문맥상 가장 적절한 것은? (3점)

① I wish I could live in Alaska.
② I wish I could live in the cave.
③ Alaska is a wonderful place to live.
④ Which house would you most like to live in?
⑤ I would travel to many places with my family.

[12~14] 다음 대화를 읽고 물음에 답하시오.

Jinho: I think living in a jungle would be really exciting. Don't you think so?

(A) I would explore it. Maybe I could make some animal friends.
(B) I know. But the jungle is full of adventure. I wish I could live there.
(C) But there are some dangerous animals in the jungle, Jinho.
(D) What would you do if you lived in the jungle?

Claire: Then where would you sleep? In a cave?
Jinho: No, I would stay in a tree house. Then (가) 나는 위험한 동물들로부터 안전할 거야.
Claire: That makes sense.

[경남 ○○중]

12 위 대화가 자연스러운 대화가 되도록 (A)~(D)를 바르게 배열한 것을 고르면? (4점)

① (A) - (C) - (B) - (D)
② (A) - (D) - (C) - (B)
③ (B) - (A) - (D) - (C)
④ (C) - (B) - (A) - (D)
⑤ (C) - (B) - (D) - (A)

[경남 ○○중]

13 밑줄 친 (가)의 표현을 영어 두 단어를 추가하여 완성하시오. (4점)

> (가) 나는 위험한 동물들로부터 안전할 거야.
> → I would be _____ from _____ animals.

→ _____, _____

14 위 대화를 통해 대답할 수 <u>없는</u> 질문은? (3점)

① When will Jinho go to the jungle?

② What would Jinho do in the jungle?

③ Where would Jinho sleep in the jungle?

④ What does Jinho think the jungle is full of?

⑤ How would Jinho be safe from dangerous animals?

15 다음 대화에 대한 내용으로 가장 적절한 것은? (3점)

> 휘빈: Minwoo, we need to start our project on our dream country to visit.
>
> 민우: That's right. Which country do you want to visit?
>
> 휘빈: In my case, I want to visit Spain.
>
> 민우: What would you do if you visited Spain?
>
> 휘빈: I'm interested in buildings. So I would go see *La Sagrada Familia*.
>
> 민우: Isn't that the church Antoni Gaudi designed?
>
> 휘빈: Yes, it is. It would be interesting to see how his design was inspired by nature.
>
> 민우: Hmm... How about *Gaudi and Spain* as the title for our project?
>
> 휘빈: I love it!

① 휘빈이와 민우는 꿈에 그리던 시골을 방문할 예정이다.

② 휘빈이는 스페인을 여러 번 갔던 경험이 있다.

③ 휘빈이는 스페인의 상업에 관심이 많다.

④ 민우는 Gaudi and Spain을 프로젝트의 주제로 하려 한다.

⑤ 민우는 교회를 보고 그 교회가 건축된 시기를 추측할 수 있었다.

[16~17] 다음 글을 읽고 물음에 답하시오.

> Venice has 118 small islands. On weekends, I would travel from island to island by a *vaporetto*, a water bus. At high tide, the water from the Adriatic Sea often (가)[full / leaves / rises / and / the streets] of water. However, (나)나는 가교 통로로 도심 주변을 걸어다닐 수 있을 것이다.

16 위 글의 밑줄 친 (가)를 문맥에 맞게 배열하시오. (4점)

(가) [full / leaves / rises / and / the streets]

→ _____

17 위 글의 밑줄 친 (나)를 영어 세 단어를 추가하여 완성하시오. (6점)

(나)나는 가교 통로로 도심 주변을 걸어 다닐 수 있을 것이다

→ I would be ⓐ_____ to walk ⓑ_____ the town through the ⓒ_____ walkways

ⓐ_____

ⓑ_____

ⓒ_____

When you visit Korea, you might wonder where you can stay. Why don't you stay in a <u>hanok</u>? A hanok is a traditional Korean house. If you stayed in a hanok, you would (ⓐ_____) because there are no beds. Hanok houses are mostly built with (ⓑ_____) materials such as wood, stone, straw, paper, and earth. These materials help you keep your skin healthy. In the cold winter, the warm ondol floors heat your body. The doors in hanok are covered with thin paper. They help keep you cool in (ⓒ_____)

18 위 글의 흐름상 빈칸 ⓐ~ⓒ에 들어가기에 가장 알맞은 내용으로 짝지어진 것을 고르시오. (3점)

	ⓐ	ⓑ	ⓒ
①	sleep on the floor	natural	summer
②	sleep on the roof	natural	winter
③	sleep on the roof	unnatural	winter
④	sleep on the floor	unnatural	summer
⑤	sleep on the floor	natural	winter

19 위 글에서 한옥에 대한 설명으로 옳은 것은? (3점)

① 한옥에는 침대가 있다.

② 한옥은 세계적인 전통 가옥이다.

③ 한옥의 문들은 두꺼운 종이로 덮여 있다.

④ 추운 겨울에 온돌 바닥은 당신의 몸을 시원하게 해준다.

⑤ 한옥에 들어간 천연 재료는 당신의 피부를 건강하게 유지하도록 도와준다.

Tulou in Fujian, China

ⓐ<u>If I lived in a tulou, a huge round house in Fujian, China, I would always have friends at home to play.</u> ⓑ<u>I would sometimes hear my neighbor calling me to come over for tea or dinner.</u> In a tulou, there are usually three to five floors.

The first floor is used for cooking and eating. And people (가)<u>store</u> food and tools on the second floor. ⓒ<u>Do you wonder where would I sleep?</u> My bedroom would be on the third or fourth floor.

A tulou is like a village. ⓓ<u>The people living in a tulou mostly have the same family name.</u> Some large tulou can house up to 50 families. They work together and share many things. ⓔ<u>Living together in one building keep them safe.</u>

Homes are everywhere. But they are different all over the world. What is your home like?

20 위 글의 주제로 가장 적절한 것은? (3점)

① the examples of tulou

② different kinds of houses

③ the feature and structure of tulou

④ various materials used in buildings

⑤ outstanding value of traditional buildings

21 위 글의 밑줄 친 ⓐ~ⓔ 중 어법상 바르지 <u>않은</u> 것의 개수는?

(3점)

① 1개   ② 2개   ③ 3개

④ 4개   ⑤ 5개

22 위 글의 밑줄 친 단어 (가)store의 의미로 알맞은 것은? (3점)

① to provide a place for somebody to live

② to hit someone or something deliberately

③ to fix equipment or furniture into position so that it can be used

④ to make the information available to other people on the Internet

⑤ to put something that is not being used in a place where it can be kept safely

23 위 글의 tulou에 대한 설명과 일치하지 <u>않는</u> 것으로 짝지어진 것은?

(3점)

> (가) 토루는 대개 3층에서 5층으로 되어 있다.
> (나) 1층은 요리하고 식사하는 데에 사용된다.
> (다) 사람들은 2층에 식량과 도구를 보관한다.
> (라) 모든 종류의 토루는 50가구 이상 수용할 수 있다.
> (마) 토루에 사는 사람들은 같은 성별끼리만 거주할 수 있다.

① (가), (나)

② (가), (다)

③ (나), (마)

④ (다), (라)

⑤ (라), (마)

[24~30] 다음 글을 읽고 물음에 답하시오.

Different people ⓐ<u>live</u> in different houses. Some use ladders to enter their houses. (가)_____ live in houses on the water. And (가)_____ share their houses with many people. Imagine you live in one of these houses. How would that change your life?

Pueblos in New Mexico, USA

If I lived in a pueblo, I would climb up a ladder to enter my house. There's a ⓑ<u>hidden</u> opening on top of the house. If unwelcome visitors ⓒ<u>to be appeared</u>, I would pull the ladder up to stop them from entering. The thick walls are made of earth, straw, and water. They would keep me cool in summer and warm in winter. The houses ⓓ<u>have</u> a flat roof. I would sometimes ⓔ<u>sleep</u> up on the roof under the moon and stars.

Houses on Water in Venice, Italy

(㉠) (나)<u>내가 만약 베니스에 산다면, 나는 매일 아침 곤돌라를 타고 학교에 갈 것이다.</u> Venice has 118 small islands. On weekends, I would travel from island to island by a *vaporetto*, a water bus. At high (A)_____, the water from the Adriatic Sea often rises and leaves the streets full of water. (㉡) However, I would be able to walk around the town through the raised walkways.

Venice is known as the "floating city." In Venice, there are (B)_____ colorful houses on the water. (㉢) The old Venetians decided to live there to keep themselves (C)_____ from invaders. But it was not easy for them to build their homes on this swampy surface. So they installed more than 10 million wooden poles in the ground. (㉣) It is these wooden poles that support Venice to this day. (㉤)

24 위 글의 빈칸 (가)에 들어갈 말로 알맞은 것을 고르시오. (3점)

① Other   ② Others   ③ Another

④ The other   ⑤ The others

25 위 글의 ㉠~㉤ 중 다음 주어진 문장이 들어가기에 가장 알맞은 곳을 고르시오. (3점)

> You may wonder how and why they built the houses on the water.

① ㉠ ② ㉡ ③ ㉢
④ ㉣ ⑤ ㉤

26 위 글의 우리말 (나)를 영어로 올바르게 표현한 것은? (3점)

① If I lived in Venice, I take a gondola to school every morning.
② If I will live in Venice, I will take a gondola to school every morning.
③ If I lived in Venice, I would take a gondola to school every morning.
④ If I live in Venice, I would take a gondola to school every morning.
⑤ If I lived in Venice, I will take a gondola to school every morning.

27 위 글의 밑줄 친 ⓐ~ⓔ 중, 문법적으로 어색한 것은? (3점)

① ⓐ ② ⓑ ③ ⓒ
④ ⓓ ⑤ ⓔ

28 위 글의 빈칸 (A)~(C)에 알맞은 것은? (3점)

	(A)	(B)	(C)
①	tide	many	safely
②	stem	much	safely
③	tide	much	safe
④	stem	many	safely
⑤	tide	many	safe

29 위 글에 대한 내용으로 어색한 것은? (3점)

① 집에 들어가기 위해 사다리를 사용하는 사람도 있다.
② 푸에블로에서는 불청객이 집으로 들어오는 것을 막기 위해 사다리를 끌어올려 들어오지 못하게 한다.
③ 베니스에 산다면, 곤돌라를 타고 학교를 갈 수 있다.
④ 베니스는 물 위에 색색의 다리들이 많이 있고, '평평한 도시'로 알려져 있다.
⑤ 베니스에서는 땅에 천만 개 이상의 나무 기둥이 설치되어 있다.

30 위 글을 읽고 질문에 답할 수 없는 것을 고르시오. (3점)

① What supports the houses in Venice?
② How many small islands does Venice have?
③ Why are houses on the water colorful in Venice?
④ Why did the old Venetians build their houses on water?
⑤ How did the old Venetians build their homes on the swampy surface?

3학년 영어 2학기 기말고사(8과) 1회

반		점수	
이름			

문항수 : 선택형(24문항) 서술형(4문항)　　　20 ．　．　．

◎ 선택형 문항의 답안은 컴퓨터용 수정 싸인펜을 사용하여 OMR 답안지에 바르게 표기하시오.

◎ 서술형 문제는 답을 답안지에 반드시 검정 볼펜으로 쓰시오.

◎ 총 28문항 100점 만점입니다. 문항별 배점은 각 문항에 표시되어 있습니다.

[부산 ○○중]

01 다음 문장의 빈칸에 들어가지 <u>않는</u> 단어는?　　(4점)

> • Eleven minus five _____s six.
> • This book helped the students who _____d with math.
> • She _____d after the thief but couldn't catch him.
> • It is bad to tax too much because not money but people _____ the most.

① chase
② matter
③ equal
④ struggle
⑤ wave

[경기 ○○중]

02 다음 중 〈보기〉의 어느 문장에도 들어갈 수 <u>없는</u> 단어는? (3점)

> • _____ : 12 o'clock at night
> • _____ : the process of choosing a person by voting
> • _____ : to say or write something again or more than once
> • _____ : wanting more money, power, food, etc. than you really need

① greedy
② relate
③ election
④ repeat
⑤ midnight

[서울 강동구 ○○중]

03 다음 밑줄 친 부분의 우리말 표현이 올바른 것은?　(4점)

① He decided to <u>read himself to sleep</u>. (읽다가 잠들다)

② Let's <u>keep in touch</u> while you are away. (고군분투하다)

③ He announced that he was going to <u>run for</u> public office. (달아나다)

④ I picked up the books on the desk and put them into my bag <u>one by one</u>. (나란히)

⑤ You start from point A and have to go <u>in the order of</u> 1→9→8→5… (거꾸로)

[부산 ○○중]

04 다음 주어진 문장과 의미가 같은 뜻의 문장을 쓰시오.(보기의 단어들을 반드시 사용할 것)　　(4점)

> 보기
>
> so / that

> The bag was too heavy for him to lift.
> → _____(10단어)

→ _____

05 다음 주어진 문장과 같은 의미가 되도록 빈칸을 완성하시오.

(4점)

조건

• to를 반드시 사용할 것.

He was so smart that he could solve the problem.

→ He was _____ _____ _____ _____ the problem.

→ _____

06 다음 ⓐ~ⓓ 중, 어법상 틀린 문장을 모두 고른 것은?　(3점)

ⓐ My brother is too angrily to talk with me.
ⓑ This bread is too hard to eat it.
ⓒ The house looked so dark to go in.
ⓓ The shop is too crowded to looking around.

① ⓐ, ⓒ

② ⓐ, ⓓ

③ ⓑ, ⓒ

④ ⓑ, ⓒ, ⓓ

⑤ ⓐ, ⓑ, ⓒ, ⓓ

07 다음 중 어법상 옳은 것만을 모두 고른 것은?　(4점)

ⓐ My legs were shaking so badly that I couldn't stand.
ⓑ The questions are too difficult for me to answer them.
ⓒ He spoke too quietly for us to hear what he was saying.
ⓓ She ran so fast that I couldn't catch up with.

① ⓐ, ⓒ

② ⓑ, ⓓ

③ ⓒ, ⓓ

④ ⓐ, ⓑ, ⓒ

⑤ ⓐ, ⓑ, ⓓ

08 다음 (A)~(C) 안에서 어법에 맞는 표현으로 바르게 짝지어진 것은?　(3점)

• No one (A)[have / has] ever done this before.
• This is the factory (B)[where / which] I work in.
• The food is too expensive (C)[of / for] him to buy.

	(A)	(B)	(C)
①	has	which	for
②	has	which	of
③	has	where	for
④	have	where	of
⑤	have	which	of

09 다음 중 어법상 바른 것을 고르시오. (3점)

① No one were happy with the news.

② Nothing are impossible if we try hard.

③ Nothing have happened after the accident.

④ No one takes pictures inside the museum.

⑤ No one remember the name of the movie.

10 다음 그래프의 내용과 일치하지 않는 것은? (4점)

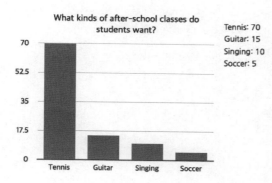

What kinds of after-school classes do students want?

Tennis: 70
Guitar: 15
Singing: 10
Soccer: 5

① A hundred students participated in the survey.

② The result says that the least students chose singing.

③ Fifteen out of one hundred students want to learn the guitar.

④ Fifteen percent of the students chose singing and soccer.

⑤ From the result, the school should have more tennis classes for after-school class.

11 다음 일기 예보를 보고 대화문의 빈칸 ⓐ~ⓑ에 들어가기에 가장 알맞은 내용으로 짝지어진 것을 고르시오. (4점)

Monday　　**Tuesday**　　**Wednesday**

A: Can we ride our bikes on Tuesday?

B: I'm afraid not. Tuesday will ⓐ_____
_____.

A: Do you think we can go on a picnic on Wednesday?

B: I don't think so. Wednesday will ⓑ_____
_____.

① ⓐ be too rainy to ride our bikes

　ⓑ be too snowy to go on a picnic

② ⓐ not be so rainy that we can ride our bikes

　ⓑ be so snowy that we can't go on a picnic

③ ⓐ be too sunny to ride our bikes

　ⓑ be so cold that we can't go on a picnic

④ ⓐ be too rainy to ride our bikes

　ⓑ not be so cold that we can go on a picnic

⑤ ⓐ be too sunny to ride our bikes

　ⓑ be so sunny that we can't go on a picnic

12 다음 그래프를 보고 빈칸 수에 맞게 질문에 대한 답을 완성하시오. (5점)

Favorite Type of Movie

Total number of students : 20

Romance: 6 (30%)
Action: 5 (25%)
Comedy: 4 (20%)
Horror: 2 (10%)
Others: 3 (15%)

- What can you tell from the chart about a romance movie?

→ _____ _____ _____ _____ _____
_____ a romance movie.

[14~15] 다음 대화를 읽고 물음에 답하시오.

> B: Jina, what's the matter? You look very upset.
> G: My brother broke my computer. I'm so angry.
>
> ⓐ What do you mean?
> ⓑ Oh, I get it. I guess it's not good to stay angry for a long time.
> ⓒ Well, it takes a lot of muscles to look angry, but only a few to smile. (가)_____
> ⓓ I'm sorry to hear that, but your facial muscles must be tired.
>
> B: That's right. Remember, it's always better to smile.
>
> *B: Boy, G: Girl

14 위 대화에서 주어진 ⓐ~ⓓ를 순서대로 바르게 배열한 것은? (4점)

① ⓑ - ⓒ - ⓐ - ⓓ
② ⓑ - ⓒ - ⓓ - ⓐ
③ ⓓ - ⓑ - ⓒ - ⓐ
④ ⓓ - ⓐ - ⓑ - ⓒ
⑤ ⓓ - ⓐ - ⓒ - ⓑ

13 다음 대화의 빈칸에 들어가기에 가장 알맞은 것은? (3점)

> A: When you are making Dalgona candies, you have to make sure you add baking soda, or else it will not work. _____
> _____
> B: No, I don't understand.

① Do you see what I mean?
② What would you do?
③ What is it like?
④ Can you guess what I want for it?
⑤ What's the matter?

15 위 대화의 빈칸 (가)에 들어갈 말로 가장 적절한 것은? (3점)

① Do you see what I mean?
② Do you know why you are angry?
③ Do you know how often you smile?
④ How do you like that?
⑤ Did you know about facial muscles?

16 다음 밑줄 친 ⓐ~ⓔ 중 대화의 흐름상 어색한 것은? (4점)

> A: Yura, ⓐI did a survey on students' favorite food.
> B: ⓑThat sounds interesting. What were the results?
> A: Eighty percent of the students like fast food. Only five out of them chose salad as their favorite. ⓒDo you get it?
> B: ⓓNo, I don't. Eating a lot of fast food makes them unhealthy. ⓔI am worried about them.

① ⓐ   ② ⓑ   ③ ⓒ

④ ⓓ   ⑤ ⓔ

[17~21] 다음 글을 읽고 물음에 답하시오.

> Robin and Pascal hid up in a tree and counted the soldiers one by one. (A)
> Pascal: There are five soldiers from midnight to six in the morning. Next, there are three soldiers until noon, and then there are eight soldiers until six in the evening. (B) Lastly, there are twelve soldiers until midnight. So, you should go inside between six in the morning and noon.
> Robin: What? I don't get it.
> <Pascal drew a graph and showed it to Robin.>
> Pascal: Look, the most dangerous time is between six in the evening and midnight. Four times more soldiers work (가)at that time than from six in the morning until noon. (C)
> Robin: Aha! I got it now. Thank you so much, Pascal! (D)
> Pascal: You're welcome. (E) Now I realize the importance of graphs. (나)아무도 그것들이 더 이상 필요 없다고 말할 수 없을 거예요.

17 위 글에서 주어진 표현이 들어갈 곳으로 가장 알맞은 곳은? (3점)

> Do you see what I mean?

① (A)   ② (B)   ③ (C)

④ (D)   ⑤ (E)

18 위 글의 밑줄 친 (가)at that time에 해당되는 시간은? (3점)

① 저녁 6시~자정

② 자정~새벽 6시

③ 새벽 6시~정오

④ 정오~저녁 6시

⑤ 4시간마다

19 위 글의 (나)의 우리말을 <보기>의 단어들을 사용하여 영어로 옮기시오. (10단어로 쓸 것) (4점)

> 보기
> No one / say / that / anymore

(가)아무도 그것들이 더 이상 필요 없다고 말할 수 없을 거예요.

→ _____

→ _____

20 위 글에서 답을 찾을 수 없는 질문은? (4점)

① When was the best time to go inside?

② What did Pascal do hiding up in a tree?

③ When was the most dangerous for going inside?

④ How many soldiers did Pascal need to go inside?

⑤ What did Pascal use to help Robin understand what he said?

21 위 글의 내용과 일치하는 것은? (3점)

① 파스탈과 로빈은 병사들의 수를 장소별로 세었다.

② 가장 안전한 시간은 오후 6시부터 12시까지이다.

③ 아무도 병사가 더 이상 필요 없다고 말하지 않았다.

④ 파스칼은 로빈 덕분에 그래프가 필요한 이유를 깨달았다.

⑤ 가장 안전한 시간과 위험한 시간의 병사 수 차이는 4배이다.

[22~26] 다음 글을 읽고 물음에 답하시오.

Pascal was doing his math homework in his room. He was struggling with graphs.

"It's too hard to read and draw graphs. Why do I need these anyway? No one need graphs in real life."

He put down his pen and picked up his favorite book, *Robin Hood*. He decided to read himself to sleep. When he was about to open the book, he heard a voice. He looked up from the book to see who was talking. He couldn't believe his eyes. It was his dog, Manny, that was talking!

"Close your eyes and repeat after me. *Cogito ergo sum*," said Manny.

"You can talk?"

"Just repeat! *Cogito ergo sum*."

Pascal closed his eyes and repeated the words. Suddenly, he heard men shouting. When he opened his eyes, he saw soldiers on horses. They were chasing ⓐa man with arrows in his hand.

"Hello, my name is Robin Hood."

"Wow! Are you the Robin Hood from the book?"

"No. I'm the ⓑRobin Hood of Sherwood Forest. Who are you and why are you here?"

"My name is Pascal. I don't know why I'm here, but there must be a reason. ⓒYou saved me from the soldiers. Thank you so much. Is there anything I can do for you?"

"Well, can ⓓyou help us get back the money the king took from the people? He taxed them too much. He is so greedy that he can't share with the people. They don't have enough money to buy food. ⓔI want to help them get their money back. However, there are many soldiers in the tower, so nobody can get inside."

"Hmm... I think I have a solution. But first, can you take me to the tower? I need to count the number of the soldiers."

22 위 글에서 이야기에 등장하지 <u>않은</u> 인물은?　　(3점)

① Pascal

② Manny

③ Robin Hood

④ soldiers

⑤ Robin Hood's dog

25 다음 주어진 영영 풀이 중 위 글에 나오지 <u>않는</u> 단어는?　(4점)

① to calculate the total number of people, things, etc.

② to try very hard to do something when it is difficult

③ wanting more money, power, etc. than you really need

④ to collect money so that the government can perform public services

⑤ to mean something is important because it has an effect on you

23 위 글의 밑줄 친 ⓐ~ⓔ 중 지칭하는 것이 <u>다른</u> 하나는?　(3점)

① ⓐ a man

② ⓑ Robin Hood

③ ⓒ You

④ ⓓ you

⑤ ⓔ I

24 위 글 다음에 나올 내용으로 가장 알맞은 것은?　(4점)

① The king shares the tax money with the people.

② Pascal counts the number of soldiers.

③ The sodiers attack Robin Hood.

④ Pascal goes back to his room.

⑤ Robin Hood draws a graph.

26 위 글의 밑줄 친 문장 중 어법상 <u>어색한</u> 문장은?　(3점)

① No one need graphs in real life.

② It was his dog, Manny, that was talking!

③ Is there anything I can do for you?

④ He is so greedy that he can't share with the people.

⑤ However, there are many soldiers in the tower, so nobody can get inside.

(A) What kinds of numbers are thought to be lucky or unlucky? Do you think it is similar around the world?

(B) Usually, the number 7 is a lucky number in countries like England, the USA, and France. However, a lucky number in one country can be an unlucky number in another country. Chinese people think 7 is unlucky because July or "the seventh month" is often thought of as a month for ghosts.

(C) How about the number 4? In Germany, the number is regarded as lucky because it matches the number of leaves on a four-leaf clover. However, in China, the sound of the word is similar to that of the Chinese word for death.

(D) If you visit Oahu, Hawaii, the Pineapple Garden Maze is a must see. It is the world's longest maze, and it attracts visitors from around the world. The maze has 11,400 native plants and covers about 5 kilometers.

(E) In ancient Korea, 1 represented the sky and 2 represented the earth. 1 plus 2 equals 3, so 3 was a lucky number in Korea. However, the number 4 is still an unlucky number, just like in China.

27 (A)~(E) 중 위 글에서 내용상 <u>어색한</u> 단락은? (3점)

① (A)   ② (B)   ③ (C)

④ (D)   ⑤ (E)

28 위 글의 내용과 일치하는 것은? (4점)

① Lucky numbers around the world are similar everywhere.

② An unlucky number in one country can be lucky in another.

③ Number 4 is considered lucky in Korea because it matches the shape of the clover.

④ The number 9 and 4 are thought to be unlucky in China related to the sound.

⑤ 1 plus 2 equals 3, so it is the luckiest number in China.

◎ 선택형 문항의 답안은 컴퓨터용 수정 싸인펜을 사용하여 OMR 답안지에 바르게 표기하시오.

◎ 서술형 문제는 답을 답안지에 반드시 검정 볼펜으로 쓰시오.

◎ 총 27문항 100점 만점입니다. 문항별 배점은 각 문항에 표시되어 있습니다.

[부산 ○○중]

01 다음 단어의 영영 풀이로 알맞지 <u>않은</u> 것은? (3점)

① relate: to make a logical connection

② novel : a long written story about imaginary people and events

③ count: to calculate the total number of people or things

④ vote : to indicate your choice officially at a meeting or in an election

⑤ midnight: 12 o'clock in the middle of the day

[부산 ○○중]

02 다음 문장의 빈칸에 들어가지 <u>않는</u> 단어는? (4점)

- In ancient Korea, 1 _____ed the sky and 2 _____ed earth.
- It's hard to build _____ in a short time.
- No money but people _____ the most.
- The meaning of _____ is to make a logical or causal connection

① relate

② muscle

③ matter

④ represent

⑤ struggle

[부산 ○○중]

03 다음 주어진 문장과 의미가 같은 문장으로 바꿔 쓰시오. (보기의 단어들을 반드시 사용할 것) (4점)

> **보기**
>
> so / that

> He was smart enough to solve the problem.
> → _____(10단어)

→ _____

[경기 ○○중]

04 다음 중 어법상 의미에 맞게 전환된 것은? (4점)

① The soup is too hot for me to eat.

→ The soup is so hot that I can eat it.

② He is too young to travel alone.

→ He is so young that he couldn't travel alone.

③ The game was too popular for the king to prohibit.

→ The game was so popular that the king couldn't prohibit.

④ The pants are so small that I can't wear them.

→ The pants are too small for me not to wear them.

⑤ I am too busy to watch a movie with him.

→ I am so busy that I can't watch a movie with him.

05 다음 주어진 문장과 같은 뜻이 되도록 빈칸 수에 맞게 문장을 완성하시오. (4점)

조건
• so를 반드시 사용할 것.

She jogs every morning so that she can stay healthy.
→ She jogs every morning _____ _____ _____ stay healthy.

→ _____

06 주어진 (A), (B)가 같은 의미가 되도록 바르게 쓰인 것은? (4점)

① (A) The tea is so hot that I can't drink it.
(B) The tea is too hot to drink it.

② (A) Minji is so short that she can't get on that ride.
(B) Minji is too short not to get on that ride.

③ (A) The house was too dangerous for me to go in.
(B) The house was so dangerous that I couldn't go in.

④ (A) The laptop was too expensive for her to buy.
(B) The laptop was so expensive that she couldn't buy it.

⑤ (A) Sunday will be too cloudy to see the sunshine.
(B) Sunday will be cloudy so that we can't see the sunshine.

07 다음 문장과 의미가 같은 것을 2개 고르시오. (3점)

Jennifer는 너무 피곤해서 밖에 나가지 못했다.

① Jennifer was so tired to go out.

② Jennifer was too tired to go out.

③ Jennifer was too tired not to go out.

④ Jennifer was so tired and she could go out.

⑤ Jennifer was so tired that she couldn't go out.

08 다음 그래프의 내용과 일치하는 것은? (4점)

A survey on the books students want for their school library

Novels: 13
Science-Fiction Books: 5
History Books: 2

① Twelve students participate in the survey.

② The result says that the least students chose novels.

③ Nobody chose history books for their school library.

④ Five out of twenty students chose science-fiction books.

⑤ From this survey result, the school library should get more history books than novels.

09 다음 중 어법상 바른 문장은 <u>모두</u> 몇 개인가? (3점)

ⓐ Yujin is too youth to drive.
ⓑ I am too hungry to sleepy.
ⓒ Nobody were happy with the news.
ⓓ No one read the book before the class started.
ⓔ My brother is too angrily to talk with me.
ⓕ No one in my family watches TV.

① 1개　　　② 2개　　　③ 3개
④ 4개　　　⑤ 5개

10 다음 그래프를 보고 〈보기〉의 단어를 사용하여 질문에 답하시오. (4점)

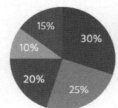

Favorite Type of Movie

Total number of students : 20

Romance: 6 (30%)
Action: 5 (25%)
Comedy: 4 (20%)
Horror: 2 (10%)
Others: 3 (15%)

보기
of　　　like

What can you tell from the pie chart about action movies?

→ ＿＿＿＿＿＿＿＿＿＿＿＿＿＿＿(8단어)

→ ＿＿＿＿＿＿＿＿＿＿＿＿＿＿＿＿

11 다음 ⓐ~ⓓ 중 어법상 틀린 문장을 <u>모두</u> 고른 것은? (4점)

ⓐ His problems were too serious to solve them.
ⓑ Her speech was too slow to be finished on time.
ⓒ No one come to the party without a present.
ⓓ I found that nobody were at home.

① ⓐ, ⓑ
② ⓐ, ⓒ
③ ⓑ, ⓒ
④ ⓐ, ⓒ, ⓓ
⑤ ⓑ, ⓒ, ⓓ

12 다음 중 어법상 옳은 것만을 〈보기〉에서 <u>모두</u> 고른 것은? (4점)

보기
ⓐ She's too scared to do it. ⓑ It's pretty that she is. ⓒ It was the test result that made me sad. ⓓ The laptop was so expensive that he couldn't buy. ⓔ It is in this restaurant that we have dinner every Friday.

① ⓐ, ⓒ
② ⓑ, ⓓ
③ ⓐ, ⓒ, ⓔ
④ ⓑ, ⓓ, ⓔ
⑤ ⓑ, ⓒ, ⓓ, ⓔ

13 다음 중 두 문장의 의미가 <u>다른</u> 것은? (3점)

① Minji is so short that she can't get on that ride.

→ Minji is too short to get on that ride.

② It is too late. So we can't change the design.

→ It is too late for us to change the design.

③ The tea is so hot and we can't drink it.

→ The tea is too hot for us to drink it.

④ He was too tired to finish the work.

→ He was so tired that he couldn't finish the work.

⑤ The car is so expensive that she can't buy it.

→ The car is too expensive for her to buy.

14 다음 글에서 밑줄 친 It이 가리키는 것은? (4점)

> B: These days, you don't need <u>it</u> to watch a movie or go to a concert. You just need to store <u>it</u> in your cell phone. Then show <u>it</u> on your phone's screen before you go in. You don't need to go through the trouble of printing out <u>it</u>. Do you see what I mean?

① money

② a mobile ticket

③ a document

④ a paper ticket

⑤ a tool

15 다음 대화의 빈칸에 들어갈 말로 적절하지 <u>않은</u> 것은? (4점)

> Mina: Henry, what are you doing?
>
> Henry: I'm writing an article about students' favorite snacks. I'm worried about their health.
>
> Mina: Why?
>
> Henry: Well, I surveyed 100 students and the results show that eighty percent of the students liked pizza and fried chicken for snacks. (가)_____
>
> _____
>
> Mina: Oh, I get it. Students really like fast food. What else did they like?
>
> Henry: Twelve percent of the students chose chocolate cake as their favorite.
>
> Mina: Wow, students should really try to eat healthier snacks!

① Do you get it?

② Do you get the point?

③ Do you see what I mean?

④ Do you know what will happen?

⑤ Do you understand what I am talking about?

16 다음 대화 중 가장 <u>어색한</u> 것은? (4점)

① A: What would you do if you visited Spain?

B: I'm interested in buildings. So I would go see La Sagrada Familia.

② A: I wish I could live in Alaska. Then I could go sledding all day!

B: No kidding! Alaska is a very cold place.

③ A: It would not be easy to live in this house because the inside is also upside down.

B: Really? But I want to try living there.

④ A: What kind of house would you build?

B: I would build a house that is completely covered with mirrors.

⑤ A: Those cave houses look so unique, don't they?

B: Me, too! I live in a cave house.

17 다음 글의 내용과 일치하지 <u>않는</u> 것은? (4점)

Usually, the number 7 is a lucky number in countries like England, the USA, and France. However, a lucky number in one country can be unlucky in another. Chinese people think 7 is unlucky because July or "the seventh month" is often thought of as a month for ghosts.

Many people in Western countries such as the USA and Norway don't like the number 13. There are even scary movies about Friday the 13th. However, in Italy, the number is related to a good person, St. Anthony. He prayed for lost things or people. Now, people celebrate the day he died, June 13th.

How about the number 4? In Germany, the number is regarded as lucky because it matches the number of leaves on a four-leaf clover. However, in China, the sound of the word is similar to that of the Chinese word for death.

① Not only in England but also in the USA, the number 7 is a lucky number.

② Not only Chinese people but also French people think 7 is unlucky.

③ People in the USA as well as in Norway don't like the number 13.

④ People in Italy celebrate the day St. Anthony died, June 13th.

⑤ In Germany, the number 4 is regarded as lucky.

Pascal was doing his math homework in his room. He was struggling with graphs.

"It's too hard ㉠to read and draw graphs. Why do I need these anyway? No one ㉡needs graphs in real life." ⓐHe put down his pen and picked up his favorite book, *Robin Hood*. He decided to read ㉢themselves to sleep. When he was about to open the book, he heard a voice. He looked up from the book to see who was talking. ⓑHe couldn't believe his eyes. (가)His dog, Manny, was talking!

"Close your eyes and repeat after me. *Cogito ergo sum*," said Manny,

"ⓒYou can talk?"

"Just repeat! *Cogito ergo sum*."

Pascal ㉣closed his eyes and repeated the words. Suddenly, he heard men shouting. When he opened his eyes, he saw soldiers on horses. They were ㉤chasing a man with arrows in his hand. The man saw Pascal and shouted.

"It's too dangerous for ⓓyou to stand there. Come on." The man pulled Pascal onto his horse and rode into the woods.

When they arrived at a house, the man stopped and got off his horse.

"Hello, my name is Robin Hood."

"Wow! Are you the Robin Hood from the book?"

"No. I'm the Robin Hood of Sherwood Forest. Who are ⓔyou and why are you here?"

18 위 글을 읽고, (A)~(E)의 문장을 사건이 일어난 순서대로 배열한 것으로 가장 적절한 것은? (4점)

(A) Robin took Pascal to the woods.
(B) Robin introduced himself to Pascal.
(C) Pascal complained about learning graphs.
(D) Manny told Pascal to repeat what he said.
(E) Pascal was surprised to hear a voice from his dog.

① (B) - (D) - (C) - (A) - (E)
② (C) - (A) - (D) - (E) - (B)
③ (C) - (E) - (B) - (D) - (A)
④ (C) - (E) - (D) - (A) - (B)
⑤ (E) - (C) - (A) - (B) - (D)

19 위 글의 밑줄 친 ⓐ~ⓔ 중 지칭하는 것이 나머지 넷과 <u>다른 것</u>은? (4점)

① ⓐ   ② ⓑ   ③ ⓒ
④ ⓓ   ⑤ ⓔ

20 위 글의 밑줄 친 ㉠~㉤ 중 문맥상 단어의 쓰임이 적절하지 <u>않</u>은 것은? (3점)

① ㉠ to read
② ㉡ needs
③ ㉢ themselves
④ ㉣ closed
⑤ ㉤ chasing

21 위 글의 밑줄 친 (가)를 〈보기〉와 같이 표현한 것으로 가장 적절한 것은? (3점)

> **보기**
> The accident took place <u>in 1995</u>.
> → It was in 1995 that the accident took place.

① It is Manny that his dog is talking!

② It was talking who his dog, Manny!

③ It is his dog that Manny was talking!

④ It was his dog, Manny when was talking!

⑤ It was his dog, Manny, that was talking!

22 위 글의 (A)~(E) 중 주어진 문장이 들어갈 알맞은 위치는? (4점)

> So, you should go inside between six in the morning and noon.

① (A)　　② (B)　　③ (C)

④ (D)　　⑤ (E)

[22~25] 다음 글을 읽고 물음에 답하시오.

(A) Pascal hid up in a tree outside the tower and counted the soldiers one by one. (B)

"There are five soldiers from midnight to six in the morning. (C) Next, there are three soldiers until noon, and then there are eight soldiers until six in the evening. Lastly, there are twelve soldiers until midnight. (D)

"What? I don't get it. (E)"

Pascal thought for a moment, 'Hmm... a graph might make this easier to understand.'

Pascal drew a graph and showed it to Robin.

"Look, the most dangerous time is between six in the evening and midnight. Four times more soldiers work at that time than from six in the morning until noon. Do you see what I mean?"

"Aha! I get it now. Thank you so much, Pascal!"

"You're welcome. Now I realize that (가)_____

_____."

Next morning, Robin successfully entered the tower thanks to Pascal's advice. Pascal who was outside the tower saw Robin waving at him. Pascal waved back and said to himself. "It was a great adventure. How do I go back? Oh, I know. I should say the words *Cogito ergo sum*!"

23 위 글의 흐름상 빈칸 (가)에 들어갈 말로 가장 적절한 것은? (4점)

① drawing graphs takes too much time

② graphs don't matter when I explain my ideas

③ graphs can be effective tools of communication

④ graphs are unhelpful in giving information clearly

⑤ I should try not to use graphs because they only make confusion

24 위 글에서, Pascal의 graphs에 대한 생각은?　(3점)

① No one needs graphs anymore.

② Graphs are not good ways to make things clear.

③ Graphs are not important in explaining something.

④ Graphs might be useful to make things easier to understand.

⑤ Good explanation is more important than using a graph to understand.

[26~27] 다음 글을 읽고 물음에 답하시오.

> "My name is Pascal. I don't know why I'm here, but there must be a reason. (A) You saved me from the soldiers. Thank you so much. (B) Is there anything I can do for you?"
>
> "Well, can you help us get back the money the king took from the people? He taxed them too much. (C) They don't have enough money to buy food. (D) l want to help them get their money back. However, there are many soldiers in the tower, so nobody can get inside.
>
> "Hmm... I think I have a solution. (E) But first, can you take me to the tower? I need to count the number of the soldiers."

26 위 글의 흐름상 다음 주어진 문장이 들어가기에 가장 적절한 곳은?　(4점)

> He is so greedy that he can't share with the people.

① (A)　　② (B)　　③ (C)

④ (D)　　⑤ (E)

25 위 글을 읽고 내용상 옳은 것만을 〈보기〉에서 있는 대로 고른 것은?　(4점)

> 보기
>
> ⓐ Pascal checked the number of soldiers, hiding up in a tree.
> ⓑ Pascal told Robin when the good time to go inside the tower was.
> ⓒ Robin understood Pascal's explanation without graphs.
> ⓓ The worst time to get into the tower was between six in the evening and midnight.
> ⓔ Pascal and Robin entered the tower together.

① ⓐ, ⓑ

② ⓑ, ⓒ

③ ⓐ, ⓑ, ⓓ

④ ⓐ, ⓓ, ⓔ

⑤ ⓒ, ⓓ, ⓔ

27 위 글을 읽고 대답할 수 <u>없는</u> 질문은?　(3점)

① What did Robin ask Pascal to do?

② Why did Pascal feel thankful to Robin?

③ Why couldn't Robin get inside the tower?

④ Why did Pascal want to go to the tower?

⑤ What is the solution to get into the tower?

정답 및 해설

Lesson 5 (중간)

01 ② 02 ④ 03 Arriving 04 ② 05 ④ 06 ④ 07 ②
08 ② 09 ③ 10 ②
11 Is it possible to go to Terminal 2 by subway?
12 ② 13 ⑤ 14 ② 15 I was worried that you were lost.
16 How do I get to your place
17 ③ 18 ① 19 The labyrinth has no dead ends.
20 Following the path all the way to the end 21 ⑤ 22 ④
23 Looking at them closely, you may find the beauty of order
   and regularity.
24 ① 25 ③ 26 ③ 27 ① 28 ③ 29 ④ 30 ②

01 '어떤 사람이 어떤 나쁜 일이나 그/그녀가 일으킨 일에 대해 책임이 있다고 믿거나 말하다'라는 영영 풀이가 가리키는 것은 ② blame(비난하다)이다.

02 '공공 건물에서 나가는 길'이라는 영영 풀이가 가리키는 것은 exit(출구)이다. 따라서 ④ '화재가 났을 경우에는 출구를 찾아야 한다'는 문장에 들어가는 것이 적절하다.

03 분사구문은 「접속사+주어+동사」로 이루어진 부사절을 분사를 포함하는 부사구로 표현한 것으로 시간, 이유, 원인, 조건 등을 나타낸다. 분사구문은 접속사와 주어를 생략하고 동사원형에 ~ing를 붙여 만든다.

04 주어진 문장을 분사구문을 이용한 문장으로 바꾸면, 'Feeling disappointed, I didn't do anything.(실망했기 때문에 나는 아무것도 하지 않았다.)'이 된다.

05 ④ '어머니의 생신을 위해 파이를 만든 후에, 아버지에게 그것을 상자에 넣어달라고 부탁했다.'라는 의미의 문장이다. 따라서 부정대명사 one은 대화 중 이미 언급되었거나 이야기하고 있는 특정한 것을 가리키는 인칭대명사 it으로 고치는 것이 적절하다.

06 ④ Knowing not him → Not knowing him으로 고쳐야 어법상 적절한 문장이 된다.

07 (A) Confusing → Confused / (C) He feeling sleepy → Feeling sleepy / (E) Knowing not → Not knowing으로 고쳐야 어법상 적절한 문장이 된다.

08 ②의 빈칸에는 부정대명사 one이 들어가는 것이 적절하다. 나머지 빈칸에는 대화 중 이미 언급되었거나 이야기하고 있는 특정한 것을 가리키는 인칭대명사 it이 들어가는 것이 어법상 적절하다.

09 B의 질문에 대한 A의 대답이 "그곳에 기차 아니면 버스를 타고 갈 수 있어."였다. 따라서 빈칸에 들어갈 B의 말로 가장 적절한 것은 ③ How can you get there?(너는 그곳에 어떻게 갈 수 있니?)이다.

10 위 대화에서 Henry는 공항에 가는 방법으로 버스와 지하철, 두 가지 방법이 있다고("We have two choices, bus or subway.") 언급했다.

11 "Is it possible to ~?"는 "~하는 것이 가능하니?"라는 의미의 문장이다. to 뒤에는 동사원형이 오는 것이 어법상 적절하다.

12 "내 펜을 여기 두고 온 것 같아."라는 A의 말에 대해 "펜 하나가 여기 있나 살펴보자."라는 B의 대답은 어법상 적절하지 않으므로 부정대명사 one을 인칭대명사 it으로 고치는 것이 적절하다.

13 위 대화에 따르면, 엄마는 아들이 말타기 대신 미로 공원을 방문하고 싶다고 하자 일정을 바꿨고 아들이 만족해하는 걸 보고 기뻐하고 있다. 따라서 ⑤ you decided to stop changing your mind(네가 마음을 바꾸는 걸 멈추기로 결정했다는 걸 들어서 기쁘다.)는 흐름상 적절하지 않다.

14 위 대화에 따르면, 아들은 원래는 말타기 체험을 하고 싶어했지만 마음을 바꿔서 미로 공원에 가고 싶어 한다고("I know, but I heard the park is a lot more fun. Please.") 언급되어 있다.

15 "네가 길을 잃었을까봐 걱정했어."라는 의미의 문장이므로 현재분사 losing은 '길을 잃은'이라는 뜻을 가진 과거분사 lost로 고치는 것이 적절하다.

16 "How do I get to ~?"는 "~에 어떻게 가야 하나요?"라는 의미의 문장으로 길을 묻는 표현이다. to 뒤에는 장소를 나타내는 명사가 오는 것이 적절하다.

17 위 대화에서 휘빈이는 민준이와 상현이가 이미 자신의 집에 있다고만 언급했을 뿐이다.

18 ⓐ Compared → Comparing으로 고쳐야 어법상 적절한 문장이 된다.

19 대명사 this는 앞서 언급된 단수 명사 또는 앞서 언급된 내용이나 문장을 대신한다. 위 글에서는 labyrinth에는 막다른 길이 없다(There are no dead ends.)는 내용, 즉 'The labyrinth has no dead ends.'라는 내용을 대신하는 대명사로 사용되었다.

20 분사구문은 「접속사+주어+동사」로 이루어진 부사절을 분사를 포함하는 부사구로 표현한 것으로 시간, 이유, 원인, 조건 등을 나타낸다. 분사구문은 접속사와 주어를 생략하고 동사원형에 ~ing를 붙여 만든다.

21 마지막 문단에서 maze에 대해서 'If you are not careful, you can easily lose your way.'라고 언급되어 있다.

22 위 글에서는 labyrinth와 maze에 대해서 소개하면서 비교, 설명하고 있다. 따라서 제목으로 가장 적절한 것은 ④ The Differences between Labyrinths and Mazes이다.

23 분사구문은 접속사와 주어를 생략하고 동사원형에 ~ing를 붙여 만든다.

24 (B)의 우리말과 일치하도록 주어진 단어를 배열하면 'it will be worth visiting'이 된다.

25 (가) frustrate: 좌절시키다
   (나) keep ~ing: 계속해서 ~하다
   (다) lose one's way: 길을 잃다

26 '미로는 벽과 방, 산울타리, 벽돌, 거울과 심지어 눈과 같은 다양한 재료로 만들어진다.'라는 문장이 들어가기에 가장 적절한 곳은 미로가 실은 종이 위에 그려지거나 인쇄될 수도 있다고 말하는 곳 앞인 (C)이다.

27 조동사 may는 '~일지도 모른다'는 의미로 어떤 일에 대한 추측을 나타낸다. 또한 의문사가 쓰인 간접의문문이므로 문장의 순서는 '의문사+주어+동사'의 형태가 되어야 어법상 적절하다.

28 (라)one은 부정대명사로 대화 중 앞서 언급한 특정하지 않은 명사를 대신한다. 위 글에서는 문맥상 앞 문장의 solution(해결책)을 가리킨다.

29 마지막 문단에 따르면, 이탈리아의 빌라파사니 미로의 산울타리는 너무 높아서 사람들은 그 너머를 볼 수가 없다고('They are so high that people can't see over them.') 언급되어 있다.

30 위 글에서는 세계 곳곳의 미로에 대해서 소개하고 있다. 따라서 제목으로 가장 적절한 것은 ② Mazes Around the World(세계 곳곳의 미로들)이다.

Lesson 5 (중간) 2회

01 ① **02** ④ **03** ①

04 Looking at the map closely, you can find our school.

05 Seeing the stranger, the dog began to bark.

06 ④ **07** ③

08 (A) How do I get to the library?
(B) Turn right at the crossroad.

09 ④ **10** possible, borrow **11** ③ **12** ③

13 (B) Go straight for one more block. (C) turn right
(D) go straight for about 100 meters

14 (가) Almost. (나) All right. **15** ⑤ **16** ①, ③

17 (가) What a great idea!
(나) Killing two birds with one stone.

18 ④ **19** ③ **20** ② **21** ⑤ **22** ⑤

23 We have to keep making decisions about which way to go.

24 ② **25** ⑤

26 (나) how creative human beings are
(다) It will surely be worth visiting!

27 ⑤

28 (A) When you compare the two pictures below
(B) If you follow

29 ⓐ The labyrinth ⓑ The labyrinth has no dead ends

30 ⑤

01 ① certain은 '확실한'이라는 뜻을 가진 단어이다. 따라서 '무엇을 하거나 믿어야 할지 모르는, 또는 어떤 것에 대해서 결정할 수

없는'이라는 영영 풀이와는 뜻이 반대이다.

02 위에서부터 순서대로, ① influence(영향을 미치다), ② material(재료), ③ exit(출구), ⑤ leap(뛰어오르다)가 들어가는 것이 문맥상 가장 자연스럽다.

03 ①에서 '필통을 잃어버려서 하나 사야 한다'는 의미의 문장이다. 인칭대명사 it은 대화 중 이미 언급되었거나 이야기하고 있는 특정한 물건을 가리킨다. 따라서 대화 중 앞서 언급한 특정하지 않은 명사를 대신하는 부정대명사 one으로 바꾸는 것이 어법상 적절하다.

04 분사구문은 「접속사+주어+동사」로 이루어진 부사절을 분사를 포함하는 부사구로 표현한 것으로 시간, 이유, 원인, 조건 등을 나타낸다. 분사구문은 접속사와 주어를 생략하고 동사원형에 ~ing를 붙여 만든다.

05 분사구문은 「접속사+주어+동사」로 이루어진 부사절을 분사를 포함하는 부사구로 표현한 것으로 시간, 이유, 원인, 조건 등을 나타낸다. 분사구문은 접속사와 주어를 생략하고 동사원형에 ~ing를 붙여 만든다.

06 ⓐ a new it → a new one / ⓓ is considered → considers / ⓕ safely → safe로 고쳐야 어법상 적절한 문장이 된다.

07 ③의 문장은 '책을 읽는 것은 어려운 일일지 모르지만, 언제나 당신의 영혼에 유익하다'라는 의미의 문장으로 분사구문이 쓰인 문장이 아니다. Reading은 동명사로 문장에서 주어 역할을 하고 있다.

08 (A) "How do I get to ~?"는 "~에 어떻게 가야 하나요?"라는 의미의 문장으로 길을 묻는 표현이다. to 뒤에는 장소를 나타내는 명사가 오는 것이 적절하다
(B) turn right: 우회전하다, crossroad: 교차로

09 B(주원이)가 무엇을 읽고 있냐고 Alice에게 묻자, Alice는 미궁의 기원에 대한 책이라고 대답한다(C). 주원이는 미궁이 반인반수를 가두는 오래된 신화에 나오는 감옥이 아니냐고 되묻자(B), Alice는 주원이가 그 이야기를 알고 있냐고 묻자(D), 주원이는 그렇지 않다고 대답하면서 신화 속 나오는 괴물의 이름을 잊어버렸다고(A) 말하는 순서로 이어지는 것이 흐름상 가장 자연스럽다.

10 "Is it possible to ~?"는 "~하는 것이 가능하니?"라는 의미의 문장이다. to 뒤에는 동사원형이 오는 것이 어법상 적절하다.

11 위 대화에 따르면, 주원이는 신화 속의 괴물 이름을 잊어버렸다고 ("Not really, I forgot the name of the monster.) 언급했으므로 주원이는 그들의 대화 주제에 대해서 완전히 알고 있지 않다고 볼 수 있다.

12 수지의 말에 이어 Andrew는 자신의 집으로 오는 길을 알려주고 있다. 따라서 빈칸 (A)에 ③ How long does it take to go to your house from here?(여기서 너희 집까지 시간이 얼마나 걸리니?)는 적절하지 않다.

13 위 대화와 그림에 따르면, 현재 수지는 우체국이 보이는 곳에 서 있다. (B)에는 "한 블록 더 직진해."가 적절하다. 이후 Kim's Bakery가 보이면 우회전을 해서 100미터 정도 직진하면 Andrew의 집에 도착할 수 있다. 따라서 (C)에는 turn right, (D)에는 go straight for about 100 meters가 들어가는 것이

적절하다.

14 여학생이 엄마에게 제주로 가는 가족 여행 동안에 어디를 방문할지 결정했냐고 물어보았고, 엄마는 거의 됐다고 말하면서 자신의 계획을 와서 보라고 대답한다. 따라서 (가)에는 "Almost.(거의.)"가 적절하다. 여학생이 여성에게 말타기 대신 미로 공원에 가고 싶다고 말했고 여성은 일정을 변경하자고 대답한다. 따라서 (나)에는 "All right.(그래.)"이 적절하다.

15 위 대화에서 여학생은 엄마에게 둘째날에 거울 미로 공원에 가자고 제안하고 있다. 따라서 ⑤ why do you want to visit(왜 둘째날에 거울 미로 공원에 가고 싶어해요?)는 문맥상 적절하지 않다.

16 위 글에 따르면, 엄마는 딸이 승마를 하고 싶어 해서 승마 체험을 계획했지만("It sounds exciting, but I remember you said you wanted to go horseback riding.") 딸은 승마 대신 미로 공원에 가고 싶어 한다고 말해서 일정을 변경했다("Let's change our schedule for the second day.").

17 (가) 여학생이 새 기타를 사기 위한 돈을 모금하고 신곡을 발표할 수 있는 기회인 공연을 열자고 말하자, 남학생은 좋은 생각이라고 ("What a great idea.") 대답한다.
(나) 남학생은 여학생의 계획이 일석이조("Killing two birds with one stone.")라고 생각한다.

18 A가 도움이 필요하냐고 묻자, B가 이 건물의 괜찮은 중식당을 추천해줄 수 있냐고 물어보면서, 두 곳 중에 결정을 못하겠다고 말한다(ⓑ). A는 Papa Chen's가 어떠냐고 제안하면서, 음식도 맛있고 가격도 합리적이라고 말한다(ⓐ). B는 좋은 생각이라고 말하면서, 그곳까지 어떻게 가냐고 묻는다(ⓓ). 이에 A가 4층에 있다고 대답하면서 엘레베이터 옆에 있으므로 엘레베이터를 이용하라고 (ⓒ) 말하는 순서로 이어지는 것이 흐름상 가장 자연스럽다.

19 '가장 쉽고 믿을 만한 해결 방법은 맨 처음부터 손을 한 쪽 벽에 두는 것이다.'라는 문장이 들어가기에 가장 적절한 곳은 미로 안에서 길을 잃지 않는 방법으로 벽에 손을 두고 계속 벽을 따라가라고 말하는 곳인 (C)이다.

20 ⓐ 미로에서 길을 잃지 않는 방법으로 가장 쉬운 방법은 벽에 손을 두고 난 후 계속 벽을 따라가는 것이라고 말하고 있다. 따라서 Then(그러고 나서)이 적절하다. / ⓑ 미로를 걷는 것이 어두운 방에서 걷는 것과 같다고 말하면서, 벽에 손을 대고 걷는 이 가장 쉬운 방법이 어떤 종류의 미로에는 통하지 않는다고 말하고 있다. 따라서 Unfortunately(불행히도)가 적절하다.

21 위 글에 따르면, 사람들이 기꺼이 미로를 방문해서 미로의 '계획된 혼란'을 즐긴다는 내용이다. 따라서 빈칸에는 ⑤ planned confusion이 적절하다.

22 마지막 문단에서 미로를 걷는 가장 쉽고 믿을 만한 방법도 어떤 종류의 미로에서는 통하지 않을 수도 있다고('Unfortunately, this simple method may not be effective in certain types of mazes, especially when all of the walls are not connected') 말하고 있다.

23 위 글에 따르면, 미로에서는 어느 방향으로 가야 하는지에 대해서

계속 결정을 내려야 한다고('You have to keep making decisions about which way to go.) 언급되어 있다.

24 미로가 여러 종류의 재료로 만들어졌다고 말하면서(B), 미로는 종이 위에 인쇄되거나 그려질 수도 있으며(A), 미로가 종이 위에 그려지는 숫자 미로(C)에 대해서 설명하는 순서로 이어지는 것이 흐름상 가장 자연스럽다.

25 (가)order는 '순서', '질서'라는 뜻으로 사용되었다. / ①, ②, ④: 주문, ③: 명령

26 (나) 의문사를 이용해 문장 내에서 목적어가 될 수 있는 간접의문문을 만들 수 있다. 이때 간접의문문은 명사절로 취급하고, '의문사+주어+동사' 순으로 쓴다.
(다) be worth ~ing: ~할 가치가 있다

27 위 글에서는 labyrinth와 maze에 대해서 소개하면서 비교, 설명하고 있다. 따라서 제목으로 가장 적절한 것은 ⑤ The Differences between Labyrinths and Mazes이다.

28 분사구문을 부사절로 바꿀 경우, 분사구문의 의미에 따라 부사절의 접속사가 달라진다. (A)는 '아래의 두 사진을 비교해 볼 때'라는 의미의 문장이므로 접속사 when을 쓰는 것이 적절하다. (B)는 '마지막까지 길을 쭉 따라가게 되면'이라는 의미의 문장이다. 따라서 접속사 if를 쓰는 것이 적절하다.

29 ⓐ 대명사 it은 앞서 언급된 단수명사를 가리킨다. 위 글에서는 문맥상 the labyrinth를 가리킨다. / ⓑ 대명사 this는 앞서 언급된 단수 명사 또는 앞서 언급된 내용이나 문장을 대신한다. 위 글에서는 labyrinth에는 막다른 길이 없다(There are no dead ends.)는 내용을 대신하는 대명사로 사용되었다.

30 위 글에 따르면, labyrinth에 들어가서 길을 쭉 따라가면 중심에 이를 수 있다고('Following the path all the way to the end, you will reach the center.') 언급되어 있다.

Lesson 6 (중간) 1회

01 ⑤ **02** ② **03** ② **04** ④ **05** ③
06 (A) It is at the park that I ride a bike.
　　(B) It was Tom that[who] broke the window.
07 ② **08** ④ **09** ⑤ **10** ① **11** ② **12** ④ **13** ④
14 It means "Have a nice day."
15 What do you think of these acronyms, Mom?
16 ⑤ **17** ⑤ **18** ⑤ **19** ⑤ **20** ② **21** ④
22 Killing two birds with one stone.
23 ④ **24** 네가 하는 것은 네가 말하는 것보다 더 중요하다.
25 ① **26** ③ **27** ④ **28** ⑤ **29** ④
30 It is you that should decide what is best for you.

01 빈칸에 공통으로 들어갈 단어는 '유지하다', '가지고 있다'라는 뜻을 가진 동사 keep이다.

keep in touch: 연락을 유지하다

keep the chance: 기회를 가지다

02 disagree는 '동의하지 않다'라는 뜻을 가진 단어이다. 주어진 영영 풀이가 가리키는 것은 agree(동의하다)이다.

03 동사를 강조할 경우에는 대동사 do를 원래 동사 앞에 써서 'Sean did meet Jane at the station.'이라고 바꾸는 것이 어법상 적절하다.

04 ④는 '유민이가 시험에서 만점을 받을 것이라는 것은 사실이다.'라는 의미의 문장이다. 나머지는 모두 It-that 강조 구문이다.

05 however는 '그러나'라는 의미의 접속부사로 앞뒤 문장의 의미가 반대될 때 쓸 수 있다.

06 It-that 강조 구문은 강조하고자 하는 부분을 It is/was와 that 사이에 넣고, 나머지 부분을 that 뒤에 써서 나타낸다. '…한 것은 바로 ~이다/이었다'라고 해석한다.

07 (A) fascinating: 매혹시키는, 매혹적인

(B) take away: ~을 빼앗아 가다

08 A가 Emma에게 쉬자고 말하자(C), Emma는 공부한지 30분 밖에 안 되었다고 대답한다(D). A가 '일만 하고 놀지 않으면 우둔한 사람이 된다'는 속담을 말한다(B). 이에 Emma가 알겠다고 말하면서, 이 부분만 끝내고 쉬자고(A) 말하는 순서로 이어지는 것이 흐름상 가장 자연스럽다.

09 A의 질문에 대한 B의 대답이 "난 그것이 건강하지 않다고 생각해."였다. 따라서 빈칸에 들어갈 A의 말로 가장 적절한 것은 ⑤ What do you think of(~에 대해서 어떻게 생각하니?)이다.

10 위 대화에서는 다른 사람이 없을 때 그 사람의 이야기를 하지 말아야 한다고 이야기하고 있다. 따라서 빈칸에 들어갈 말로 가장 적절한 것은 ① Walls have ears.(낮말은 새가 듣고 밤말은 쥐가 듣는다.)이다.

11 위 대화에서는 환경을 보호하지 않으면 결국 후회하는 것은 우리가 될 것이라고 말하고 있다. 따라서 빈칸에 들어갈 말로 가장 적절한 것은 ② What goes around comes around.(남에게 잘못한 만큼 자신에게 돌아오는 법이다.)이다.

12 ⓓ: I still think they are useless.는 I still think they are useful.로 고치는 것이 적절하다.

13 ⓓraise는 '모금하다'라는 뜻으로 쓰였다.

14 위 대화에 따르면, 두문자어 HAND는 "Have a nice day.(좋은 하루 보내.)"를 의미한다고 언급되어 있다.

15 "What do you think of ~?"는 "~에 대해서 어떻게 생각하니?"라는 의미의 문장으로 상대방의 의견을 묻는 표현이다.

16 위 대화에서 엄마는 친구로부터 받은 메시지의 몇몇 글자들을 이해하지 못하겠다고("Well, I got a message from my friend, but I don't understand what some letters of it mean.") 언급되어 있다.

17 "사진을 인터넷에 올리는 것에 대해 어떻게 생각하니?"라는 A의 질문에 대해 "난 반대해. 어떤 사람들은 너의 사진들을 악용할 수도 있어."라는 B의 대답이 흐름상 가장 자연스럽다.

18 위 대화에서 B가 유라에게 무엇을 하고 있냐고 물어보자 유라는 인터넷에 사진을 올리고 있다고 대답하면서 와서 보라고 말한다. B는 네 일상을 보여주는 사진이 많다고 하면서 그것이 위험하지 않냐고 묻는다(ⓓ). 유라는 자신의 친구들도 사진을 많이 올리기에 그것이 서로를 알아갈 수 있는 좋은 방법이라고 생각한다고 대답한다(ⓒ). B는 동의하지 않는다고 말하면서, 그것을 악용하는 사람들이 있을 수 있다고 말한다(ⓑ). 이에 유라가 생각해 보니, 사진 올리는 것에 더욱 주의해야겠다고 대답하면서 충고 고맙다고 (ⓐ) 말하는 순서로 이어지는 것이 흐름상 가장 자연스럽다.

19 '그 결과, 우리가 수정하는 데 더 많은 시간이 들게 될 거야.'라는 문장이 들어가기에 가장 적절한 곳은 곰곰이 생각하지 않고 어떤 것을 한다면 실수할 수 있다고 말하는 곳 뒤인 (E)이다.

20 위 글에서 주어진 속담은 '돌다리도 두드려 보고 건너라.'이며 Brian Pearson은 기회는 자주 오지 않는다고 말하면서 이에 대해 반대하고 있다. 따라서 빈칸 (가)에 들어갈 속담으로 알맞은 것은 ② Strike while the iron is hot.(쇠뿔도 단김에 빼라.)이다.

21 give it a second thought는 '한 번 더 곰곰히 생각해 보다'라는 뜻을 가진 표현이다.

22 <보기>의 설명처럼, 한 가지 행동으로 두 가지 문제를 해결하는 것은 '일석이조'라는 뜻을 가진 영어 표현인 'Killing two birds with one stone.'이다.

23 위 글에 따르면, 수지는 '돌다리도 두들겨 보고 건너라.'는 속담에 대해 동의하면서 결정하기 전에 신중하지 않으면 실수할 수 있다고 ("Also, we'll make mistakes if we do something without giving it a second thought.") 말하고 있다.

24 관계대명사 what은 선행사를 포함하는 관계대명사로 명사절을 이끌며, '~하는 것'으로 해석된다.

25 위 글에서는 '행동이 말보다 중요하다'라는 속담을 설명하면서 다른 의견을 가진 사람들도 있다고 언급하고 있다. 따라서 문맥상 빈칸에 들어갈 말로 적절한 것은 순서대로 ⓐ words, ⓑ actions, ⓒ words이다.

26 몇몇 사람들은 말보다 행동으로 보여주려고 노력하지만 다른 몇몇 사람들은 다른 의견을 갖고 있다는 내용이다. 따라서 빈칸 (B)에 들어갈 가장 알맞은 표현은 ③ However(그러나)이다.

27 위 글에서는 말의 지혜가 사람들에게 영향을 주고 그들의 삶을 바꾼다고 설명하고 있다. 또한 속담에 대한 상반되는 의견이 있을 수 있다고 말하면서 그 예시를 살펴보자고 이야기하고 있다. 따라서 다음에 이어질 내용으로 알맞은 것은 ④ '다양한 의견을 가질 수 있는 속담 제시'이다.

28 ⓔ that make → that makes로 고쳐야 어법상 적절한 문장이 된다.

29 위 글에서는 '눈에서 멀어지면, 마음에서도 멀어진다.'라는 속담에 대해서 이야기하고 있다. Anna Brown은 자신의 초등학교 친구를 예시로 들면서 이에 대해 동의하고 있다.

30 It-that 강조 구문은 강조하고자 하는 부분을 It is/was와 that 사이에 넣고, 나머지 부분을 that 뒤에 써서 나타낸다. '…한 것은 바

로 '~이다/이었다'라고 해석한다.

Lesson 6 (중간)

01 ②	02 ⑤	03 ③	04 ⑤	05 ②	06 ②	07 ①	08 ②
09 ④	10 ①	11 ③	12 ⑤	13 ⑤	14 ①	15 ①, ④	
16 ⑤	17 ③	18 ④	19 ②	20 ①			

21 Opportunities, often　　　　22 ④

23 If there is a chance, we should grab it.　　24 ②, ⑤

25 ④　26 Strike while the iron is hot.　27 ③　28 ③　29 ③

30 (a) cold → hot (b) could → may (c) what → that

01 두 문장의 빈칸에 들어갈 단어로 가장 적절한 것은 ② influence (영향; 영향을 미치다)이다.

02 reliable은 '신뢰할 수 있는'이라는 의미의 단어이다.

03 frightening: 무시무시한, 무섭게 하는 / cause: 야기하다, 발생시키다

04 ⑤ It was threw away that I trash yesterday. → I did throw away the trash yesterday.로 고쳐야 어법상 적절한 문장이 된다.

05 ① was → is / ② March → in March / ④ who he → who / ⑤ It was went hiking that Lisa with Jinsu last Friday. → Lisa did go hiking with Jinsu last Friday.로 고쳐야 어법상 적절한 문장이 된다.

06 "늦지 마! 내일 시계탑 앞에서 오전 11시에 만나는 거야."라는 A의 질문에 대해 "알겠어."라는 B의 대답이 흐름상 가장 자연스럽다.

07 A는 뒷담화하는 것에 대해서 어떻게 생각하는지 B에게 물어보았고, B는 그것이 무례하다고 생각한다고 말하고 있다. 따라서 빈칸에는 ① Walls have ears.(낮말은 새가 듣고 밤말은 쥐가 듣는다.)가 적절하다.

08 대명사 they, them은 앞서 언급된 복수 명사를 가리킨다. 위 대화에서는 문맥상 ② 'AI robots'를 가리킨다.

09 ⓓ agree → disagree로 고쳐야 문맥상 적절한 문장이 된다.

10 위 대화에서 경빈이는 도일이가 자신의 일상 사진을 인터넷에 올리는 것에 대해 반대하면서, 좀 더 조심해야 한다고 충고하고 있다. 따라서 빈칸에 들어갈 경빈이의 말로 가장 적절한 것은 ① "사진을 악용하는 사람이 있을 수도 있어."(There might be some people who will use your pictures in a bad way.)이다.

11 ⓒ should allow → should be allowed로 고쳐야 어법상 적절한 문장이 된다.

12 위 글에서는 ⑤ What does Claire think they should use to reserve the music rooms?(Claire는 음악실을 예약하기 위해 무엇을 사용해야 한다고 생각하는가?)에 대해서는 언급된 바 없다.

13 (A) ASAP는 as soon as possible(가능한 한 빨리)을 의미한

다. / (B) ASAP과 HAND는 acronyms(두문자어)의 예이다. / (C) 위 대화에서 두문자어에 대해 엄마는 언어를 파괴할 수 있다고 우려하는 반면 Jacob은 그것이 재미있고 사용하기 쉽다고 의견을 표현하고 있다. 따라서 opinion이 적절하다.

14 위 대화에 따르면, Jacob의 엄마가 친구로부터 ASAP과 HAND라는 두문자어가 포함된 문자를 받았고 Jacob에게 무슨 뜻인지 물어보고 있다.

15 위 글에서 재하는 자신의 이웃과 거리가 멀어졌지만 시간이 가도 여전히 그 친구를 보고 싶어 하고 있고, 사람들이 서로를 생각하는 것은 같이 보낸 시간의 질이라고 말하고 있다. 이에 대해 마지막 문단에서 당신의 의견이 무엇인지 물어보면서, 정답은 없으며 자신에게 가장 잘 맞는 대답을 결정해야 한다고 말하고 있다. 따라서 빈칸에 들어갈 말로 가장 적절한 것은 ① 'You should decide what is best for you.', ④ 'It is you that should decide what is best for you.'이다.

16 주어진 문장은 '백지장도 맞들면 낫다.'라는 의미의 속담이다. 따라서 이와 같은 의미의 문장은 ⓐ '다른 사람들로부터 훌륭한 아이디어를 얻을 수 있다,' ⓒ '일을 빠르게 완성할 수 있다.'이다. / ⓑ: 결정하기 전에 너무 많은 시간을 할애할 수 있다, ⓓ: 너무 많은 정보로 인해 혼란스러워질 수 있다, ⓔ: 일을 완성할 때 더 도움이 되는 것은 나 자신의 생각이다.

17 '그러나, 몇몇 사람들은 다른 의견을 갖고 있다.'라는 문장이 들어가기에 가장 적절한 곳은 행동보다 말이 더 중요하다고 생각하는 사람들이 있다고 말하는 곳인 (C)이다.

18 (ㄱ)은 '당신이 행하는 것이 말하는 것보다 더 중요하다'라는 의미라고 언급되어 있다. 따라서 빈칸 (ㄱ)에 들어갈 표현으로 가장 적절한 것은 ④'Actions speak louder than words.'이다.

19 (가) It-that 강조 구문이 쓰인 문장으로, '행동보다 더 중요한 것은 말이다.'라는 의미의 문장이다. / (나) 가주어It - 진주어 to부정사 구문이 쓰인 문장으로, '다른 생각을 갖는 것은 자연스럽다.'라는 의미의 문장이다.

20 말의 지혜가 사람들에게 영향을 주고 그들의 삶을 바꾼다고 설명하고 있다. 또한 속담에 대한 상반되는 의견이 있을 수 있다고 말하면서 그 예시를 살펴보자고 이야기하고 있다. 따라서 제목으로 가장 적절한 것은 ① Proverbs Upside Down(거꾸로 보는 속담)이다.

21 opportunitiy: 기회

22 (A) 수지는 결정을 내리기 전에 신중해야 한다고 말하면서, 충분히 시간을 갖지 않으면 후회할 수 있다고 말하고 있다. 따라서 However(그러나)가 적절하다. / (B) 곰곰이 생각하지 않고 결정을 내리면 실수를 할 수 있고 그 결과 그 실수를 만회하는 데 더 많은 시간이 들 수 있다는 내용이므로 빈칸에는 As a result(그 결과)가 적절하다.

23 조건을 의미하는 접속사 if를 이용해서 'If there is a chance, we should grab it.'이라고 영작할 수 있다.

24 위 글에서 Suzi는 '돌다리도 두들겨 보고 건너라.'라는 속담에 완전히 동의한다고 말하고 있다.

25 위 글에 따르면, Brian은 '돌다리도 두들겨 보고 건너라.'라는 속담에 동의하지 않는다고 말하면서 기회가 왔을 때 잡아야 한다고 생각한다. 그 예로 자신이 하키 팀의 주장이 되어달라는 요청을 받았을 때 너무 신중하게 생각했고 결국 다른 사람이 주장이 되었다고 말하면서 후회하고 있다고 언급하고 있다.

26 위 글에 따르면, Brian은 '돌다리도 두들겨 보고 건너라.'라는 속담에 동의하지 않는다고 말하면서 기회가 왔을 때 잡아야 한다고 생각한다. 그 예로 자신이 하키 팀의 주장이 되어달라는 요청을 받았을 때 너무 신중하게 생각했고 결국 다른 사람이 주장이 되었다고 말하면서 후회하고 있다고 언급하고 있다. 따라서 빈칸 (다)에 들어갈 말로 가장 적절한 속담은 'Strike while the iron is hot.'(쇠뿔도 단김에 빼라.)이다.

27 ⓐ closely → close / ⓓ when makes people remember each other → that makes people remember each other / ⓔ that is best for you → what is best for you로 고쳐야 어법상 적절한 문장이 된다.

28 (가) stop ~ing: ~하는 것을 멈추다
(나) spend a lot of time ~ing: ~하면서 많은 시간을 보내다
(다) I haven't seen her since: 그 이후로 그녀를 보지 못했다

29 위 글에 따르면, Jenny의 가족이 3년 전에 다른 곳으로 이사를 갔다고('Then her family moved away three years ago.') 언급되어 있다.

30 (a) 이 글에서는 '쇠뿔도 단김에 빼라.'는 속담에 대해서 이야기하고 있다. 따라서 cold는 hot으로 고치는 것이 적절하다. / (b) 생각할 시간을 갖지 않으면 결정에 대해 후회할 수도 있다는 내용이므로 조동사 could는 may로 고치는 것이 적절하다. / (c) It-that 강조 구문은 강조하고자 하는 부분을 It is/was와 that 사이에 넣고, 나머지 부분을 that 뒤에 써서 나타낸다. 따라서 what은 that으로 고치는 것이 적절하다.

Lesson 7 (기말) [1회]

> **01** ② **02** ⑤ **03** If it snowed a lot, we would go sledding.
> **04** ① **05** ④ **06** ③ **07** ③, ⑤ **08** ② **09** ④
> **10** Antoni Gaudi designed
> **11** how his design was inspired by nature
> **12** (가) Why? (나) That would be cool,
> **13** ⑤ **14** ① **15** ① **16** ④ **17** ② **18** ②
> **19** 그 집들은 평평한 지붕이 있어. **20** ④ **21** ③
> **22** to keep themselves safe from invaders
> **23** ④ **24** ④ **25** ② **26** ④ **27** lived, would, to
> **28** (1) live → living (2) has → have **29** ① **30** ①, ④

01 '어떤 사람으로 하여금 당신을 예찬하거나 존경하도록 만들다'라는 영영 풀이가 가리키는 것은 ② impress(깊은 인상을 주다)이

02 support는 '지지하다', '부양하다'라는 뜻을 가진 단어이다.

03 가정법과거 문장은 'If+주어+were/동사의 과거형 ~, 주어+조동사의 과거형(would/should/could/might)+동사원형 ….'의 형식으로 현재 사실과 반대되는 가정을 나타낼 때 쓸 수 있다.

04 가정법과거 문장은 'If+주어+were/동사의 과거형 ~, 주어+조동사의 과거형(would/should/could/might)+동사원형 ….'의 형식으로 현재 사실과 반대되는 가정을 나타낼 때 쓸 수 있다.

05 ① warmly → warm / ② worriedly → worried / ③ surprising → surprised / ⑤ doing easily → easy to do로 고쳐야 어법상 적절한 문장이 된다.

06 ⓒ If I lived in a jungle(정글에 산다면) - ⓜ I would go to Mars first(최초로 화성에 갈 텐데.)는 흐름상 적절하지 않다.

07 과거 사실과 반대되는 내용을 가정할 때에는 'If+주어+had p.p+~, 주어+조동사의 과거형(would/should/could/might)+have+p.p ….'의 형식의 가정법 과거완료 형식을 쓰는 것이 어법상 적절하다.

08 "그래서, 그 집에 산다면 뭘 할 건데?"라는 문장이 들어가기에 가장 적절한 곳은 주어진 질문에 대한 대답으로 심해에 있는 집에 산다면 심해를 탐험하고 특이한 해양 동물을 찾을 것이라고 말한 곳 앞인 (B)이다.

09 대명사 it은 앞서 언급된 단수 명사 혹은 앞 문장 전체를 가리킨다. 위 대화에서 (가)it이 가리키는 것으로 가장 적절한 것은 ④이다.

10 과거의 일이므로 시제는 과거형이 되어야 한다.

11 의문사를 이용해 문장 내에서 목적어가 될 수 있는 간접의문문을 만들 수 있다. 이때 간접의문문은 명사절로 취급하여 문장 내에서 주어, 목적어, 보어 역할을 한다. '의문사+주어+동사' 순으로 쓴다.

12 B가 완전히 거울로 덮인 집을 지을 것이라고 말하자, G가 왜 그런지 이유를 물어본다. 이에 B가 거울이 집을 거의 눈에 보이지 않게 만들 것이기 때문이라고 대답하자, G가 멋지다고 대답하는 것이 흐름상 자연스럽다.

13 위 대화에서 두 화자는 해외여행을 하고 있는 친구가 보낸 사진을 보면서 대화하고 있다.

14 유민이는 터키를 여행하고 있는 Julia로부터 사진을 받았다고 한다.

15 위 대화에 따르면, 진호는 정글에 사는 것이 정말 신날 것이라고("I think living in a jungle would be really exciting.") 언급하고 있다.

16 푸에블로의 두꺼운 벽은 흙과 지푸라기, 그리고 물로 만들어졌다고('The thick walls are made of earth, straw, and water.') 언급되어 있다.

17 위 글에서는 다양한 형태의 집과 주거 형태에 대해서 설명하고 있다. 따라서 빈칸 (A)에 들어갈 말로 가장 적절한 것은 ② Different people live in different houses.(다양한 사람들은 다양한 집에서 산다.)이다.

18 주어진 우리말을 영작하면, 'If unwelcome visitors appeared.

I would pull the ladder up to stop them from entering.'이 된다. 따라서 순서대로 unwelcome(환영받지 못하는), pull(당기다), stop ~ from -ing(~가 …하지 못하게 하다) 이 들어가는 것이 적절하다.

19 flat: 평평한, roof: 지붕

20 위 글에서는 이탈리아의 베니스가 물 위에 떠 있는 주거 형태를 갖게 되었는지에 대한 이유와 어떻게 그것을 건축했는지에 대해서 이야기하고 있다. 따라서 제목으로 가장 적절한 것은 ④ The Floating City: How and Why?(물에 떠 있는 도시: 어떻게 그리고 왜?)이다.

21 위 글에서는 이탈리아의 베니스가 물 위에 떠 있는 주거 형태를 갖게 되었는지에 대한 이유와 어떻게 그것을 건축했는지에 대해서 이야기하고 있다. 따라서 빈칸 (가)에 들어갈 내용으로 가장 적절한 것은 ③ floating city(물에 떠 있는 도시)이다.

22 keep A safe from ~: ~로부터 A를 안전하게 지키다

23 위 글에서는 ④ '거리가 물에 잠겼을 때 걸을 수 있는 가교 통로의 이름은?'에 대해서는 언급된 바 없다.

24 위 글에서는 이탈리아의 베니스가 물 위에 떠 있는 주거 형태를 갖게 되었는지에 대한 이유와 어떻게 그것을 건축했는지에 대해서 이야기하고 있다. 따라서 ⓓ '많은 방문자들은 그 도시의 숲을 보고 영감을 얻는다.'라는 문장은 흐름상 적절하지 않다.

25 (A) by+교통수단: ~를 타고
(B) high tide: 만조
(C) leave A full of ~: A를 ~로 가득찬 채로 두다

26 첫 문단에서 중국의 tulou라는 주거 형태가 3층에서 5층으로 이루어져 있다고 말한다. 1층은 주방과 식당으로, 2층은 음식과 도구를 저장하며 침실은 3층 또는 4층이다(C). tulou는 마을과도 같으며 같은 성을 가진 사람들이 같이 일하고 많은 것들을 공유한다(A). 집은 어디에나 있지만 전 세계가 모두 다르다. 당신의 집은 어떤 모습인지에 대해 묻는(B) 순서로 이어지는 것이 흐름상 가장 자연스럽다.

27 가정법과거 문장은 'If+주어+were/동사의 과거형 ~, 주어+조동사의 과거형(would/should/could/might)+동사원형 ….'의 형식으로 현재 사실과 반대되는 가정을 나타낼 때 쓸 수 있다. 따라서 우리말에 맞게 빈칸을 완성하면, 'If I lived in a tulou, I would always have friends at home to play with.'가 된다.

28 (1) The people이 주어이자 선행사이므로 live in은 (who are) living in의 형태가 되는 것이 적절하다.
(2) 주어가 복수인 The people이므로 동사는 have가 되는 것이 적절하다.

29 의문사를 이용해 문장 내에서 목적어가 될 수 있는 간접의문문을 만들 수 있다. '의문사+주어+동사' 순으로 쓴다.

30 위 글에 따르면, Tulou에는 항상 집에서 함께 놀 친구들이 있으며('If I lived in a tulou, I would always have friends at home to play with.'), Tulou의 주민들은 대부분 같은 성씨라고('The people living in a tulou mostly have the same family name.') 언급되어 있다.

Lesson 7 (기말)

2회

> **01** ③ **02** ③ **03** He kept the door closed.
> **04** (예) If I were a bird, I would fly in the sky.
> **05** ③ **06** ③, ④ **07** ②
> **08** Because I don't have enough money, I can't buy a better computer.
> **09** ④ **10** ⑤ **11** ① **12** ⑤ **13** safe, dangerous
> **14** ① **15** ④ **16** rises and leaves the streets full
> **17** ⓐ able ⓑ around ⓒ raised **18** ① **19** ⑤ **20** ③ **21** ③
> **22** ⑤ **23** ④ **24** ② **25** ③ **26** ③ **27** ③ **28** ⑤ **29** ④
> **30** ③

01 위에서부터 순서대로, earth(땅), walkway(통로), tide(조류, 밀물과 썰물), invader(침략자)가 들어가는 것이 문맥상 가장 자연스럽다.

02 ③ invasion은 '침략'이라는 뜻을 갖는 단어이다.

03 'keep+목적어+목적보어'는 '(목적어)가 (목적보어)하도록 유지하다'라는 의미를 갖는다. 이때 목적보어는 목적어와의 관계에 따라 현재분사(능동), 과거분사(수동)를 쓸 수 있다.

04 가정법과거 문장은 'If+주어+were/동사의 과거형 ~, 주어+조동사의 과거형(would/should/could/might)+동사원형 ….'의 형식으로 현재 사실과 반대되는 가정을 나타낼 때 쓸 수 있다.

05 ③ will → would로 고쳐야 어법상 적절한 문장이 된다.

06 ① happily → happy / ② waited → waiting / ⑤ warmly → warm으로 고쳐야 어법상 적절한 문장이 된다.

07 주어진 문장은 '나는 카메라가 없기 때문에 사진을 찍지 않는다.'라는 의미의 문장이다. 따라서 현재 사실과 반대되는 내용을 가정하는 가정법과거 문장을 이용해서 ② If I had a camera, I would take pictures.(내가 카메라를 갖고 있다면, 나는 사진을 찍을 텐데.)라고 영작할 수 있다.

08 가정법과거 문장은 'If+주어+were/동사의 과거형 ~, 주어+조동사의 과거형(would/should/could/might)+동사원형 ….'의 형식으로 현재 사실과 반대되는 가정을 나타낼 때 쓸 수 있다. 따라서 주어진 문장을 접속사 Because를 사용한 문장으로 바꾸면, '돈이 없어서 더 좋은 컴퓨터를 살 수 없다.'라는 문장으로 쓸 수 있다.

09 A가 자신의 꿈의 집이라고 말하면서 Alice의 생각을 묻자(ⓒ), Alice는 그것이 심해에 있어서 특이해 보인다고 대답하면서 그런 집에 살면 무엇을 할 것인지 묻자(ⓑ), A는 심해 탐험을 하고 특이한 해양 동물을 발견할 것이라고 대답한다(ⓐ). 이에 Alice가 멋지다고(ⓓ) 말하는 순서로 이어지는 것이 흐름상 가장 자연스럽다.

10 위 대화에서는 ⑤ When will Taeho move to Alaska?(태호는 언제 알래스카로 이사할 것인가?)에 대해서는 언급된 바 없다.

11 위 대화에서 태호는 선물로 받은 썰매를 타보고 싶어 하지만 눈이 오지 않아서 실망하고, 알래스카에서는 하루 종일 썰매를 탈 수 있을 것이라며 아쉬워하고 있다. 따라서 빈칸에 들어갈 말로 가장 적

절한 것은 ① I wish I could live in Alaska.(알래스카에 살면 좋을 텐데.)이다.

12 진호가 정글에서 사는 것이 재밌을 것이라고 말하면서 Claire의 의견을 묻는다. Claire는 정글에 위험한 동물들이 많다고 말하자(C), 진호는 알지만 정글은 탐험으로 가득 차 있어서 그곳에 살고 싶다고 대답한다(B). Claire가 정글에 산다면 무엇을 할 것인지 물어보자(D), 진호가 정글 탐험을 하면서 동물 친구들도 만들 수 있을 것이라고(A) 말하는 순서로 이어지는 것이 흐름상 가장 자연스럽다.

13 주어진 우리말을 영작하면 'I would be safe from dangerous animals.'가 된다.

14 위 글에서는 ① When will Jinho go to the jungle?(진호는 정글에 언제 갈 예정인가?)에 대해서는 언급된 바 없다.

15 위 대화에 따르면, 휘빈이와 민우는 방문하고 싶은 나라에 대한 발표 주제로 스페인 출신 건축가 Antoni Gaudi가 지은 건축물인 La Sagrada Familia를 선택하는 것에 대해서 논의하고 있다.

16 위 글에 따르면, 베니스에서는 밀물 때에 아드리아해의 물이 차오르면 거리를 물로 가득하게 한다고 이야기하고 있다. 따라서 영작하면 'At high tide, the water from the Adriatic Sea often rises and leaves the streets full of water.'가 되는 것이 적절하다.

17 주어진 우리말을 영작하면 'I would be able to walk around the town through the raised walkways.'가 된다.

18 ⓐ sleep on the floor: 바닥에서 자다
ⓑ natural: 자연적인
ⓒ help keep you cool in summer: 여름에 시원하게 지내도록 돕다

19 위 글에 따르면, 'Hanok houses are mostly built with natural materials such as wood, stone, straw, paper, and earth. These materials help you keep your skin healthy.'라고 언급되어 있다.

20 위 글에서는 중국의 거주 형태 중 하나인 tulou에 대해서 소개하고 설명하고 있다. 따라서 위 글의 주제로 가장 적절한 것은 ③ the feature and structure of tulou(tulou의 특징과 구조)이다.

21 ⓐ play → play with / ⓒ where would I → where I would / ⓔ keep → keeps로 고쳐야 어법상 적절한 문장이 된다.

22 (가)store는 '저장하다'라는 의미로 사용되었다.

23 위 글에 따르면, (라) 어떤 토루는 50가구 이상 수용할 수 있다고 언급되어 있다. 또한 (마) 토루에 사는 사람들은 같은 성별이 아니라 같은 성(family name)을 갖고 있다고 한다.

24 첫 문단에서 몇몇 사람들은 집에 들어가기 위해 사다리를 사용하고, 다른 몇몇 사람들은 물 위의 집에서 거주하며, 다른 몇몇 사람들은 많은 사람들과 같은 집에서 산다고 언급되어 있다. 따라서 빈칸에 들어갈 말로 가장 적절한 것은 ② Others이다.

25 '당신은 어떻게 그리고 왜 그들이 물 위에 집을 지었는지 궁금할지도 모른다.'라는 문장이 들어가기에 가장 적절한 곳은 베니스 사람들이 물 위에 집을 지은 이유와 방법에 대해서 설명하는 곳 앞인 ⓓ이다.

26 가정법과거 문장은 'If+주어+were/동사의 과거형 ~, 주어+조동사의 과거형(would/should/could/might)+동사원형 ….'의 형식으로 현재 사실과 반대되는 가정을 나타낼 때 쓸 수 있다.

27 ⓒ to be appeared → appeared로 고쳐야 어법상 적절한 문장이 된다.

28 (A) At high tide: 밀물 때, 만조에 (B) many: 뒤에 셀 수 있는 명사인 houses가 왔으므로 many가 적절하다. / (C) keep themselves safe from invaders: 침략자들로부터 자신들을 안전하게 지키다

29 마지막 문단에서 'Venice is known as the "floating city."(베니스는 물 위에 떠 있는 도시라고 알려져 있다.)'라고 언급되어 있다.

30 위 글에서는 ③ Why are houses on the water colorful in Venice?(베니스의 물 위의 집들이 왜 다양한 색깔을 가지고 있는가?)에 대해서는 언급된 바 없다.

Lesson 8 (기말)

1회

> **01** ⑤ **02** ② **03** ①
> **04** The bag was so heavy that he couldn't lift it.
> **05** smart enough to solve **06** ⑤ **07** ① **08** ① **09** ④
> **10** ② **11** ①
> **12** Six out of twenty students like a romance movie.
> **13** ① **14** ⑤ **15** ① **16** ④ **17** ③ **18** ①
> **19** No one can say that we don't need them anymore. **20** ④
> **21** ⑤ **22** ⑤ **23** ④ **24** ② **25** ⑤ **26** ① **27** ④ **28** ②

01 위에서부터 순서대로, equal(동등하다), struggle(고군분투하다), chase(뒤쫓다), matter(중요하다)가 들어가는 것이 문맥상 가장 자연스럽다.

02 위에서부터 순서대로, midnight(자정), election(선거), repeat(반복하다), greedy(탐욕스러운)가 들어가는 것이 문맥상 가장 자연스럽다.

03 keep in touch: 연락을 계속하다 / run for: ~에 입후보하다
one by one: 하나씩 / in the order of: ~의 순서로

04 'too ~ to+동사원형' 구문은 '너무 ~해서 …할 수 없다'라는 의미로 'so ~ that 주어+can't[couldn't]' 구문으로 바꿔 쓸 수 있다.

05 'so ~ that 주어+동사' 구문은 '너무 ~해서 …하다'라는 의미이다. 따라서 '형용사/부사+enough to+동사원형' 구문으로 바꿔 쓸 수 있다.

06 ⓐ angrily → angry / ⓑ too hard to eat it → too hard to eat / ⓒ so dark to go in → too dark to go in / ⓓ to looking around → to look around로 고쳐야 어법상 적절한 문

장이 된다.

07 ⓑ too difficult for me to answer them → too difficult for me to answer / ⓓ catch up with → catch up with her로 고쳐야 어법상 적절한 문장이 된다.

08 (A) 부정대명사 No one은 단수 취급한다. 따라서 has가 적절하다. (B) 선행사 the factory를 수식하는 절로 I work in이 쓰였으므로 관계부사 where가 아니라 관계대명사 which가 적절하다. (C) 의미상 주어로 for가 적절하다.

09 ① were → was / ② are → is / ③ have → has / ⑤ remember → remembers로 고쳐야 어법상 적절한 문장이 된다.

10 위 그래프에 따르면, 학생들이 가장 덜 선호하는 방과 후 수업은 축구이다.

11 위 그림에 따르면, 화요일에는 비가 오기 때문에 자전거를 탈 수 없다. 따라서 빈칸 ⓐ에는 'be too rainy to ride our bikes'가 적절하다. 수요일에는 눈이 오기 때문에 소풍을 갈 수 없다. 따라서 빈칸 ⓑ에는 'be too snowy to go on a picnic'이 적절하다.

12 위 그래프에 따르면, 로맨스 영화는 20명의 학생 중에서 6명의 학생이 가장 좋아하는 영화다.

13 A의 질문에 대한 B의 대답이 "아니, 이해 못했어."였다. 따라서 빈칸에 들어갈 A의 말로 가장 적절한 것은 ① Do you see what I mean?(무슨 말인지 알겠니?)이다.

14 남학생이 여학생에게 화나 보인다고 말하자, 여학생은 자신의 남동생이 컴퓨터를 망가뜨려서 화가 난다고 대답한다. 남학생은 그 말을 듣고 유감이라고 말하면서 여학생의 얼굴 근육이 피곤하겠다고 말한다(ⓓ). 여학생이 그게 무슨 말이냐고 묻자(ⓐ), 남학생은 화나 보이려면 많은 근육이 쓰인다고 말하면서 자신의 말이 무슨 의미인지 알겠냐고 묻는다(ⓒ). 이에 여학생이 알겠다고 대답하면서, 오랫동안 화난 채로 있는 것이 좋지 않다고(ⓑ) 대답하는 순서로 이어지는 것이 흐름상 가장 자연스럽다.

15 위 대화에서 남학생은 화가 난 여학생에게 화가 난 표정을 하면 얼굴 근육이 피곤하다고 말하면서 자신의 말이 무슨 의미인지 알겠냐고("Do you see what I mean?") 말하는 것이 문맥상 가장 적절하다.

16 A가 B에게 80퍼센트의 학생들이 가장 좋아하는 간식으로 패스트 푸드를 골랐고, 5퍼센트의 학생들만이 샐러드를 뽑았다고 이야기 하면서 무슨 의미인지 알겠냐고 묻고 있다. 이에 B가 패스트푸드를 많이 먹는 것은 학생들의 건강을 해친다고 대답했다. 따라서 ⓓ "No, I don't."는 흐름상 적절하지 않다.

17 "제 말이 무슨 뜻인지 아시겠어요?"라는 문장이 들어가기에 가장 적절한 곳은 파스칼이 로빈에게 탑 안으로 들어갈 안전한 시각이 아침 6시부터 정오 사이라고 설명하는 곳인 (C)이다.

18 파스칼이 로빈에게 탑 안으로 들어갈 안전한 시각이 새벽 6시부터 정오 사이이며, 저녁 6시부터 자정까지는 12명의 군사가 있는 가장 위험한 시간대라고 설명하고 있다. 따라서 (가)at that time에 해당되는 시간은 ① '저녁 6시~자정'이다.

19 주어진 우리말을 영작하면 'No one can say that we don't need them anymore.'가 된다. 이때 부정대명사 no one은 단수 취급한다.

20 위 글에서는 ④ How many soldiers did Pascal need to go inside?(파스칼은 안에 들어가기 위해 얼마나 많은 병사가 필요했는가?)에 대해서는 언급된 바 없다.

21 위 글에서 "Four times more soldiers work at that time than from six in the morning until noon."이라고 언급되어 있다.

22 위 글에서는 로빈 후드의 개에 대해서는 언급된 바 없다.

23 ⓓ you는 'Pascal'을 가리킨다. 나머지는 모두 로빈 후드를 가리킨다.

24 위 글에서는 그래프를 공부하던 Pascal이 자신의 개 Manny에 의해 소설 속 인물인 Robin Hood를 만나게 되었다. 자신을 구해준 로빈으로부터 탑 안에 들어갈 수 있게 도와달라고 요청을 받은 Pascal은 자기에게 해결책이 있다고 말하면서 병사들의 수를 세야 한다고 말하고 있다. 따라서 다음에 나올 내용으로 가장 알맞은 것은 ② 'Pascal counts the number of soldiers.'이다.

25 ① count(세다), ② struggle(고군분투하다), ③ greedy(탐욕스러운), ④ tax(세금을 매기다)를 가리키는 영영 풀이다.

26 ① No one need graphs in real life. → No one needs graphs in real life.로 고쳐야 어법상 적절한 문장이 된다.

27 위 글에서는 국가별로 행운의 숫자와 불행의 숫자에 대해서 설명하고 있다. (D)문단에서는 하와이의 파인애플 미로에 대해서 설명하고 있으므로 위 글의 주제와 관계 없다.

28 위 글에서는 국가별로 행운의 숫자와 불행의 숫자에 대해서 소개하면서, 한 국가의 행운의 숫자가 다른 국가에서는 불행의 숫자일 수 있다고 설명하고 있다.

Lesson 8 (기말) 2회

01 ⑤ 02 ⑤
03 He was so smart that he could solve the problem.
04 ⑤ 05 so as to 06 ④ 07 ②, ⑤ 08 ④ 09 ②
10 Twenty-five percent of the students like action movies.
11 ④ 12 ③ 13 ③ 14 ④ 15 ④ 16 ⑤ 17 ② 18 ④
19 ③ 20 ③ 21 ⑤ 22 ④ 23 ③ 24 ④ 25 ③ 26 ③
27 ⑤

01 midnight은 밤 12시, 즉 '자정'을 의미하는 단어이다.

02 위에서부터 순서대로, represent(의미하다), muscle(근육), matter(중요하다), relate(관련시키다)가 들어가는 것이 문맥상 가장 자연스럽다.

03 '~할 만큼 충분히 …한'이라는 뜻의 '형용사/부사+enough to+동사원형' 구문은 '너무 ~해서 …하다'라는 의미의 표현 'so+형

용사/부사+that+주어+동사' 구문으로 바꿔 쓸 수 있다.

04 ① The soup is so hot that I can eat it. → The soup is so hot that I cannot eat it. / ② couldn't → can't / ③ The game was so popular that the king couldn't prohibit. → The game was so popular that the king couldn't prohibit it(the game). / ④ The pants are too small for me not to wear them. → The pants are too small for me to wear.로 고쳐야 어법상 적절한 문장이 된다.

05 '~하기 위해서, ~하도록'이라는 의미를 나타내는 표현으로 「(so as) to+동사원형」, 「in order to+동사원형」, 「so that+주어+can/may ~」, 「in order that+주어+can/may ~」 등을 쓸 수 있다.

06 ① The tea is too hot to drink it. → The tea is too hot for me to drink. / ② not to get on that ride → to get on that ride / ③ The house was so dangerous that I couldn't go in. → The house was so dangerous that I couldn't go in it. / ⑤ cloudy so that → so cloudy that으로 고쳐야 어법상 적절한 문장이 된다.

07 'so ~ that 주어+can't[couldn't]' 구문은 '너무 ~해서 …할 수 없다'라는 의미로 'too ~ to+동사원형' 구문으로 바꿔 쓸 수 있다.

08 위 그래프에 따르면, 20명의 학생 중에 5명의 학생이 학교 도서관에서 원하는 책으로 공상과학 소설을 골랐다고 한다.

09 ⓐ youth → young / ⓑ sleepy → sleep / ⓒ were → was / ⓔ angrily → angry로 고쳐야 어법상 적절한 문장이 된다.

10 위 그래프에 따르면, 20명의 학생 중에 5명의 학생이 액션 영화를 가장 좋아하는 영화로 골랐다. 따라서 '25퍼센트의 학생이 액션 영화를 좋아한다'고 볼 수 있다.

11 ⓐ too serious to solve them → too serious to solve / ⓒ come → comes / ⓓ were → was로 고쳐야 어법상 적절한 문장이 된다.

12 ⓑ 의미상 'She is pretty.'라는 문장으로, pretty는 주어 she의 보어 역할이지만 보어는 강조 표현을 쓰지 않는다.
ⓓ The laptop was so expensive that he couldn't buy. → The laptop was so expensive that he couldn't buy it.으로 고쳐야 어법상 적절한 문장이 된다.

13 ③ The tea is too hot for us to drink it. → The tea is too hot for us to drink.로 고쳐야 어법상 적절한 문장이 된다.

14 대명사 it은 앞서 언급된 단수 명사 혹은 앞 문장 전체를 가리킨다. 위 글에서 밑줄 친 it이 가리키는 것으로 가장 적절한 것은 ④ paper ticket(종이 티켓)이다.

15 위 대화에 따르면, Henry는 미나에게 자신이 학생 100명을 대상으로 한 가장 좋아하는 간식에 대한 설문조사의 결과를 말해주고 있다. Henry는 80퍼센트 이상의 학생이 피자와 닭튀김을 가장 좋아하는 간식으로 뽑았다고 말하면서 무슨 말인지 이해하겠냐고 묻고 이에 미나는 학생들이 패스트푸드를 좋아한다고 말하는 것이 흐름상 자연스럽다. 따라서 빈칸에 들어갈 말로 적절하지 않은 것은

④ Do you know what will happen?(무슨 일이 일어날지 알겠니?)이다.

16 "그 동굴 집들은 참 특이해 보인다, 그렇지 않니?"라는 A의 질문에 대해 "나도 그래! 난 동굴 집에 살아."라는 B의 대답은 흐름상 자연스럽지 않다.

17 첫 문단에 따르면 중국인들은 숫자 7을 불행한 숫자라고 생각한다고 언급 되어 있다. 프랑스 사람들은 숫자 7을 행운의 숫자라고 생각한다.

18 위 글에 따르면, Pascal은 그래프를 배우는 것에 대해 불평을 하고 있었고(C), 자신의 개인 Manny가 말을 하는 것을 보고 놀랐다(E). Manny는 Pascal에게 눈을 감고 말을 따라 하라고 시켰고(D), Pascal은 감았던 눈을 뜨자 병사들에게 쫓기는 로빈을 보았고 그는 Pascal을 숲 속으로 데려갔다(A). 숲 속에서 두 사람이 자신을 소개하는(B) 순서로 이어지는 것이 흐름상 가장 자연스럽다.

19 ⓒYou는 Pascal의 개인 'Manny'를 가리킨다. 나머지는 모두 Pascal을 가리킨다.

20 ⓒ themselves는 himself로 고쳐야 어법상 적절하다.

21 <보기>의 문장은 It-that 강조 구문으로, 강조하고자 하는 부분을 It is/was와 that 사이에 넣고, 나머지 부분을 that 뒤에 써서 나타낸다. '…한 것은 바로 ~이다/이었다'라고 해석한다. 따라서 (가)를 It-that 강조구문을 이용해 영작하면, ⑤ 'It was his dog, Manny, that was talking!'이 된다.

22 '그러니까 당신은 새벽 6시와 정오 사이에 들어가야 해요.'라는 문장이 들어가기에 가장 적절한 곳은 파스칼이 로빈과 탑 안의 군사의 수를 세고 나서 로빈에게 언제 들어가야 할지 조언을 하는 곳인 (D)이다.

23 위 글에 따르면, 파스칼은 로빈과 탑 주위의 병사의 수를 세다가 언제 들어가야 할지 말해 주었지만 로빈이 이해하지 못했다. 파스칼은 그래프를 이용해서 로빈이 몇 시에 성 안에 들어가야 하는지 쉽게 설명해 주었다. 따라서 빈칸 (가)에 들어갈 말로 가장 적절한 것은 ③ graphs can be effective tools of communication(그래프는 의사소통하는 데 효과적인 도구가 될 수 있구나.)이다.

24 위 글에 따르면, 파스칼은 그래프를 이용해서 로빈이 탑 안에 들어갈 수 있도록 도와주었고 그로 인해 그래프가 어떤 것을 이해하기 쉽도록 만들기 위해서는 유용하다는 것을 깨달았다고 언급하고 있다.

25 위 글에 따르면, 로빈은 파스칼이 그래프를 보여주자 파스칼의 말을 이해했다(ⓒ). 파스칼은 탑 바깥에서 로빈이 탑 안에 들어가는 것을 보았다고(ⓔ) 언급되어 있다.

26 '그는 너무 탐욕스러워서 사람들과 나누지 않아.'라는 문장이 들어가기에 가장 적절한 곳은 왕이 백성들에게 너무나 많은 세금을 물려서 사람들이 식량을 살 돈이 없다고 말하고 있는 곳인 (C)이다.

27 위 글에서는 ⑤ What is the solution to get into the tower?(탑 안에 들어갈 수 있는 해결책은 무엇인가?)에 대해서는 언급된 바 없다.

적중 1OO + 특별부록

Plan B

우리학교
최신기출

지학 · 민찬규 교과서를 배우는

학교 시험문제 분석 · 모음 · 해설집

전국단위 학교 시험문제 수집 및 분석
출제 빈도가 높은 문제 위주로 선별
문제 풀이에 필요한 상세한 해설

중3-2
영어

지학 · 민찬규